United States Firearms The First Century 1776-1875

United States Firearms The First Century 1776-1875

David F. Butler

illustrated by the author

WINCHESTER PRESS

Library of Congress Catalog Card Number 77-146062
ISBN: 0-87691-030-04

Published by Winchester Press
460 Park Avenue, New York 10022

Printed in the United States of America

ACKNOWLEDGEMENTS

The creation of a book usually involves the assistance of many friends and associates. Particular thanks are given to:

Mr. Thomas E. Hall, Curator of the Winchester Gun Museum for many illustrations and invaluable consulting advice.

Mrs. Carolyn M. Chesto, who typed the manuscript with great skill—making smooth copy where rough had gone before.

Mr. Edward D. Lowry, Director of Winchester Exploratory Research for many discussions on long range ballistics. Mr. Walter M. Bellemore, Staff Engineer, Winchester Research who consulted and made his records available on early cartridge dimensions and ballistics.

Appreciation is expressed to Mr. Lawrence Faeth, and the Winchester Research Photograph Staff, and to consultant friends particularly Fred G. Parisi and Daniel H. Sise who have shared knowledge in many discussions. Thanks are also given to Mrs. Geraldine A. Patti who typed thousands of words on an earlier draft of the manuscript.

Appreciation is expressed to Col. Berkeley R. Lewis and the Smithsonian Institution for permission to quote from *Small Arms and Ammunition in the United States Service,* and to the National Rifle Association for permission to use information and illustrations contained in an article by the author in the Special Centennial Issue of *The American Rifleman,* January 1971. Thanks are expressed to *The Gun Report* for permission to use data and illustrations from the author's article in the October 1970 issue, and to Mr. E. S. McCawley, Jr. and S. M. Alvis of Remington Arms Co. who have provided information on early Remington firearms.

The first draft sections of manuscript date back to 1951, and information has been added to build this present book during the intervening twenty years. My field of firearms and ammunition research and design is a constant exploration of new ideas and a gathering of technical information. To this basic search in a professional career I have been fortunate in adding many additional contacts through discussions with other gun collectors and hobbyists at gun shows. Much has been learned in participation at rimfire, centerfire and pistol matches, and in shooting antique muzzle loading and single shot rifles. The patience and understanding of my wife, Ann, and our two boys, David and Donald, has been a great help. David has made a particular contribution in indexing this volume.

My hope is that you find this book interesting and of value in your own explorations.

CONTENTS

INTRODUCTION

The century following the American Revolution witnessed a truly remarkable demonstration of ingenuity and inventiveness. At the opening of the Revolution the armies of the world were equipped with smoothbore flintlock muskets which had an effective range of hardly a hundred yards. The muskets often misfired even in good weather and were almost useless if the weather were damp or raining. America was an agricultural colony with crude tools and few manufacturing facilities.

A century later, the United States had been transformed into a highly creative and productive nation. The transcontinental railway had been completed, and Americans were streaming westward carrying lever-action repeating rifles capable of a high rate of fire and accurate enough to hit a mark a quarter-mile away. These tremendously improved firearms used metallic cartridges which sealed a pointed lead bullet, charge of powder, and reliable priming into a rugged, water-tight package. The round lead ball of the flintlock musket rattling down a smoothbore barrel had been replaced by a tightly fitting, swaged lead bullet which was spun at a high rate of speed by the rifling in the barrel, so that serious hunting could be accomplished at ranges exceeding 400 yards.

In the early 1800's, American inventors were encouraged to develop new and more complex firearms designs. Thousands of experiments gradually filtered out the good ideas, and the United States Army actually adopted a breech-loading flintlock rifle as early as 1819! The designs taxed the production capabilities of the small manufacturing plants then in operation. Hand forging, filing, and grinding operations were replaced by water power and, later, steam engines. Improved manufacturing processes were developed, and by the 1830's breech-loading percussion rifles were in use, and Colt started manufacturing radically new percussion revolvers by high-precision manufacturing techniques.

The inventors of the 1840's, such as Christian Sharps, created designs which led to the powerful single-shot rifles of the Civil War and the buffalo hunting period. Although the Civil War Sharps were loaded with paper cartridges they proved powerful and accurate in the hands of skilled marksmen such as Berdan's Sharpshooters. Northern cavalry of the Civil War found their Sharps carbines fast loading and very effective. Improved Sharps and Remington single-shot rifles of the 1870's firing powerful center-fire cartridges delivered superb accuracy for long-range shooting. These rifles were widely used for buffalo hunting on the Western plains at extremely long ranges. In 1874, an American rifle team armed with these "new-fangled" breechloading rifles beat the world-champion Irish rifle team (firing traditional muzzle loading rifles) at ranges exceeding half a mile!

Inventors had experimented with repeating rifles for hundreds of years in Europe. None of the designs were successful. In the 1840's, inventors on both sides of the Atlantic tried again with improved designs firing paper cartridges. The experiments continued in the 1850's, and crude metallic ammunition showed the possibility of success. Experiments by Walter Hunt, Lewis Jennings, and Christopher Spencer started the trend toward the first really successful repeaters — the lever-action Spencer and Henry rifles of the Civil War. Over 100,000 repeaters were used in the conflict, firing more than 60,000,000 copper-cased rimfire cartridges.

In the postwar years, hunters, trappers, and farmers carried rapid-firing Henry, Winchester, and Spencer lever-action rifles. These firearms permitted rugged individualists to survive in the wilderness where the odds were almost always against the pioneer. The rugged reliability of American firearms helped tremendously in the settling of the nation and earned a worldwide reputation for technical excellence.

United States Firearms The First Century 1776-1875

Early Muskets and Muzzle-Loading Pistols

CHAPTER 1

The earliest settlers in the United States carried firearms that were incredibly crude by modern standards. These early arms were matchlocks and consisted of a heavy iron barrel mounted on a large, straight, awkward-looking wooden stock. In most cases the muskets were so heavy that the musketeer carried a prop that was stuck in the ground to help hold up the forward end of the gun for firing. Ignition was by means of a smoldering rope that had been dipped in saltpeter so that it burned slowly — much like a modern cigar. To fire the musket a charge of powder was measured and poured in the muzzle, a spherical bullet was rammed down the barrel, with or without wadding, and some loose powder trickled into a small pan which was fastened to the breech. The smoldering rope was held in an iron arm that pivoted on a shaft and was connected to the trigger. As the trigger was pulled, the arm rotated, lowering the smoldering rope down into contact with the powder in the pan. With luck the powder ignited and the flame flashed through a small hole lighting the main powder charge in the barrel. The gas pressure drove the bullet down the barrel bouncing from side to side, and finally shot out of the muzzle in the general direction of the enemy. The musket ball was surrounded by a cloud of dense smoke primarily composed of unburned components of the gunpowder.

The matchlock had many disadvantages: It was slow to load, inaccurate, and required a lighted match for ignition. There were three steps from the crude matchlock of the 15th century to the flintlocks of the American Revolution: The Wheellock, the Snaphaunce, and the Miquelet.

THE WHEELLOCK

In order to eliminate the need for carrying a smoldering match with the musket, the wheellock was invented. An iron pan, very similar to the "pan" of the flintlock rifle shown in Figure 1-1, was attached to the barrel. A serrated iron wheel protruded up through the bottom of the pan and was surrounded by the priming powder. A powerful spring was wound up and locked by the "sear." A piece of iron pyrites was placed in the jaws of a hammer somewhat similar to that of the flintlock rifle, and the hammer was lowered so that the iron pyrites was spring-loaded against the wheel. When the trigger was pulled the powerful main spring rotated the serrated wheel against the iron pyrites developing a shower of sparks which ignited the priming powder in the pan. The powder flash passed through a small hole into the barrel, igniting the main charge, and the main charge in turn propelled the bullet out of the barrel.

The wheellock was a very expensive firearm to man-

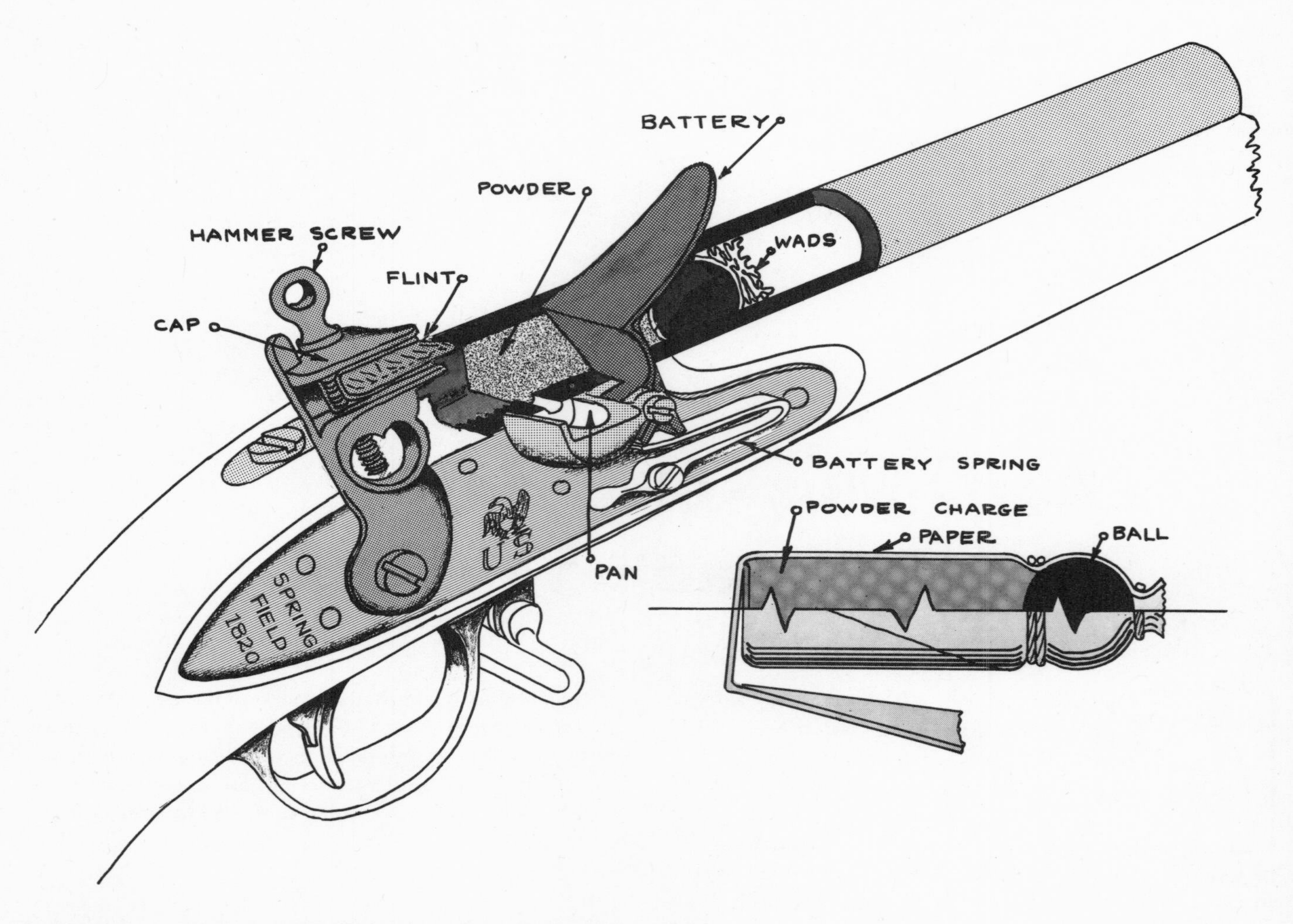

FIGURE 1-1 Cutaway of flintlock musket and ammunition.

ufacture and required watchmaker precision for success. Maintenance of these complex mechanisms was very difficult so that they were both too expensive and too delicate to become popular either in Europe or in the New World.

THE SNAPHAUNCE

In the mid-16th century a simplified design was created. The Snaphaunce design was similar to that of the flintlock shown in Figure 1-1, except that the "battery," the mechanism to spark the powder flash in the pan, consisted only of the curved plate which was struck by the flint. The pan was covered by a little lid which was an entirely separate piece. The Snaphaunce lock was still fairly complex. When the trigger was pulled the hammer rotated, carrying a piece of flint in its jaws. A linkage mechanism connected to the hammer moved the priming pan lid forward, uncovering the loose powder in the pan. The flint struck the battery sending a shower of sparks down into the pan and igniting the priming powder. The flash of flame communicated through a small touchhole, igniting the main charge in the barrel of the musket. The main charge drove the ball down the smoothbore barrel and out the muzzle.

THE MIQUELET

The next development was the Miquelet which is said to have been first produced during the mid-16th century in Europe. In the Miquelet lock the general arrangement of components was similar to that of the flintlock muskets shown in Figure 1-1. The pan cover and battery were combined into one unit. The main difference between the Miquelet and the flintlock was that the hammer spring was external, that is, it was mounted on the outside of the lock plate and was fully visible. The battery or "frizzen" was very often grooved vertically, with the ridges being hit by the flint and the valleys guiding the sparks downward into the priming pan.

THE FLINTLOCK

By 1650 the flintlock design had taken form. This gun mechanism combined the elements shown in Figure 1-1 into an inexpensive, sturdy, and reasonably reliable ignition system. The design was so successful that it remained the primary method of firearms ignition for 200 years until it was supplanted by the percussion system in the 1840's. During the 17th century the designs reflected the personal ideas of private contractors in England and on the Continent. In 1717 the French standardized the design of their Army musket which was manufactured at the armories of Charleville, St. Etienne, and Mauberge.

Early in the 18th century the British also standardized their musket designs, and created the Long Land Service Musket which became famous around the world by its nickname "Brown Bess."

Design of the Flintlock Musket

The construction of a typical flintlock musket is shown in Figure 1-1. The cartridge is at the right side of the illustration, and although crude by modern standards it represented a very important improvement over the use of loose powder and ball.

The long barrel of the flintlock musket was usually .69 to .80 inches in inside diameter. It was a smooth bored tube and had a threaded area at the breech into which a solid steel plug was screwed. This "breech tang" had a bar extending to the rear of the threads and this tang was fastened to the wooden stock with a vertical screw which went down through the tang and threaded into the trigger guard. The heaviest section of the barrel was at the breech where the threads were cut and where the gas pressure was the highest. In order to keep the weight to a reasonable level, the barrel was tapered from the breech to the muzzle. Although these muskets have the appearance of massive ruggedness, careful examination will show that the forward half of the barrel is extremely thin and has the appearance of a modern shotgun barrel. It is a tribute to the contractors of this early day that, despite their crude machinery, they could turn out barrels that proved reliable in rugged Army service.

A hole drilled in the side of the barrel at the breech end was lined up with the pan which was usually part of the lock plate. The pan was covered with the "L" shaped piece of steel known as the battery or frizzen. The battery is shown in a raised position, ready to receive an 8- to 12-grain charge of loose powder for priming.

After priming, the battery was snapped shut and the battery spring held it in a closed position, protecting the priming from accidentally being shaken out or getting wet in a light rain.

The large powder charges, shown to the rear of the musket barrel, were compressed between the breech plug and the round soft lead ball in the barrel. The ball was held in place by paper wadding from the cartridge.

Loading the Flintlock Musket

The soldier was supplied with paper cartridges. (See the right side of Figure 1-1.) The top half shows what the inside of the cartridge looked like. The cartridge was manufactured by rolling up a tube of paper around a wooden dowel the diameter of the soft lead ball. The dowel was partially withdrawn, and one end of the paper tube was gathered in and tied with a piece of string. The soft lead musket ball was then dropped in the open end of the tube. The string was brought around the ball and wrapped twice around the paper tube to constrict the section behind the ball, thus holding it in position.

The heavy charge of black powder was poured in the open end of the paper tube and the open end was twisted and folded over to hold the powder in position.

The design shown is a typical American cartridge which was used occasionally during the Revolution and became increasingly standardized and popular in the early 19th century. The French and British cartridges were somewhat different in design. The British generally tied off the tube at one end and then dropped the musket ball in and held it in place with the powder charge, thus eliminating the loops of string which retained the musket ball at the front of the cartridge. The French often folded over one end of the paper tube and pasted it shut. They did not usually use string to retain the ball at the front of the cartridge. As a result a French cartridge often looked like a simple paper cylinder with one end twisted over and folded in place.

During the American Revolution the cartridge supply for the Continental Armies was somewhat chaotic. Some French cartridges were used and limited quantities of the American design were produced, but most of the Continental soldiers carried loose powder and shot and measured the proper powder charge during the loading sequence. For the Continental soldiers who were skilled in the use of the rifle and musket, this was a good system, but the use of paper cartridges was a tremendous advantage for most troops. The loading sequence with a flintlock musket was complex at best and the paper cartridge insured that all the elements were available in their proper proportions and thus simplified loading.

Some of the early arms manuals of the Revolutionary period list twenty-two separate steps for loading a flintlock musket! Even without the formalized motions of a drill manual, the following basic steps were required:

1. Place the hammer in a half-cock position and snap the frizzen open to uncover the priming pan.
2. Lift the cover of the leather cartridge box on your belt and withdraw a cartridge with your right hand.
3. Open the cartridge. Since you are holding the musket with your left hand and have the cartridge in your right hand, you obviously need a third hand to tear off the top of the cartridge. This was usually solved by biting the end of the cartridge and tearing off the end of the paper tube.
4. Pour eight to twelve grains of powder into the priming pan and snap the frizzen shut.
5. Pour the remaining powder down the muzzle of the musket.
6. Wad up the paper cartridge and stuff the paper cartridge and ball into the muzzle.
7. Withdraw the ramrod from underneath the barrel.
8. Drive the musket ball and paper wadding down to the breech end of the barrel.
9. Replace the ramrod in the guides beneath the barrel.
10. Cock the hammer.
11. Aim the musket and fire.

As the trigger was pulled, the hammer fell under the pressure of the powerful mainspring hidden on the inside of the lockplate. The flint struck the curved face of the battery, lifting the battery off the pan and sending a shower of sparks downward into the priming charge. Usually (but not always) the priming charge ignited with a great whoosh. Flame and smoke went in all directions, and some fire passed through the flash hole to ignite the main charge. After a fraction of a second the main charge ignited and drove the patched ball rattling up the barrel. Less than 50 percent of the powder charge turned into gas, the remainder coating the inside of the musket or rifle barrel or being ejected as a dense cloud of burning and solid particles of charcoal, sulphur and saltpeter.

The efficiency of flintlocks was low, since the powder was inefficient. There was considerable leakage around the ball and a jet of flame flared out from the chamber through the flash hole. When all these factors are considered it is no wonder that you were pretty safe 200 yards in front of a musket, provided it was aimed at you!

The standard French flintlock muskets and the later American muskets had barrels which were .690 of an inch in inside diameter. With the crude manufacturing techniques this dimension could not be held exactly, but good barrels generally ranged from .690 to .705 of an inch, a spread of .015 of an inch. The musket balls were not completely round since they were cast in brass or iron molds made with crude tools. From the American Revolution through about 1830 the standard American musket ball was .640 of an inch in diameter. After 1830 more accurately cast bullets were available, and development of the compression process of manufacturing musket balls permitted their nominal diameter to be increased to .650 of an inch.

The difference between the musket ball diameter and the barrel diameter was called "windage." With a .640-inch ball and a .690-inch barrel the clearance was .050 of an inch and this gap was filled with the paper wadding of the cartridge. In essence, the .050 inch clearance was a "tolerance absorber" to take care of three inaccuracies:

1. Musket balls were not perfectly round, and varied in diameter from mold to mold.
2. The barrels were not uniform in inside diameter, either from one end to the other in a single musket, nor from musket to musket.
3. The inside of the barrel accumulated fouling from firing, and the buildup was most severe just forward of the chamber.

The improved process of manufacturing musket balls by compression instead of casting in the late 1830's essentially eliminated the first inaccuracy and allowed the windage to be decreased from .050 of an inch to .040 of an inch with a significant improvement in velocity and efficiency. Even so, the efficiency of the average military flintlock was pretty poor.

Colonel Berkely Lewis, in his *Small Arms and Ammunition in the United States Service,* reports that

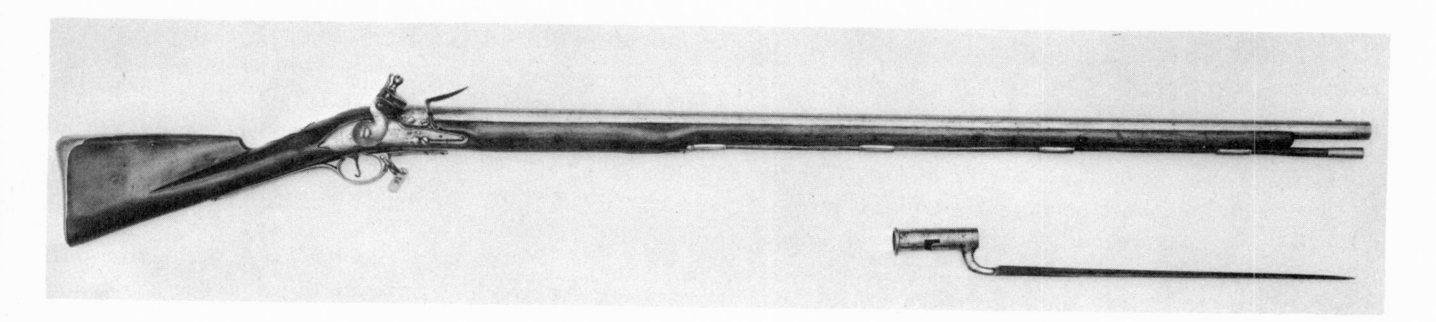

FIGURE 1-2 Early British "Brown Bess" musket with wooden ramrod.

extensive tests at West Point in 1837 established that the standard flintlock musket with single ball cartridge was fired at the rate of 2.53 shots per minute. The standard "buck and ball" cartridge of one musket ball and three buckshot was fired at three shots per minute. Penetration in a white oak plank with the single ball cartridge was 1 inch at 100 yards, 0.55 of an inch at 200 yards, and only a shallow dent at 300 yards.

BRITISH LONG LAND SERVICE MUSKET "BROWN BESS"

Early in the 18th century the British standardized their flintlock musket design, and established a new "Ordnance System of Manufacture." The idea was to give long-term contracts to contractors who could specialize in the manufacture of complex gun components, and become very skilled. The early arms models were officially known as the Long Land Service Muskets, and unofficially known as "Brown Bess" around the world. Special Sea Service Muskets were designed for the Navy.

Under the Ordnance System contracts were given to private contractors in central England near Birmingham to manufacture locks and barrels. Manufacture of the 46-inch long barrels with a ¾-inch inside diameter was a very time-consuming and laborious process, and this system allowed certain contractors to specialize and manufacture barrels year after year. The quality of the barrels was proven by firing each barrel with an excessive charge of powder under the watchful eye of a government inspector. The acceptable barrels were then stamped by the inspector and shipped to the Tower of London for storage.

The second complex element in the flintlock musket was the lock mechanism. Great care was required in manufacturing the complicated parts with the crude tools available in the 17th and 18th centuries. Most of the metal work of these early times utilized copper, brass, pewter or soft iron and none of these materials would stand up under the stresses and strains of a flintlock mechanism. The lock mechanism had three springs, one to control the position of the frizzen, one to keep the sear in engagement, and the main spring to power the hammer. These springs had to be formed to complex shapes and then hardened and tempered to the resiliency and toughness required for long service. The point of contact between the tip of the sear and the hammer notch was crucial to the safety of the musket. Soft metals in this area would wear rapidly or break off, making the gun either unserviceable or liable to accidental firing.

The other components were considerably simpler to manufacture, such as the trigger guards, triggers, butt plates, and ramrod pipes. These components were known as furniture, and until 1725 iron was specified for them. Although brass was a more expensive material it could be cast, filed, and polished cheaper than iron could be forged and finished, so brass furniture gradually became standard for the service. These simpler components were contracted for on a pound weight basis, and then also stored. When additional muskets were needed, barrels, locks and furniture were withdrawn from storage and delivered to gunmakers near London. In a relatively short time these gunmakers could manufacture stocks and assemble the finished muskets "lock, stock and barrel."

The British Government had found that when they contracted for the entire musket on an emergency basis with fast deliveries required prices tended to be quite high and the quality very uneven. At times the British Government had to purchase muskets on the Continent to fill emergency needs, and this resulted in further design and caliber variations and quality problems. The ordnance system allowed contractors to plan their production carefully and take the time required to manufacture components of the highest practical quality. It had the further advantage of providing more standardized musket designs.

REVOLUTIONARY PERIOD MUSKETS

The Long Land Service Muskets saw extensive service in America. British and colonial troops carried them in frontier skirmishes, and in the French and Indian Wars from 1756 to 1763. The appearance of the typical Brown Bess used from 1717 through the Revolution is shown in Figure 1-2. In actuality this is a fairly early musket, probably assembled about 1740. The lock was manufactured by Jordan in 1733. The official name for this musket is the Long Land Service Musket and it was a refinement of the British musket designs of the 17th century. The barrel was 46 inches long with a smooth inside bore of .750 of an inch nominal diameter. There was a small rectangular stud on top of the barrel two inches from the muzzle which served as a crude front sight and also as a bayonet catch. At the breech end the barrel was marked with the broad arrow denoting it as property of the British Crown. Inspection and proofing marks were also stamped into the barrel at the breech to show that it had been proven.

The stock was of walnut and was cut off about four inches from the muzzle to make room for the bayonet. After 1725 the muskets were generally manufactured with brass fittings. This illustration clearly shows the cast brass butt plate, which formed a protective shield over the butt end of the gun. The trigger guard was made of another heavy brass casting with thick sections and a long tail which extended down to the rear of the grip of the stock. A brass plate was cast and fastened on top of the grip of the stock. This was a decorative plate in which numbers were cut to identify the gun's storage rack.

One way to identify this as an early Brown Bess musket is the fact that it is fitted with a wooden ramrod. The ramrod was fitted with an iron tip and was held in its position below the barrel by four brass "thimbles" or "pipes." Some steel ramrods were used in the Brown Bess muskets as early as 1724. There was strong sentiment for the wooden ramrod among British officers. Although steel ramrods were used on all muskets manufactured after 1750, General Howe's army in Boston still had the old wooden ramrod models in 1776.

The barrel was held into the stock with cross pins passing transversely through the wooden stock and through lugs welded to the bottom of the musket barrel. The lock with its graceful gooseneck hammer was held into the stock by heavy screws. At first these screws just passed through the wood, but it was soon found the lock tended to work loose. This was solved by setting an ornamental brass bar in the wood on the left side of the stock to hold the heads of the lock-plate screws. In this way the screws could be drawn up very tightly and the lock plate held firmly in position in the stock.

Flint-Lock Mechanism

The British flint-lock typical of those in use at the time of the American Revolution is shown in Figure 1-3. This lock is part of the Winchester Gun Museum collection and was manufactured in 1729. It was apparently stored in the Tower of London and may never have been assembled into a firearm, for it shows no evidence of significant wear. Careful examination of the lock, manufactured with the crude tools of 240 years ago, leaves one with a real appreciation for the artistic feeling of the craftsmen of that day. The lock components are far more ornate and artistic than required simply for function. The exposed side of the lock is shown on the left-hand side of the illustration. The lock plate is rounded and the section to the rear of the hammer has engraved lines forming a triangular border inside which the word Tower, and the date of manufacture are engraved. The hammer has rounded contours and a graceful gooseneck shape. The hammer spur has been forged as an integral part but then has been sculptured as a pillar rising out of the smooth sculptured S shape of the hammer. The upper part of the hammer spur has been rounded and curled over with an ornamental detail at the extreme top. Sculptured edges on the lower jaw sweep around the gooseneck of the hammer and then flare out on the main body of the hammer to give an accented detail which emphasizes the free flowing curves of the hammer design. The flintlock hammer is basically a complex shape with the necessity of providing a completely exposed clamp for a piece of flint stone held in a leather or lead cushion. Every attempt has been made to make the Brown Bess hammer, hammer cap (which formed the upper anvil of the vise), and the cap screw in smooth, rounded and artistic shapes.

Forward of the hammer a large crown has been engraved on the side of the lock plate with GR below the crown to indicate that it was Crown property and at least nominally owned by King George. (King George in Latin is spelled Georgius Rex, hence the GR.) The engraved crown was done with considerable detail — with ornamental curlicues, internal details showing diamond shapes and a maltese cross surmounting the top of the crown. Forward of the engraved crown was a stamped broad arrow and a smaller stamped crown on its side, indicating that the finished lock had been inspected and accepted as Crown property.

Immediately above the inspection mark is the iron pan which held the priming charge. This pan was forged integral with the lock plate — no small trick with the crude tools available in 1729. The smoothly curved pan had a projection forming a vertical lip at the back, commonly known as a "fence to the rear," to prevent the priming charge from flashing back toward the shooter. This type of design is known as a "flat pan" since the top surface of the pan is parallel to the axis of the barrel and the top surface of the lock plate. The flat pan with fence to the rear was the standard design of the French Charleville musket of 1763 and was the style of design commonly used on U.S. Army flintlocks and commercial American flintlocks on the frontier.

SHORT LAND SERVICE MUSKET

Many British soldiers found the Brown Bess to be a clumsy and awkward musket. In the 1750's the clamor became so loud that a new model was designed with a 42-inch barrel. The marines and the Militia were armed with this musket late in the 1750's. The appearance was very similar to Figure 1-2. The shorter barrel was found to be a very definite improvement and had no effect on range or accuracy. In 1768 the new musket design was standardized and plans drawn up to manufacture 100,000. The conservatism of the British military establishment was such that small quantities of the Long Land Service Muskets continued to be manufactured until the 1790's.

The French Charleville muskets of 1717 were very similar in appearance to the Brown Bess. In 1763 the French adopted a much more "modern" design which later served as the pattern for the first American muskets.

Despite continued complaints of the awkwardness, weight and inaccuracy of the Brown Bess muskets, there was little change in the design between 1776 and 1814 when Colonel Hanger, a British Army officer, said.

> "A soldier's musket, if not exceedingly ill-bored (as many are), will strike the figure of a man at 80 yards; it may even at a hundred, but a soldier must be very unfortunate indeed who shall be wounded by a common musket at 150 yards, provided his antagonist aims at him; and, as to firing at a man at 200 yards, with a common musket, you may just as well fire at the moon. No man was ever killed by a musket at 200 yards by the person who aimed at him."

A common military rhyme about musket shooting went:

> "One went high,
> and one went low,
> and where in Hell
> did the other one go?"

COMMITTEE OF SAFETY MUSKETS

Despite the shortcomings of the British musket, the first approach to arming the Colonies was to encourage local manufacture of flintlock muskets designed to specifications virtually identical to the Brown Bess. In 1775 some Colonies set up specifications, and Massachusetts was typical, specifying a barrel to fire a one-ounce ball, and that for muskets to "resemble and, as nearly as may be, equal in goodness with the King's new arms there shall be allowed . . . the sum of three pounds."

By November 1775 the Continental Congress made an attempt to unify the muskets procured for the Continental Army by passing the following resolution:

> "Resolved, that it be recommended to the several assemblies or conventions of the Colonies respectively, to set and keep their gunsmiths at work to manufacture good fire locks, with bayonets, each

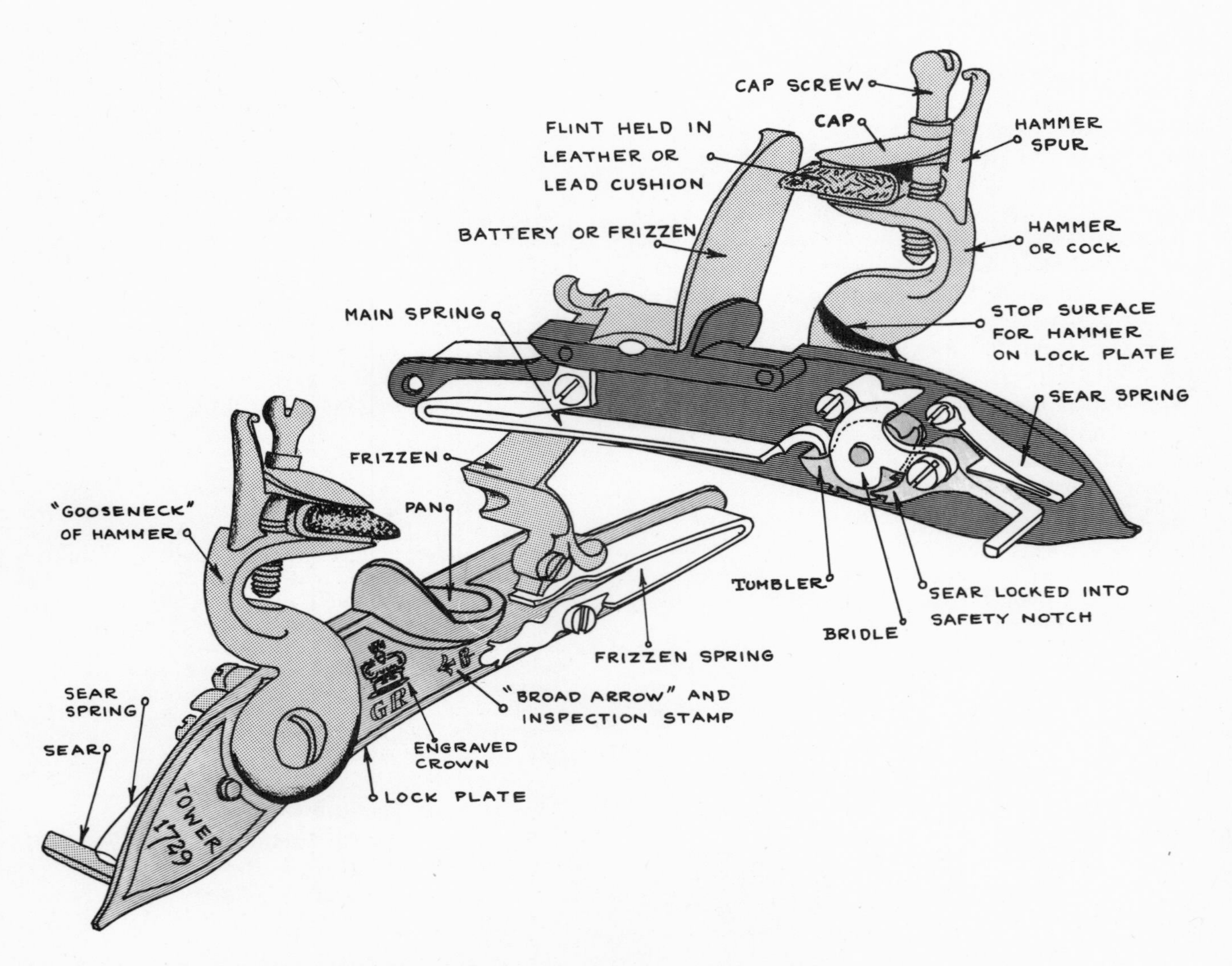

FIGURE 1-3 Lock from "Brown Bess" flintlock musket.

fire lock to be made with a good bridle lock, ¾ of an inch bore, and of good substance at the breech, the barrel to be 3 feet 8 inches in length, the bayonet to be 18 inches in the blade, with a steel ramrod, the upper loop thereof to be trumpet mouthed: that the price to be given be fixed by the assembly or convention, or committee of safety of each colony . . ."

Contracts were let to various small American gunmakers, many adhering to the specifications recommended by the Continental Congress in Philadelphia. The Committee of Safety Muskets were made in small quantities, and generally did not have any barrel bands. The barrel was held to the stock with cross pins through the wood, and through slots in lugs on the underside of the barrel.

Most Committee of Safety Muskets were manufactured by the American contractors using Brown Bess muskets as models for the shape and size of the parts. The appearance was so similar that Figure 1-2 may be used to illustrate both muskets, except that the Committee of Safety Muskets had iron ramrods. Since the small American shops had only crude tools, and virtually no fixtures and gauges to measure finished parts, the dimensions varied greatly. Often one man would file out all the parts of a lock using hand files with the parts clamped in a vise. In later years production was started the same way at Springfield Armory, and it is recorded that filing a lock by hand took a skilled workman three days. The author believes this refers to the time to finish the parts, starting with rough shaped parts from the blacksmith's forge. The hand-filed finished parts were not interchangeable from gun to gun, and the variations in size and shape were a persistent cause for complaint by the Army's ordnancy staff. The wide variations in American manufacture muskets remained a serious problem through the 1820's.

The Brown Bess and Committee of Safety Muskets both used balls of close to .700 of an inch in diameter. From a careful study Colonel Berkeley Lewis states:

> The "Brown Bess" used a ball supposedly standardized at 15 per pound, or caliber 0.688. From an examination of 70 bullets found on British campsites it appears that they varied from 0.687 to 0.700 of an inch in diameter, with an average of 0.694. The British charge was 6 drams (or 163 grains). The cartridge tube was tied with string ahead of the bullet and filled with powder, and the end twisted tightly.

The pan was covered with a frizzen which is shown in open position in the left-hand illustration and snapped shut to protect the priming charge in the right-hand illustration. The powerful frizzen spring held the frizzen firmly in either a fully opened or fully shut position. The design of the frizzen again shows considerable interest in artistic appearance. There is an ornamental tail which has many smoothly shaped flowing curves. The tail is definitely necessary to prevent the frizzen from snapping too far open after being struck by the hammer, but the ornamental curlicues are purely for appearance. The design of this lock and frizzen can be compared to the much plainer design of the American muskets of 1816; see Figure 1-12. The American lock differs in having a perfectly plain functional tail on the frizzen to control the distance that the frizzen snaps open. The entire pan has been tilted forward to protect the shooter against the powder flash, and the fence has been eliminated. Notice that the rear surface of the pan is considerably higher than the top of the lock plate. A comparison of the two designs shows that the frizzen spring has also been simplified and the hammer has been made of a simpler design with a reinforcing loop up to the lower jaw for added strength.

Internal details of the Brown Bess are shown on the right-hand side of Figure 1-3. The mainspring is very powerful and held to the lock plate by a screw. The moving end of the spring has an arched shape to exert heavy downward pressure on the "tumbler." This tended to rotate the tumbler counterclockwise. A shaft on the tumbler passes through the lock plate and through the hammer. The tumbler shaft extension was usually square in cross section, with a matching hole in the hammer. A large screw held the hammer firmly to the tumbler shaft, making it one rigid assembly.

As the tumbler was driven counterclockwise by the mainspring the hammer was carried forward and the flint gripped in the jaws struck the battery or frizzen. This motion drove the frizzen forward, uncovering the pan and sending showers of sparks down into the loose powder in the pan. The excess energy of the hammer was absorbed by a shoulder on the hammer surface striking the upper surface of the lock plate at the end of the hammer motion.

The hammer is shown in a half cocked position in both these illustrations. The sear was held against the tumbler by the sear spring, and the illustration shows the searing surface deeply engaged in the safety notch. The safety notch was used during the loading process and when carrying a fully loaded musket. The hammer was drawn back to a shallower notch, which is shown just under the bridle—when the soldier was ready to fire. As the trigger was pulled, a bar on the trigger contacted the right-angle tail of the sear, driving it upward. This disengaged the sear from the tumbler, allowing the hammer to fall.

The sear and tumbler were held in position by a fixed piece known as the bridle which was held to the lock plate by two screws. The rear bridle screw formed a shaft on which the sear rotated. The bridle had a hole through the center which formed an inboard bearing for the tumbler.

The components for a high quality lock with design features typical of the period of the American Revolution are shown in Figures 1-4 and 1-5. The drawing shows a good quality commercial lock slightly less ornate and smaller in size than the Brown Bess lock of Figure 1-3. This is a better than average lock, however, designed and manufactured with care to give long and reliable service.

The lock plate is shown in the upper right-hand corner of Figure 1-4. Since the flintlock mechanisms were very difficult to manufacture with the crude machinery available in America, great numbers were imported from Europe. The American locks often had a flat lock plate with a pan bolted on. This lock had the pan forged integral with the lock plate which required fairly heavy machinery for forging or a great deal of time on the part of the blacksmith and machinists. The lock plate is cut like a piece of Swiss cheese with eleven holes. In the section to the rear of the pan there are five holes, one a large hammer hole .400 of an inch in diameter and four threaded holes with 3/16 inch thread. The function of these holes may be seen by referring back to Figure 1-3. The hole immediately behind the pan was used for the

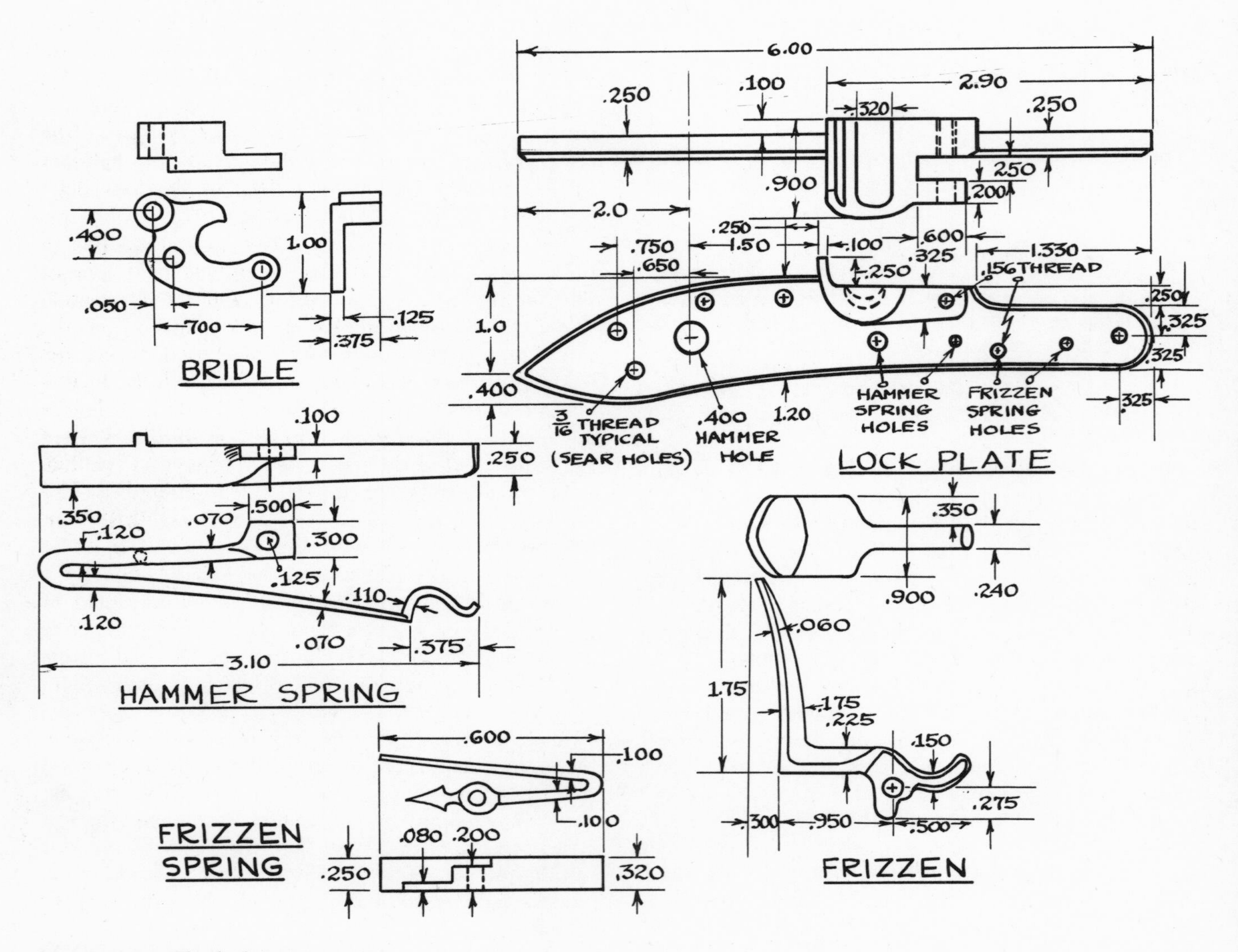

FIGURE 1-4 Flintlock components.

large screw which passed transversely through the stock and clamped the lock plate to the wood. The pan projected inward from the inner face of the lock plate by .100 of an inch. This allowed the pan to fit solidly against the side of the barrel and the pan trough would channel the powder flash directly into the touch hole. A slot is cut in the metal forward of the pan and a tapped hole is drilled crosswise to provide pivot for the battery or frizzen. The forward section of the lock plate has two holes for the hammer spring and two holes for the frizzen spring. In each case there is a threaded hole for the screw to retain the spring and a small hole forward for a small projection on the spring. These two points locked one end of the spring rigidly in position and the working end of the spring flexed relative to these two fixed points.

The frizzen is shown in the lower right side of Figure 1-4. This was basically an "L"-shaped forging and there is a small ornamental detail on the tail. This tail was quite important in controlling the distance to which the frizzen snapped open. The frizzen spring held the frizzen firmly in position to keep the pan covered and also provide resistance to the blow of the flint. As the hammer rotated forward, the flint

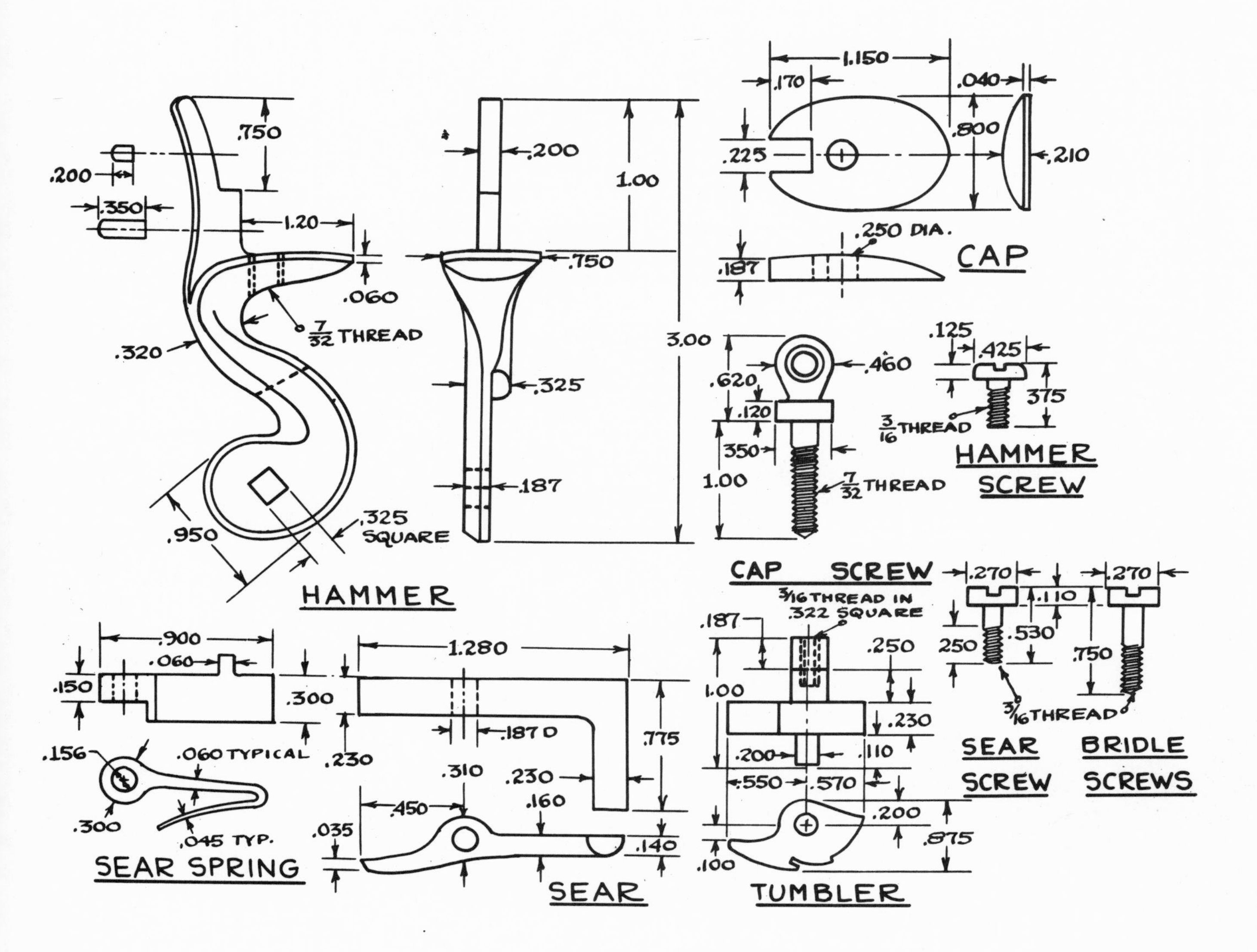

FIGURE 1-5 Flintlock components.

scraped down the frizzen generating a shower of sparks, and the cover was forced back uncovering the pan. The tail on the frizzen controlled the distance to which it rotated after the blow was absorbed. The face of the frizzen needed to be very hard for flint is an extremely tough material and a soft frizzen would be rapidly gouged by blows of the flint.

The frizzen and hammer springs are shown in the lower left side of the illustration. These were very tricky components to manufacture. In each case they had to be forged carefully to a rather complex shape and then heat treated to a hard and relatively brittle condition. The hammer spring was a particularly powerful spring — at full cock the curved end often pressed down on the tumbler with almost 100 pounds of force. At the same time the allowable deflection of the spring was relatively short. This meant that the spring had what is known as a very high "rate". For example: if the spring had a rate of 200 pounds per inch it meant that it would require 200 pounds of force to compress it one inch. In the relaxed condition it exerted no force at all, but if the tail was pushed up ¼-inch it would exert a force of 50 pounds. At ½-inch deflection the spring would push down with 100 pounds, and at ¾-inch it would push down with 150 pounds.

When the Colonial blacksmith tempered his springs some came out as shown in the drawing and some came out with a wider angle at the bend and some with a smaller angle. Once a spring was tempered, it was difficult to change the angle, for it was brittle after heat treatment and would crack through the bend. At the same time if the gunsmith assembled these springs with the various angles to his lock mechanisms, the springs with a very tight angle at the bend would give very little force, resulting in a hammer that was easy to cock but would often misfire. The springs with a wide open angle would make a hammer very difficult to cock, which would tend to break flints rapidly and cause excessive damage to the frizzen.

There were two ways to solve the problem. One was to anneal the spring to a dead soft condition again, bend it to a slightly better angle and reheat treat it, hoping that the final angle would be more nearly correct. The other approach was to file the surfaces on the tumbler or move the location of the hammer spring screw so that the deflection was in the proper range for functioning.

The bridle is shown in the upper left-hand illustration. This little part looks fairly innocuous, but it was a very important element for it determined the pivot positions of both the hammer and sear. If the sear was not properly aligned with the hammer, the lock was not very safe and did not function well. The bridle had an additional function in that the upper hooked surface formed a solid stop preventing the tumbler from rotating too far. Normally on a flintlock this surface was never used for it only came into action if the lock was accidentally snapped with the hammer removed. Later in the percussion era it became the primary means for preventing over rotation of the hammer and tumbler if the lock was removed from the gun.

The design of the ornate hammer is shown in Figure 1-5. This is basically a flat forging and on the better guns it was formed into an artistically pleasing "S" shape with smooth flowing lines and carefully sculptured contours. The curves swirled around with artistic care and flared out to form the lower jaw which held the flint. Rising from the back of the "S" shape was the hammer spur which served to guide the cap. The hammer spur provided the "line of strength" absorbing part of the shock of the flint slamming into the frizzen. The hammer spur also prevented the cap screw from getting bent due to the heavy blows of the flint.

The cap is shown in the upper right-hand illustration. There were two basic designs of cap. The earlier design is shown in Figure 1-3. There was a small groove cut in the face of the hammer spur and a matching projection on the cap rode inside this groove. The design shown in Figure 1-5 first appeared before 1750 and became increasingly common in the latter part of the 18th century. In this design a groove was cut into the cap which surrounded the hammer spur. The slot in the cap plus the screw aligned the axis of the cap with the axis of the hammer. The piece of flint slid into the opening between the cap and the hammer and then the cap screw was tightened down firmly in place.

Some cap screws had a hole through the center as shown in Figure 1-5. Others had a cross slot as shown in the Brown Bess lock of Figure 1-3. In some locks both features were provided. The threads on these early locks are incredibly crude. The thread profiles are often rounded and the threads are only partially cut. On this example, the cap screw threads, which took a lot of stress in being tightened hard to hold the flint, are cut about half the depth of a modern 7/32 inch thread. The thread on the hammer screw shown in the right side of Figure 1-5 is even shallower, having the appearance of only a third to a quarter the depth of a modern 3/16-inch thread. The sear screw is shown in the lower right side of Figure 1-5 and there were two bridle screws identical in shape, one of which served as the sear pivot. Three screws are not shown. One was the screw which held the hammer spring or mainspring to the lock plate. This was almost identical to the hammer screw but had a .156 of an inch thread. The frizzen spring screw was virtually the same as the mainspring screw. The screw which formed the cross pivot for the frizzen was very similar to the bridle screw with a long shank, but had a slightly smaller head and a smaller thread .156 of an inch in diameter.

The sear and frizzen springs are shown in the lower left side of Figure 1-5. They were not as critical as the mainspring, but were tricky to make with the crude machining and heat-treatment methods available in the 18th century. The sear design remained virtually unchanged for 200 years and is a typical design used in all side lock mechanisms, appearing even on many breech-loading rifles.

The tumbler is shown in the lower right side of Figure 1-5. This little part provided the transfer of powerful forces within the flintlock mechanism and had to be forged and machined very carefully. It can be seen in its proper position in the right side of Figure 1-3 slightly hidden behind the bridle. The powerful mainspring pushed down on the sloping surface forward of the pivot. On the lower surface a deep safety notch was cut and then a shallower firing notch to the rear. There was a .200 of an inch diameter pivot on the inboard side which passed through the bridle and positioned the inboard end of the tumbler. A shaft .400 of an inch in diameter passed through the lock plate and flats were filed into the outer end of the shaft so that the rotational torque developed by the powerful mainspring could be transferred to the hammer causing it to rotate and slam the flint into the frizzen. In addition the square-ended shaft had a hole drilled and tapped to hold the hammer screw. The tumbler was small but it was like the crankshaft of a modern engine, and absolutely essential to the functioning of the flintlock mechanism.

FRENCH MUSKETS IN THE AMERICAN REVOLUTION

The French had been active in the research and development of improved military firearms, in the late 17th and early 18th centuries. In 1702 they standardized on the use of paper cartridges and by 1717 had developed a standard musket design, very much like the British Long Land Service Musket (Brown Bess) shown in Figure 1-2. The French manufactured muskets at the Royal Armories at St. Etienne, Mauberge, and Charleville, and held them in storage until needed. This provided a tight government control over military musket production and allowed good standardization of design for the 18th century.

New designs were studied, and by 1763 the French had evolved an excellent musket containing very modern features for its day. During the early years of the American Revolution, the Colonists received a great boost in their war effort with shipments from France of substantial quantities of the .69 caliber French Charleville muskets, most of which were the Model 1763 design. Shipments of 101,918 French muskets of designs dating from 1718 to 1768 were documented during the Revolutionary War. The average price paid was only about $5.00 per musket, compared to a purchase cost of $12.30 per musket for the Committee of Safety Muskets manufactured in the Colonies.

CHARLEVILLE MODEL 1763

Caliber — .69, smoothbore
Barrel length — 44¾ inches
Stock — black walnut, 57 inches long
Ignition — flintlock
Overall length — 59½ inches
Weight with 14-inch bayonet — 9¾ pounds

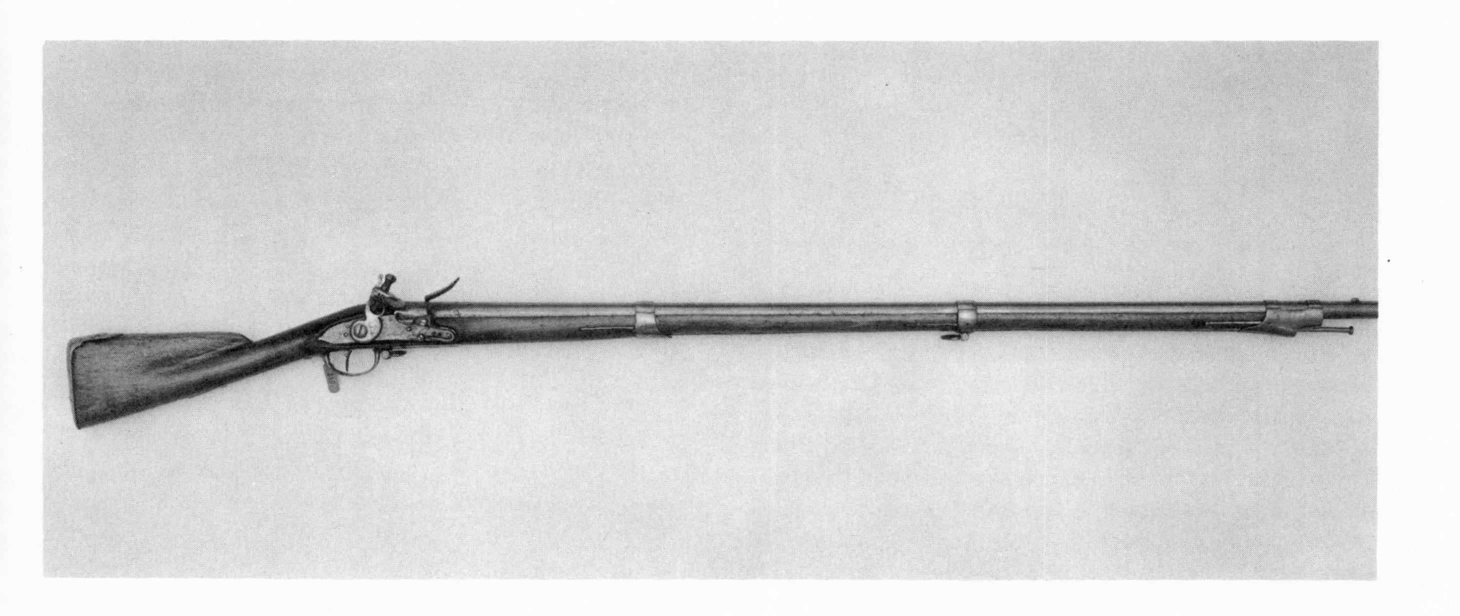

FIGURE 1-6 French Model 1763 "Charleville" flintlock musket.

The French muskets were made at many arsenals, but the majority came from the Charleville Armory, and the name is often used to describe any French musket. With their smaller caliber and lighter ball these muskets were quite satisfactory and were used all through the Revolutionary War. A Charleville Model 1763 musket is shown in Figure 1-6. It differs in several respects from the Brown Bess. The barrel was held on with three steel bands, rather than with cross pins. Other differences were the smaller caliber of .69 of an inch compared with the .75 caliber Brown Bess. This was a 15 percent reduction in cross-section area of the bore, and the Charleville naturally fired a lighter musket ball (370 grains compared with 500 for the Brown Bess).

The amount of recoil a soldier could stand did not vary much from one army to the other, and to keep the recoil within reasonable limits required that the 500-grain ball from the Brown Bess be fired at about 200 feet per second less velocity than the ball from the French Charleville.

United States Model 1795 Flintlock Musket

The performance of the Charleville muskets was so satisfactory that when Congress passed an Act in 1794 establishing National Armories the Charleville Model 1763 was used as the model for the first standard United States musket. The first armory was established at Springfield, Massachusetts, in buildings which had existed since the Revolution.

MODEL 1795

Caliber — .69, smoothbore
Barrel length — 44¾ inches
Stock — black walnut, 56⅝ inches long
Ignition — flintlock
Overall length — 59½ to 60 inches
Weight — average, 8 pounds 14 ounces

The Springfield model of 1795 was a very close copy of the French Model 1763 with the same caliber, barrel length and other specifications. The weight without bayonet was slightly under nine pounds. The appearance of the musket is shown in Figure 1-7. The close similarity to the Charleville Model of 1763 is clearly shown. The French muskets were made with two types of hammers — a graceful gooseneck as shown on the Brown Bess in Figure 1-2, and a doubled necked hammer with a reinforcing loop under the jaw. The double necked hammer was standard on the Model 1795 Springfield.

The first American muskets of this design were assembled at Springfield as early as 1778, using parts made by local contractors. Springfield was established as a storage depot during the Revolution, and the manufacturing functions were added by Congressional action in 1794. The manufacture of muskets in Colonial America was a very time-consuming process, and the barrels were particularly difficult. Since large bars of steel and deep-hole drills were not available, the barrels were laboriously made by wrapping a red hot strip of steel spirally around a mandril, and forge-welding the strips together by hammering. The welded barrels were then reamed and polished on the inside and smoothed to a tapered contour on the outside.

The 44¾-inch barrel, twice as long as most modern rifle barrels, was necessary because of the very poor quality of musket powder available in the 18th century. Enormous charges of 160 to 190 grains of black powder were used to propel a 370- to 500-grain soft lead ball at 1,000 to 1,400 feet per second velocity. A very long barrel gave additional time for the poor quality powder to be churned up and mixed and burned during the passage of the paper-patched bullet down the bore. A second reason for the long barrel was that the infantry were sometimes called upon to act as pikemen in resisting a cavalry or infantry charge. Fitting a 14-inch or longer bayonet at the end of the long musket barrel provided an over-all weapon of over six feet. At the same time practical experiments had shown that longer barrels were impractical since the soldiers of the day found it awkward to load a musket with so long a barrel.

Manufacture of the lock for the musket was also very difficult in an agricultural country like the United States. The flintlock musket represented a highly refined product for its day, and the procurement of good quality iron, the forging and machining of complex shapes, such as hammers, frizzens, pans, triggers and "Vee" springs, were formidable problems for a new nation.

When production was started at Springfield Armory there were very few machine tools, jigs and fixtures. The early hand production methods were gradually improved with the addition of tools to do specific operations, but wide variations in part size and quality remained a very serious problem through the 1820's.

In the early 19th century water power was used more frequently to provide power for manufacturing. This substitution of water for muscle power on some of the heavier operations such as drilling, grinding and turning, plus the development of specialized tools and crude gauges, added up to more accurate production techniques.

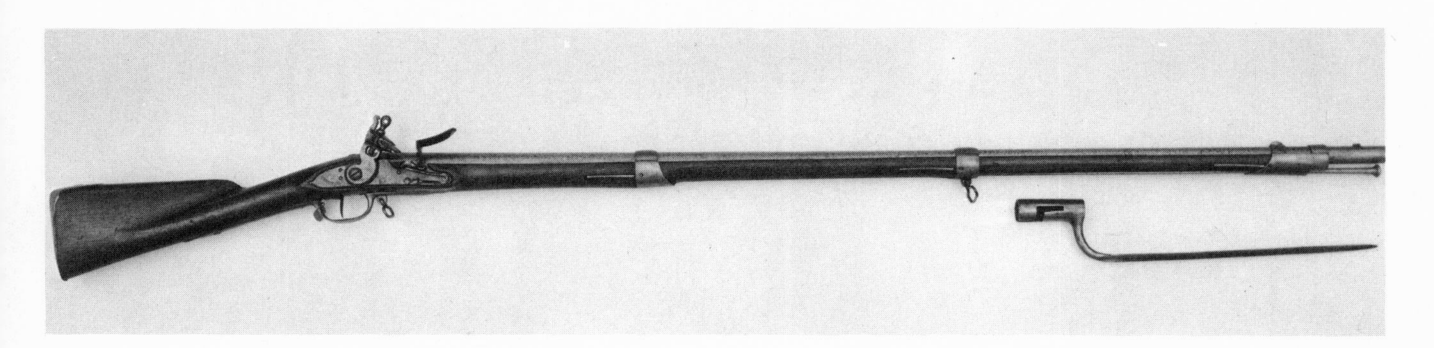

FIGURE 1-7 United States Model 1795 flintlock musket

CHANGES IN MUSKET DESIGN FROM 1795 TO THE 1840's

The design of the Model 1795 Springfield musket proved to be very satisfactory. The same basic pattern of musket was continued for almost fifty years until replaced by a percussion musket in the early 1840's. The design was so successful in fact that it requires a close examination of the early 19th century muskets to discern the subtle changes that occurred. Features that remained common on all flintlock muskets manufactured for regular Army units were:

1. Caliber .690 of an inch (with the crude manufacturing tolerances of the day, the barrels generally ran from .690 of an inch to .705 of an inch.)
2. Barrels were held to the stock with three bands.
3. A steel ramrod with a mushroom tip was fitted into a channel cut into the stock and retained by a spring retainer at the breech end of the rifle.
4. A long black walnut stock was fitted with a straight grip and a forearm which extended to within a few inches of the muzzle of the barrel.
5. Two sling loops were fitted, one on the middle barrel band, and the second either immediately in front of the trigger guard or as part of the forward loop of the trigger guard.
6. Double necked hammers were fitted to the muskets. (Early muskets such as the Brown Bess, Committee of Safety and some of the French Charleville muskets had an S shaped or gooseneck hammer. The double necked hammer had a reinforcing loop on the front side running up to the hammer jaw).
7. All the muskets had a front sight formed as part of forward barrel band. The muskets were so inaccurate that no rear sights were fitted.

The Model 1795 muskets were manufactured both at Springfield Armory and after 1801 at Harper's Ferry Armory in Virginia. They were also manufactured by a number of small contractors at a price of $13.40 per musket. Not all these muskets agree in design. For example muskets contracted by Eli Whitney of New Haven in 1798 incorporated features from the French Charleville design of 1777, including a tilted brass pan on the lock, a feature which did not become standardized in this country for another fifteen years. Whitney also included a rounded hammer rather than the flat beveled hammer standard on the Charleville model 1763 and the Springfield model 1795 design. These features are both shown in the lock detail in Figure 1-12.

FIGURE 1-8 Infantry of American Continental Army, 1779-1783.

U.S. Musket Model of 1808

The first changes in musket design that are significant enough to be considered a new model occurred in 1808. The Model 1808 muskets were manufactured at Springfield and at Harper's Ferry as well as by a large number of Government contractors.

Musket production received a major impetus in 1808 when Congress passed an act for arming the Militia of the states with an annual appropriation of $2,000,000 per year for the manufacture of new muskets to a standard pattern.

This Congressional action followed a confrontation between the British ship Leopard and the American ship Chesapeake on the high seas. The British ship stopped the Chesapeake and drafted the American sailors on board, claiming they were still British citizens even though the Revolutionary War was long over. Protests by President Thomas Jefferson did not resolve the conflict. Although Jefferson was strongly against war, calling it "the scourge of mankind," he found it necessary to greatly increase preparedness in the United States for a war with Britain appeared to be materializing rapidly and did occur in 1812. In June, 1808, the Congressional action provided for an annual production of 40,000 muskets at the National Armories. Springfield and Harpers Ferry were each tooled up for manufacture of 20,000 muskets a year. Other long-term contracts were given to private manufacturers. The Congressional action also provided for the manufacture of rifles, pistols and swords.

Although at this point in history we were known around the world as a nation of riflemen, the fact is that the smoothbore muskets were the mainstay of American defense. They constituted 80 to 90 percent of the long arms purchased. The State Militia were an important element in the United States defense plans. Many states contracted directly with private manufacturers for militia muskets. These varied slightly in pattern from the national designs and this sometimes led to confusion. Eli Whitey, for example, had large contracts with New York State for the manufacture of muskets, and he was careful to specify that the muskets manufactured for the Federal Government incorporate some of the features for which he had already tooled up for the New York State muskets. Whitney was a progressive manufacturer and incorporated more modern features than some of the standard Federal designs in the same period, but these differences in design resulted in a lot of controversy in the administration of contracts.

On October 29, 1808, President Jefferson, through the Secretary of War, contacted the governors of all the states and territories and asked them "to take effectual measures to organize, arm and equip, according to law, and hold in readiness to march at a moment's notice" their State Militia numbering almost 100,000 men. The Congressional Act of March 1808 provided for the manufacture of sufficient muskets by the National Armories and private manufacturers to meet the requisitions of the regular Army, and also of all State Militias requesting muskets. In order to set up the production on an orderly basis, private companies were given five-year contracts for the fabrication of muskets ranging in quantities from 2,500 to 10,000 in number. The contractors were furnished "pattern muskets" which were fabricated at the National Armories and provided a standardized design to use as a guide. Their appearance is shown in Figure 1-9.

During the first decade of the 19th century the Ord-

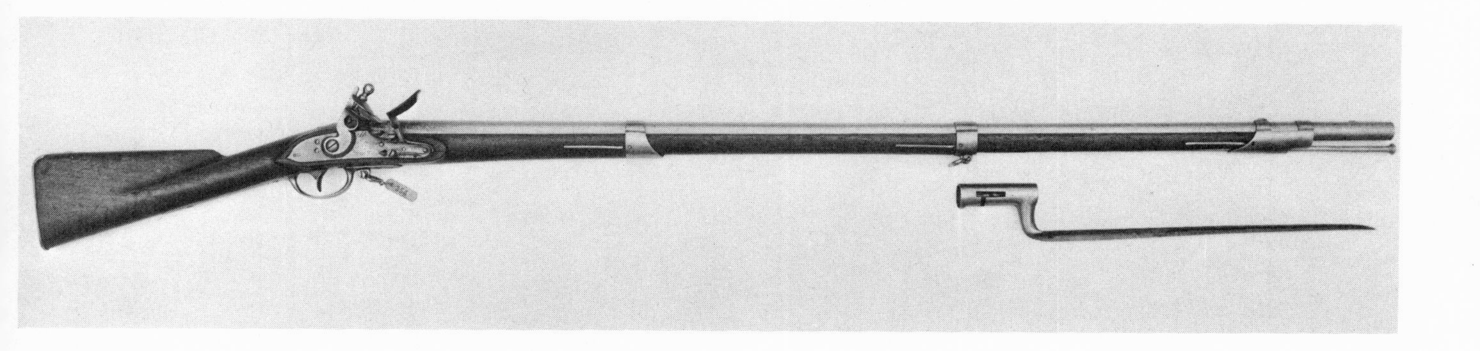

FIGURE 1-9 United States Model 1808 flintlock musket.

nance experts at Springfield and Harper's Ferry Armories had done what we at the present time call a "value engineering study." Each component in the musket was examined to determine if it performed its function in the most efficient manner and if the design could be simplified to improve its function or to make it cheaper to manufacture. Changes made in the Model 1808 included:

1. Elimination of an ornamental tail on the frizzen.
2. The pan was rounded in design and forged integral with the lock plate. This construction would not have been practical with the crude tooling available in 1800. Apparently more elaborate tooling allowing the more difficult process of forging the pan integral was developed in the first decade of the 19th century.
3. The stock was shortened by one inch and the groove running from the comb of the stock toward the butt plate was considerably shortened.
4. The over-all length of the musket was reduced by about an inch. Barrels were reduced by about a quarter inch.
5. The "value engineers" really went to work on the trigger guard, shortening it by about two inches and changing the long pointed ornamental ends of the guard into shorter plain round ends.

U.S. Muskets, Model of 1812

By 1812 the Ordnance Department was unhappy with contractors taking liberties with the muskets and variations in the sizes of the parts added to the confusion. The Government felt that more exact specifications were needed to assure uniformity of future production. Special "model muskets" were fabricated at Harper's Ferry Armory in 1812 with the intention that these would provide guides in establishing production standards at Springfield, Harper's Ferry and

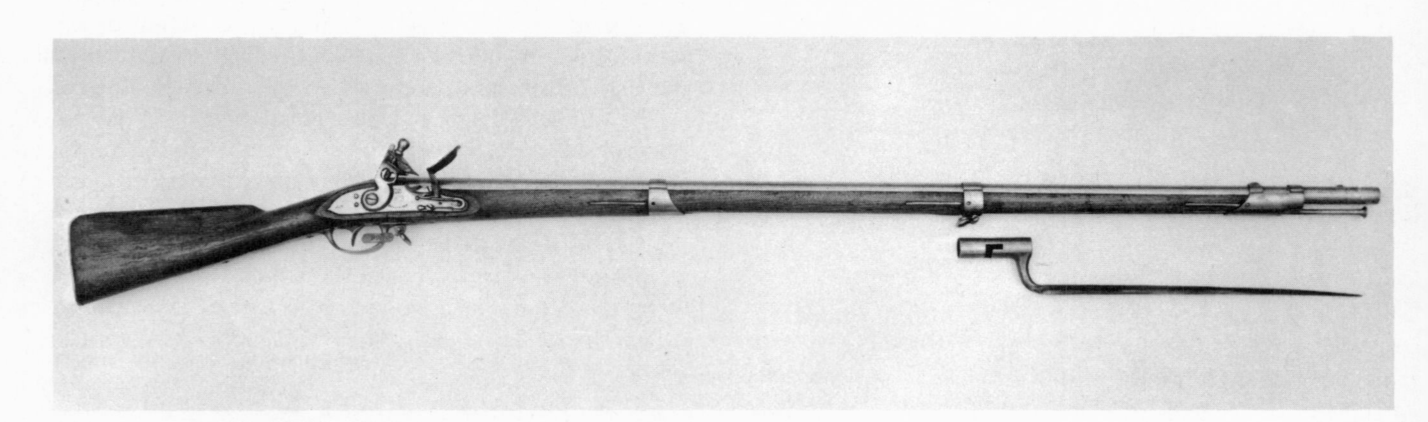

FIGURE 1-10 "First Style" United States Model 1812 flintlock musket.

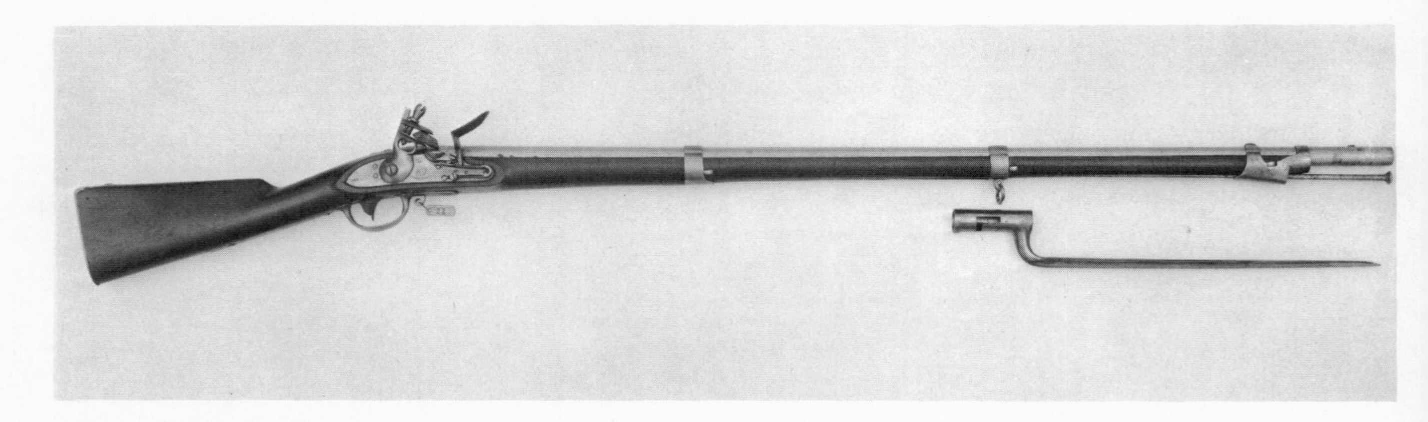

FIGURE 1-11 "Second Style" United States Model 1812 flintlock musket.

FIGURE 1-12 Lock details of United States Model 1816 contract musket.

with the private contractors. The locks, plates, furniture and screws were to be standard and interchangeable on these future models. The price for the new models was established at $13.00 per musket, compared with $10.75 paid in 1812 for the manufacture of Model 1808 muskets.

The Model 1812 muskets are broken down by the student of early firearms into first, second and third types plus contract muskets. A first style musket is shown in Figure 1-10. The second type musket had a very unusual retaining catch for the forward barrel band, which is shown in Figure 1-11. This illustration shows the rounded hammer design, which was much more common on the Model 1812 muskets than the flat beveled design shown in Figure 1-10. Both examples are from the Winchester Gun Museum in New Haven, Connecticut. The principal differences between the Model 1812 muskets and the 1808 design were that in the later model the surfaces of the double necked hammer were rounded and the pan was forged integral with the lock plate and was rounded at the bottom. The muskets manufactured at the armories retained the flat type of pan with a fence to the rear, while the Whitney Model 1812 contract muskets used a tilted pan as shown in Figure 1-12.

The length of barrel on the 1812 muskets was reduced to forty-two inches and it was made slightly heavier than the earlier barrels. A peculiar cut in the cheek of the butt stocks was hollowed out to fit the shooter's face. The lock plate on the 1812 muskets was shorter than on the earlier muskets. The butt stock was shortened again and did not have the long cut extending back from the comb of the stock. The Model 1812 musket continued the practice of the earlier designs in having an iron butt plate, iron trigger guard and trigger plate, iron barrel bands and a steel ramrod.

The War Department took into account the fact that there were many stocks of old parts at the armories and at contractors' plants. These continued to be assembled into muskets after 1812. The result was that the situation became increasingly more confused until in 1815 the Ordnance Department decided to take a strong stand and straighten out the situation.

U. S. Musket, Model 1816

On June 10, 1815, Chief of Ordnance recommended the adoption of a new standard musket and rifle. The intention was to lay down the exact specifications and

Musket	Caliber	Barrel Length	Overall Length	Weight, Pounds
Early "Brown Bess" (Long Land Service Pattern) 1717-1780	.75	46″M	62″M	10.7M
Late "Brown Bess" (Short Land Service Pattern) 1768-1800	.75	42M	58M	10.0M
French Charleville M 1763	.69	44¾M	59½M	8.9M
Springfield Model 1795	.69	44½M	59½M	8.6M
Springfield Model 1808	.69	44½M	59¼M	9.4M
Springfield Model 1812	.69	42	57½	9.5
U.S. Musket, Model 1816	.69	42	58	9.5
U.S. Musket, Model 1822	.69	42M	58M	9.6M
U.S. Musket, Model 1835	.69	42M	58M	9.6M
U.S. Percussion Musket, Model 1842	.69	42M	58M	9.1M

M = MEASURED WINCHESTER GUN. MUSEUM

FIGURE 1-13 Specifications of flintlock muskets.

to have the National Armories fabricate muskets which agreed with each other in all features and distribute these to the private contractors to define the pattern of future designs. In May 1816 the Superintendent of the Springfield Armory was directed by the Ordnance Department to make three muskets. After approval, six more muskets were fabricated together with six sets of taps, dies, gauges and patterns to be used by Springfield and Harper's Ferry Armory. The major difference between the Model 1816 muskets and the earlier designs was the use of a tilted brass pan on the lock plate. The brass pan was similar to the design of the French Charleville musket of 1777 and was a separate piece attached to the iron lock plate. In addition the muskets had rounded hammers and the rear of the lock plate was rounded to a convex surface in back of the hammer. These details are clearly shown in Figure 1-12.

Uniformity of manufacture continued to be a major problem. One of the Model 1816 muskets in the Winchester Gun Collection was manufactured at the Virginia Manufactury. It has a brass pan, but it is flat as on the Model 1795 musket, and has a fence to the rear. Furthermore, the hammer is flat and beveled. These kinds of variations continued so that in 1822 another attempt was made to establish more uniform specifications.

U.S. Musket, Model 1822

This is a minor variation of the Model 1816, and some refer to this as the Model 1816, second type. An excellent example of the Model 1822 musket is shown in Figure 1-14. This musket has a rounded hammer and a rounded lock plate to the rear of the hammer. A tilted brass pan is fitted. Most of the Model 1822 muskets had barrels, barrel bands, trigger guards and butt plates finished by the Browning process, whereas all earlier muskets had been finished bright. In 1831 the Browning process was dropped and the bright finish was renewed.

Minor changes from the earlier models of 1812 muskets included a lengthening of the lock plate by ¼ inch and bending the top of the frizzen away from the hammer.

The Models 1816 and 1822 were excellent, and thou-

MODEL 1822 SPECIFICATIONS

Caliber: .69 smoothbore
Overall length: 58 inches
Weight: 9.6 pounds
Lock plate: flat surface forward of hammer, rounded surface to rear of hammer
Barrel: 42 inches long
Stock: black walnut, very low comb, no comb, flutes, 54 inches long.

sands were manufactured at Springfield and Harper's Ferry Armories, and by many private contractors.

The period from 1795 to 1825 saw the establishment of greatly improved manufacturing capabilities in the National Armories and by private contractors. Eli Whitney established an armory in New Haven, Connecticut, and built a dam to provide waterpower to operate gunmaking machinery. The Armories were also changing over from hand-forging and turning processes to the use of waterpower for forging locks, for forge welding, reaming and grinding barrels, and for grinding and polishing the components to final dimensions. It was a period when the Armories started making elaborate gauges to inspect the contours of the lock plates, barrels, hammers and stock for conformity to the model dimensions. An excellent set of these early gauges are on display at the Smithsonian Institution and they show great care in construction.

There was still a great deal of hand labor in the manufacture of muskets, but the early 19th century saw the changeover from muskets made by hand techniques, with poorly finished internal components of widely varying dimensions, to components of uniform size and good finish. An important incentive for this change was the Congressional Act of 1808 which provided a long-term government financial commitment for musket manufacture.

Private contractors such as Henry Deringer, Eli Whitney, Simeon North, N. Starr, L. Pomeroy and Asa Waters developed private armories to manufacture "contract muskets" to the established pattern. Highly skilled mechanics and inventors such as John Hall (inventor of a breech-loading flintlock rifle!), Marine T. Wickham and others worked at the National Armories to develop improved designs and manufacturing techniques.

There were many frustrations. The Government contracting responsibility was changed in 1812 from Tenche Coxe, "Purveyor of Public Supplies," to a different office headed by a commissary general named Callender Irvine. General Irvine and the private contractors fought continuously. He insisted on the letter of the contracts, which the private manufacturers could not meet to his satisfaction. In reading Irvine's letters to Simeon North and Eli Whitney, the tremendous friction is obvious. Irvine repeatedly recommended to the Secretary of War that the contracts be canceled, and the impression is strong that under Callendar Irvine's approach there would have been little procurement until the manufacturing processes were sufficiently good to give truly interchangeable manufacture of parts.

A barrel-grinding machine was installed at Springfield Armory in 1818, and it was enthusiastically endorsed as providing higher quality barrels of more uniform wall thickness, with lower costs than hand processes. Major manufacturers today use barrel-grinding machines to provide the uniform outside contours and wall thicknesses on shotgun barrels, which are similar in manufacturing difficulty to the musket barrels of 150 years ago, but made of stronger steels and held to much closer inside and outside tolerances.

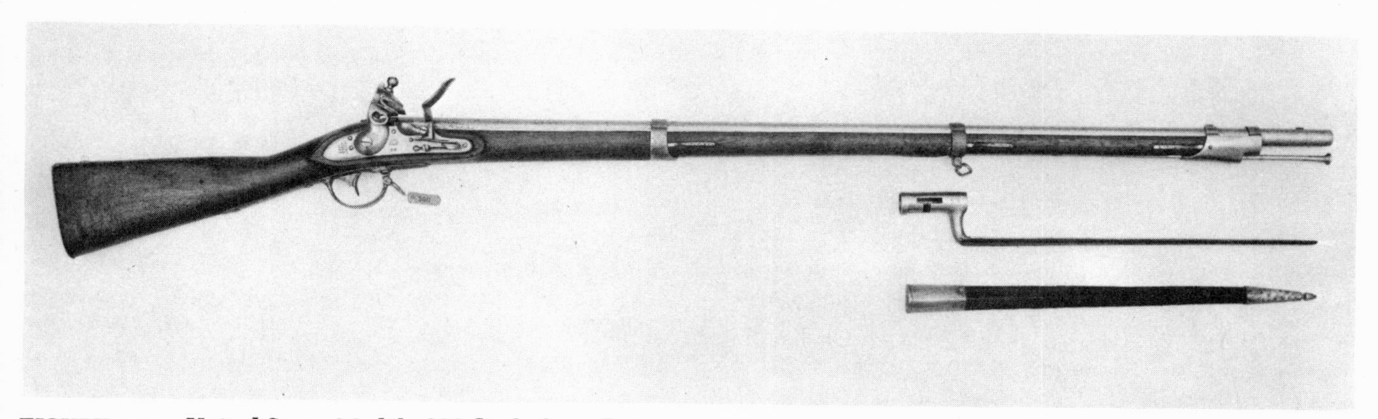

FIGURE 1-14 United States Model 1822 flintlock musket.

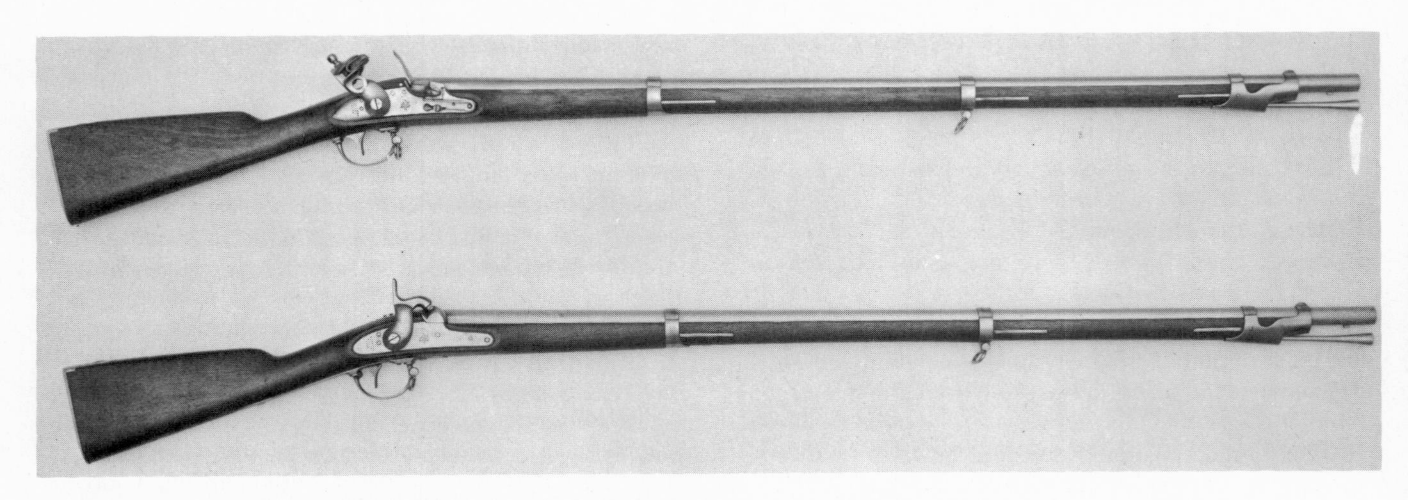

FIGURE 1-15 Upper: United States Model 1835 flintlock musket.
Lower: United States Model 1842 smoothbore percussion musket.

FIGURE 1-16 Left: Model 1835 flintlock musket details.
Right: Model 1842 percussion musket details.

U.S. Musket, Model 1835

During the 1830's Ordnance considered modification in flintlock musket design to incorporate improvements that were standardized in the French musket of 1822. Development of the specifications of the new model dragged on through 1833 and 1834, and the specifications were finally written in 1835. Production of the new design began late in 1839 and continued for five years. These muskets are quite rare, for only 30,421 were produced and 26,841 were converted to percussion muskets at Springfield Armory between 1849 and 1851. A typical model 1835 musket is shown as the upper musket in Figure 1-15, and on the left side of Figure 1-16. This specimen, from the Winchester Gun Museum, was manufactured at Harper's Ferry Armory. One of the most interesting features is that the pan on this musket is very similar to that on the Springfield Model 1795 musket in having a flat top surface parallel to the barrel center line and a fence to the rear. The pan was removable on both designs. In the Model 1835 musket the pan was made of brass while in the Model 1795 it was made of iron. The lock plate on the Model 1835 musket is rounded at the rear of the hammer, and the hammer itself is double necked and rounded. The frizzen had a small section at the tip bent forward as on the Model 1822 muskets. The Model 1835 was the last flintlock musket in the United States Service.

MODEL 1835 SPECIFICATIONS

Caliber: .690 bore minimum, .705 bore maximum.
Barrel: 42 inches long, bright finish.
Stock: Black walnut, 54¾ inches long with a higher comb than Model 1835 but not fluted.
Trigger guard: Iron with finger ridges on trigger plate to rear of guard.
Weight: 9.6 pounds, average.

There was a slight change in the design of the ramrod which was flared to a conical end instead of having a mushroom shaped end as on earlier muskets. The butt plate, trigger guard and barrel bands continued to be made of iron. There was only a front sight, which was on the front loop of the front barrel band.

U.S. Percussion Musket, Model 1842

In 1842 the design of the U.S. smoothbore percussion musket was standardized. The musket was very similar in appearance to the flintlock musket, Model 1835, shown in Figure 1-16, except for the use of a percussion ignition, rather than a flint-type ignition system. The design of the two muskets can be compared by examining Figures 1-15 and 1-16. Both muskets were fitted with 42-inch smooth bore .69 caliber barrels. The barrels were held to the stock with three barrel bands fastened by spring clips. The steel ramrods, with their conical flared ends, were similar on the two muskets as were the trigger guards with the sling swivel attached to the front bow of the guard. All of the furniture of the Model 1842 musket, such as barrel bands, butt plate and trigger guard, were made of iron and were finished bright. The stock was black walnut, 55 inches long with a regular comb and no comb flutes. The weight of a Model 1842 musket in the Winchester Museum measured a surprisingly low 9.1 pounds. Some reduction is due to the elimination of all the pan and frizzen machinery, but not enough to account for a half-pound weight difference between Model 1835 and 1842 muskets — both in "new" condition.

This weight of 9.1 pounds may be unusually light, for analysis of data on a Model 1842 musket tested at Washington Arsenal in the 1840's gives a test weight of ten pounds.

The main differences from the Model 1835 design is the great simplification in the breech area, most clearly shown in Figure 1-16. The percussion system was mounted in a "cone seat" welded to the rear of the barrel. The hammer was entirely different from that of the flintlock muskets in being one piece and having a solid surface to slam the percussion cap down on the cone to cause ignition. Since the cone was nearer the center line of the musket than the pan of the flintlock designs, the hammer had to have a considerable offset to the left to line up properly with the cone.

In the early 1840's considerable emphasis was put on conversion of earlier muskets to the percussion design. This was generally accomplished by dovetailing and brazing on a block of iron which was then machined and threaded to receive the cone for the percussion cap. New offset hammers were fabricated to replace the flintlock assembly. This simple conversion permitted modernization of a large number of good quality muskets at very low expense.

It is a commentary on the ruggedness of frontier conditions that in many sections the flintlock musket was preferred, even after the invention of percussion. The reason was that a flintlock firearm was serviceable with only powder and ball which were relatively easy to obtain even on the frontier. The percussion musket also required percussion caps and these were hard to find in many of the far frontier locations.

During the middle 1850's, many of the percussion muskets were altered to fire a Minié type bullet. The musket barrels were rifled with shallow grooves and rear sights were added to take advantage of the greatly increased accuracy of the rifled arms. Since the musket barrels were .69 caliber to start with, and had thin walls, the resulting "rifles" were far from ideal. The Minié bullets were heavier than musket balls, and typical ballistics given for tests conducted in 1843 showed the differences:

	"Old Musket" (Round Ball)	"Altered Rifle Musket" (Minié Ball)	Army Modern M-14 Rifle
Caliber	.69 (Smooth)	.69 (Rifled)	.30 (Rifled)
Bullet Weight	412 Grains	740 Grains	150 Grains
Powder Charge	110 Grains	70 Grains	46.5 Grains
Muzzle Velocity	1500	954	2800
Muzzle Energy*	2059	1496	2612
Test Weight of Musket*	10.0	10.0	9.7
Free Recoil Velocity of Rifle/Musket Due to Bullet Alone	8.83 Ft/Sec	9.36 Ft/Sec	6.2 Ft/Sec
Calculated True Free Recoil Velocity* [BRL Formula]	12.3 Ft/Sec	12.2 Ft/Sec	8.77 Ft/Sec
"K" Factor for Powder Gases	.507	.507	1.00
Calculated Recoil Energy of Rifle/Musket*	23.5	23.3	11.6
"Muzzle Impulse" of cartridge pound-seconds*	3.55	3.5	2.65

*Calculated on ballistics computer program

The performance of the old percussion musket firing a round ball is compared with the converted muskets firing the elongated Minié ball which weighed 740 grains. As a modern comparison the Army's .30 caliber rifle, the M-14, is shown in the third column. The shift from a round ball to an elongated ball in the old musket increased the bullet weight from 412 to 740 grains. In order to keep the recoil within bearable limits, the muzzle velocity was cut from 1500 feet per second to 954 feet per second, according to tests performed by Captain Alfred Mordecai at Washington Arsenal in 1843 and 1844.

The test reports include data on the distance the rifle or musket would recoil in one foot if suspended freely on wires. These are given as 8.83 feet for the round ball musket and 9.36 feet for the "rifle-musket."

Calculated on a modern computer, an analysis of this data shows that the velocities given are for the impulse due to the musket ball alone and do not take into account the impulse due to the powder charge. The next line down shows the calculated true free recoil velocity using the latest formula developed by the Ballistics Research Laboratories in Aberdeen, Maryland, and modified by the author to reflect black powder rather than smokeless powder ballistics.

The data shows the powder charge of the rifled .69 caliber muskets was adjusted so that the recoil velocity and the recoil energy remained virtually identical to that with the heavier powder charge of the round ball load. Even so, the recoil velocity of 12¼ feet per second of the 10-pound musket gave a tremendous recoil energy of 23 foot-pounds.

These recoil velocities and energies compare with measured recoil velocities of 8.77 feet per second for the Army's modern M-14 rifle and a recoil energy of only 11.6 foot-pounds. Late in 1969 the Army announced that it was replacing the M-14 with an even lighter rifle — the .22 caliber M-16 rifle. One of the major reasons is the heavy weight of the rifle and the "heavy recoil" which makes it extremely difficult for the average soldier to control the rifle in full automatic fire. Since the old muzzle-loading muskets were fired much less frequently than a modern automatic rifle, the soldiers of a century ago could absorb much more recoil per shot. The recoil velocity and recoil energy of the old muzzle-loading muskets are really much closer to the performance of a modern shotgun with magnum or rifled slug loads than to the modern military rifle.

Recoil was a severe problem even at the time of the American Revolution. The weight of a musket ball increases as the cube of the diameter, and the average British Brown Bess ball of 0.694 inches diameter weighed about 500 grains. There are 7,000 grains to the pound, so the weight may be calculated by dividing 7000 grains by "14 to the pound", which is the way the weight is listed on the old tables of the Revolutionary period.

The 163-grain charge of black powder was divided, with about 10 grains placed in the "pan" and 153 grains in the barrel. From calculations of the ballistics of a large number of muzzle-loading military muskets and rifles the author has found that a "muzzle impulse" of 3.5 pound-seconds was about the maximum that a soldier could stand, and practically no military firearms ever exceeded this figure.

According to Newton's second law, each action has an equal and opposite reaction. The "muzzle impulse" is the momentum delivered to the musket ball, wads and powder out the muzzle of the musket, and this is balanced by an equal and opposite shove of 3.5 pound-seconds on the shooter's shoulder.

The muzzle velocity of the Brown Bess may be estimated as follows:

$$\text{Muzzle Impulse} = \frac{(W_b + W_w + K \cdot W_p)\ V_o}{\text{gravity}}$$

$$W_b = \text{weight of ball, pounds} = \frac{\text{weight of ball, grains}}{7000}$$

V_o = muzzle velocity of ball

$$W_p = \text{weight of powder, pounds} = \frac{153 \text{ grains}}{7000}$$

$$W_w = \text{weight of wadding, pounds} = \frac{10 \text{ grains}}{7000}$$

gravity = acceleration of gravity = 32.16 ft./sec.^{2}

$$3.5 \text{ lb.-sec.} = \frac{(500 + 10 + 1.0 \times 153)}{7000 \times 32.16}$$

V_o = 1200 Feet/Second Muzzle Velocity

The muzzle energy of the ball would be:

$$E_o = \frac{1200^2 \times 500}{7000 \times 2g} = 1600 \text{ Foot-pounds}$$

Note: the "K" factor deserves much study. A detailed analysis by the author leads to an estimate of:

K = 1.0 for Revolutionary war muskets

K = 1.6 for 20th century black powder cartridges

K = 1.53 for .375 and .458 magnums with heavy bullet

K = 1.35 for the M-14 (.30 caliber)

K = 1.05 for the M-16 (.22 caliber)

K = .84 for the .220 Swift.

The ballistician measures the efficiency of firearms by the amount of muzzle energy delivered per grain of propellant, and this may be estimated as:

$$\text{Efficiency} = \frac{1600 \text{ foot-pounds}}{153 \text{ grains in the barrel}}$$

Efficiency = 10½ foot-pounds per grain of propellant [there are 7000 "grains" per pound]

These estimates are for a new musket fired with good quality powder of the Revolutionary War period. Many Brown Bess muskets were made with oversize bores, some as large as .800 inches, and these would be very inefficient with the standard ball.

The wide variations in Brown Bess muskets drew many disparaging comments from contemporary writers, and some considered it the worst flintlock used by any European power. It was probably as good as the muskets of the other major powers. French muskets

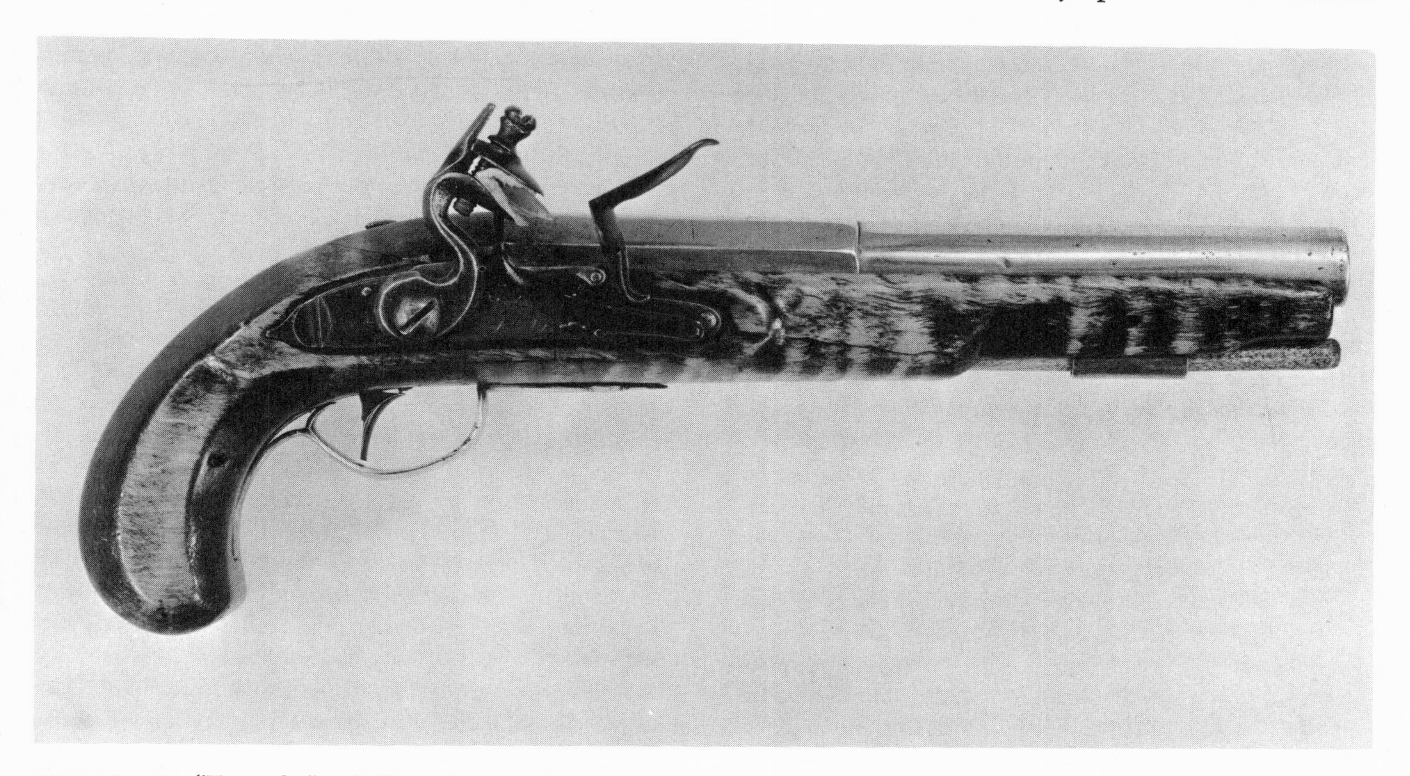

FIGURE 1-17 "Kentucky" style flintlock smoothbore pistol.

of the same time period in the Winchester Gun museum also show wide variations in bore diameter. The estimates given above for performance would be with the best of the muskets, with a difference in diameter between barrel and ball (windage) of .050 inches.

MUZZLE-LOADING PISTOLS

The development of flintlock pistols in the United States very closely paralleled the long arms. Since pistols were primarily designed for personal defense, the emphasis was on creating a compact, lightweight firearm which would have a great deal of "punch" at close range.

A commercial flintlock pistol dating from the American Revolution is shown in Figure 1-17. The .45 caliber smoothbore brass barrel was mounted on a one-piece walnut stock. The barrel length was only 6¾ inches and was machined octagonal for the rear half and turned round for the front half. No sights were fitted and the short wooden ramrod was held by a single brass pipe inletted and cross-pinned into the wooden stock. This brass trigger guard was relatively simple but did include an ornamental detail extending forward under the stock. A vertical screw extended down from the tang of the barrel through the stock and retained the trigger assembly. The screw may be seen extending slightly above and below the stock.

Since the emphasis of pistol design was on light weight and compactness, they were generally fitted with small, lightweight lock plates. The flintlock mechanism on this pistol was slightly smaller than that used on the Kentucky rifles and much smaller than the locks used on military muskets.

The pistol was manufactured by Jacob Grubb of Pennsylvania between 1770 and 1780. The lock work has typical design features of the period with a flat, beveled gooseneck hammer. The construction of the hammer spur and cap are typical of the late 18th century designs. The flat pan is designed with rounded contours and a fence to the rear. The frizzen is nicely detailed complementing the modest engraving on the lock plate.

The pistol has no sights, in keeping with its basic objective — personal defense at close range.

The efficiency of most pistols was relatively low. Actual ballistic tests on a .44 caliber flintlock pistol with a patched round ball of 120 grains and 40 grains of FFFg black powder gave a muzzle velocity of 1050 feet per second and 290 foot-pounds of muzzle energy. The efficiency was slightly over 7 foot-pounds per grain of propellant.

MILITARY FLINTLOCK PISTOLS

The pistols used in the American Revolution were either imported from Europe or commercial designs similar to the Kentucky pistol shown in Figure 1-17. The first standardized for the United States Army was the Model 1799. This was manufactured by Simeon North of Connecticut, and closely followed the designs of the French Army pistol of 1777. This was an unusual pistol design with a short stock and a peculiar trumpet-shape mounted at an angle to the barrel. Simeon North was given two contracts, totaling 2000 pistols in 1799, and 1800.

In 1805 Henry Dearborn, Secretary of War, instructed Harpers Ferry Armory to manufacture 4000 .54 caliber smoothbore pistols. These were larger than the Kentucky pistols shown in Figure 1-17, with 10-inch barrels and an over-all length of 16 inches. The butt of the pistol was reinforced with a metal cap and the stock was cut off a short distance in front of the lock plate. A rib was soldered to the underside of the barrel and the ramrod was retained up against the rib by a single ramrod pipe.

In 1807 an even larger pistol was manufactured at Springfield Armory. This was a .69 caliber smoothbore model with a barrel 10.8 inches long and an over-all length of 17⅜ inches. The stock was extended out nearer the muzzle of the pistol and the fore-end was retained to the barrel with an assembly similar to that used on early muskets. The assembly included a front sight for the pistol and a spring retainer to hold the barrel band in position.

The War of 1812 caused a serious shortage of pistols, and additional contracts were given to Simeon North of Middletown, Connecticut, for slightly smaller .69 caliber smoothbore pistols. These had barrels 9 inches long and an over-all length of 15.3 inches. The Simeon North pistols continued the design features of the Springfield models but differed slightly in lock details. The locks were designed with a flat beveled surface in front of the hammer and a rounded contour to the rear. The double necked hammer had rounded contours and a tilted pan was fitted to the lock. Simeon North built a new factory to manufacture the pistols, and this delayed delivery, much to the annoyance of the Government. Quality was satisfactory and the contracts were continued. In 1816 the caliber was changed to .54 caliber smoothbore but the other specifications remained the same. The .54 caliber became the standard pistol size and small quantities were manufactured through the 1820's and 1830's.

The last flintlock was the Model 1836 pistol which was fitted with an 8½-inch long round smoothbore barrel of .54 caliber, and had an over-all length of 14¼ inches.

PERCUSSION MUZZLE-LOADING PISTOLS

In 1842 two styles of percussion muzzle-loading pistols were standardized, both in .54 caliber. The standard model was manufactured at Springfield Armory with an 8½-inch smoothbore barrel and an over-all length of 14 inches. The lock and percussion mechanisms were very similar to the design of the Model 1842 percussion musket.

The loss of pistol ramrods was a frequent problem on earlier pistols, and this was solved on the Model 1842 by permanently retaining the ramrod with a small swinging stirrup assembly. The design had a double swivel joint so that the ramrod could be withdrawn, pivoted 180 degrees and raised up to the axis of the barrel and used to ram the ball down on the powder charge. The ramrod could then be withdrawn from the barrel and returned to its storage position without ever disconnecting it from the stirrup mechanisms. The pistols were normally finished with brightly polished iron barrels and polished brass furniture.

More compact .54 caliber smoothbore pistols were also specified in 1842. These models had 6-inch barrels and an over-all length of slightly under 12 inches. They were manufactured during the decade of the 1840's by Henry Aston, Middletown, Connecticut; Henry Deringer of Philadelphia, and N. P. Ames. These pistols all fired the half-ounce round ball of .525 diameter which was standard for the muzzle-loading rifles in the United States Service. The powder charge was reduced to keep the recoil within reasonable limits. The pistols were very effective at close range, but accuracy was poor and it is doubtful that these pistols were effective at ranges much over 100 feet.

Muzzle-Loading Ammunition

CHAPTER 2

Developing an accurate picture of the performance of flintlock muskets during the American Revolution is difficult because there was no reliable way to measure velocities in the United States and there were wide variations in the muskets and ammunition. Both the British and French had developed standardized musket designs early in the 18th century, and the French had been issuing paper cartridges to soldiers in the field for 75 years prior to the Revolution. The quality of black powder was so poor that in the early 18th century, musket barrels close to 4 feet long were necessary to churn the ingredients adequately, burn up the powder, and propel the musket ball at a reasonable velocity. The balls were cast in relatively crude metal molds and were often "out of round" by .020 to .030 inches. The standard British Brown Bess muskets at the time of the Revolution generally fired balls from .687 to slightly over .700 inches in diameter. The paper cartridge powder charge was 163 grains compared with charges of 46 grains of smokeless powder for our modern .30 caliber Army cartridge, and only 28.5 grains of powder for the new 5.56 mm (.22 caliber) Army cartridge.

The French Charleville musket of 1763, which came closest to being standard United States musket during the Revolution, fired a .627 inch diameter ball weighing 370 grains with an enormous black powder charge of 189 grains. If the musket ball had fitted tightly in the barrel and provided a good gas seal, the poor underfed Revolutionary soldier would have gone head over heels from the recoil. The French muskets had a basic barrel diameter of .690 of an inch and due to the crude manufacturing techniques, this often varied to .015 of an inch larger for a maximum diameter of .705 of an inch on a new musket. With a maximum diameter barrel and a .627-inch musket ball the difference in diameters was .080 of an inch — over 1/16-inch! Even with the ball surrounded by the paper cartridge wadding the gas leakage was tremendous and the muzzle velocities moderate.

Both the British and French loaded their ammunition into paper cartridges. Just as the British and French differed in the design of their muskets, so they differed slightly in their approach to making cartridges. A typical French cartridge with a straight seam and designed for the Charleville musket is shown in upper Figure 2-1. The French often utilized old government documents for cartridge paper — an effective way to clean out the files, for the information would literally be blown to the four winds. After the cartridge tube was completed the musket ball was dropped in the open end and the 189-grain charge of black powder measured into the cartridge with a small metal dipper. The end of the tube was twisted and folded over to retain the powder charge.

A typical British musket cartridge is shown in Fig-

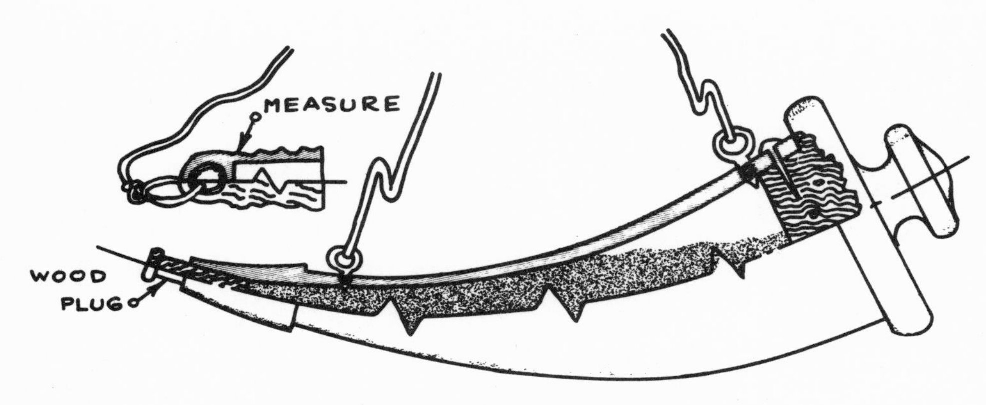

TYPICAL 18TH CENTURY HORN

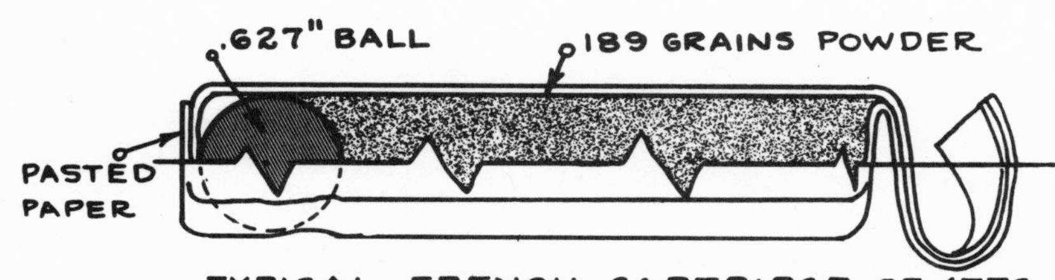

TYPICAL FRENCH CARTRIDGE OF 1776

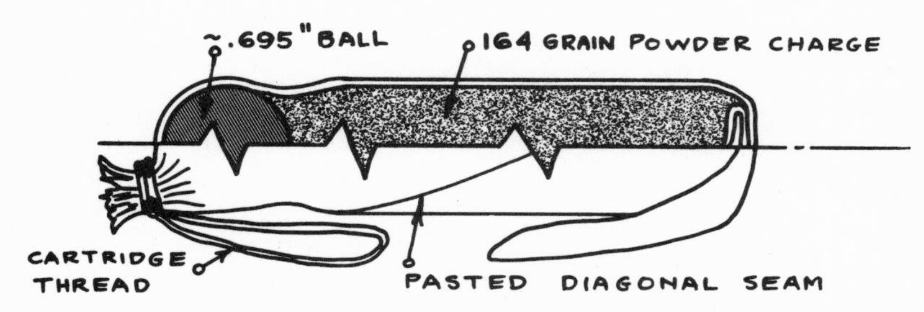

TYPICAL BRITISH CARTRIDGE OF 1776

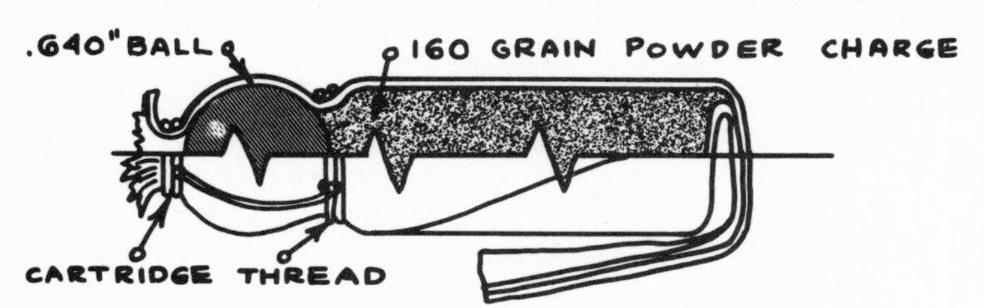

TYPICAL AMERICAN CARTRIDGE OF 1800

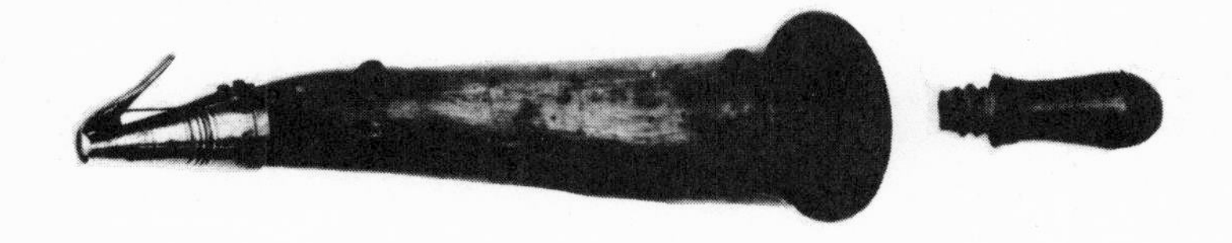

TYPICAL 19TH CENTURY POWDER HORN

FIGURE 2-1 American, British and French cartridges, and powder horns.

ure 2-1. The paper tube was generally pasted up with a diagonal seam. One end was gathered in over the end of the forming dowel and then choked off with several turns of string which were tied. The heavy musket ball of .687- to .700-inch diameter was dropped in the open end of the tube and the heavy powder charge measured out and poured in on top. The open end of the tube was then twisted over and folded back, alongside the cartridge.

The American Army utilized both French and British cartridge designs and gradually evolved their own design which became more and more standardized during the early 19th century. This design is shown in the third illustration down in Figure 2-1. A paper tube with a spiral seam was rolled up and pasted. One end was tied off with string as in the British design. By the time of the first standard musket design in 1795, a musket ball of .640-inch diameter and almost 400 grains in weight was specified. This was dropped in the open end of the paper tube and then the string was led around the ball and circled the paper tube several times to hold the ball in position. The powder charge for the United States Model 1795 musket was generally 167 grains of black powder. This was measured out and poured in the tube and then the end was twisted and folded over to retain the powder.

THE POWDER HORN

The Americans used standard French Charleville musket cartridges when available, but supplies were desperately short during the Revolution, and in most cases the American muskets were loaded with round balls, loose powder and paper wadding. The American soldiers and frontiersmen generally carried their powder in a horn such as that shown in the upper illustration of Figure 2-1. The upper half of the horn has been cut away to the center to show the interior construction. The horn was hollowed out to a thin shell. The large end was permanently closed by a wooden plug carved to design reflecting the skill and interests of the owner. Grooves were often cut in the upper plug to hold a rawhide carrying string. Sometimes the rawhide was fastened to rings screwed to the horn. The lower end of the horn was often fashioned with a small step to hold the rawhide string in place. A hole was drilled in the cut-off small end of the horn and this was plugged with a small wooden dowel to retain the powder.

Soldiers on tedious duty at frontier forts often spent hundreds of hours carving elaborate designs on their powder horns. Some valuable examples of this art are found in museums across the country. The soldier often carved his name, regiment and location in ornate script or shaded block letters, and then added ornamental designs. The powder horn itself did not provide any means to measure the powder charge, which was accomplished by two methods. One common approach was to place the musket ball in the soldier's hand and pour powder over the ball until the conical pile just hid the ball. This was considered an appropriate charge for a rifle or musket. The second, and more scientific method, was to take the rifle or musket out on a wintry day when there was fresh fallen snow. A relatively small powder charge would be loaded and fired, and the quantity would be increased gradually until the shooter noticed unburned powder grains on the snow in front of the muzzle. The powder charge would then be slightly reduced to insure that all the expensive and precious powder was being burned in the barrel. Often a small deer antler was hollowed out by drilling and then cut off to provide a little cup or measure holding the exact powder charge for the rifle or musket. This is shown in the left-hand side of Figure 2-1, and was often attached to the powder horn or cartridge bag by a rawhide thong.

Skilled frontier riflemen sometimes developed the appropriate charge for their rifle by running accuracy and penetration tests at the average hunting range of 50 to 100 yards. When they found the load which gave best accuracy with good penetration, they would fashion a measuring cup to hold this powder weight.

A late style of powder horn is shown in the lowest illustration of Figure 2-1. It is a 19th century horn of the type often used for "priming" a muzzle-loading cannon by trickling a charge of fine black powder into the vertical touchhole at the breech after the cannon was fully loaded. This type of horn was also used by riflemen in the early 19th century. It differs from the earlier horn in several respects. A large wooden plug has been permanently fixed to the large end of the horn, with a coarse wooden screw thread cut into the center. A removable wooden handle has been carved with matching thread. This allowed the powder horn to be filled from the large end and then closed off with the plug.

The lower end of the horn was closed off with a conical brass cap. This was permanently attached to the horn with small screws or nails. The cap was carved and had ornamental grooves rolled in the middle section. Two small brass plates were soldered vertically near the nose of the cap. A small brass lever was fitted which closed off the end of the powder horn, and a leaf spring held the lever in a closed position.

This style of powder horn still did not measure a powder charge. In use, the rifleman lifted the powder horn and placed the small end over his powder mea-

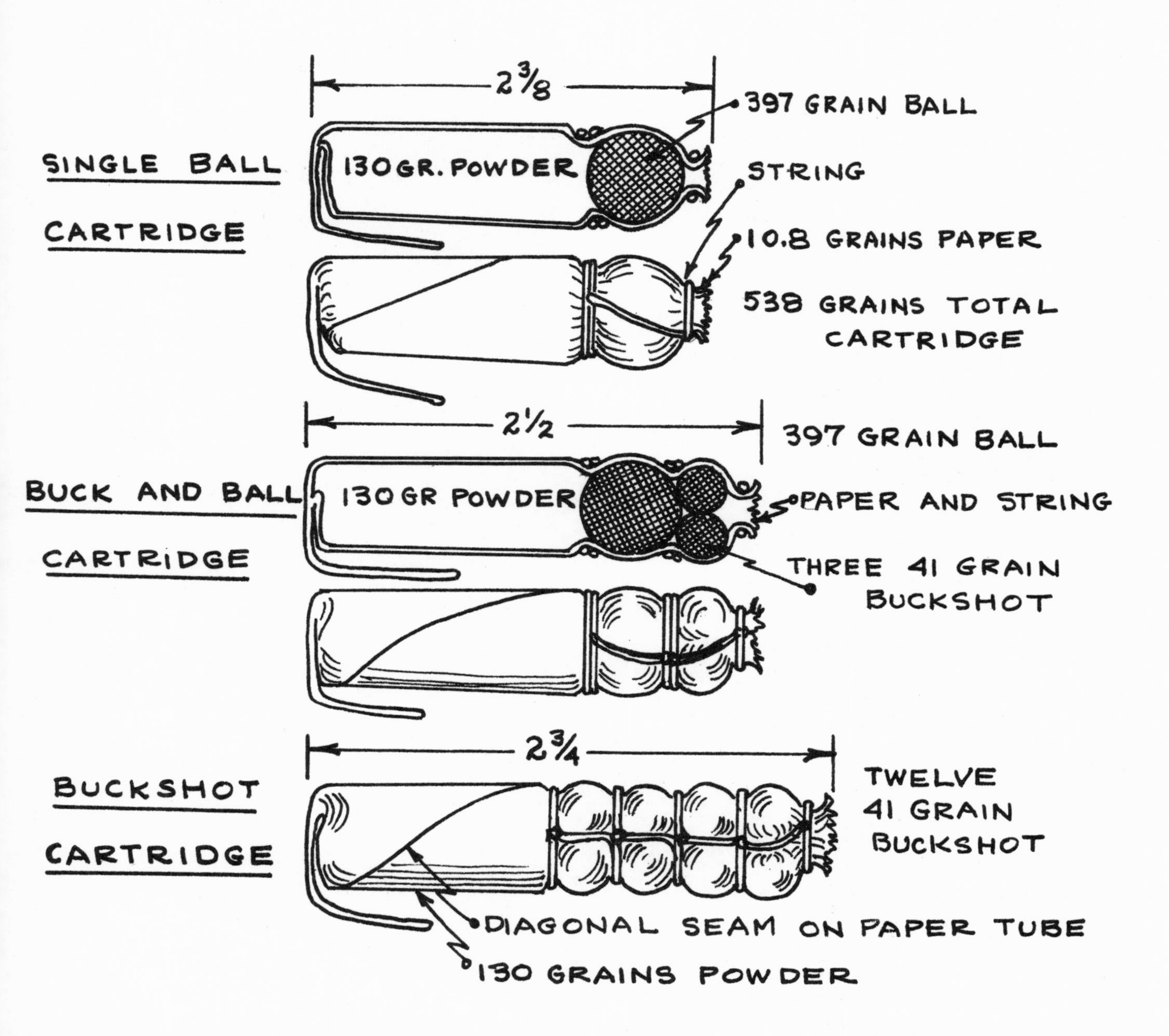

FIGURE 2-2 American cartridges for flintlock muskets (1841 specifications).

sure, then depressed the powder release lever until his measure was full. This type of powder horn was quicker and more convenient for two reasons. One was that the powder horn could be opened with one hand where two would be required to remove the plug on the earlier horn. The second was that the horn could be refilled more rapidly by removing the wooden plug in the large end of the horn.

MUSKET CARTRIDGES

During the American Revolution there were wide variations in powder quality, variations in the amount of charge thrown by powder flasks, and variations in the quality of the musket balls. The French muskets were of of excellent quality, but used, and the American Committee of Safety, muskets were relatively

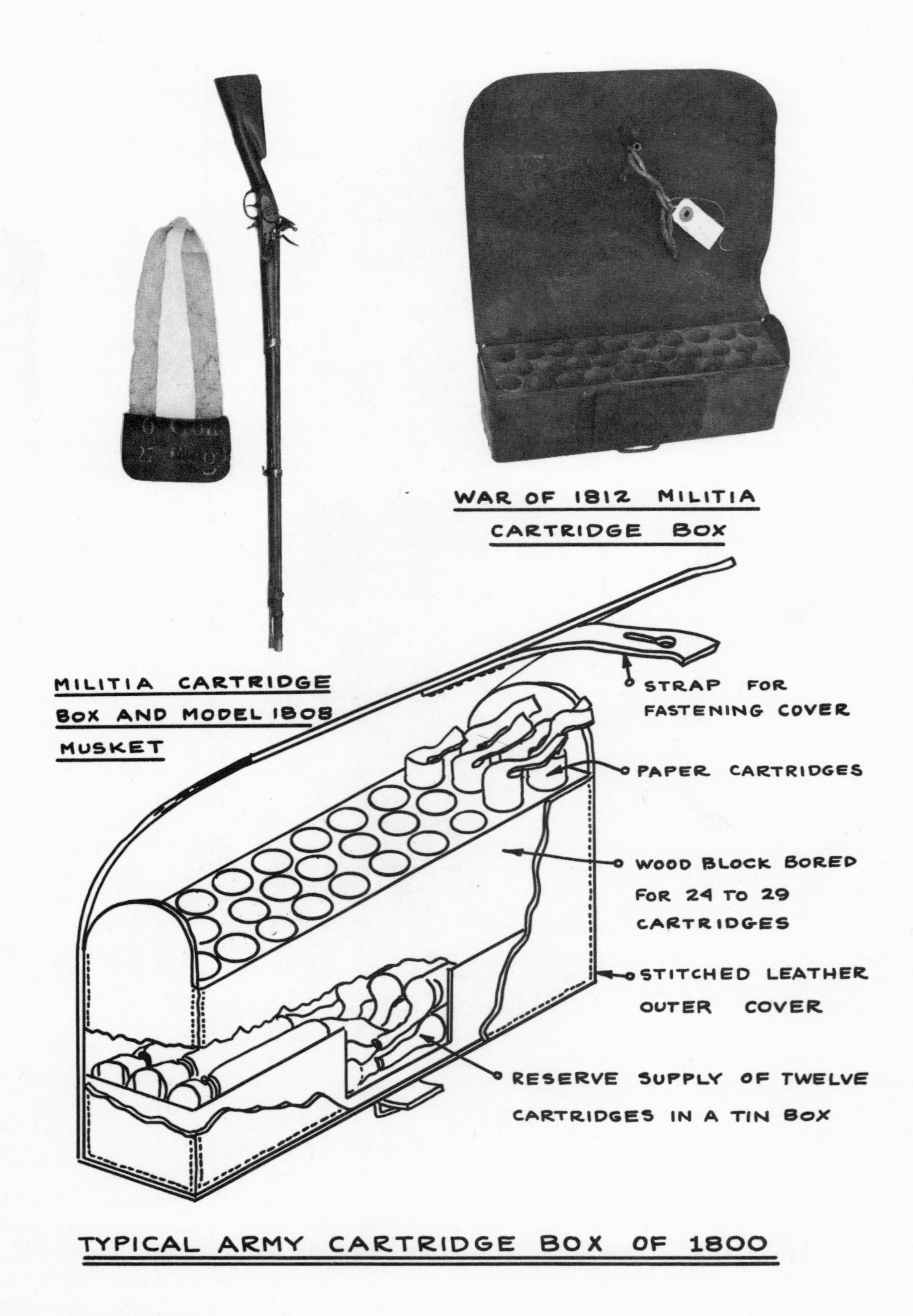

FIGURE 2-3 American cartridge boxes.

crude due to the very limited manufacturing facilities available. When all these variations were compounded by rusting and accumulation of dirt under severe field conditions, the result was wide variations in actual performance of American firearms during the Revolution.

Cartridges were a big advantage to the soldier in the field by providing him with the ball, or the musket ball plus three buckshot or twelve buckshot, all counted and packaged together as a unit. The proper powder charge was measured out and the paper cylinder of the cartridge provided wadding for the musket. The cartridge relieved the soldier from getting a ball from one pouch, measuring powder from the horn and securing his wadding from a third location. The wadding was essential on two counts — it had to absorb the large differences in diameter between the musket ball and the interior of the barrel, and it retained the musket ball and powder charge at the breech end of the barrel if the musket muzzle was tilted downward.

One of the main advantages of the musket was its flexibility. While it is normally considered to have been loaded with a single ball, three separate types of cartridges were widely used in the military musket. These cartridges are shown in Figure 2-2. These drawings reflect the Ordnance Specifications of 1841. The single ball cartridge is shown in the upper illustration, loaded with 397-grain ball of .640-inches diameter and a 130-grain black powder charge. The cartridge has all the characteristics shown in the earlier illustration, with a pasted diagonal seam and string to hold the ball in position.

Combinations of a large round ball and three buckshot were a popular load. In fact, one order from Continental Army Headquarters in October 1777 specified "Buckshot are to be put in all cartridges which shall hereafter be made." This combination of "buck and ball" is shown in the second cartridge down in Figure 2-2. The end of the paper cylinder was choked off with string and then three buckshot were dropped into the bottom of the tube. This was followed by the standard 397-grain single ball and then string was looped around and tied to hold both the buckshot and single ball in position. The standard powder charge for the time period was measured in and the end of the cartridge folded over to retain the charge. This combination of buck and ball remained popular for almost 100 years. It was widely used through the War of 1812 and in the 1850's was still considered useful for guard duty, Indian fighting or for any operations in brush country. It gave the soldier the heavy impact of the standard ball load plus three additional buckshot which gave a pattern to overcome much of the inaccuracy of the standard military musket.

The Ordnance Manual for 1841 printed the sizes of buckshot and ball to be loaded into the standard cartridges. The standard buck and ball had a .640-inch diameter ball weighing 18 to the pound. In addition to the 397-grain ball, three 41-grain buckshot were loaded into the cartridge. This was followed by the standard powder charge of 130 grains of musket powder. Eight to twelve grains of this charge were used to prime the pan of the flintlock, leaving about 120 grains in the main charge rammed down the barrel. By the 1840's powder quality had improved considerably, and the enormous charge of 120 grains of black powder in back of 520 grains of buckshot and balls must have given a horrendous recoil.

The third style of cartridge is shown in the lower illustration of Figure 2-2. This was the full buckshot load with twelve 41-grain buckshot giving a total weight of projectiles of 492 grains. This again was loaded with standard powder charge of 130 grains. In this buckshot load the paper cartridge was crumpled up after the powder had been poured down the barrel and the entire paper cylinder plus buckshot were inserted in the barrel as an assembly. While the paper provided some gas seal, the leakage must have been pretty severe. Modern buckshot cartridges for shotguns utilize several sturdy fiber wads to provide an effective gas seal in the bore.

CARTRIDGE BOXES

Since paper cartridges were quite fragile, they needed protection both from rough handling and from the weather. Many different designs evolved, but by the late 18th century the Americans were using two common types. The boxes basically consisted of a wooden block bored with 24 or more holes to hold cartridges. A typical box is shown in the lower illustration in Figure 2-3. A block bored for 29 cartridges was one of the most popular sizes. The block held the paper cartridges vertically with the folded over tail projecting above the top of the block so that they could be removed easily.

The wooden block was completely surrounded by a fitted leather cover. There were end plates with a semicircular section to protect the cartridges from a driving rain. Sometimes this was simply nailed to the wooden block in the back, but on the better boxes the wooden block was completely enclosed in a leather box. The large leather flap went up the back, over the top, and down the front, and was fastened on the underside of the cartridge box. A little leather door in the lower center portion of the leather cover provided access to a reserve cartridge compartment located below the wooden block. This was the soldier's emergency supply which was generally kept in a small tin box with two sides. Often about a dozen cartridges were stacked in this box six on each side. The area in the center was used to store spare flints, tools, oil and cleaning patches. The cartridge box was either worn on the belt or carried on a shoulder strap.

Militia Cartridge Box

An important part of the U.S. military was the militia. During the period of peace following the Revolutionary War the Regular Army was reduced to insignificant numbers and major emphasis for national defense was placed on the state militia. At the time of the War of 1812, for example, the state militia numbered over 100,000 men, while the Regular Army consisted of only a few thousand troops. The militia cartridge box was simpler in construction and two views of this are shown in the upper section of Figure 2-3. On the right side is shown the cartridge box with the cover open and on the left side is a smaller view of the cartridge box with its leather cover closed and the 2½-inch wide canvas shoulder strap stretched out. This cartridge box belonged to a Connecticut Yankee named Deacon Collins, whose name appears on the rolls of the Connecticut Militia, 6th Company, 27th Regiment, in 1799. The regiment and company numbers are painted on the cover of the cartridge box. The illustration shows the box with the Model 1808 musket carried by Deacon Collins during the War of 1812.

This box has been carefully measured by Thomas E. Hall, Curator of the Winchester Gun Museum. It contains 29 holes of .765-inch diameter and 2 11/16 inches depth. The standard cartridges of 1812 were of an .675 inch in diameter and 3½ inches long so that about ¾ inch of cartridge extended above the box. The sample cartridge of this period in the Winchester Museum is typical of the French musket cartridge with a fully glued construction.

There is a small leather pocket sewn to the front of the cartridge box, but this was merely a pocket to store flints, oil and patches. There was no reserve cartridge supply with this style of militia box.

BLACK POWDER

The performance of all ammunition is highly dependent on the quality of powder available. At the beginning of the American Revolution, the Americans recognized their need for this critical commodity and raided many British powder storage areas. Close to 100,000 pounds of powder were secured from these raids and private storage sources, but most of this was expended before the Army had been properly organized. Few of us can imagine the problems faced by General Washington and his staff in trying to keep some kind of effective army in operation with desperate shortages of every kind of supplies. The Americans tried to make powder by extracting saltpeter from local sources. Most of the powder manufactured in the United States was made from the almost half million pounds of saltpeter imported from France. At the same time we imported nearly a million and a half pounds of manufactured gun powder.

Black powder is by far the oldest explosive—known and used in Europe and China by the 13th century. It is a mechanical mixture of different chemical ingredients — quite different from modern smokeless powders where many chemical ingredients are blended into chemical structures with carefully engineered burning characteristics. Black powder is made of three ingredients: The fuel is charcoal, refined as closely as possible to pure carbon, and ground up into small dust grains. The oxygen needed for charcoal to burn was provided by saltpeter or potassium nitrate. Potassium nitrate is a relatively unstable compound and under heat and pressure it releases oxygen which then combines with the carbon to burn to carbon dioxide. The third ingredient is sulphur. Sulphur was found to provide a means for modulating the burning and also greatly improved the generation of powder gas.

The basic principle behind the effectiveness of black powder as a propellant is the change from a very small volume of dry powder into a very large volume of gas. Endless experiments were performed during the 500 years prior to the American Revolution to find what blend of ingredients would provide the most gas, be most reliable, and leave the least residue in the gun barrel. The final proportions used throughout the world were approximately 75 percent saltpeter, 15 percent charcoal, and 10 percent sulphur. As the black powder burned, many intermediate products were formed. Ultimately three different gases were generated: Nitrogen from the saltpeter, and carbon monoxide and carbon dioxide from the carbon and oxygen. A number of unwanted solid products were also developed, including the unburned carbon grains, potassium carbonate, potassium sulphate, and potassium sulphides. With most black powders slightly over 55 percent of the powder comes out as solid residue and only 45 percent is turned into gas.

In the Middle Ages the three ingredients were kept separately and mixed at the battlefield by the gunners.

Approximate Dates	Firearm (Musket)	Caliber	Diameter of ball inches	Weight of ball grains	Powder charge including priming	Muzzle velocity feet/sec	Muzzle energy foot-pounds	Muzzle impulse pounds-seconds	Efficiency: energy per grain of propellant
1763-1800	French Charleville Model 1763	.69	.627	370	189	1,400	1,610	3.47	9.0
War of 1812	Springfield Model 1795	.69	.640	397.5	167	1,440	1,825	3.6	11.6
1830's	Springfield Model 1822	.69	.640	397.5	146.5	1,440	1,825	3.47	13.4
1840-1845	Springfield Model 1840	.69	.640	397.5	130	1,499	1,980	3.5	16.5
1845-1850	Springfield Model 1840	.69	.650	412	110	1,410	1,817	3.26	18.2
1850-1860	Springfield Model 1840	.69	.650	412	110	1,500	2,060	3.48	20.6

FIGURE 2-4 Ballistics of flintlock muskets.

After many gunners blew themselves up instead of the enemy, processes were gradually developed to perform these operations at a factory. The safest manufacturing procedure was to grind the chemicals into extremely fine powders in separate processes and then mix them and add water to make a sticky, gooey mess. The water mixture was allowed to dry out in cakes and then was broken up and reground into the proper size granules for use with firearms. The finest powder is known as FFFFg and this is used for priming in flintlock mechanisms and for use in ignition trains of cannon. The next size powder — FFFg — is used for small pistol cartridges and in small shotgun loads. FFg was used in large pistols and small bore rifles while the large grained Fg powder was used for flintlock muskets and large caliber rifles. Even larger granulations were used for cannon and for blasting. Black powder is still widely used today, even in some highly advanced military ammunition. Black powder is easy to ignite, where modern smokeless powders can be extremely difficult to start burning. A very effective method of ignition is to have a primer ignite a charge of black powder which then blasts out flaming particles of sulphur and carbon into the tightly packed smokeless powder, providing an excellent booster to set the main charge burning.

Black powders during the American Revolution were relatively poor in quality. During the early 19th century the quality improved and, as the power increased, so did the recoil felt by the poor soldier. Periodically complaints from the field became so loud that the Ordnance Department took notice, ran a series of tests, and specified new standard cartridges with bearable recoil limits.

At the time of the changeover from round balls to the hollow-base Minie bullets with cylindrical body and conical head, recoil became a very severe problem and writings of that time admit that the common soldier often would throw part of his powder charge away to avoid the punishing recoil of the musket.

Powder charges were gradually reduced over the years and from calculations of many different sets of data this author concludes that *powder charges were modified over the years so that the muzzle impulse*

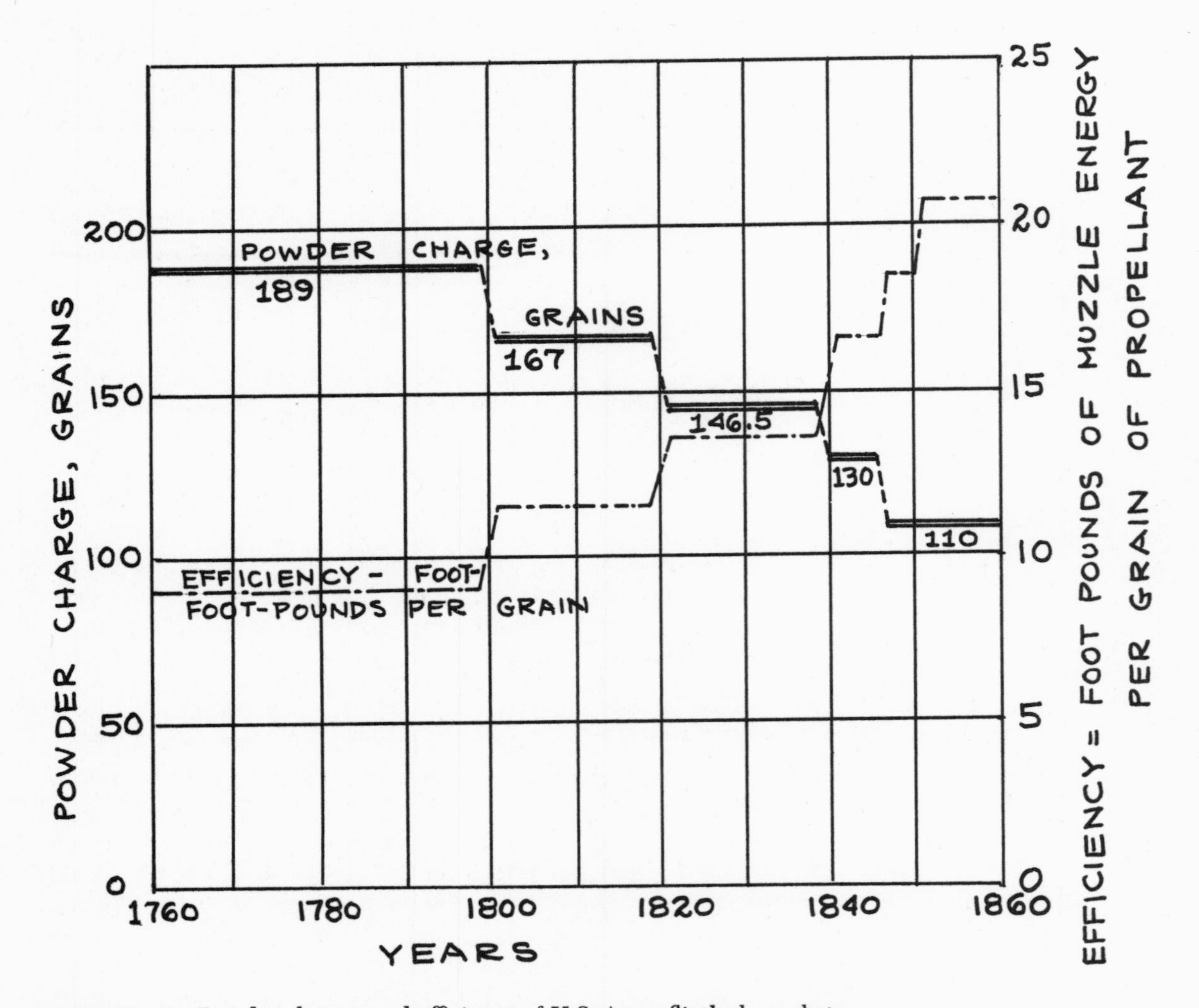

FIGURE 2-5 Powder charges and efficiency of U.S. Army flintlock muskets.

of the musket did not exceed 3.5 pound-seconds. The recoil momentum of the muskets was equal to the muzzle impulse and 3.5 pound-seconds is an extremely high recoil level.

The famous .30 caliber Garand (M1) rifle of World War II had only 2.7 pound-seconds recoil and the new M-16, .22 caliber rifle widely used in Southeast Asia has only 1.224 pound-seconds. Since the soldiers of the Revolution and the early 19th century were generally smaller and lighter than today's vitamin-filled Americans, the musket recoil was formidable indeed.

BALLISTIC TESTS

The first reliable ballistic tests in the United States were performed with a special pendulum constructed on a French ordnance design. A careful and comprehensive series of tests was made at Washington Arsenal in 1843 and 1844 on various types of gun powder by Captain Alfred Mordecai of the Ordnance Department. These experiments and later tests by him provide the first logical and systematic testing of small arms in the United States.

The ballistic pendulum is basically a very simple device. It consists of a heavy weight, usually a large wooden block, suspended on thin wires. The bullet is fired horizontally into the stationary block, and the movement of the pendulum is measured, either as an angular motion of the wires, or as a distance the block moves. The practice at Washington Arsenal was to measure the angular motion, which ranged from 3½ to 10 degrees with small arms ammunition.

The velocity of the musket ball is calculated from momentum formulas, which state that the momentum before and after the impact of the bullet in the block must be equal. The formulas can be simplified to:

$$W_1V_1+W_p\times0=(W_1+W_p)\ V_2$$

where

W_1=weight of bullet in pounds

W_p=weight of pendulum block, pounds

V_1=velocity of bullet just before impacting block

0=velocity of block before impact

V_2=velocity of the pendulum with the bullet buried in the block after impact

V_2 is calculated from the angular motion of the pendulum, and then V_1 can be calculated.

Calculations based on some of these early tests are shown in Figures 2-4 and 2-5. In all cases the data in this chapter should be understood to refer to muskets in excellent working condition with good quality powders and balls of the periods. Alfred Mordecai's experiments showed what would be considered extremely high efficiencies for flintlock muskets.

The test results of the standard load of the early 1840's is shown on line 4. With a .640-inch diameter ball of 397.5 grains and a 130 grain powder charge a muzzle velocity of 1499 feet per second was recorded. This was the average velocity of a long series of carefully measured tests, and there is every reason to believe this is an accurate figure.[1] This performance calculates out to a muzzle energy of 1980 foot-pounds and an efficiency of 16.5 foot-pounds of muzzle energy per grain of propellant. The momentum of this load is approximately 3.5 pound-seconds.

A standard load of the 1830's tested by Captain Mordecai utilized the same 397.5-grain ball but a heavier powder charge of 146.5 grains. This provided a muzzle velocity of 1440 feet per second and the efficiency was slightly lower at only 13.4 foot-pounds of energy per grain of propellant. The muzzle impulse of this load was 3.47 pound-seconds.

In his description of the test results, Alfred Mordecai commented that the standard load of the 1830's with the 146.5-grain powder charge was equal to the Revolutionary War load of 189 grains due to the poorer quality powder of the 18th century. The Revolutionary War Load used a 370-grain projectile, but the very heavy powder charge would give about the same muzzle impulse as a load from the 1830's. The muzzle velocity is calculated at 1400 feet per second to equal the muzzle impulse and musket recoil of the standard 1830 load.

[1] B. R. Lewis, *Small Arms and Ammunition in the U.S. Service*, Smithsonian, 1968. Page 99.

The corresponding muzzle energy of a Revolutionary War load is 1610 foot pounds and the efficiency was only 9.0 foot-pounds of muzzle energy per grain of propellant.

Alfred Mordecai's recommendation of the proper powder charge for use in the 1840's with an improved "A-4" black powder is shown in the next to bottom line of Figure 2-4. The 110-grain powder charge included 100 grains for propelling the ball and 10 grains for priming the flash pan. Since tolerance of the musket barrels and ammunition had improved, Alfred Mordecai recommended decreasing the clearance between the lead ball and the inside of the musket barrel from .050-inches to .040-inches.

With this same 110-grain powder charge in the Model 1842 percussion musket an initial velocity of 1500 feet per second was measured. The velocity from a flintlock musket would be slightly lower due to three factors. First, approximately 10 grains of the powder charge were used in the flash pan rather than to propel the bullet, and second the flint ignition required there be an open flash hole between the barrel and pan from which a jet of flame would emerge all the time there was pressure in the musket barrel. The third factor was that the hot flame from the fulminate priming compound in a percussion musket gave a much hotter start to the propellant ignition. Some very interesting tests were performed by Captain Mordecai using a regular Model 1835 flintlock musket and leaving the vent to the pan wide open but *adding a percussion ignition system*. It was found that the hotter ignition flame of the percussion cap increased muzzle velocity 15 to 24 feet per second over the slower and gentler ignition of the flash from the powder pan of the same model of flintlock musket.

Notice on Figures 2-4 and 2-5 how the efficiency of the flintlock muskets increased over the years as better powders became available, more uniform bullets were manufactured, and better control of the interior barrel diameter was achieved through improved manufacturing processes.

Calculating all these factors into the equations for muzzle energy and efficiency, we come out with an estimated velocity of 1410 feet per second for the .69 caliber flintlock musket with a 110-grain powder charge of the then new and improved "A-4" powder. This new black powder of the 1840's with the larger .650-inch diameter musket ball would deliver about 1815 foot-pounds of muzzle energy, and the efficiency was considerably increased to a little over 18 foot-pounds of muzzle energy per grain of propellant.

During the early 19th century inventors were very active in England and on the Continent trying to develop better types of military ammunition. As human ingenuity was applied to the development of improved machinery the crude manufacturing processes of earlier centuries were being rapidly improved. The early 19th century was a time when the steam engine was under rapid development and was becoming widely used for powering railroads, steamships, and pumping water. Boring the large cylinders for steam engines was very difficult, and there was great need for improved machinery to manufacture engine parts to closer tolerances. The same emphasis was applied to firearms technology. At the time of the American Revolution, the European specification for the inside diameter of musket barrels generally allowed a tolerance of .015 of an inch above the nominal dimension. Thus a new French musket could vary in bore diameter from .690- to .705-inch. American muskets were not always held this closely and there is some evidence that British muskets at times greatly exceeded this tolerance. By the 1840's the interior diameter of American rifle barrels was being held to .540 of an inch plus .0025-inch, thus the maximum dimension was only .5425-inch. Obviously, with such a spread of dimensions as in Revolutionary muskets, the bullets must necessary fit loosely in the average musket or they could not be loaded into muskets with a small barrel. By the 1840's, this problem had been solved and both barrels and bullets could be manufactured to quite close dimensions.

The inventors were looking for the "universal answer" — a single firearm which would perform the functions of both the traditional musket and the slow loading rifle. The experiments probed in many directions. The British developed new forms of rifling. One was a concept where the barrel was oval in cross section and the long axis of the oval took a spiral path from breech to muzzle. When an elliptical bullet was rammed down on top of the powder charge it was forced to follow the spiral path as it accelerated up the barrel to the muzzle. A second approach was to develop a spherical ball with a belt around the middle much like the rings of Saturn. The barrel was manufactured with two deep and rounded rifling grooves. The bullet had to be lined up with these grooves before ramming, and accuracy was very poor.

Some excellent British designs were developed in the 1850's including an hexagonal-bore rifle developed by Sir Joseph Whitworth, one of the leading British manufacturers of steel products including artillery. Bullets with an hexagonal cross section were manufactured to be used in the Whitworth rifles, and these gave excellent accuracy and long-range performance.

The French made a major discovery in rifling techniques in converting some old smoothbore muskets into rifled firearms. Since the barrels were fairly thin at the muzzle, they could not cut the rifling as deeply as they wished. The rifling was cut a proper depth at the breech end of the barrel where the walls were thicker and was tapered down to a shallower depth at the muzzle. To everyone's surprise these rifled muskets gave a significant improvement in accuracy and the design spread rapidly. It was standardized for the United States Civil War rifles, which had three rifling grooves — deep at the breech and shallow at the muzzle.

A second line of experimentation was concentrated on developing bullet designs which would be easy to load and would still spin as the rifle was fired. This was a problem experimenters had been working on for 500 years. If a barrel was clean and made to proper dimensions, it was quite possible to take a slightly oversized lead ball and engrave the rifling into it by hammering it into the muzzle with a small mallet. Once the rifling had been cut into the lead ball, it could be forced the rest of the way with the ramrod. Accuracy was not very good-for the soldier did not engrave the ball uniformly shot after shot. The amount of "upset" depended on how hard he had struck the bullet with the mallet. As the rifle was fired, powder deposits built up in the barrel, but not uniformly. The heaviest deposits were just forward of the chamber. This meant that the bullets could be rammed most of the way with the ramrod and then the mallet had to be used again to force the bullet the final few inches to the chamber. The over-all result was a very slow loading process and poor accuracy.

A major improvement developed with the use of the patched lead bullet in which a resilient material, such as leather or cloth, was used to wrap the ball before loading in the barrel. This patch accomplished two things: First, the rifling did not have to be cut into the bullet itself. The rifling could grip the patch which in turn would spin the bullet due to friction sending the bullet out of the muzzle in a true spherical shape. Second, the rifle remained easy to load, even as some powder residue built up at the breech. Frontiersmen often tried to loosen the powder residue by soaking the patch in saliva before ramming the bullet and patch down the barrel.

Although the patched bullet was a substantial improvement, loading was still fairly slow and the round ball lost its velocity and accuracy rapidly. Experimenters in the early 19th century tried an incredible number of different designs in their search for the perfect answer.

Inventors in the United States performed many experiments. In addition, we kept careful track of European developments, sending technical commissions, to discuss small arms and artillery developments with the Continental powers. In the mid-1850's tests of European and American designs at Washington Arsenal led to the specifications of the 1855 series of rifles and muskets.

EXTERIOR BALLISTICS

A bullet leaves the muzzle of a rifle at its highest velocity and immediately begins to slow down due to air resistance. The spherical bullet slows down rapidly, for it has a large-cross sectional area in comparison with its weight. The spherical ball is not a very efficient shape to displace air during its flight. Since it is relatively blunt, air pressure builds up at the front of the ball rather than flowing smoothly around it and a vacuum forms behind it, both slowing the ball. These factors combine to make the ball a short-range projectile. The best way to overcome these limitations is to make the spherical balls of very heavy material, and lead is excellent from this standpoint. Even so, the modern shotgun firing fine shot has an effective range of less than 50 yards. With buckshot or round balls the effective range is still under 150 yards. The ballistic performance of round balls can be improved further by making them of extremely high density materials such as tungsten or uranium, but these are solutions for special applications and not for the average sportman's pocketbook.

The obvious way to improve exterior ballistic performance was to reduce the air drag on the projectile during flight. There were two ways of doing this. One was to decrease the diameter of the bullet for a given weight, and the second was to give it a pointed shape which would displace the air more easily. Literally hundreds of designs were experimented with, and some are so weird in appearance it is hard to believe people spent money to test them. Some of the weird designs included two balls that were held together by a stud-and-socket joint, two musket balls cast together in the form of a figure 8, hollow spherical bullets, and spherical bullets with long tapered noses which obviously would be unstable in flight. The successful designs rapidly settled into a pattern of a cylindrical section with a pointed nose. Every conceivable shape of nose was tried, from hemispherical to a long conical cap and all possible shapes in between. Careful experiments showed that an "ogive" was the most practical design. An ogive is simply the arc of a circle much larger in radius than the radius of the projectile. Experimenters found that this type of shape allowed the air to flow much more easily over the surface of the projectile and that more velocity was retained at long range.

EASE OF LOADING AND ACCURACY

The second major problem was to develop designs which would be easy to load and stilll accurate in flight. Ingenious experimenters saw that if the ball could be loaded from the breech of the firearm the problem would be solved. The British Captain Patrick Ferguson came up with one of the best solutions with his musket which was closed at the breech by a vertical screw. With the action open, a slightly oversized ball could be slid into the chamber and the powder charge poured in on top of it. When the rifle was fired, the ball was driven into the slightly smaller diameter rifled section which engraved and spun the bullet in flight. The Ferguson rifle was successfully used during the American Revolution until the inventor was badly wounded in a skirmish and his skilled group of riflemen broken up for political reasons.

An American inventor, John Hall, invented a breech loading flintlock rifle with a "tip up" chamber. His rifle also used a bullet slightly larger than bore diameter. Both of these designs were way ahead of their time, for the manufacturing techniques were so crude that there was considerable gas leakage at the breech and the soldiers did not like the noise and flame.

An ingenious European solution was to make the powder chamber at the breech end of the rifle smaller in diameter than the remainder of the barrel. For example, suppose you had a .60 caliber rifle with a one-inch section at the breech which was only .55 of an inch in diameter. A .590 inch ball dropped freely down a clean barrel, but stopped when it struck the shoulder at the powder chamber. A few hard raps with the ramrod caused the bullet to expand radially into the rifling grooves. This system was developed by a Captain Delvigne, using a slightly elongated bullet or "oval ball."

Another approach was the "Thouvenin system" in which the rifle barrel had a uniform diameter but a sharp-pointed iron stake was screwed into the breech plug and extended up through the powder chamber. An elongated bullet with a flat base was used. The slightly undersized bullet was dropped down the barrel onto the powder charge, resting on the sharp stake. A few blows of the ramrod caused the stake to be driven into the base of the bullet expanding it radially. This provided a good gas seal and gave enough grip by the rifling to spin the bullet. This system had two disadvantages: The powder chamber

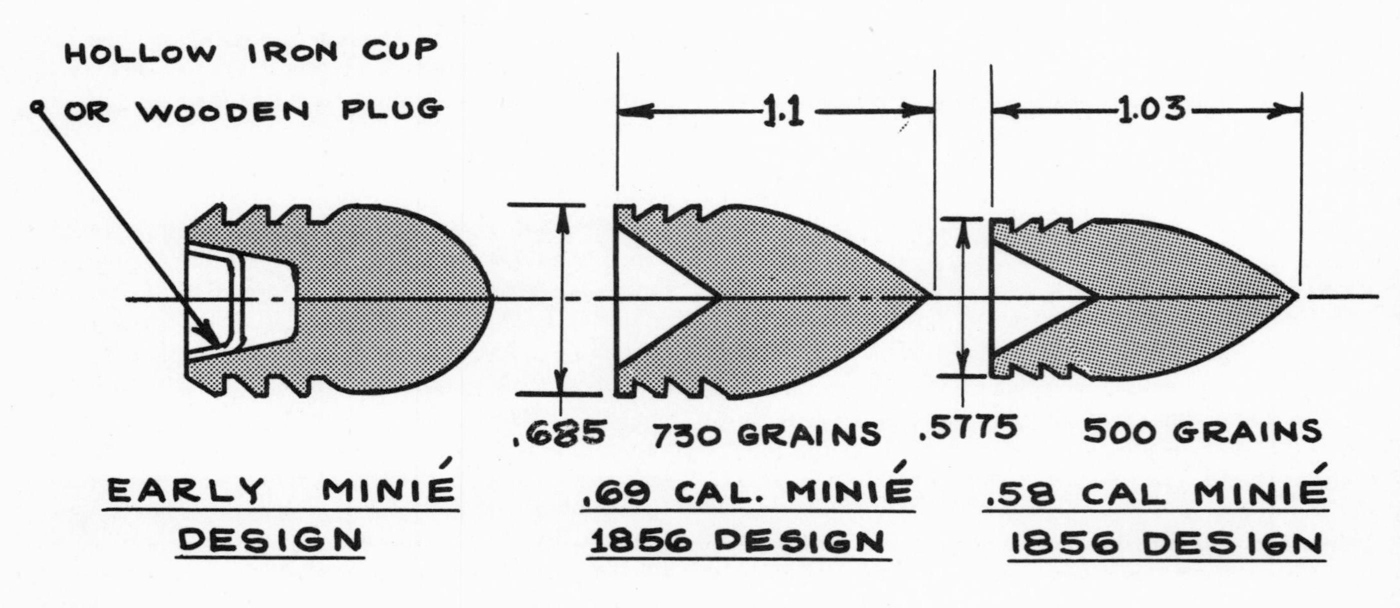

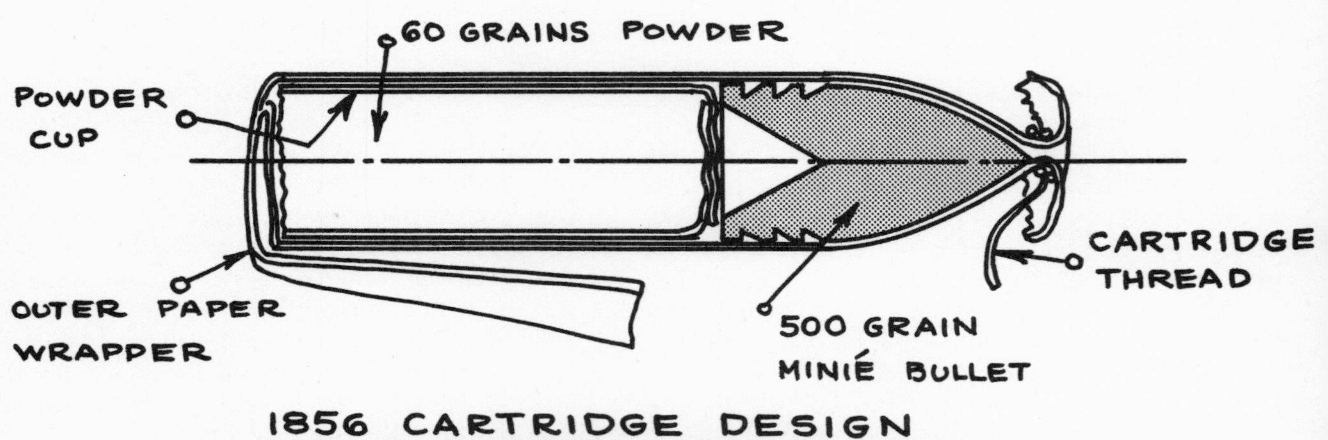

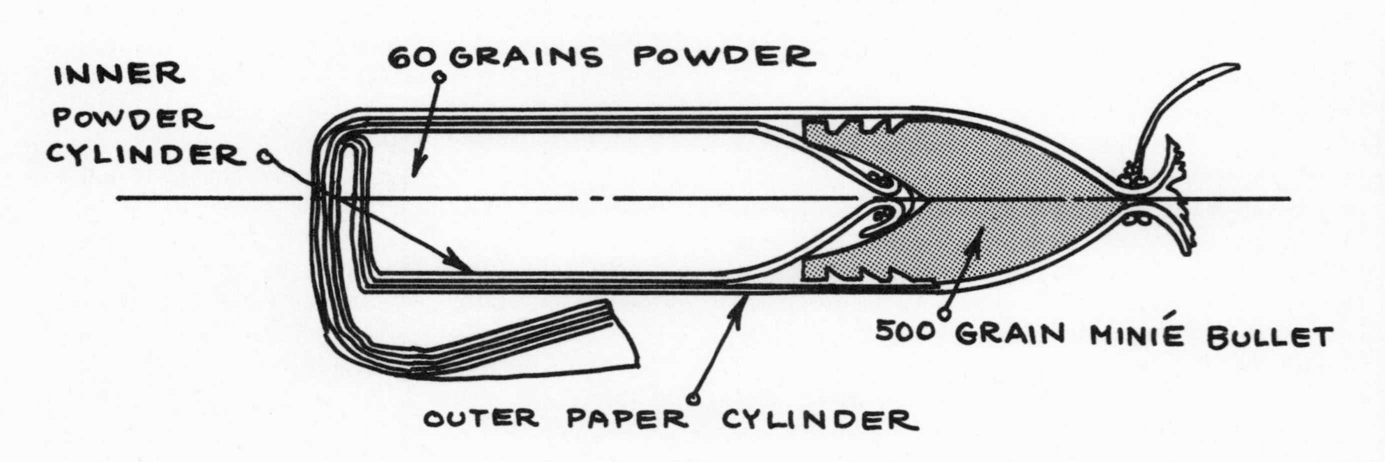

FIGURE 2-6 Designs of Minié Bullets.

was very difficult to clean with the sharp stake up the center and accuracy was not too high as the soliders did not upset the bullet uniformly.

Minié Bullets

Captain C. E. Minié of the French Army developed what was to become by far the most successful system based on extensive experiments in the 1840's. By 1850 he had developed a "Cylindro Conoidal ball" with an iron cup in its base. The design of the American version of his bullet is shown in Figure 2-6. The complicated name simply means a cylindrical bullet surmounted by a conoidal or ogive-shaped point. The original bullets had an iron cup in the base as shown in the left upper illustration of Figure 2-6. The principle was very simple. The bullet was slightly smaller than the bore diameter of the rifle. After the powder charge was poured in the barrel the bullet was dropped in from the muzzle with the hollow base downward. A couple of light blows of the ramrod seated the bullet firmly on the powder charge. When the rifle was fired the gas pressure drove the iron cup into the hollow base of the lead bullet expanding the lead skirt outwards providing an excellent gas seal and a strong grip between the rifling and bullet skirt. Ratchet-shaped grooves were cast or swaged into the bullet to scrape out powder residue as the bullet traveled up the barrel. The bullet was very slightly under bore diameter. For example, the Army Manual of 1856 specified a .5775-inch diameter bullet to be used in the .58 caliber musket. This is only one half of one-thousandth of an inch (.0005) under the nominal bore diameter and was probably a maximum dimension. The bullets for the .69 caliber converted rifle-muskets were specified as .685-inch in diameter or .005-inch smaller than the bore diameter. In either case these bullets were extremely effective for they were easy to load and gave excellent accuracy and greatly improved range over the round ball.

New paper cartridges were developed of more complex construction. First the bullets were lubricated with a mixture of one part beeswax and three parts tallow. Care was used to keep grease out of the hollow cavity and off the base of the bullet where it might contaminate the powder. A separate chamber for the powder was rolled up using two sheets of paper, and the diagonal seam and one end were pasted shut to make a hollow paper cup for the powder. A large "outer wrapper" of trapezoidal shape was rolled up over a .58 caliber wooden dowel and the diagonal seam was glued shut. The final assembly is shown in the second line of Figure 2-6. The paper powder cup was inserted in one end of the open tube and the Minié bullet was pushed into the front end. The front of the cartridge was choked around the point of the bullet and held shut with several turns of "cartridge thread" tied with half hitches. The cartridge was then turned bullet end down and the powder cavity filled with a measured quantity of black powder. The open end was twisted over and folded parallel to the side of the cartridge as shown in Figure 2-6.

Loading the Rifle-Musket

The Ordnance Manual of 1856 says about loading: "To use this cartridge, tear the fold and pour out the powder; then seize the ball firmly between the thumb and forefinger of the right hand and strike the cylinder a smart blow across the muzzle of the piece (rifle). This breaks the cartridge and exposes the bottom of the ball (Minié bullet). A slight pressure of the thumb and forefinger forces the ball into the bore clear of all cartridge paper."[2]

CIVIL WAR CARTRIDGES

By 1861 the manufacture of the new types of cartridges had been well established and the design slightly simplified. The bullets were made on swaging machines similar in operation to those used for making modern .22 rimfire bullets, although the Civil War machines were much larger and slower in operation. The lead was first cast into round cylindrical bars .58 of an inch in diameter. These bars were rolled down to .46 of an inch in diameter and 2 feet long in a swaging or rolling machine. The lead bars were fed into a cutoff machine which cut off slugs of slightly over 500 grains in weight. The slugs were then transferred to a die cavity in the bullet-swaging machine. It is probable that as the machine slammed shut a pointed punch drove the slug forward in the die cavity. The punch "had" the shape of the hollow base of the Miníe bullet. As it drove the slug forward into the conical shaped cavity, the nose ogive was formed and the lead was expanded radially. Sharp rings in the die cavity formed the grooves in the bullet. Excess lead was forced out as a thin flash around the bullet. After the bullets were ejected from the machine the thin lead was cut off by hand with a knife, and the bullets dimensions were checked.

The Ordnance Manual of 1861 stated that one man could manufacture 30,000 bullets in 10 hours using the swaging machine. One man could cast 1500 bars in 10

[2] *Ibid.* P 183

hours and one man could trim and roll 2000 bars in 10 hours. These sound like extremely high production rates for Civil War type machinery, and probably represented the maximum calculations of an efficiency expert rather than realistic production figures.

The bullets were then lubricated by being placed base downward on a tin frame capable of holding about 50 bullets. The frame was immersed in a melted mixture one part tallow and eight parts beeswax until the cylindrical parts of the bullets were covered. The frame and bullets were then removed and allowed to cool. The excess lubricant probably was removed after cooling by pushing the bullets through a metal die with a hole .5775 of an inch in diameter.

A slightly simplified procedure had been developed for rolling up the paper cartridges, utilizing two trapezoidal sheets of paper. The "inner cylinder" was rolled up around a pointed wooden dowel and the diagonal seam was glued. One end of the tube was gathered around the pointed wooden stick and the end tied shut with a piece of cartridge thread. The conical end was then inserted into the hollow base of a Miníe bullet and a second sheet of cartridge paper wrapped around the Minié bullet, the tube of cartridge paper and the wooden former. The second piece of cartridge paper was then gathered around the nose of the bullet and it, in turn, was also tied with a piece of cartridge thread. The standard 1861 cartridge is shown in the third illustration down in Figure 2-6. The cartridge was loaded with bullets of .575 to .5775-inch diameter weighing 500 to 510 grains and carrying a powder charge of 60 grains. These cartridges were manufactured in very large quantity — almost half a billion were produced during the Civil War. A quarter of a billion other paper cartridges were manufactured to fit the .69 caliber rifle-muskets and special foreign muzzle-loading rifles.

The Confederacy also manufactured the .58 caliber paper cartridge in smaller quantities as its standard Civil War ammunition. Many southern cartridges were simplified in construction by eliminating the entire outer wrapper. These cartridges had the entire bullet exposed and the paper powder cylinder was inserted and glued into the hollow base of the Minié bullet.

Special Civil War Cartridges

In addition to the standard Minié bullet loads, blank cartridges were manufactured, which consisted of an inner powder cavity with one end pasted over to form a square end. This was then filled with powder and the tail folded over much as a standard cartridge was manufactured. Over 21,000,000 blank cartridges were produced.[3]

The 1861 Ordnance Manual also specified a buckshot load similar to that used in muskets loaded with 15 spherical lead shot. According to one table of specifications the buckshot load was used only in the .69 caliber muskets with a 110-grain powder charge. The .69 caliber rifled muskets normally fired a 730-grain Minié bullet of .685-inch diameter with a powder charge of 70 grains. The Civil War cartridge for smoothbore muskets was loaded with a .650-inch diameter ball weighing 412 grains and a powder charge of 110 grains.

The standard .58 caliber cartridges and blanks were loaded with 60 grains of powder. Special lighter cartridges were designed for the cadet rifles, Model 1857, and these fired a 450-grain Minié bullet with a powder charge of 50 grains.

Shaler's Sectional Bullet

Buckshot cartridges had been very popular loads for military muskets. They were excellent for guard duty, or combat in brush where targets were indistinct. The buck and ball load was also widely utilized by the Revolutionary and early 19th century soldiers. The effectiveness of both these loads was dependent on a smoothbore barrel. Rifling gave a spin to the buckshot, so that they fanned out rapidly into a conical pattern which was useless at most fighting ranges. Inventors puzzled over this, and an ingenious design was developed during the Civil War to provide multriple shot capability in a rifle or rifle-musket. An inventor named Shaler came up with an ingenious cartridge shown in the lower illustration in Figure 2-7. Three bullets were loaded into each cartridge. The front bullet had a hollow base and a single wide driving band at the base. The forward section of the bullet was dome-shaped with a fairly blunt point. Into the hollow base of the bullet was inserted a second bullet which also had a hollow cavity in the base, and a broad driving band, but this one was designed with a shorter conical nose. Into the base of the second bullet was inserted a flat-based bullet with a conical nose and a relatively short driving band. The very skilled cartridge collector can identify these cartridges, since they are generally found with the front bullet exposed and the rear of the bullet tied off with cartridge string.

These bullets were apparently quite successful and five design variations of the Shaler sectional bullet have been identified.[4] The illustration in Figures 2-7 is a typical design.

[3] *Ibid.* P 188
[4] *Ibid.* Plate 28.

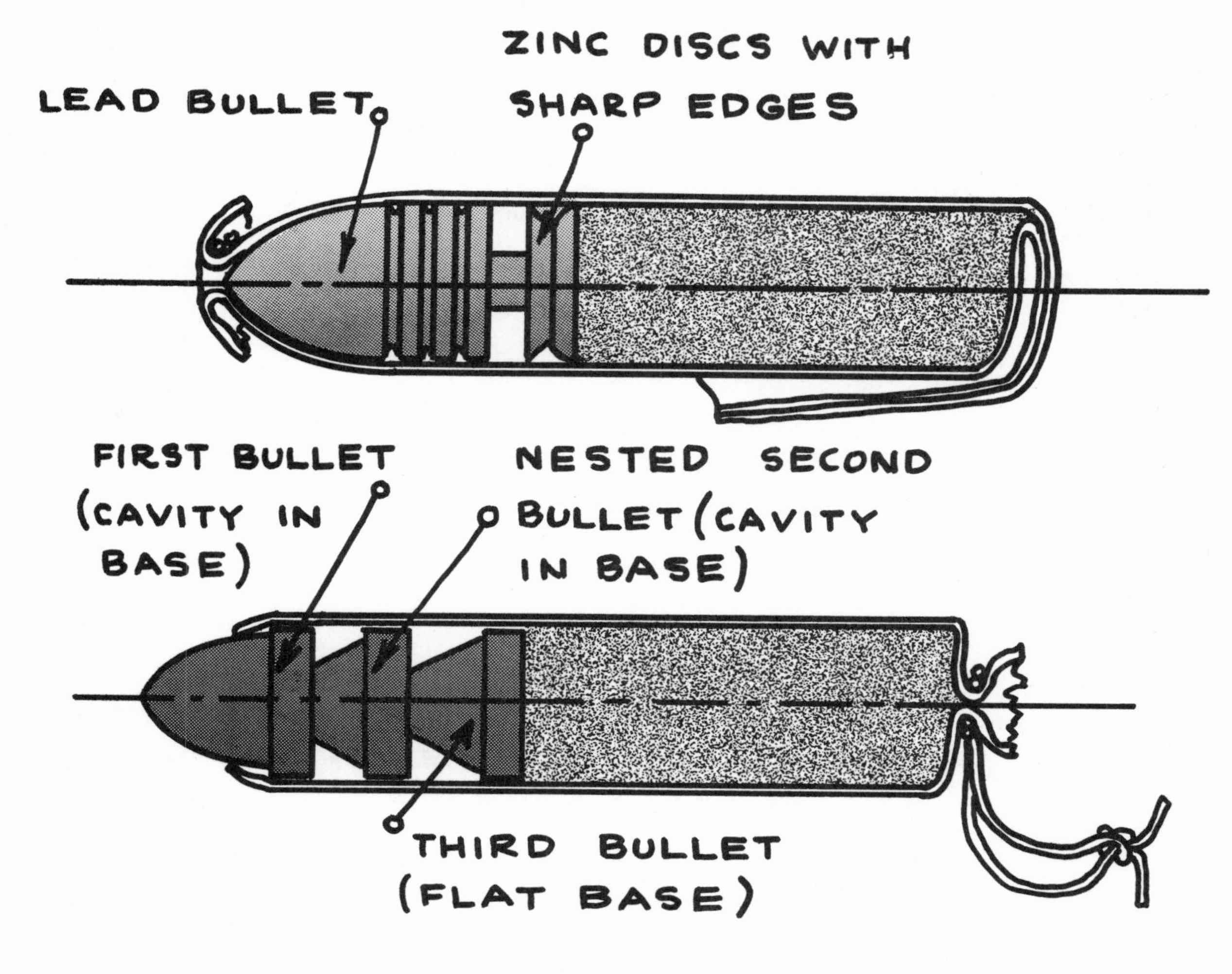

FIGURE 2-7 Design of .58 caliber Williams (top) and .58 Shaler sectional bullets in paper cartridges.

Williams' Bullets

Cleaning a muzzle-loading rifle was always a big problem for field soldiers and this was particularly true when the troops were involved in heavy combat with forced marches between engagements. The Civil War armies — like most armies — were generally filled with extremely tired men driven to the edge of physical endurance — men who were in no mood to spend more than the bare minimum of time on such arduous tasks as cleaning their rifles. At the same time, powder residue built up in the firearms as the black powder cartridges were fired. The design of the Minié bullets with ratchet-shaped grooves helped clear some of the fouling on each shot. An inventor named Williams came up with another idea. He made a bullet consisting of a lead nose and a slightly conical shaped zinc washer at the base. This washer was held to the bullet by a lead disc and plug. The design is shown in the upper illustration of Figure 2-7. When the cartridge was fired gas pressure drove the lead disc

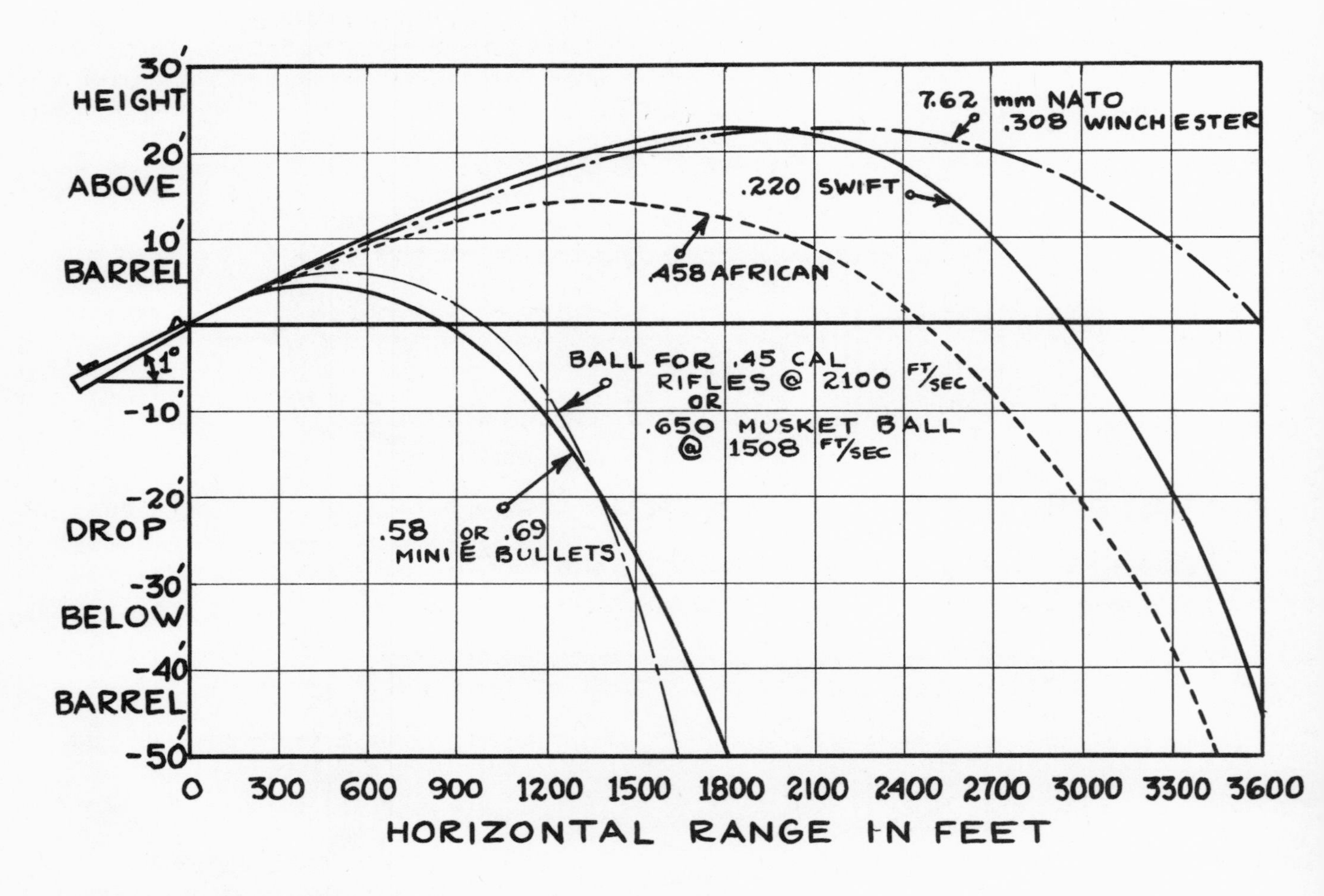

FIGURE 2-8 Exterior ballistics of rifles and muskets.

against the conical zinc washer, flattening it and forcing it to expand radially. The hard, sharp edge of the zinc washer then served to scrape the barrel of the rifle as it accelerated up the bore. There were several effective variations of this bullet. Original tests were performed in late 1861 and until near the end of the Civil War one Williams cartridge was included in every package of .58 caliber muzzle-loading cartridges.[5]

Explosive Bullets

It is interesting that both the Union and the Confederacy experimented with and used explosive bullets during the Civil War. Neither side admitted the use of explosive bullets and each charged the other with using them. Explosive bullets were also developed in Europe. A typical design consisted of a lead bullet with a copper or iron tube set into the front. The tube was filled with black powder and a percussion cap or similar priming device containing fulminate of mercury was used to close off the front of the powder cavity. These cartridges could be effective if properly designed and manufactured but they were also extremely dangerous to use. If the soldier rammed the cartridge too hard he was liable to set off the explosive bullet with disastrous results. A better design of bullet was developed by an inventor named Gardiner. This was patented in 1863 and is described as follows:

> A copper vessel, like a miniature bottle, was cast into the bullet with its neck opening at the bullet's base. The cavity was filled with powder, and the neck was plugged with slow burning powder. On firing of the rifle the powder in the base of the bullet was

[5] *Ibid.* P 125

ignited and when it had burned through to the inside, the bullet exploded. This was timed to occur 1¼ seconds after firing. It appears that while in flight this bullet had a tracer effect probably the first on record — but its possibilities went unnoticed for 40 to 50 years. The Gardiner bullet can be recognized by the nozzle like projection at the base, communicating with the interior. Some are now considerably corroded around the fuze hole from deterioration of the powder within. Ordnance records show that a total of 33,350 Gardiner explosive bullets or musket shells — were issued to the troops. They were used in calibers, .54, .58 and .69. The caliber .54 bullet weighed 363 grains, the caliber .58, 451 grains.[6]

EXTERIOR BALLISTICS OF MUZZLE LOADING AMMUNITION

A comparison of exterior ballistic performance of modern and muzzle-loading ammunition is shown graphically in Figure 2-8. The calculations have been performed for muskets, muzzle-loading rifles and modern rifles, with the muzzle in each case elevated at an angle of 1 degree above horizontal. The trajectories have been calculated out to 2000 yards or slightly over a mile. In order to illustrate the differences the vertical scale on the graph has been greatly expanded. For example, each horizontal grid represents 300 feet and each vertical grid represents only 10 feet. One degree elevation is not a very big angle and yet the modern 7.62 mm NATO cartridge [also known as .308 Winchester] sends a sharply pointed 150-grain bullet 3613 feet before it comes back down to the same elevation as the barrel. The time to travel this distance is only 2.3 seconds and the bullet, starting at 2800 feet per second, retains a velocity of 1000 feet per second at this extended range.

A modern .220 Swift cartridge fires a 48-grain bullet at the highest commercial muzzle velocity of 4110 feet per second. This bullet, fired at the same 1 degree angle, eventually rises 23 feet above the elevation of the barrel at a range of 1847 feet from the muzzle. It travels 2950 feet before returning to the elevation of the barrel and covers this distance in only 2.19 seconds. With such a light projectile most of the velocity is gone. The velocity has dropped to only 745 feet per second and retains only 60 foot-pounds of energy.

The very heavy .458 Winchester African cartridge (which is used for elephant hunting and other large and dangerous game) launches a round nose 500-grain bullet at 2130 feet per second. If this cartridge is fired at the same 1 degree elevation, the bullet would reach a maximum height of 14 feet above the barrel at 1400 feet from the muzzle and would travel 2458 feet or almost half a mile before returning to the height of the barrel. At this range it would retain a velocity of 963 feet per second and 1030 foot-pounds of energy.

The performance of Civil War ammunition was very different from these modern cartridges. The .58 caliber hollow Minié bullet — the standard Civil War load — left the muzzle at 1005 feet per second with an energy of 1132 foot-pounds. If launched at the same 1 degree angle, it would reach a maximum height of 4.26 feet at a range of 465 feet from the muzzle. After only 893 feet of travel it would return to the same height of the barrel and at this range it would retain 773 feet per second velocity, and 670 foot-pounds of energy. To cover 3600 feet the .58 Minié bullet would require a flight time of 5.96 seconds and the bullet would retain a velocity of only 421 feet per second at this range and 198 foot-pounds of energy. After traveling 3600 feet the Minié bullet would have fallen to 375 *feet below the height of the barrel.*

The performance of the .69 caliber Minié bullet was quite similar. Launched with a muzzle velocity of 954 feet per second, it had a higher energy level at 1495 foot-pounds. It reached a maximum height of 3.93 feet after 432 feet of travel and dropped back to the height of the barrel after only 834 feet of travel. The time needed to cover 3600 feet horizontal range was very similar to the Miníe bullet at 6.08 seconds. The retained velocity was also very similar, at 419 feet per second and the retained energy was 288 foot-pounds. The .69 caliber Minié bullet would have fallen to 397 feet below the height of the barrel after traveling 3600 feet.

The calculations were also performed for a modern 12-gauge rifled slug load. The bullet, weighing 544 grains, was launched at 1470 feet per second. The ballistics of this load were almost identical to the .58 caliber Miníe bullet with the exception that the blunter nose caused the velocity to fall off more rapidly at extended range. For example, at 3300 feet of range calculations indicate it would be traveling downward at an angle of 76 degrees and that it would never reach the 3600-foot range from the muzzle.

EXTERIOR BALLISTICS OF SPHERICAL BULLETS

The exterior ballistics of spherical bullets is quite surprising. The standard load in the Revolutionary War was a .627-inch diameter ball at an approximate muzzle velocity of 1400 feet per second and slightly

[6] *Ibid.* P 127

over 1600 foot-pounds of muzzle energy. This was a typical load for the French Charleville Model 1763 musket using a powder charge of 189 grains. If the musket was fired at 1 degree elevation and the bullet came out reasonably straight, it would reach a height of 5.49 feet at a distance of 530 feet from the muzzle. The bullet would fall back to the height of the barrel after a range of 933 feet at which time it would still retain 563 feet per second velocity and 260 foot-pounds of energy. This Revolutionary War bullet would also run out of steam at a horizontal range of about 3700 feet.

The best smoothbore musket ballistics were for the early 19th century .650-inch diameter balls, fired from the Model 1835 or 1842 muskets at a muzzle velocity of 1508 feet per second and a muzzle energy of 2080 foot-pounds. This ball would reach a maximum height of 5.95 feet at a range of 566 feet from the muzzle. The ball would travel 988 feet before falling back to the height of the barrel and the flight would take 1.19 seconds. The 412-grain lead sphere would retain 561 feet per second velocity and an energy of 288 foot-pounds.

The ballistics of a typical .45 caliber Kentucky rifle loaded with a .435-inch diameter ball weighing 135 grains and launched with a muzzle velocity of 1700 feet per second would give almost identical ballistics to the .650-inch musket ball. If the powder charge in the Kentucky rifle was increased to 100 grains, the bullet came whistling out of the muzzle at 2100 feet per second velocity. The 135-grain ball had a muzzle energy of 1322 foot-pounds. The bullet would reach a maximum elevation of 7.2 feet above the muzzle at a distance of 630 feet. It would fall back to the height of the rifle barrel at 1050 feet from the muzzle after a flight of 1.28 seconds. At this range it would retain only 475 feet per second velocity and an energy of only 68 foot-pounds. These ballistics represented about the maximum limit to which a round ball could be driven and much unburned powder would be spewed out of the muzzle with this heavy a powder charge. Even so, the bullet theoretically would travel only 3065 feet horizontally before it was falling vertically. Toward the end of the trajectory the angle sloped rapidly downward. For example, it would take 11 seconds to reach a range of 2700 feet and the bullet would be falling at an angle of 68 degrees. After another 10 seconds the bullet would only have reached a range of 3000 feet and would be falling at an angle of 86 degrees.

During the first half of the 19th century, the standard United States rifles were .54 caliber firing a round lead bullet .525 of an inch in diameter. The tests by Major Alfred Mordecai in the mid-1840's showed a launch velocity of 1750 feet per second for the standard cartridge. The bullet weighed 218.5 grains and had a muzzle energy of 1486 foot-pounds. If fired at a 1 degree elevation the bullet would reach a height of 6.4 feet at a range of 582 feet from the muzzle. It would drop back to the height of the barrel after only 992 feet of travel and a flight time of 1.22 seconds. The retained velocity would be 508 feet per second and the retained energy 125 foot-pounds. Calculations indicate that the extreme range of this bullet would be 3250 feet. It would take 14.5 seconds for the bullet to travel 3000 feet from the muzzle and at this range it would have a velocity of 183 feet per second along the flight path and would be dropping at an angle of 77 degrees. The figures demonstrate the dramatic improvement in exterior ballistic performance which has been accomplished by modern science and technology in the field of firearms.

Muzzle-Loading Rifles

CHAPTER 3

The development of rifled firearms is lost in the history of the Middle Ages. Some crossbows were designed to impart a spiral motion to the bolt or arrow in order to give better stability in flight. There is an oft-repeated story that rifling grooves were originally cut straight in the musket barrels to serve as recesses into which dirt could accumulate for the sole purpose of making loading easier. While this design was undoubtedly tried, European records indicate that spiral rifling was well known in the 16th century. Rifling is sometimes credited to Gaspard Kollner of Vienna in the late 15th century and at other times to Augustus Kotter of Nuremberg about 1520.

Whether smoothbore or rifled, these early firearms posed many difficult problems. The barrels were not smooth inside and were not a uniform diameter from one end to the other. The bullets were cast in crude molds and were not round. The earliest attempts to make a gas tight seal utilized a wooden plug or sabot which was rammed down on top of the powder and served as a base wad much as fiber wads are used in our shotshells today. The use of a wooden sabot under the ball was continued in artillery practice to the end of the muzzle-loading era and was a common design used during the American Revolution and through the Civil War.

Augustus Kotter used a star-grooved rifling design about 1520. This is a rifling pattern where eight or more narrow rifling grooves are cut into the bore of the barrel. This type of rifling is a logical first step, for the process of cutting the grooves was so laborious the tendency would be to make the grooves narrow so that not very much material had to be removed to form the rifling. The first patent for rifling gun barrels in England was issued to one Arnold Rotsipen in 1635. By 1600 the Germans and Swiss were skilled rifle makers, and the greatly increased accuracy of rifle projectiles was well known through Europe. This makes one ponder why the smoothbore musket remained the standard infantry arm for another 240 years — and there were excellent reasons.

The smoothbore musket could be loaded with a loose-fitting ball and the windage or clearance between the musket ball and bore was taken up with paper wadding. Infantry tactics called for volley firing between close ranks of standing infantry followed by a bayonet charge. The smoothbore musket fired a large ball which had tremendous power at close range and the musket could be reloaded fairly rapidly.

If a loose-fitting ball was placed in a rifle barrel, the ball would simple rattle down the bore like a musket ball on firing and fail to spin, resulting in poor accuracy. This posed a very difficult problem for neither the barrels nor bullets could be made to close tolerances and a tight fit of the lead bullet in the barrel was essential so that the rifling would bite and give the bullet proper spin. The general solution was to provide the rifleman with a sturdy iron ramrod and a mallet so that he could

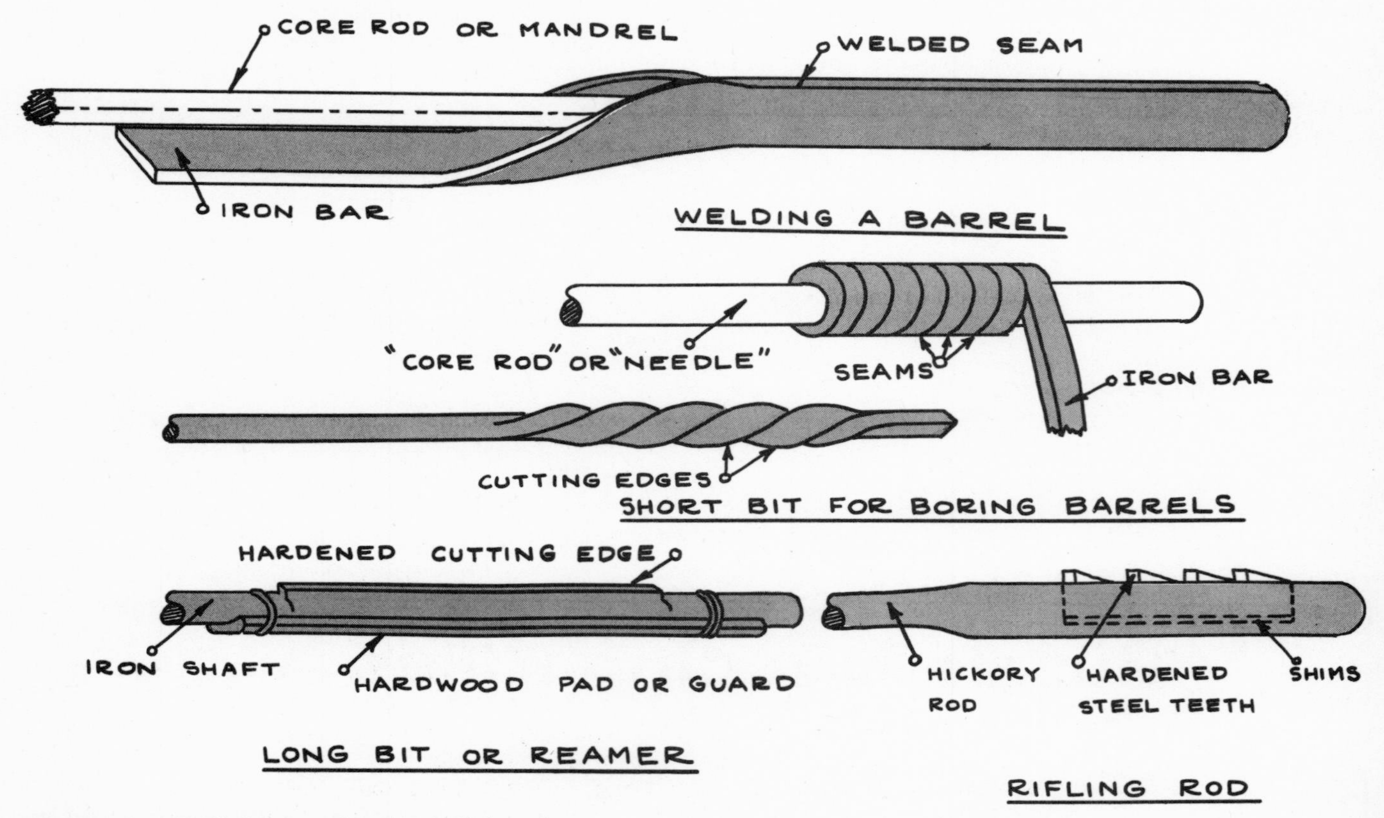

FIGURE 3-1 Tools for manufacturing rifle barrels.

literally drive a slightly oversize lead bullet the length of the rifle barrel during the loading process. One can imagine a 16th century battle scene with 5 percent of the riflemen firing and 95 percent in the various stages of reloading their cumbersome weapons. The image of hundreds of men in ranks pounding away on iron ramrods with mallets to drive the bullets down in the midst of a hot battle helps one visualize why the rifles remained a very specialized weapon issued only to select troops.

The rifle was brought to the United States during the second half of the 17th century. The first rifles were very heavy German designs with relatively short barrels and large bore diameters. Since powder and lead were extremely expensive in the Colonies, the design was gradually modified to a smaller diameter barrel and a longer bore to get a little more efficiency out of the powder, and to reduce the amount of lead required for each bullet. By 1700 the use of a very thin leather or cloth patch, generally circular, was well known in Germany and Switzerland, and its use had become popular in the United States. The tough leather or cloth patch accomplished many things to make the rifle a much more practical firearm than it had ever been before:

1. It served as a "tolerance absorber" so that bullets of slightly differing diameter could be fired effectively through the same barrel.
2. The bullet was not deformed by being driven into the rifling. The bullet was slightly smaller than the inside diameter of the barrel. The patch material was forced out into the rifling grooves and was spun as the bullet and patch moved up the barrel. The rotary motion was transmitted from the patch to the spherical bullet by the friction of the resilient patch material. When the bullet left the barrel the patch quickly fell away due to air resistance, and the smooth spherical ball, unmarked with rifling grooves but stabilized by spinning traveled accurately to the target.
3. The resilient patch greatly reduced the amount of force required to load the rifle. There was no need for an iron ramrod and mallet for the resilient patch could accommodate changes in barrel diameter due to fouling.

The rifle was always the weapon of the skilled shooter. Anyone experienced with the early flintlock rifles knows that considerable experimentation is required to achieve good accuracy. Once the frontiersman found the magic combination of powder charge and bullet diameter, he would cut his powder horn to throw this exact charge. He could do extremely effective shooting with his unique combination of bullet, type of patch, and carefully measured powder charge.

The United States was fortunate in having skilled riflemen available in moderate numbers during the Revolution and in the War of 1812. These were generally volunteers who came into the Service with their own rifle and hunting equipment. With their lifelong shooting experience and the toughness that frontier conditions demanded they were extremely effective troops.

The manufacture of rifles and muskets with the crude tools available in the United States in the 18th century required tremendous patience and ingenuity. Techniques were evolved which utilized the same manufacturing processes as in the far better equipped Royal Armories and commercial factories of Europe but with tools and machinery which utilized wooden components wherever possible. There were three processes for manufacturing barrels. The most common technique is shown in the upper illustration of Figure 3-1. An iron sheet was hammered out on the blacksmith's forge with the width equal to the circumference of the finished barrel and a length slightly shorter than the finished barrel. An iron rod the same diameter as the inside of the barrel was cooled in water while the strip of iron was being heated. Very often this strip of iron was made up from scrap iron which the blacksmith had collected from various sources. There was one theory that used horseshoes had been toughened by the impact of the horses' hooves on the roadway and were especially suitable for use in barrels.

When the strip was red hot it was withdrawn from the forge and placed on the anvil. The blacksmith placed the mandrel or "core pin" in about the center of the barrel and started hammering up the edges of the strip to form a tube around the mandrel. Periodically the mandrel had to be knocked loose and cooled and the rough barrel would be returned to the forge for reheating. The upper illustration of Figure 3-1 shows the barrel when half done. The edges of the strip have been joined on top of the mandrel and have been forge-welded into a seam with the blacksmith's hammer. Half the barrel has been finished and the blacksmith is now ready to repeat the process on the other end, first curving the sides of the material upwards, then forming a loop over the top of the mandrel and forge-welding the seam into a strong joint. It is obvious that the quality of the barrel depends entirely on the skill of the blacksmith. Barrels would often have to be reheated more than a dozen times before the forging process was complete and really strong welded joints achieved.

The second major technique for making rifle and musket barrels is shown in the second illustration of Figure 3-1. A small iron bar about ½ inch x ½ inch in cross section has been made up by the gunsmith. This iron bar is heated up in the forge and then wrapped spirally around the cold mandrel or "needle." As the bar was wrapped around, it was hammered to thin the material down to the approximate finished thickness of the barrel and the spiral joints were forge-welded into a solid and strong structure. This process was often known as the Damascus process and was much used in making shotgun barrels during the 18th century. In the Damascus method the slender iron bar usually was given a spiral twist before it was wrapped around the mandrel. The finished Damascus barrel has the appearance of a rope wrapped around the mandrel with many beautiful patterns showing in the texture of the steel.

The third process for making rifle or musket barrels utilized two strips of steel and a forging process similar to that shown in the upper illustration of Figure 3-1. By using two strips the forming process was considerably simplified. The strips could be preformed into a dished shaped by laying the strip in a trough and bending it into a semicircular shape by driving in a mandrel the diameter of the inside of the barrel. The disadvantage of this process was that there were two longitudinal seams along the length of the barrel and a careless workman might produce a barrel that would open up like a banana.

After the forging process was completed, both the inside and outside surfaces had to be finished. The bore was generally drilled out with a short bit as shown in the third illustration down in Figure 3-1. This bit was made from a piece of hardened steel which was first forged to a square cross section then heated very hot and given a spiral twist. It was then quenched in water or oil to make the cutting edges much harder than the rifle barrel. The short bit was attached to a long shaft not shown in the illustration. Some of the better equipped gunsmiths developed a crude version of a lathe and had a foot treadle to rotate either the barrel or the bit during boring. In the early 19th century, the National Armories and some of the larger manufacturing plants converted to water power for these kinds of boring operations. Many of the backwoods gunsmiths in Kentucky, Tennessee, and Pennsylvania continued into the 20th century to use treadles or hand-operated lathes for boring and reaming rifle barrels.

After the barrel was completely drilled out the inside

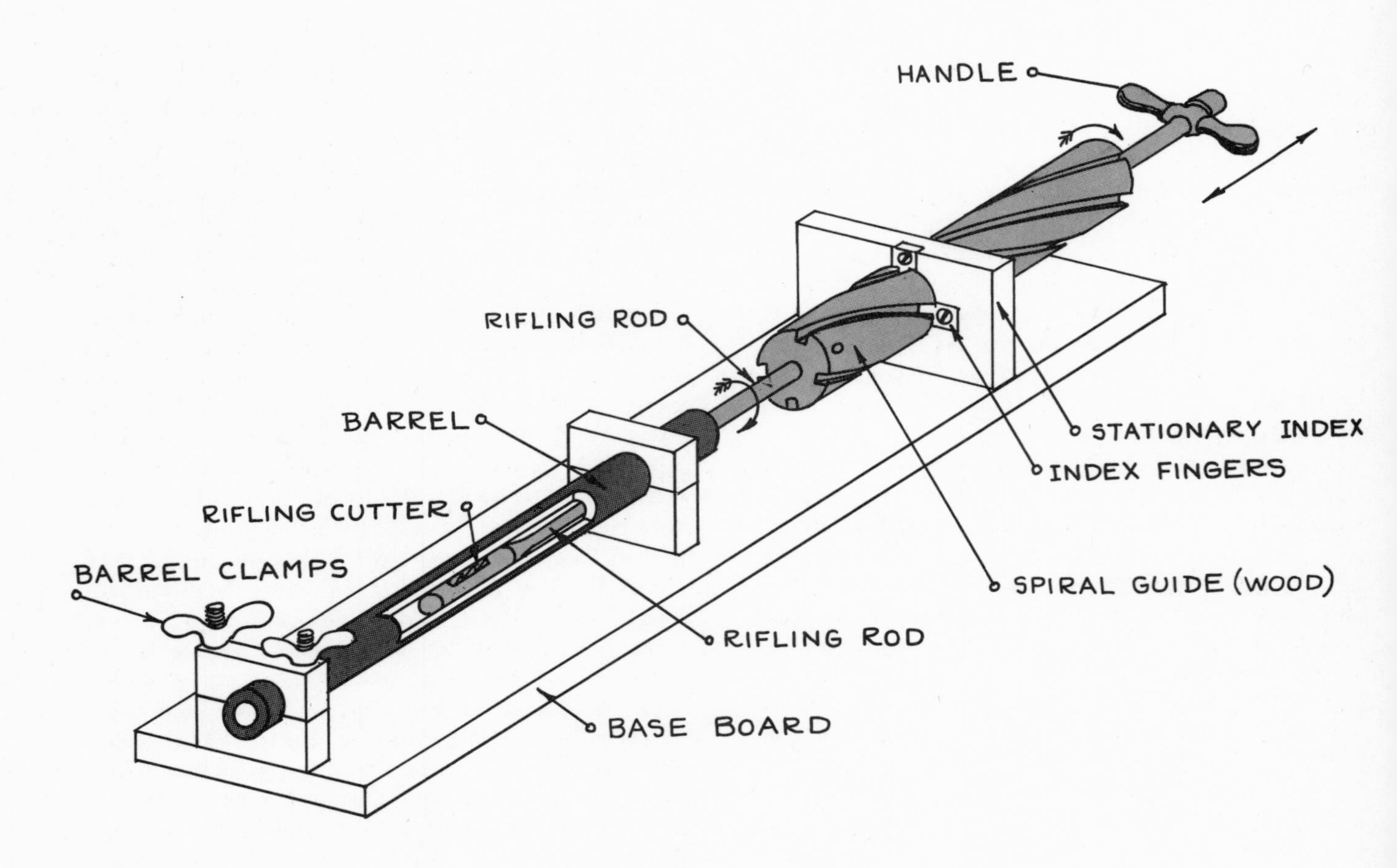

FIGURE 3-2 Rifling machine.

of the bore was reamed smooth with a "long bit" or reamer. This is shown in the lower left illustration of Figure 3-1. The reamer consisted of a long straight cutting edge which had been filed or ground very sharp and then hardened. The diameter of the reamed hole was controlled by fitting a hardwood pad or bearing on the side opposite the cutting edge. This hardwood pad was held in place with wire, rawhide or string. After the first cuts had been completed, the gunsmith increased the diameter of the cut slightly by removing the hardwood pad and adding a small shim of thin metal between the hardwood pad and the reamer.

The reamer was then oiled and fed back slowly into the revolving barrel. Photographs of some of the early wooden lathes which were used for boring and reaming operations makes one wonder how smooth, straight barrels could have been manufactured with this equipment. The interior surface of the barrel was finally reamed smooth after many, many cuts. The barrel was then removed from the lathe and the straightness checked by an instrument which looked very much like a small Indian bow. A small string or wire was threaded through the hole in the barrel and fastened to the ends of a long slender stick which was bent into an arc. The string formed a straight line through the barrel and the skilled barrel maker could determine if the hole was straight by bringing the string over so that it touched one side of the bore. If the contact between the string and the bore was continuous for the entire length, the barrel was straight. If it was not, the high points or gaps were readily apparent. The barrel was then marked and the string withdrawn. The barrel was laid on a hollow anvil and struck with a lead hammer and the straightness checked again.

It is easy to imagine that a great deal of skill was required to know how hard and exactly where to strike the barrel to make it true. Barrel straightening has continued as an art through the centuries, and is still an operation that requires a highly skilled workman. The modern technique is to put a cross-hair pattern on a sheet of lighted, frosted glass. The skilled barrel maker sights through the barrel and sees the optical pattern of the cross hair along the length of the bore. He then places the barrel in a powerful bending fixture and applies just enough pressure to compensate for the bend in the barrel. It is not a matter of bending the barrel exactly straight since the barrel steels are resilient. The art lies in overbending the barrel so that after it springs back from the extreme position it is exactly straight.

RIFLING THE BARREL

After the barrel had been reamed and straightened it was ready for the rifling process. The earliest equipment was made entirely of wood and was incredibly crude by modern standards. Some of the rifling benches were left outside year-round for the gunsmith rarely used his rifling machines. A typical early rifling tool is shown in the lower illustration of Figure 3-1. Surprisingly enough, the rifling rods were generally made of hard wood such as hickory. The rifling cutter was a small piece of hardened steel with saw type teeth filed and then honed to a sharp edge. A slot was whittled into the hickory rifling head and the cutter dropped into place.

Now imagine that the rifle barrel, reamed and straightened, is fastened down to a bench. The rifling cutter with a dimension to the top of the rifling teeth of about .0002 of an inch larger than the diameter of the barrel was placed into one end of the barrel and pulled through with the long hickory shaft. As the sharp rifling cutters traveled down the barrel each tooth would take a very fine shaving from the surface of the bore. When the cutter emerged from the other end of the barrel you would have a long relatively straight groove .0002-inch deep the length of the barrel. There would be two serious problems. One is that the rifling would be straight and not twisted and the second is that you would have no reliable way to line the cutter up with the groove to make a second deeper cut.

These problems led to the development of the rifling machine or rifling bench as shown in Figure 3-2. This illustration shows the parts in a simplified form for clarity. The machines were built on a heavy wooden baseboard and the barrel was rigidly clamped to the board by two guides. In Figure 3-2 the barrel has been partially cut away to show the rifling cutter and the rifling head cutting a groove inside the barrel. The rifling head is being pulled through the bore by tension on the hickory rifling rod which in turn is cross-pinned to the large spiral guide. The spiral guide was normally made of hardwood and was 3 or 4 inches in diameter and as long as the longest barrel to be manufactured. The spiral guides were often over 4 feet long. At the far end of the spiral guide another shaft was fitted together with a freely turning handle.

The spiral guide was held in a "stationary index" which had a series of wooden or metal index fingers which rode in the long slots which had been laboriously carved into the outside surface of the spiral guide. As the barrel maker pulled on the handle, the spiral guide was forced to rotate by the index fingers and it in turn forced the rifling rod and rifling head to rotate inside the barrel. Figure 3-2 shows the spiral guide with four slots. Most were actually made with seven or eight slots, equal to the number of grooves to be cut in the barrel.

The rifling cutter was kept well oiled and as the handle reciprocated back and forth the rifling cutter would dig deeper and deeper into the barrel, cutting a single groove. When the cut reached a depth where no more metal was removed the spiral guide was rotated one groove and the process was repeated again. After about 40 back and forth motions the rifle barrel shown in Figure 3-2 would have four shallow grooves half a thousandth of an inch deep. The rifling head was then removed from the barrel and the rifling cutter lifted out. The chips were cleaned out and a small shim placed underneath the rifling cutter, lifting it by about .001 of an inch. The process was then repeated another forty strokes resulting in four slightly deeper grooves perhaps .001 of an inch deep. With good equipment and a strong gunsmith a barrel could be completely rifled in about a half a day. Because the process was so laborious the tendency was to have a large number of fairly narrow, shallow grooves. It did not require much twist to stabilize the spherical bullet and twists of one turn in four feet were commonly used.

Modern barrels are rifled by four different processes. The process used in many of the older shops throughout the world is a direct descendant of the old process used by the early gunsmiths and is called "hook rifling." A hardened steel rifling cutter on a long steel shaft is reciprocated back and forth in the barrel to cut the grooves one at a time. The spiral motion of the cutter is generally developed by what is called a "sine bar." The machine looks like a large cast-iron lathe with a heavy frame. The sine bar lies at one end of the machine. If the angle of the sine bar is close to the axis of the barrel a very slow pitch of rifling will be cut. If the sine bar is tilted at a sharp angle to the axis of the barrel the twist becomes faster, and some modern barrels are cut with twists as short as one turn in 9 inches. Experimental twists of one turn in 6 inches have been cut in .22 caliber barrels, but experimental work in the Winchester Research Laboratories showed that the chamber pressures rose very fast as the rifling twists were decreased to these extreme values.

A second process for rifling barrels is known as "broaching." The broaching process can be visualized by thinking of a string of pearls strung on a very strong wire. Suppose that the first pearl is the bore diameter of the barrel and each succeeding pearl is .0002 inch bigger in diameter. Each pearl has a complete rifling pattern cut into its surface. As the string of pearls is pulled through the barrel each pearl would take a fine cut so that by the time the last pearl finished traveling the length of the barrel the rifling is cut to full depth. In actual manufacturing practice the "pearls" are knobbly cutters on a hardened steel shaft. This process has the advantage of providing a finished rifling configuration with a single pass of the tooling. The disadvantages are the very expensive tooling and machinery required and a tendency for the barrel to have fine longitudinal scratches along the rifling.

A third process to rifle modern barrels is to make a single button or pearl of an extremely hard material such as tungsten carbide. Tungsten carbide is so hard that the rifling pattern must be ground into the surface with diamond grinding wheels. To rifle a barrel by this "button rifling" process, the tungsten carbide button is placed in one end of the barrel and pushed through the barrel by a powerful hydraulic press. This process involves tremendously high forces and if the lubrication film breaks down, both the barrel and the tungsten carbide button will be ruined.

Some of the finest barrels for target shooting made by custom makers are fashioned by combining the first and third processes. The barrels are first rifled by the hook rifling process and then the scratches are removed by pushing a hardened tungsten carbide button through the barrel to establish the final shape and smooth the interior surface.

The final modern process for manufacturing modern barrels is very unusual. In this process the barrel is drilled oversize. The barrel is placed in a large powerful machine and slowly rotated. When the machine is turned on a series of hammers literally pound the barrel inward around a mandrel which has been machined to the rifling shape. As a result of the hammering and pounding the interior diameter of the barrel is decreased and it takes on the shape of the rifling. The outside of the barrel is also decreased in diameter and the barrel becomes longer. This process is used by some of our largest manufacturers, for it results in a barrel with a very smooth interior surface and the rotary hammering increases the strength of the steel.

BARREL MANUFACTURE DURING THE CIVIL WAR

The U.S. Ordnance Manual of 1861 describes the standard process for manufacturing rifle barrels at the time of the Civil War as follows:

> The barrel is made from a short, flat bar of iron, which is first formed into a hollow cylinder and then welded and drawn out to the required size, length, and taper, by passing it through a series of rolls for that purpose.
>
> Materials — Best refined iron, free from slag and other impurities, of uniform texture, without hard spots: in plates 14″ long, 5½″ wide, .5625″ thick; the edges are so beveled that they shall form a close joint when the plate is formed into a cylinder. English iron, Marshall brand, is generally used.

The specifications note that the "best bituminous coal" should be used in the reverberating furnace and the "best anthracite coal" used in the forge. The tools to be used for the barrel making process were also specified. Primarily these were large machines which had grooved rollers designed to properly shape the flat strip into a tubular barrel. The process continues:

> To form the cylinder — the plates are put into the furnace and raised to a white heat, and then passed through the rolls, each groove in succession. The first groove forms the plate into a trough-shape; the second and third grooves contracted gradually; the fourth turns the two edges inward and the fifth completes the cylinder. The operation is performed at one heat.
>
> A day's work — three men can form 450 cylinders in 10 hours.
>
> To weld and shape the barrel — the fireman places two cylinders in the furnace and brings them to welding-heat; the foreman thrusts the largest mandrel [a long steel bar with an egg shaped bulb on each end. The mandrels were .46 of an inch to .71 of an inch in diameter] through one of the welded barrels while *yet in the furnace* and, taking it to the rolls puts the mandrel through the frame, introduces the end into the first groove, and a cylinder is drawn over the bulb of the mandrel which is held by the collar.

By this process the barrel was being swaged on both the inside and the outside at the same time. The bulb-shaped end of the mandrel was slightly larger than the inside diameter of the barrel. As the barrel was being pulled over the egg shaped end of the mandrel the rollers were squeezing down the outside forcing the hot edges of the rolled up plate to become welded together. The process continues:

> The first assistant, standing on the opposite side of the rolls, catches the barrel as it passes through, with a pair of tongs, and hands it to the second assistant, who stands on the same side as the foreman, and he receives it with a small short mandrel, which he thrusts into the barrel and straightens it by striking it two or three times on the flat table. He then replaces it in the furnace, and it is raised to a welding heat a second time . . . .
>
> When the barrel is brought to a welding heat the second time, the foreman takes it with the next smaller mandrel and passes it through the second groove [there were a series of graduated grooves in the rollers, the first groove being the largest, the second next largest, etc.].

In passing through the second groove the barrel was reduced in diameter and lengthened. It was then straightened by shoving a 3-foot long cylindrical mandrel into the bore and whacking the barrel on a flat iron table until the mandrel would pass easily into the bore of the barrel. After this straightening the barrel was again returned to the furnace and brought up to welding heat. The third and remaining grooves in the rollers provided the tapered shape to the outside of the barrel. This is described as follows:

> The third and remaining grooves taper so as to give the barrel the shape of a frustrum of a cone, each succeeding groove reducing the size of the barrel and making it longer. The rolls are of such a size that a single revolution takes the barrel through; as they continue to revolve without stopping it requires care and dexterity on the part of the foreman to insert the barrel in the groove at the proper time, bringing the end against the shoulder in the large part of the groove.
>
> The barrel is so much chilled by passing over the mandrel, that it is necessary it should be straightened and reheated before passing it through the next grooves; a high red heat is required.
>
> After the barrel has been passed through the first 8 grooves with their corresponding mandrels, it is taken with tongs and passed twice through the last groove, for the purpose of making it round and smooth.

There were additional machines to straighten the barrels. The straightening machine had two long dies with half the shape of the barrel cut into each die. The dies were opened and closed by a powerful shaft driving an eccentric cam which opened the dies and then slammed the dies shut 60 times a minute. To straighten the barrel:

> The foreman inserts the muzzle end of the barrel in the dies and turns it around gradually, when the dies are opened, pushing it further into the dies until its whole length is embraced by them. The barrel then receives the pressure of the dies from 10 to 15 times, when it will be found to be straight.

The barrel then went to a trip-hammer with specially formed dies. An iron boss or "cone-seat" was swaged to the proper shape under the trip-hammer and then it, in turn, was forge-welded to the breech end of the barrel to provide extra material into which the "cone" or nipple could be screwed. A short mandrel was placed in the breech end of the barrel to keep the inside bore true and the dies of the triphammer were carefully designed to maintain the proper shape of the cone seat and then this extra piece of material was forged onto the barrel by the triphammer. The Ordnance Manual noted that "four men can form and weld from 75 to 80 barrels in 10 hours."

The interior surface of the barrel was then bored out, and the exterior was turned or ground to a smooth surface. The barrel was straightened again and proved by firing with an excessive charge of powder. The barrels were inspected eight times during the manufacturing process. The first inspection was made after the cone-seat was forged onto the barrel. The second inspection was after the barrel had been bored for the third time. The third inspection was after the exterior diameter had been ground smooth.

The fourth inspection was after the barrel had been proved. The normal powder charge was 60 grains of musket powder with the standard 500 grain Minié bullet. The barrels were first proved with a monstrous charge of 280 grains of powder topped with a wad made of a sheet of paper 32 inches long by .01 of an inch thick. The wad when folded up occupied a length of about ¾ of an inch in the barrel. On top of the wad a 500-grain bullet .570 of an inch in diameter was rammed and then another of the long wads was rammed into place.

If the barrel survived this first proving it received a second blast consisting of 250 grain of powder with the same wads and bullet. After this inspection the barrel was sent for filing the exterior surface, then inspected and, if passed, sent into the boring operations.

Apparently boring the interior surface of the barrels was still an extremely laborious process for no less than six boring passes were required before the interior surface was finished. The barrel was then inspected and sent to be rifled. The seventh inspection was after the rifling and the eighth inspection was after the breech plug had been assembled and the barrel was completed.

CAST STEEL BARRELS

It was during the 1840's that a great new process was developed for making very high quality, high strength rifle barrels. These were generally used for relatively expensive rifles firing heavy bullets with very heavy powder charges. The process was known as "cast steel." Regular iron was converted into steel by adding proper amounts of carbon and cast into small ingots about a foot long and four inches on a side. These ingots were sent through a series of rollers which forged and rolled the steel into long round or octagonal bars. These cast-steel barrel blanks ended up 12 to 16 feet long. The barrel maker would then cut off the length he desired for the barrel and laboriously drill a hole the entire length of the barrel.

A second and somewhat cheaper method of making barrels from cast steel was to punch a hole through the center of the short-fat ingot before rolling. The small ingot was reheated extremely hot and a hole punched lengthwise through it. A small-diameter mandrel — slightly smaller than the finished inside diameter of the rifle barrel — was chilled in cold water, and then placed through the ingot during the rolling process so that when the 12- to 16-foot long octagonal bar was finished the barrel hole was already through the entire length of the bar.

During the 1850's experiments in England developed a process known as "Whitworth fluid compressed steel." Under this process after the ingot of steel was cast, and while it was still very hot, it was placed in a hydraulic press and subjected to hundreds of tons of pressure which tended to eliminate any voids or blow holes in the material. Cast steel and Whitworth fluid compressed steel came into wide use in the United States for high quality rifles in the 1850's and through the 1880's.

The great majority of Civil War muzzle-loading rifles were made by the welding process. It is obvious that if these barrels could stand 280 grains of powder (4½ times the normal powder charge) that the forge-welding process had been developed to a high degree of perfection which allowed the production of inexpensive barrels with more than adequate strength levels for muzzle-loading firearms.

COMMERCIAL FLINTLOCKS

Three typical "Kentucky rifles" are shown in Figure 3-3. This very interesting illustration shows typical details of American flintlocks at the turn of the 19th century, and highlights the difference between American historical tradition and fact. Close examination reveals that two of the three "Kentucky rifles" were designed and built as smoothbores. By far the largest number of these flintlock firearms were manufactured in Pennsylvania by Dutch and German gunsmiths.

The upper rifle in the illustration was probably made in New England about 1780. It has a full octagon barrel 43¼ inches long and an over-all length of 59 inches. The .52 caliber barrel is rifled with seven grooves with a very slow twist. It is a good, solid, standard rifle typical of the ones that would be sold in wholesale quantities to the Government or private dealers for about ten dollars apiece. The retail price varied with what the traffic would bear but probably averaged about fifteen dollars. The rifle was fitted with a full-length stock and three brass pipes to hold the iron ramrod. A brass tip covers the front of the forearm and comes flush with the muzzle of the barrel. Lugs were welded to the bottom of the barrel and the barrel and stock were held together with three cross pins. The pins, which may be faintly seen in the illustration, passed through the wooden stock and through holes drilled in the lugs welded to the bottom of the barrel.

The lock is a typical commercial lock with a gooseneck hammer and a tilted pan with a fence to the rear. The lock plate is flat and the hammer is flat with beveled edges. The rifle is fitted with brass furniture such as the ornate cast trigger guard and butt plate. The rifle has an early type of checkering on the small of the stock.

The middle illustration of Figure 3-3 shows a Pennsylvania flintlock with a smoothbore barrel. The lack of rifling was definitely the owner's choice for the elaborate carving and scroll work on the small of the grip plus the ornamental brass work around the patch box indicate that it was a relatively expensive and high quality firearm. The design of this flintlock is typical of the period of 1780 to 1810. It has a very long barrel, 47⅞ inches, and the over-all length is 63½ inches. The rear 15 inches of the barrel is octagonal, then there is a transition section with an ornamental band, and the remainder of the barrel is turned round. Although smooth bore, a blade front sight and open "V" rear sight were fitted to the barrel. The rear of the barrel is marked J. P. Beck, identifying it as one of the firearms made by John Philip Beck of Dauphin County, Pennsylvania. There is a brass forearm tip which comes up flush with the muzzle of the rifle and four brass ramrod pipes underneath the stock hold a wooden ramrod. The barrel is held to the wood with steel wedges which pass horizontally through the forearm wood and through vertical lugs which were welded to the bottom of the barrel. The ornamental trigger guard was cast in brass and a fancy brass butt plate and patch box were fitted to the flintlock. The ornamental brass plate containing the patch box was held to the stock with no less than 9 screws. The wood

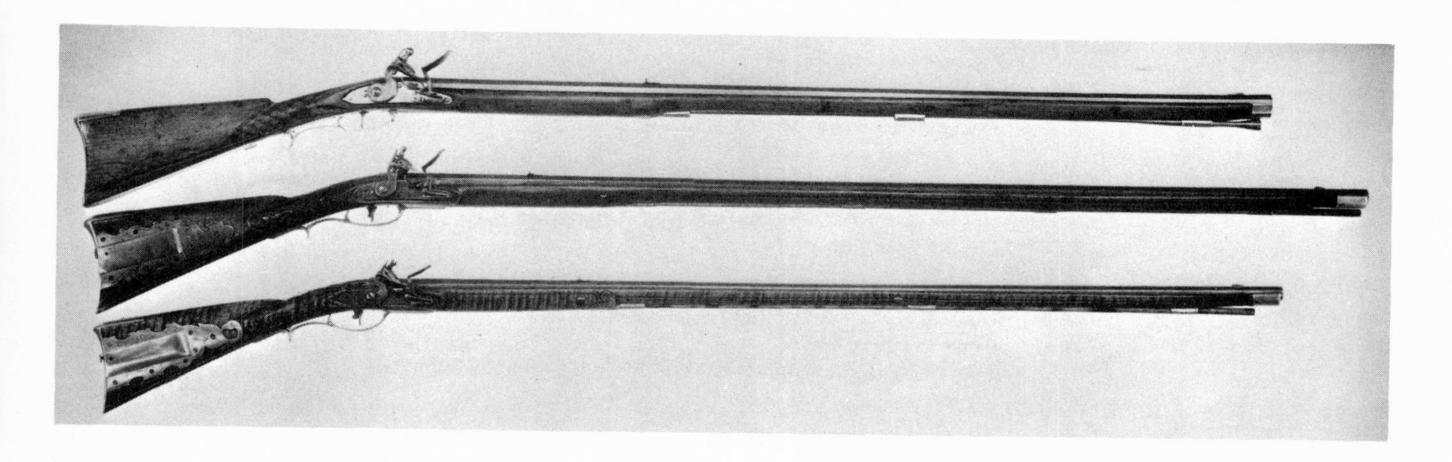

FIGURE 3-3 Three Kentucky flintlocks: UPPER; .52 caliber rifle; MIDDLE; smoothbore flintlock by John Philip Beck; LOWER; smoothbore flintlock by Nicholas Beyer.

beneath the plate was hollowed out and a spring-operated brass cover was hinged at the front end of the patch box. The small release button is barely visible as a bump on the butt plate. When this button is depressed an internal catch is released and the cover to the patch box jumps part way open.

This flintlock has seen hard service for the original lock was apparently worn out and a new lock manufactured by R. Hislop has been fitted. This was not uncommon, for on the frontier firearms were used almost daily and the lock mechanism was the part most likely to wear out. The Hislop lock does not fit the opening in the wooden stock properly and contains later features than the remainder of the flintlock. One of the features that identifies the Hislop lock as a later design is a roller bearing fitted to the frizzen spring to reduce friction and wear as the frizzen snapped open and shut.

The lowest illustration in Figure 3-3 is a smoothbore "Kentucky" manufactured by Nicholas Beyer of Lebanon, Pennsylvania, about 1800. There are records which indicate that Nicholas Beyer may have been an apprentice to John Philip Beck. Again, this flintlock was made smoothbore by choice since it is a very deluxe firearm with an elaborately carved wooden stock and forearm and a very ornate brass patch box. The barrel is 44½ inches long and is octagonal for the rear 15 inches. There is a transition section with an ornamental band and the front 30 inches of the barrel are turned round. Both of the smoothbore flintlocks in this illustration were primarily designed for relatively accurate shooting with a single ball since rifle type sights were fitted. This flintlock has a brass blade front sight and a V type open rear sight. The stock is made of tiger-striped maple which gives it a very ornamental appearance. The barrel is held to this forearm by a brass forearm cap plus cross wedges which pass though the wooden forearm and through slotted lugs welded to the bottom of the barrel. The wooden ramrod is held in three brass ramrod pipes. All the pipes are fairly ornamental with decorative ridges in both ends of the brass tube.

The cast-brass trigger guard and butt plate are typical Pennsylvania designs but the brass work around the patch box is extremely ornate — cut in the design of a fanciful bird with its neck craned rearward and the beak touching the bird's back. The brass work is held to the stock with 9 screws and again contains a spring-loaded brass cover which is held in place by an internal catch.

The release button for the patch box cover projects from the center of the butt plate. The design looks as if the patch box would automatically fly open every time a shot was fired. The lock contains later features than the uppermost illustration in having a roller fitted to the frizzen spring to reduce the friction as the frizzen snapped open when the shot was fired.

The use of smoothbore barrels on expensive "Kentucky" patterned flintlocks does not agree with the romantic tradition of American history where every frontiersman was a Daniel Boone who could unerringly hit his target every shot at 200 yards. It appears that up to half of the Kentucky or Pennsylvania "rifles" were actually left smoothbore as an owner's preference. The fact that sights were fitted to the barrel indicated that they were primarily designed for use with single lead balls enclosed in a leather or cloth patch. They obviously were intended for accurate shooting for both front and rear sights were fitted to the barrel. Military flintlock muskets of the era often had a front but no rear sight.

The owners apparently felt that the smoothbore barrel provided sufficient accuracy for the short hunting ranges of 1800 along with the additional flexibility of being able to utilize the flintlock as a shotgun for wild fowl and small game. While shot could be loaded into a rifle barrel even the slow twist of the early periods would tend to spin out the shot in contact with the bore. Since the barrels were fairly small in diameter the shot column would tend to be long and a high proportion of the pellets would receive a tangential spin, resulting relatively poor patterns. Thus the frontiersman made their own form of trade-off decision in choosing their firearm, and about half chose the wider flexibility of the smoothbore flintlock compared to the longer range accuracy and lack of effective shotgun capability of the rifle design.

The ornamental detail that went into many of these early flintlocks indicated great pride on the part of the gunmakers and a willingness on the part of the customers to pay a great deal extra in the hard earned cash of that early day for high quality art work. For example, the lower flintlock in Figure 3-3 had a great deal of extra effort put into the carving of the wooden stock and into the artistic shaping of all the metal furniture, such as forearm tip, ramrod pipes, trigger guard, butt plate and patch box assembly. Much extra hammering, filing and polishing were required for these elaborate designs. In addition to the brass work this flintlock had an 8-point silver star inletted into the cheek rest on the left side of the stock. Silver was extremely scarce on the frontier and this cost a great deal extra.

Ballistic tests were performed by Winchester Research and Thomas E. Hall, Curator of the Winchester Gun Museum, with a .40 caliber flintlock rifle similar to that shown in Figure 3-3. The rifle fired a 91-grain ball covered with a linen patch. Sixty-five grains of FFG powder were placed in the barrel and a priming charge of FFFG powder was in the pan. The ball had a muzzle velocity of 1875 FPS, giving a muzzle energy of 710 foot-pounds. This works out to an efficiency of about 11 foot-pounds of muzzle energy per grain of propellant charge. The ball did not have very long range, despite the high muzzle velocity, for it was light, and had high air resistance due to its spherical shape. Exterior ballistic calculations, based on firing tests by Ballistic Research Laboratories at Aberdeen Proving Ground, Maryland, indicate:

RANGE, YARDS	VELOCITY FEET SECOND	ENERGY IN BALL FOOT/POUNDS
0	1875	710
50	1284	333
100	948	182
200	607	75
300	416	35
400	286	12
500	195	8.5

These calculations indicate that the rifle would be pretty useless beyond 200 yards, and accuracy would be quite sensitive to side winds due to the lightness of the ball.

The performance of a .45 caliber flintlock rifle very similar to that shown in Figure 3-3 was thoroughly tested at the University of California in 1935. The results of these tests are shown in Figure 3-4. The rifle fired a 135-grain ball with a greased patch. It was tested with a series of powder charges starting with 30 grains and working up to a full 100-grain charge. Analysis of the test data shows that the efficiency of the rifle was greatest at a 40-grain powder charge where an efficiency of 18 foot-pounds of muzzle energy per grain of propellant was achieved. As the powder charge increased the muzzle velocity and muzzle energy also increased, but the efficiency tended to decline to 14 foot-pounds per grain of propellant with the 100-grain charge. With a 100-grain charge driving the light bullet a muzzle velocity of 2100 feet per second was achieved. Despite this high velocity the long range ballistics were not very good. The 135-grain bullet had 1322 foot-pounds of muzzle energy, but the spherical shape held its velocity very poorly and very little energy remained beyond 200 yards.

RANGE, YARDS	VELOCITY FEET SECOND	ENERGY IN BALL FOOT/POUNDS
0	2100	1322
100	1160	404
200	764	175
300	551	91
400	409	51
500	303	28

Closeup details of three other American flintlocks are shown in Figure 3-5. The same three firearms are shown full length in Figures 3-5a and 3-6. The upper firearm in the illustration is a short rifle with a heavy octagonal barrel. The comb of the stock is straight and there is beautiful ornamental brass work on the butt making it a very handsome firearm. Although the barrel is only 33½ inches long, it is of such heavy cross section that the rifle weighs 9 pounds 7 ounces. The barrel measures 1.080 inches across the flat at the breech and .980 of an inch across the flat at the muzzle. It is rifled with 12 very deep narrow grooves. The bore diameter is .360 of an inch and the diameter to the bottom of the grooves near the muzzle is .400 of an inch. The over-all length of this rifle with the short barrel is only 49½ inches. This is an excellent quality firearm with interesting features. The hammer has a fairly graceful contour but a double necked design. The end of the cap screw shows clearly in the

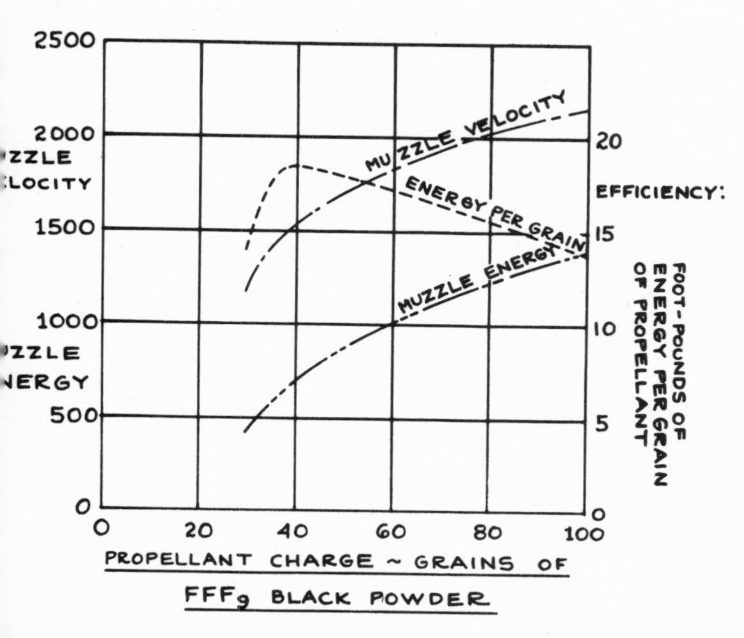

FIGURE 3-4 Performance of a .45 caliber flintlock rifle.

window machined through the hammer just below the lower jaw. The hammer has been carved with an engraving of leaves on a stalk and there is ornamental carving at the border of the hammer which is flat and beveled. The lock plate is flat and is stamped with the word "Warranted" down near the bottom and forward of the hammer. There is ornamental scrollwork and engraving on the lock plate and an ornamental vertical line near the back. The frizzen is nicely designed with ornamental detail such as the gracefully shaped tail which prevents overrotation when hit by the flint. The stock has been carefully shaped with excellent detail around the lock plate. A "tiger flame" design has been burned into the stock giving it a very ornamental appearance. The cast brass trigger guard is ornate with excellent detail. The patch box is set into the butt end of the stock and has been designed with very ornate scrollwork and is held to the stock with seven screws. A great deal of cutting and filing of the brass work and careful inletting of the wood was required to set this much ornamentation into the stock. The left side detail of this rifle is shown in Figure 3-6. The rifle has a small cheek piece on the left side. The lock is held by only a single screw passing through a brass escutcheon. Three ramrod pipes are fitted to hold the wooden ramrod. A handsome cast brass forearm cap protects the fore-end of the rifle and comes nearly to the muzzle.

The middle rifle in Figures 3-5 and 3-6 is another ornate example of early Americana. The flat locked plate is marked "S. Home." There is a very elaborate zigzag design on the rounded back of the lock plate. Eighteenth century locks generally had a pointed tail while the later flintlocks usually had rounded lock plates. This design would indicate that the lock was fairly late in the flintlock era and the second method of dating the lock is the fact that there is a roller on the frizzen spring to minimize wear as the frizzen snapped open and shut.

This is a beautifully engraved rifle. The goosenecked hammer has slender contours and looks quite fragile. It is flat with a beveled edge and an engraved border has been incised around the edge. There is very artistic ornamental detail in the pan. The metal is cut away immediately to the rear of the pan so that there is a dip between the pan and the fence. The frizzen is also formed with artistic detail. The upper surface of the frizzen is bent away from the hammer which is another detail from the early 19th century. The tail on the frizzen is likewise formed in a flowing shape to give it a graceful appearance. The cast-brass trigger guard is quite ornate with excellent flowing lines and careful finishing.

The barrel on this flintlock rifle is octagonal full length with a bore diameter of .440 of an inch and 7

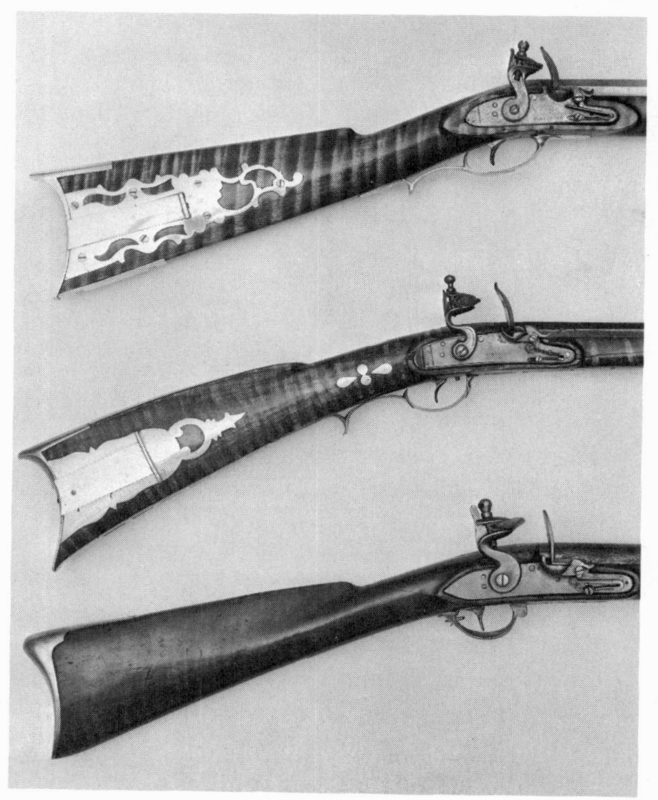

FIGURE 3-5 Details of three American flintlocks: UPPER, .36 caliber heavy rifle; MIDDLE, .44 caliber rifle; LOWER, 20 gauge smoothbore.

deep grooves measuring .470 of an inch to the bottom of the grooves near the muzzle. The barrel is 38¾ inches long and is .820 of an inch across the flats at the breech, and .740 across the flats at the muzzle. Over-all length of the rifle is 53½ inches. Although the barrel is five inches longer than on the upper rifle, the fact that it is smaller in width and has a slightly larger bore results in a drastic reduction in weight to only 6 pounds 9 ounces. The stock is extremely ornate as shown in Figure 3-5 and especially in Figure 3-6. The patch box is moderately elaborate and is held to the stock with 16 fasteners. The gunsmith really went wild on the left side of the stock. The cheekpiece has a large brass eagle inletted with stars under each wing. Underneath the cheekpiece another elaborate brass detail has been inletted into the stock with two more stars. There are six brass stars inletted just forward of the cast brass butt plate and a silver medallion has been cut in the shape of the man in the moon and inletted in the stock between the butt plate and the cheekpiece.

There is an ornamental detail of two teardrops and a figure 8 brass section inletted into the small of the stock on each side. Four brass escutcheons have been inletted into the fore-end of the stock where the cross wedges go through to retain the barrel. There is a brass forearm cap and three brass pipes to hold the wooden ramrod. The butt end of the stock has the "Roman nose" shape which was typical of the 18th century firearms.

The lowest firearm in Figures 3-5 and 3-6 is a smoothbore flintlock weighing 7 pounds 4 ounces. This has a very long barrel at 43.8 inches and an over-all length of 59.6 inches. The round barrel has an inside diameter of .610 of an inch which is 20 gauge. The smoothbore flintlock probably dates from the early 19th century. Thomas Hall, Curator of the Winchester Gun Museum, has examined this smoothbore and has come to the conclusion that it started off as a smoothbore flintlock, was converted to percussion, and at some later time was converted back to flintlock utilizing a lock which fits the opening very well. Careful examination of all three of these firearms shows gaps between the lock plate and the wood. This is most noticeable on the upper rifle which has a substantial gap just below the frizzen spring. The smoothbore flintlock at the bottom of the illustration has a lock with a pointed tail typical of the Revolutionary War period. The flat goosenecked hammer with beveled edges is also typical of the Revolutionary period as is the flat lock plate with beveled edges. The frizzen spring has a roller which places manufacture of this lock in the 19th century. A careful examination of the interior elements of the lock show that it was manufactured at a much later date than the remainder of the firearm.

This is a good solid smoothbore that probably saw extensive service as a working firearm. The stock is straight grained and sturdy but without any ornamental details. There is considerable corrosion around

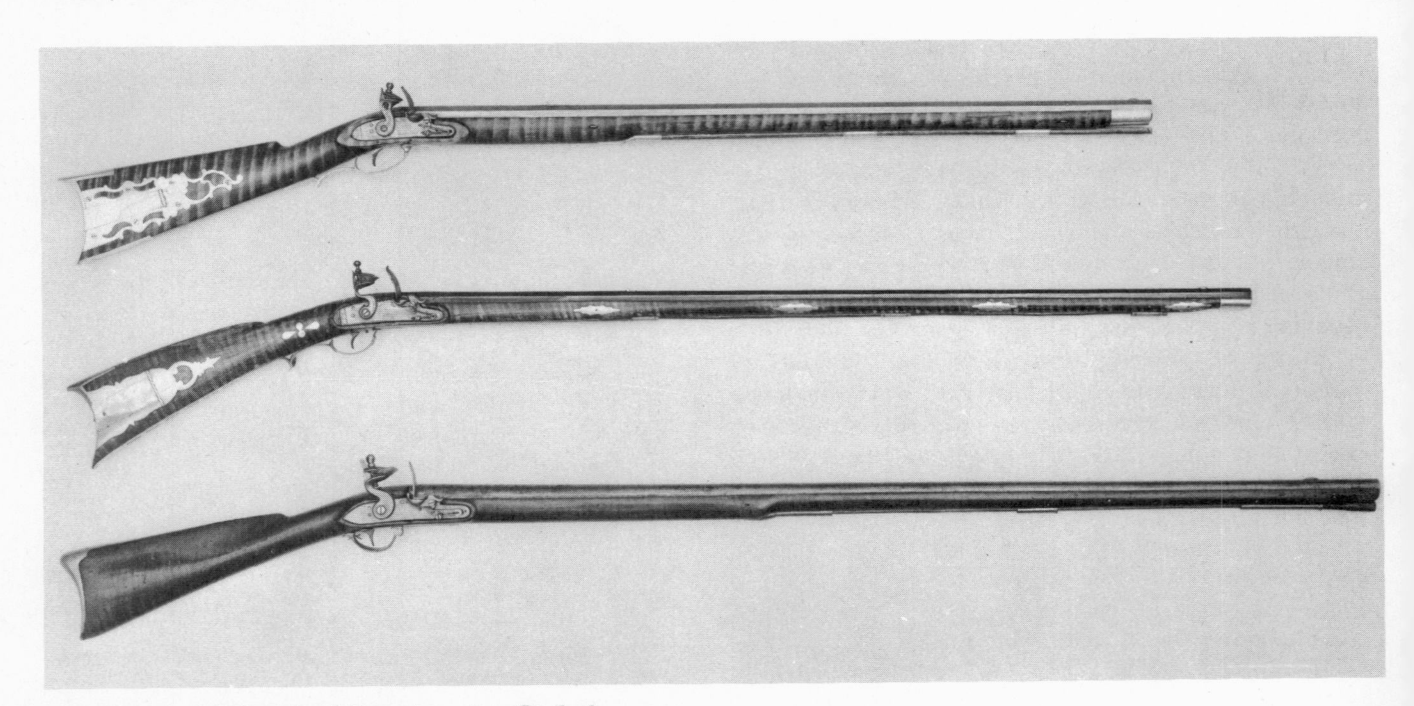

FIGURE 3-5 Right side of three American flintlocks.

the breech end of the barrel and the wood is burned away near the breech. Both factors are probably due to years and years of exposure to the flashes of powder in the pan.

These firearms show considerable contrast of features. The top and bottom flintlocks have straight stocks — popular in the 19th century. The middle rifle has a Roman nose type of curved drop to the comb, more typical of 18th century design. The two lower locks have a roller on the frizzen spring — a 19th century improvement. The lowest lock has a Revolutionary War shape lock plate, while the uppermost lock, with an earlier style of frizzen spring, has the later shape of lock plate! These types of variations and blending of features from different time periods make it very difficult for the careful historian to be dogmatic in his statements!

OVER-UNDER FLINTLOCK FIREARMS

Two rare flintlock firearms are in Figure 3-7. These are over-under designs and represent the real Rolls Royces of frontier firearms. Since the barrels were superposed, the ramrod guides were placed on the side and in each case there were two ramrod pipes as well as a ramrod retainer near the breech. Both firearms have the Roman nose shape to the buttstock typical of the 18th century design philosophy. Both have excessive drop to the stock, but this was not too important as they were heavy firearms and would not recoil too much. If a lightweight firearm is designed with this much drop to the stock, there is a tendency for the rifle to rise rapidly as the gun is fired and the stock also rises smacking the shooter in the cheek.

On these firearms this was no problem for they were heavy compared to the power of the bullet. The upper flintlock, for example, weighed 11 pounds 6 ounces. The two barrels were 37½ inches long and the over-all length of the flintlock was 52½ inches. The upper smoothbore barrel was .420 of an inch in diameter and the lower rifled barrel was .460 of an inch.

The firearm really consisted of two halves. The rear half stopped immediately forward of the hammer. The front half containing the two barrels was a completely independent unit which rotated upon a shaft.

There were two barrels, two pans and two frizzens and frizzen spring assemblies. The pan for the upper barrel is shown in the open position. After the shot had been fired, the catch on the left-hand side of the flintlock was released and the barrels were rotated 180 degrees bringing the lower barrel on top. You can note in the upper illustration that the frizzen on the lower barrel is in a closed position where it would retain a priming charge in the pan. With the hammer cocked and the barrel rotated to the new position, the shooter was ready for a very fast second shot — an important safety consideration in the far frontier. The fast second shot would be particularly important with this flintlock for the hunter probably was in no

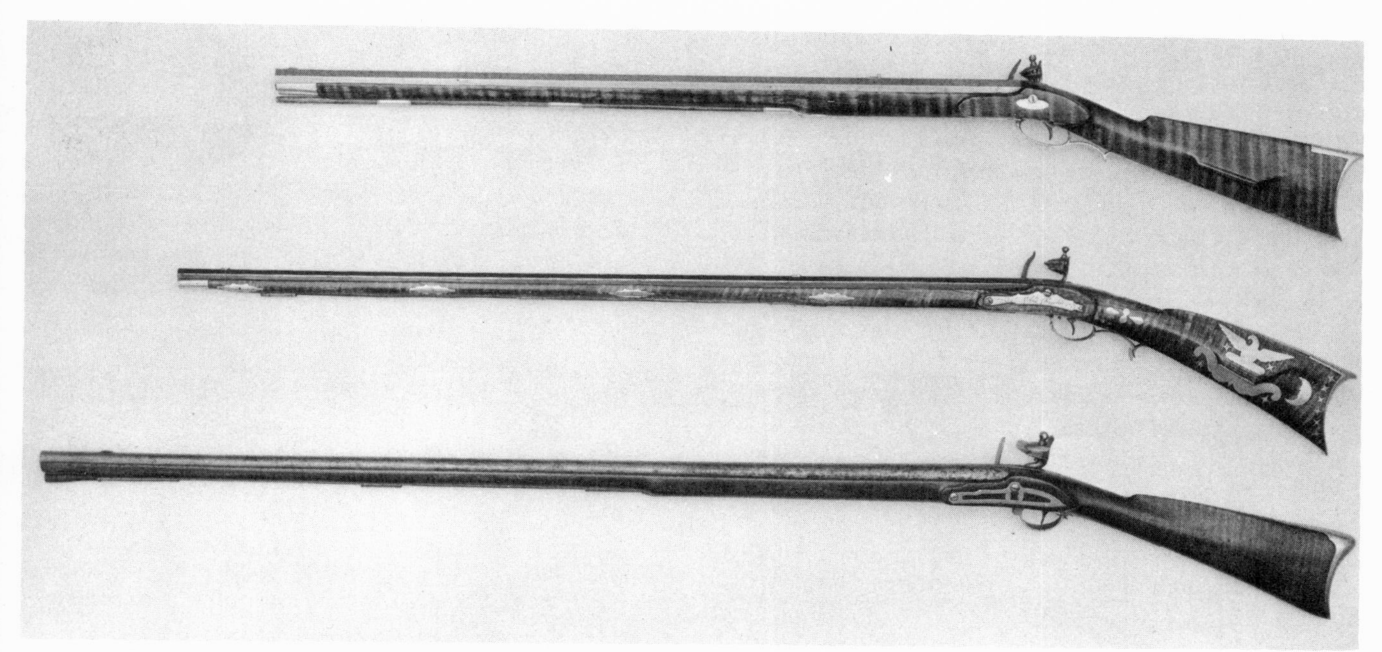

FIGURE 3-6 Left side of three American flintlocks.

shape to go through a fast reloading exercise after dragging 11 pounds 6 ounces around all day.

Both stocks have been given the tiger flame design and both have the brass patch box in the butt to carry spare flints, greased patches and cleaning equipment. Both rifles have a flat beveled lock plate, and flat, beveled hammers. The upper rifle has all 18th century features with a long tail on the lock plate, and no roller on the frizzen spring. The lower flintlock has all 18th century details on the lock except for the rounded rear to the lock plate.

The lower flintlock has even longer barrels at 38¼ inches and an over-all length of 53½ inches. Despite this the weight is much lower at 7 pounds 5 ounces. The barrels are octagonal full length and again the ramrod is inletted into a strip of wood which fitted the space between the two barrels. This flintlock is shown ready for the second shot with the pan open on the lower barrel and the hammer in the cocked position, ready to fire the second barrel. The upper barrel had a bore .435 of an inch in diameter, and the lower barrel had a bore of .400 of an inch.

The operation of these flintlocks was exactly the same as a regular flintlock rifle except for the quick second shot.

At the time of the American Revolution many of the soldiers came into the Continental Army armed with their own hunting rifles. The effectiveness of the backwoods marksmen was amply proven in many battles, particularly engagements in the forest or broken country. The use of rifles of different designs and calibers resulted in a chaotic supply situation. Standard .69 caliber cartridges, or at least standard bullets, could be issued to regiments armed with the French Charleville muskets, but a dozen different sizes of bullets might be required in a regiment of riflemen. With the extreme shortage of military equipment during the American Revolution there wasn't much chance to standardize. Even in the 1790's when a battalion of riflemen was formed for the regular Army, contracts were issued to private Pennsylvania rifle makers to provide the flintlock rifles for Army use. The resulting firearms were similar to that shown in the upper illustration of Figure 3-3. They were generally .50 to .55 caliber rifles, with a wooden stock to the muzzle and with the barrel held to the stock by cross pins. The supply situation remained chaotic for the new rifles varied in caliber, barrel length and other features.

UNITED STATES FLINTLOCK RIFLES, MODEL 1803

In 1800 Congress authorized establishment of a regiment of riflemen in the United States Army, and in 1803 the Secretary of War determined that the troops should be armed with one standard rifle of uniform design and caliber. It is interesting that the letter

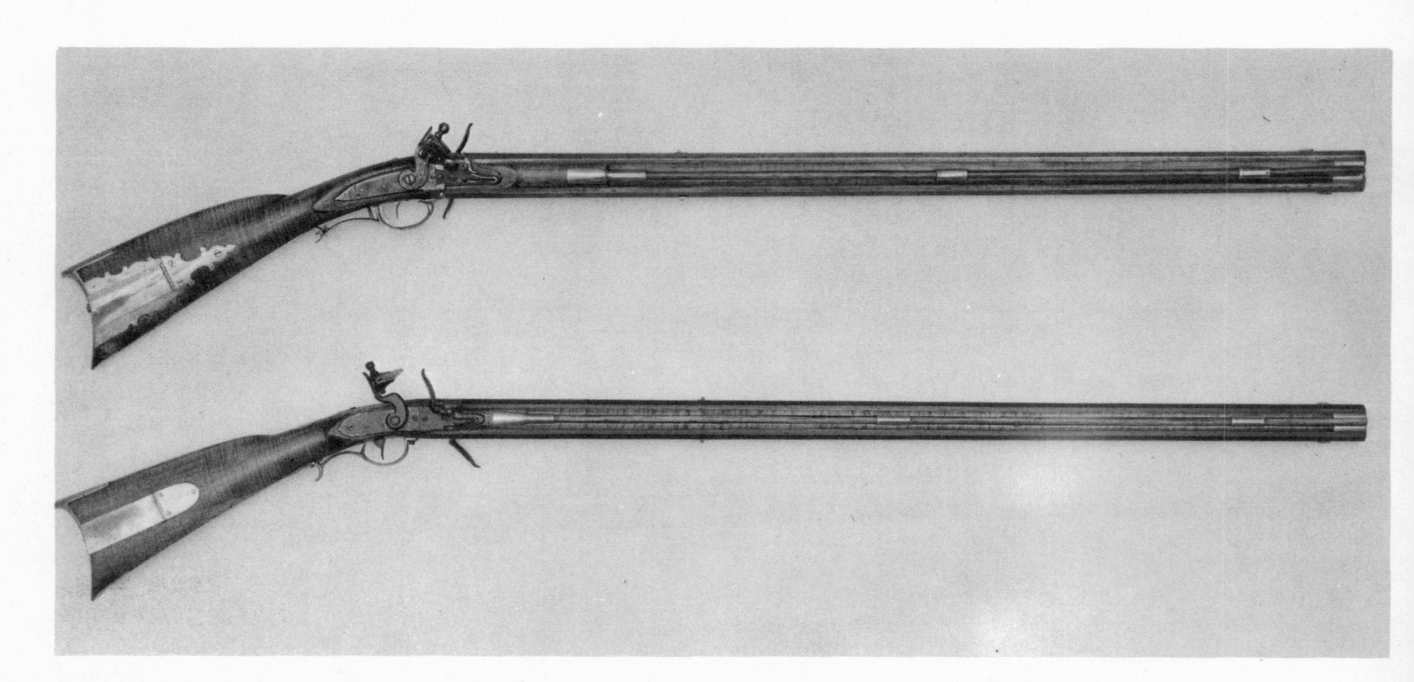

FIGURE 3-7 Two over-under flintlock rifles.

Type	Caliber	Barrel Length	Overall Length	Weight	Typical Details
Typical "Kentucky" Rifle circa 1800	.45	44	60	10m	Octagon barrel, full stock, flintlock
Typical "Kentucky" Smoothbore circa 1800	.50	44-48	60-64	10m	½ octagon barrel full stock, flintlock
U.S. Model 1803 Harper's Ferry Rifle	.54	32½	48	8m	½ octagon barrel ½ stock, flintlock
U.S. Model 1814 Harper's Ferry Rifle	.54	36	52	8.9m	½ octagon barrel ½ stock, flintlock
U.S. Rifle Model 1817 (Common Rifle)	.54	36	51	10m	Round barrel, flintlock full stock with bands
U.S. Flintlock Rifle-Musket Model 1842	.69	42	58	9.5m	Round barrel three bands full stock

FIGURE 3-8 Chart of typical flintlock rifles.

specifying the design of the Model 1803 flintlock rifle provides a charming insight into the lack of paper work in this early day. This brief letter of specification compares with at least 200 drawings and a thousand pages of written material to specify a current infantry rifle. The letter follows:

War Department
May 25th 1803

Jos. Perkin
Harpers ferry Armory

Sir.

There being a deficiency of rifles in the public Arsenals, and those on hand not being as well calculated for actual service as could be wished. It is considered advisable to have a suitable number of judiciously constructed Rifles manufactured at the Armory under Your direction. You will therefore take the necessary measures for commencing the manufactory as soon as may be after completing the Muskits now in hand. The Barrels of the Rifles should not exceed 2′ 9″ in length and should be calculated for carrying a ball of 1/30 of a pound weight — the barrels should be round from muzzle to within 10 inches of the Britch and not of an unnecessary thickness especially in the round part — the stock should not extend further than the tail pipe, from thence to within 3″ of the muzzle, an Iron rib should be substituted for that part of the stock — the ramrod should be of Steel and sufficiently strong for forcing down the ball without binding. The butt end of the ramrod should be concaved suited to the shape of the Ball — the locks should be light and well executed — the mountings should be brass — there should be at least 2,000 of these rifles made.
If you should be of opinion that any improvements may be made on the above construction or any parts thereof, you will be pleased to inform me of such improvements as you may think may be useful. I have had such convincing proof of the advantage the short rifles has over the long ones (commonly used) in actual service as to leave no doubt in my mind of preferring the short rifle, with larger Calibers than the long ones usually have and with stiff Steel ramrods instead of wooden ones — the great facility which such rifles afford in charging, in addition to their being less liable to become foul by firing, gives a decided advantage to men of equal skill and dextirity over those armed with the common long rifle.

I am very respectfully Sir
HENRY DEARBORN

Careful reading of the letter shows the casual approach to spelling in this early day. Words are capitalized throughout the letter, such as barrels, rifles, steel, and iron. The breech end of the barrel is spelled "Britch" although it is properly spelled in another letter from the Secretary of War a month later.

The design of the Model 1803 Harpers Ferry Rifle shown in the lower illustration of Figure 3-9 obviously was much closer to the commercial Pennsylvania designs than it was to the standardized Model 1795 Springfield musket. The stock had a cheekpiece and an ornate cast-brass trigger guard and curved cast-brass butt plate. A patch box was inletted into the side of the stock and covered with a flat rectangular plate which was hinged at the forward end. The fixed part of the hinge was held to the stock with three screws. The patch box cover was spring loaded into an open position and held shut by an ingenious hidden catch mechanism inletted into the butt end of the stock. The catch was released by a small button which is shown protruding from the top of the butt plate. In the patch box recess the rifleman normally carried leather or cloth patches, a pick and brush assembly used to clean out the vent hole into the barrel and brush away debris out of the pan, a "worm" which could be screwed onto the end of the ramrod and used to remove a misfired ball from the barrel and probably a small collection of spare flints.

The caliber of the new rifles was "standardized" at .540-inch diameter which required a ball .525 of an inch in diameter. The general specifications of the rifle are shown in Figure 3-8. The barrel was octagonal for about 12 inches at the breech end and then had an ornamental transition to a round section for the remainder of the length. The lock plate was flat with beveled edges, and the hammer was also flat with beveled edges and a reinforcing loop up to the lower jaw.

This was the first firearm designed at the Harpers Ferry Armory which was just getting into production. The manufacturing techniques were fairly crude so the barrels, which had a nominal length of 32½ inches, varied considerably from this figure. The inside diameters of the barrel were supposed to be .540 of an inch but this also varied considerably. The rifling also reflected the whims of the individual workmen and varied in number and depth of grooves and rate of twist. The sights were a blade front sight set into the barrel and an open rear sight which was held in a dovetail cut in the octagonal section of the barrel.

Secretary of War Dearborn, specified that 4000 rifles were to be manufactured. Surprisingly the superintendent of the Armory, Joseph Perkin, questioned whether this number of rifles would be needed and was ordered emphatically to produce the number specified. The 4000 rifles apparently met the needs of the United States Army until the War of 1812 when requirements drastically increased.

Ammunition for the Model 1803 and 1814 Rifles

The cartridge used in the early flintlock rifles was more complex than the musket cartridge. The 216-grain soft lead bullet was first wrapped in a linen or thin leather patch which was wrapped around the bullet and tied with a string. The patch was greased with tallow and the entire assembly loaded into a paper tube similar to a standard musket cartridge. The end of the paper cartridge was choked over the patched bullet assembly and tied and the paper tube was filled with about 75 grains of fine rifle powder before being twisted around and folded over.

U.S. RIFLE, MODEL 1814

As the War dragged on Congress authorized the raising of three additional regiments of riflemen. There was an insufficient quantity of Model 1803 rifles on hand, and the Ordnance Department was in the middle of its struggles to achieve true standardization of designs of small arms for the United States Service. Harpers Ferry had the tooling to manufacture the Model 1803 rifle, and skilled workmen knowledgable in production methods. The design was reviewed and a decision reached to make very minor changes, such as increasing the barrel length to 36 inches and the over-all length to 52 inches. The appearance of the Model 1814 rifle is shown in the upper illustration of Figure 3-9 and was virtually identical to the Model of 1803.

The rifle shortage was so acute that the Ordnance Department decided to start manufacture of the new rifle at both Springfield and Harpers Ferry Armories and even gave informal contracts to private manufacturers with the urgent plea to hurry the work as fast as possible. Every attempt was being made to achieve standardized designs with relatively uniform dimensions and reasonably interchangeable parts. With this view in mind "pattern rifles" were manufactured at Harpers Ferry to be a standard reference design. Experienced workmen took one copy of this rifle to Springfield Armory and instructed the personnel at Springfield in all the details of manufacture.

Manufacture of the new rifle started at Harpers Ferry in 1814, but production startup at Springfield was difficult. Only 3000 sets of parts were manufactured at Springfield and eventually the parts were shipped to Harpers Ferry for assembly into finished firearms. Some private contracts were also given to Henry Deringer in Philadelphia and a 2000-rifle contract to Robert Johnson in Middletown, Connecticut. The private manufacturers all had startup problems and the bulk of production in 1814 and 1815 was at Harpers Ferry Armory. The Model 1814 rifles continued the .54-caliber design and fired a half ounce ball (216 grains). The barrel was 36 inches long and the over-all length 52 inches. The barrel was held to the stock with cross keys rather than with barrel bands. The lock plate was flat with a beveled edge. The priming pan had a rounded bottom and had a fence to the rear. The hammer was very similar to the design used on the Springfield muskets, a flat hammer surface with beveled edges and a double necked design with a reinforcing loop up to the lower jaw. The stock was similar to many commercial rifles in coming only half way along the length of the barrel. There were two ferrules

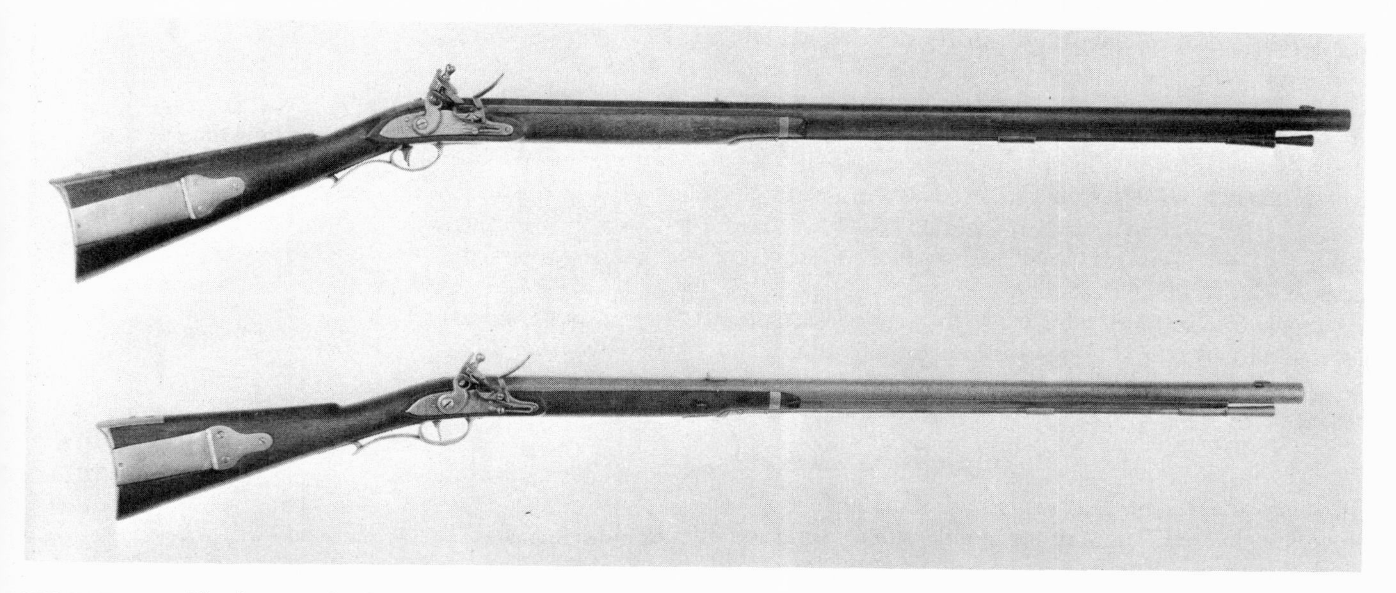

FIGURE 3-9 The first standard United States rifles: UPPER; Harpers' Ferry U.S. rifle Model 1814; LOWER; Harpers' Ferry U.S. rifle Model 1803.

or pipes to hold the steel ramrod which had a conical brass end with a recess to fit the rifle ball. The pipes were fastened to an iron rib which was soldered to the underside of the barrel and extended to within a few inches of the muzzle. The rifle had a cheek-piece on the left-hand side. The right side of the butt stock was hollowed out to form a recess for a patch box, and this opening was covered by a brass plate hinged at the front end with the stationary part of the hinge held to the stock with three screws. This patch box served the basic function of the patch boxes shown in Figure 3-5 and you can see how much the design had been simplified. The patch box cover spring loaded toward an open position and held shut by an internal catch. The cover was released by pressing a little button on the top of the butt stock. Fixed sights were fitted, a blade front and an open rear sight.

U.S. RIFLE MODEL 1817

The 1803 and 1814 rifles were copies of commercial designs at the turn of the 19th century. Military experience with these rifles was not fully satisfactory and a new design was created in 1817 reflecting a great many changes to strengthen the rifle for military service. The result became known as the "Common rifle" and was one of the handsomest military flintlock firearms ever designed. The appearance is shown in Figure 3-10. This was manufactured by Nathan Starr of Middletown, Connecticut in 1824. The caliber and barrel lengths were kept the same as the model 1814 rifle but almost all of the other details were changed to reflect the improvements in design which had been incorporated in muskets during the previous 20 years so that the appearance was entirely different from the Model 1814. The appearance of these rifles was particularly handsome, for not only were the proportions graceful but the large metal parts were finished with an antique browned color and the lock and trigger were a mottled case-hardened finish. The full length walnut stock with oiled finish offered a harmonious contrast in shade and texture to the metal components. The barrel was held to the stock with three iron bands rather than the much weaker cross wedges through the wooden stock as in the Model 1803 and 1814 rifles. The bands were held in place with spring catches. The rifles were fitted with a steel ramrod which had a brass tip with a concave surface to fit the .525-inch diameter lead ball. A fixed blade type front sight was fitted and an open type rear sight was held in a dovetail cut in the barrel.

The lock differed in many respects from the locks on the Model 1803 and 1814 rifles. The hammer had rounded contours instead of being flat and beveled. The pan was made of brass and was tilted, whereas the pans on the earlier rifles were forged integral with the lock plate, were flat, and had a fence to the rear. The lock plate on the Model 1817 was flat in the forward section with a bevel, but to the rear of the hammer it had a rounded contour and was fitted flush with the surface of the wooden stock. The design of the butt end of the

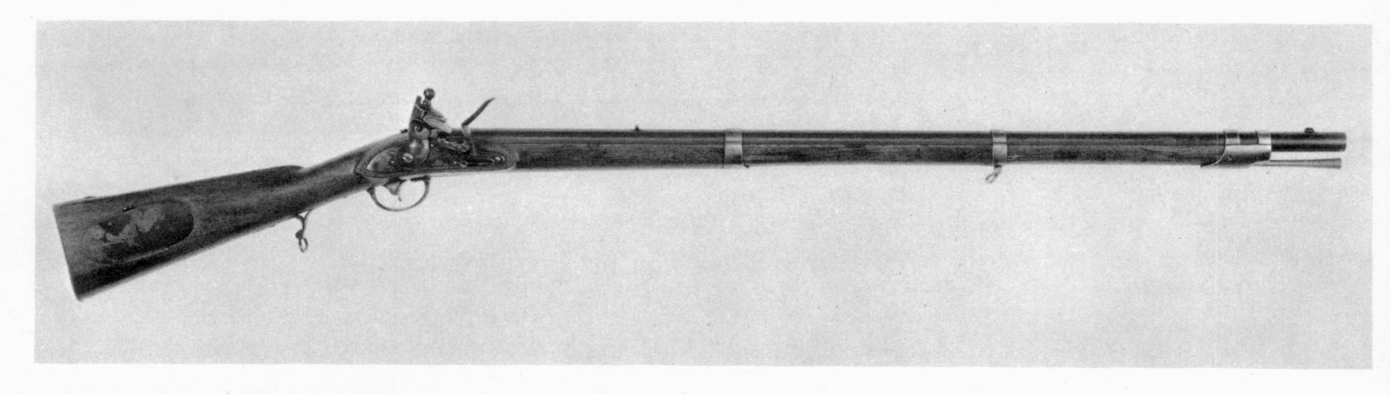

FIGURE 3-10 U.S. Rifle Model 1817 the "Common Rifle."

stock was also changed with a fairly modern flat butt plate. The patch box was also simplified with an oval shaped cover to close the recess milled into the wooden stock.

The cover was pivoted on the bottom and held shut by a small catch on the top. Furniture such as barrel bands, butt plate and patch box cover were made of iron. Instead of the cast-brass trigger guard fitted to the Model 1803 and 1814 rifles, the Model 1817 had a long trigger guard strap into which the U-shaped trigger guard itself was bolted. The strap extended to the rear and had a triangular projection on the bottom which gave something of the effect of a pistol grip to the stock. The rear sling swivel was attached on the bottom of this triangular extension.

The results of research into better designs and materials by the Armories and private contractors early in the 19th century are apparent in many small details. The finish of parts on these rifles is much improved over the rifles and muskets of the Revolutionary period. The lock, trigger, and some small parts were case-hardened to provide tougher and longer wearing surfaces. The pan was made of brass to minimize corrosion. The top of the frizzen was bent forward so that even if an oversized flint were clamped in the jaws of the hammer the action would work fairly well.

The patch box often contained many items useful to the skilled soldier. These included a spare flint and a U-shaped sheet of lead which was used to hold the flint in the jaws of the hammer plus a tool designed to tighten screws and also to tighten the top jaw of the hammer so that the flint could be gripped tightly. The rifleman's usual collection of patches were often kept in the patch box as well as a "wormer" which could be screwed onto the small end of the ramrod and used to bite into and remove a misfired bullet. The stocks were generally made of a sturdy, straight-grained walnut and had an oiled finish with very little lustre.

As a result of the War of 1812 there was an extreme shortage of military rifles. The crisis was apparently most acute in 1814 when it was simply impossible to find sufficient numbers of standard rifles for issue to the troops. Although Callender Irvine, Commissary General, had repeatedly blasted the private contractors for failure to perform in close accordance to the specifications and timing of the contracts during 1812 and 1813 and repeatedly threatened them with complete cancellation of their contracts for failure of performance, his tune changed abruptly during 1814. By then the situation was so critical that verbal contracts were made with manufacturers in the Philadelphia area for Model 1814 rifles. Later that year, written contracts were established with other private contractors, many of whom were located in Connecticut. For example, Robert Johnson of Middletown, Connecticut, secured a contract for 2000 rifles at a price of $17 each. Other contractors such as Henry Deringer of Philadelphia, R. and J. D. Johnson, and Simeon North and Nathan Starr of Connecticut also secured contracts. Many of these contractors were just getting into full scale production when the design of the Model 1817 rifle was established and many changed over their contracts to the new design.

MODEL 1842 FLINTLOCK RIFLED MUSKETS

The last flintlock rifle in the U. S. service is usually referred to as the Model of 1842. This was in fact the Model 1835 smoothbore musket which had been altered by the addition of shallow rifling cut into the barrel. The result was a rifle virtually identical in appearance to Figures 1-15 and 1-16. The .69 caliber rifle could be loaded with the standard spherical musket ball of 412 grains by enclosing the ball in a tough leather or cloth patch. Experiments with hollow bullets were active in the 1840's and a 740-grain hollow-based Minié type bullet was finally specified for this rifle. To the best of the author's knowledge this is the heaviest bullet ever specified for a United States infantry rifle and the recoil must have been terrific. When the Model 1835 musket was loaded with this .69 caliber spherical ball backed up by a 110-grain powder charge the muzzle velocity was close to 1500 feet per second. In order to keep the recoil within bearable limits, the powder charge for the 740-grain Minié bullet was reduced to 70 grains and the muzzle velocity was cut to 954 feet per second. Even so, the long-range ballistic performance of this rifle was greatly improved over that of the smoothbore musket. One of the greatest improvements was in accuracy. The spin-stabilized hollow bullet expanded to fit the bore of the rifle due to the gas pressure and was launched in a more accurate line with the axis of the barrel. All the spherical musket bullets had windage or clearance between the bullet and barrel generally of about .040 of an inch and this meant the ball rattled from side to side in the barrel as it was accelerating toward the muzzle. The direction taken by the musket ball was strongly influenced by the point at which it last bounced off the barrel. Thus the round musket ball neither retained its energy very well at long range nor provided good accuracy.

A comparison of the bullet performance of round balls and Minié bullets is shown in Figure 3-11. The range in yards is shown in the left-hand column. The second column shows the performance of the most highly developed flintlock muskets used by the United States Army. These muskets had an inside bore which varied from .690 to .705 of an inch. The soft lead ball was .650 of an inch diameter and weighed 412 grains. The paper cartridge was loaded with 130 grains of powder, of which about 10 grains were placed in the pan and the rest were used to project the bullet at a muzzle velocity of 1500 feet per second. This velocity would probably only be achieved with a properly cast bullet of .650-inch diameter and a smooth barrel close to the minimum dimension of .690 of an inch. The very rapid decline in velocity is apparent in the second row of figures. At the end of only 100 yards of travel, the bullet had lost almost 500 feet per second velocity, and by the end of another hundred yards it had lost an additional 250 feet per second. Thus at the end of 200 yards of travel the heavy musket ball was down half its launch velocity and retained only a quarter of the muzzle energy. At the end of 500 yards the musket ball's velocity was below 400 feet per second; at 800 it was below 200 fps.

	Model 1822 Or Model 1835 Musket	*Model 1842 Rifle*	*Model 1885 Rifle*
Range Yards	*130 Grains Powder 412 Grain Ball Bullet*	*70 Grains Powder 740 Grain Minié Bullet*	*60 Grains Powder 505 Grain Minié Bullet*
Muzzle	1,500	954	1,005
100	1,014	872	907
200	759	807	833
300	596	750	772
400	477	699	717
500	386	653	667
600	314	613	625
700	258	573	584
800	220	537	546
900	197	504	511
1000	191	474	478

FIGURE 3-11 Bullet velocity of muskets and rifles.

The performance of the 740-grain Minié bullet for the Model 1842 rifle musket is shown in the third column. The powder charge had been reduced to 70 grains of powder and the muzzle velocity reduced to 954 feet per second. When the figures are calculated out the free recoil velocity of the Model 1835 musket was just under 12 feet per second. The 740-grain Minié bullet at 954 feet per second gives almost exactly the same free recoil velocity — slightly under 12 feet per second. The drastic improvement in ballistic performance is apparent in the third column of figures. Where the musket ball had lost almost 500 feet per second velocity in the first 100 yards, the conical pointed Minié bullet lost only 80 feet per second and had a higher retained velocity at 200 yards than the musket ball, which was launched at 550 feet per second faster. The retained velocity of the .69 caliber Minié bullet is excellent all the way to a 1000-yard range.

After a series of tests and experiments in the early 1850's a decision was reached to standardize .58 caliber for all Army rifles. Many of the Model 1841 Mississippi rifles were bored out to the larger size and re-rifled. A new series of rifles were made in carbine, rifle, and rifle-musket size which will be described later. The last column in Figure 3-11 shows the performance of the 500- to 510-grain Minié bullet fired from a .58 caliber rifle or rifle-musket. This new rifle had many advantages. The bullet was slightly heavier than the round ball for the .69 caliber musket, but the launch velocity was much lower at only about 1000 feet per second. The result was that the free recoil velocity of the rifle was very much reduced — from slightly under 12 feet per second for the Model 1835 musket

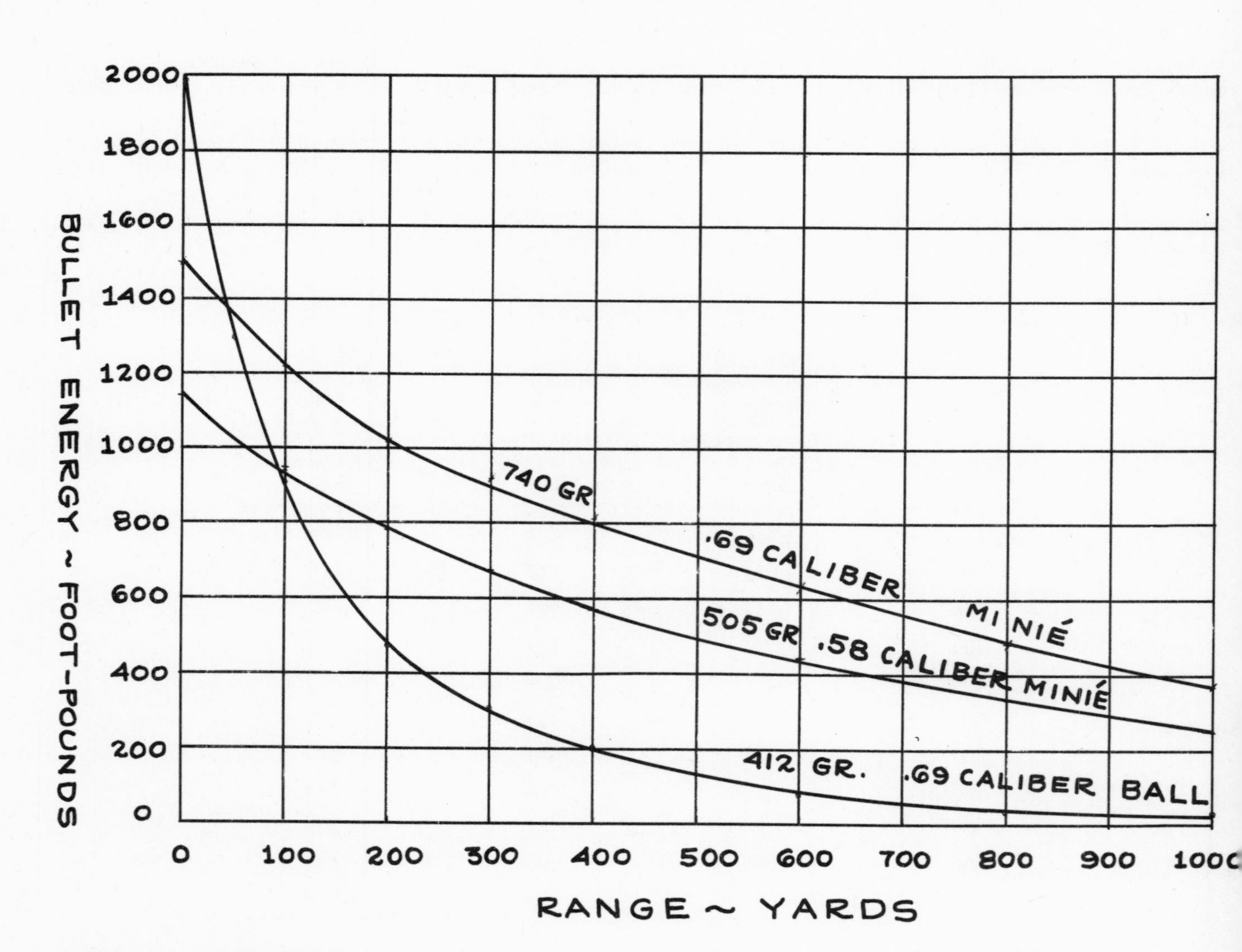

FIGURE 3-12 Graph of bullet energy versus range.

Rifle	Caliber	Barrel Length	Overall Length	Weight, Pounds
Model 1841 "Mississippi" Rifle	.54	33.0[1]	48.8[1]	9.68[1]
Model 1842 Rifle-Musket	.69	42.0[2]	57.8[2]	9.51[2]
Model 1855 Rifled Carbine	.58	22.0	36.8	6.2M
Model 1855 Rifle	.58	33.0[2]	49.3[2]	9.93[2]
Model 1855 Rifle-Musket	.58	40.0[2]	55.85	9.18[2]
Model 1858 Cadet Rifle	.58	38.0[2]	53.0[2]	8.50[2]
Model 1861 Rifle-Musket	.58	40.0	55.85	8.4M
Model 1862 Remington Zouave Rifle	.58	33.0	49.0	9.38
Model 1863 1st Type	.58	40.0	55.85	7.6-8.6M
Model 1863 2nd Type	.58	40.0	55.85	7.6-8.6M
European Rifle-Musket	.69	40.5	56.0	9.2M

1 – 1850 ORD MANUAL
2 – 1861 ORD MANUAL
M = MEASURED WINCHESTER GUN. MUSEUM

FIGURE 3-13 United States Military percussion rifles.

or Model 1842 rifle-musket to slightly under 9 feet per second for the Model 1855 rifle. This significantly lower recoil reduced the tendency of the soldiers to flinch when firing accurately aimed shots, and literally meant that the soldiers did not get banged around so much by their rifle and hence were much less tired at the end of a given number of shots.

A comparison of the retained velocities shows that both the .69 caliber and .58 caliber Minié bullets were moving at significantly the same velocity at all ranges beyond 500 yards. Even at 200 and 300 yards the velocity differs by less than 30 feet per second. In all cases the velocity retained is much higher than for the .69 caliber musket ball.

The improved long-range performance of the Minié bullet is even more sharply shown in the graph of bullet energy shown in Figure 3-12. The musket ball starts off at the muzzle with a high energy of 1985 foot-pounds. It has lost half its energy by the time it has traveled 100 yards and is down to one quarter of its muzzle energy level at 200 yards.

The .69 caliber Minié bullet starts off with a muzzle energy of 1495 foot-pounds and has retained over half its energy at 400 yards. Even at 1000 yards this bullet has retained over one quarter of its energy, or 369 foot-pounds.

The retained energy of the .58 caliber Minié bullet is similarly impressive when compared with the round ball loads. The muzzle energy is 1133 foot-pounds and over half of this energy or 578 foot-pounds is retained by the bullet at 400 yards. The retained energy at 1000 yards of 257 foot-pounds is over eight times the energy retained by the .69 caliber ball, which is coasting along with only 32 foot-pounds of energy at 1000 yards. Another factor is that both Minié bullets, if fired horizontally from a high cliff, would be moving at a downward angle of 13 degrees, while the musket ball would be falling at a 56-degree angle. The time for the .69 caliber ball to cover 1000 yards was 9.8 seconds compared with 4.7 seconds for the .58 caliber or .69 caliber Minié bullets.

PERCUSSION RIFLES

The period from 1820 to 1840 was a time of great change in the firearms industry. The flintlock had been the standard military and sporting firearm for nearly 200 years. At the same time improved production machinery made possible the manufacture of firearms to quite accurate dimensions. Work by chemists had reawakened interest in primary explosives as a means of firearms ignition. Primary explosives are unstable compounds that are very sensitive to heat or shock. They are chemical compounds which might be likened to a "house of cards" in that a relatively small blow will trigger a violent chemical reaction and the entire house of cards will collapse generating tremendous heat and pressure. Early chemical compounds were highly corrosive but in the early 19th century fulminate of mercury was developed and popularized as a primary explosive in firearms ignition. When the fulminate of mercury was blended properly with compounds which supplied oxygen, such as saltpeter, and a compound to provide an abrasive quality, such as coal dust or ground glass, the combination was a very potent priming material. This reaction was too violent to be used in the open pan of a flintlock firearm, and so designs were developed by a Scottish clergyman, Alexander Forsyth, which metered minute quantities of the fulminate of mercury powder into a tube connected to the barrel of the rifle or musket. The gun's hammer struck a firing pin, which compressed the fulminate priming charge, igniting it. The violent, hot flame passed through the tube and ignited the main black powder charge in the barrel. Mechanisms to handle and meter this violent primary explosive were very difficult and expensive to manufacture. Most popular were the "scent bottle" designs manufactured in England and Scotland.

Many inventors were working on using this primary explosive in a simpler system. The true inventor of the percussion cap has been clouded by a century of international controversy. There is considerable evidence to give credit to an Englishman, Joshua Shaw, a landscape painter, who immigrated to the United States in 1817. Shaw claimed to have invented a sturdy steel cup to hold a small charge of priming compound. This cup was placed over a tube or nipple projecting from the barrel of the rifle. When the hammer struck the steel cap the priming compound was compressed between the top of the cap and the tube, causing ignition. The steel cap effectively sealed off leakage from the breech and the flame could only escape into the main charge in the barrel of the musket. The steel caps were relatively sturdy and could be reloaded after use. Shaw claimed to have developed this invention in 1814 and to have developed a disposable percussion cap made of pewter in 1815.

In 1816 he settled on the design of a copper cap containing the fulminate charge which was used once and thrown away. Shaw's cap was formed from sheet copper with a cylindrical section closed at one end and a flanged base which made it easy to put the percussion cap on the tube. A measured small quantity of priming compound was placed in the top of the cup and covered with a thin layer of silver foil. The priming was sealed in place with shellac. Shaw apparently could support his claim to the invention, for he persuaded the United States Government to pay him $18,000 for the use of his invention.

The British arranged for comparative tests between flintlock and percussion lock guns at Woolwich Arsenal in 1834. Six thousand rounds were fired from six guns of each type of lock. The flintlocks malfunctioned nearly a thousand times while the percussion firearms misfired only thirty-six times. Even so, the British did not issue percussion firearms until 1848, some seven years after the United States had standardized on the percussion design and fifteen years after the United States first issued percussion breech-loading Hall rifles to the U.S. Cavalry.

U.S. PERCUSSION RIFLE — MODEL 1841

The first U.S. muzzle-loading percussion rifle was the Model of 1841 which is commonly known as the "Mississippi Rifle." The design continued the .54 caliber of the earlier rifles, but the barrel length was cut back to 33 inches and the over-all length reduced to slightly under 49 inches. The appearance of the rifle is very similar to the Remington "Zouave" of 1862 which is shown in Figure 3-17. The rifle had many desirable features and was considerably shorter than the standard muskets of the period. The barrel was held to the forearm with two bands. The forward band was combined with the forearm cap on the Mississippi rifle, differing slightly from the "Zouave". The patch box was similar to the Zouave design in having the hinge at the forward surface of the cover and the fixed part of the hinge was held to the stock by three screws. The cover was spring loaded and latched in place by a mechanism just forward of the butt plate. On the Model 1841 the patch box was longer, coming nearly to the comb of the stock. A button on top of the stock released the patch box cover.

The weight of the rifle was listed as 9.68 pounds in the 1850 Ordance Manual. The lock plate was flat with a beveled edge. It projected the height of the bevel above the surface of the wood of the stock. The rifles had a very elegant appearance with an oil finished walnut stock, a brass patch box, brown lacquer finished barrel and a case-hardened lock plate with a blued trigger and small parts. The 33-inch barrel had seven-groove rifling with one turn in 72 inches. The front sight was a brass blade inset into the barrel and the rear sight was an open notch design.

The name Mississippi rifle was originally applied to these Model 1841 firearms due to their issuance to the first Mississippi Regiment in 1847, which was commanded by Jefferson Davis. The Mississippi rifles were manufactured at Springfield Armory and by private contractors. Some of the largest contracts were given to E. Remington & Sons of Ilion, New York. Remington secured its first contract in 1845 for 5000 rifles at thirteen dollars each. They built up production to a rate of 1000 high-quality rifles a month, and the Ordnance Department awarded a second contract for 7500 rifles. Remington continued manufacturing the same model through the early years of the Civil War. In the late 1850's many of the Mississippi rifles were bored out to the new standard caliber of .58 and re-rifled. All the later Remington rifles were made in .58 caliber. These early contracts became the basis for Remington's large Civil War production of the famous Zouave rifles, which incorporated slight improvements that had been developed in the late 1850's The Remington Zouave models were some of the most handsome of the Civil War models, with a brown stock, blued barrel and brass furniture.

MODEL 1842 RIFLE-MUSKET

In 1842 the Army standardized its percussion smoothbore musket. This model is shown in Figure 1-15. During the early 1850's thousands of these muskets were modified by the addition of shallow rifling grooves so that they could handle the 740-grain hollow Minié bullet. It then became known as the Model 1842 rifle-musket, but the appearence was virtually identical to the smoothbore musket model.

Modifications included the addition of a rear sight with a sliding leaf which was optimistically graduated out to 900 yards. It was possible to rifle these barrels because they had a relatively heavy wall compared with the earlier flintlock muskets.

The lock design was virtually identical to that of the Model 1841 rifle, with a flat lock plate with beveled edges and a gracefully curved and rounded hammer. The percussion system was centered in a block of iron known as the cone-seat which was welded to the side of the barrel near the breech. The barrel, cone-seat, and breech tang were all made of iron but the "cone," or nipple, which held the percussion cap was made of a very hard steel with a conical surface at one end and a threaded shank at the other which screwed into the cone-seat. The cone had to be made of the best steels available for it absorbed the heavy blow of the hammer on every shot, and was further subjected to the corrosive action of the priming material in the percussion caps. The cones were designed with a tapered hole large in diameter at the upper surface tapering down to a very small diameter in the middle and then flaring out to a larger diameter again in the threaded portion. This was designed to concentrate the flame from the percussion cap through the restricted orifice and, where the passage flared out again, to allow the flame easy passage to ignite the main charge. The purpose of the restricted orifice in the center of the cone was to minimize the back flow of powder gas under the high chamber pressure after the main charge had ignited. Sometimes the percussion cap with the heavy hammer on top of it provided a good seal, but many times the fragile cap was split or shattered by the heavy hammer blow and the following explosion and did not provide a gas seal. Shattering of the percussion caps was a serious problem in the early days of percussion and many shooters lost eyes from the flying copper fragments. By the time the Model 1842 was standardized the problem had been pretty well solved by cutting a fairly deep recess in the face of the hammer so that the percussion cap was surrounded by the steel of the hammer at the time the main charge was ignited.

At the rear of the cone-seat is what looks like the fence fitted at the rear of the pan on flintlock muskets. The purpose of this fence was to contain dirt and particles of priming which spewed out from under the percussion cap as the shot was fired.

The Model 1841 rifles and Model 1842 muskets were good sturdy firearms with an excellent ignition system. These first American models performed so well, that they formed the basis for a family of firearms tailored to every military need. The Model 1842 muskets were considered well worth conversion into rifles in the latter 1850's and about 14,300 were modified.

ARTILLERY AND SAPPER MUSKETOONS — MODEL 1847

The basic percussion system was adopted to a pistol design in 1842, with a .54 caliber smoothbore barrel 8½ inches long. The lock plate was slightly reduced in size, from 6¼ inches long on the musket to 4⅞ inches on the pistol, but the appearance of the percussion lock and ignition system was virtually identical.

A series of special short firearms were manufactured for the use of the artillery troops, and for the engineering battalions who were known as "sappers" in the 19th century. The design of these .69 caliber smoothbore musketoons can be visualized by looking at Figure 1-14 and imagining that the middle barrel band had been removed, the barrel shortened from 42 inches to 26 inches and the front end assembly of the musket moved back to the shortened position.

U.S. Cavalry Musketoon, Model 1847

This musketoon was similar in specifications to the .69 caliber Artillery Musketoon with a smoothbore barrel 26 inches long and an over-all length of 41 inches. It differed in having a slightly different front end assembly with a small amount of the wooden stock showing in front of the barrel band. It also differed in having the ramrod retained by a pivoted stirrup to prevent the cavalryman from losing his ramrod in the midst of a hot engagement. In 1851 the cavalry musketoons were modified to have the ramrod retained by a small lug welded to the barrel connected to a ring on the ramrod by, of all things, a small chain. There were some minor differences in the interior construction of the lock to reflect minor improvements made in the mid-1840's, and a rear sight was added during the 1851 modifications.

UNITED STATES RIFLED CARBINE MODEL 1855

Another firearm to use the 1841 and 1842 percussion system were the rifled carbines of 1855. These were made in two models which differed very slightly in the position of the rear sling swivel, and the shape of the forearm cap. The later of the two designs is shown in Figure 3-13. It was originally planned to make this carbine the standard rifle caliber of .540 of an inch firing the .525-inch diameter round ball. During the period when the model guns were being made up in the spring of 1855, Jefferson Davis issued an order that the new caliber of .58 of an inch was to be used on all small arms as recommended by an Ordnance Board established to define the "optimum caliber" for small arms. Slightly over 1000 of the rifled carbines were manufactured in 1855 and 1856 and most, if not all, had .58 caliber barrels. These were short, light, handy firearms intended to arm the new cavalry regiments formed in 1855. They had an L-shaped rear sight allowing a quick change from short to long range, an excellent quick-change sighting system which was also used on the .30 caliber M1 carbines during World War II.

The cavalryman still had his hands full loading the percussion carbine on horseback. He first had to place the rein over his left arm and hold the carbine in his left hand. The hammer had to be moved to the safety notch and the fired percussion cap cleared away from the cone. Next, the flap of the cartridge box was lifted and a paper cartridge removed. The cartridge was held in the right hand and the paper tail torn off by the teeth. The powder charge was then poured in the barrel which was quite a trick if the horse was moving. The bullet was pushed into the barrel with the hollow base downward. The ramrod was then withdrawn from the guides beneath the barrel, rotated 180 degrees and used to ram the bullet down upon the powder charge. It was important that the hammer be at the half-cock position and the cone clear of the percussion cap so that some of the air in the barrel could escape through the vent, clearing debris from the narrow passages and insuring good ignition on the following shots. The Minié bullet was not as big in diameter as the bore so that much of the air could escape around the sides of the bullet during the ramming process. This was a very important point, for

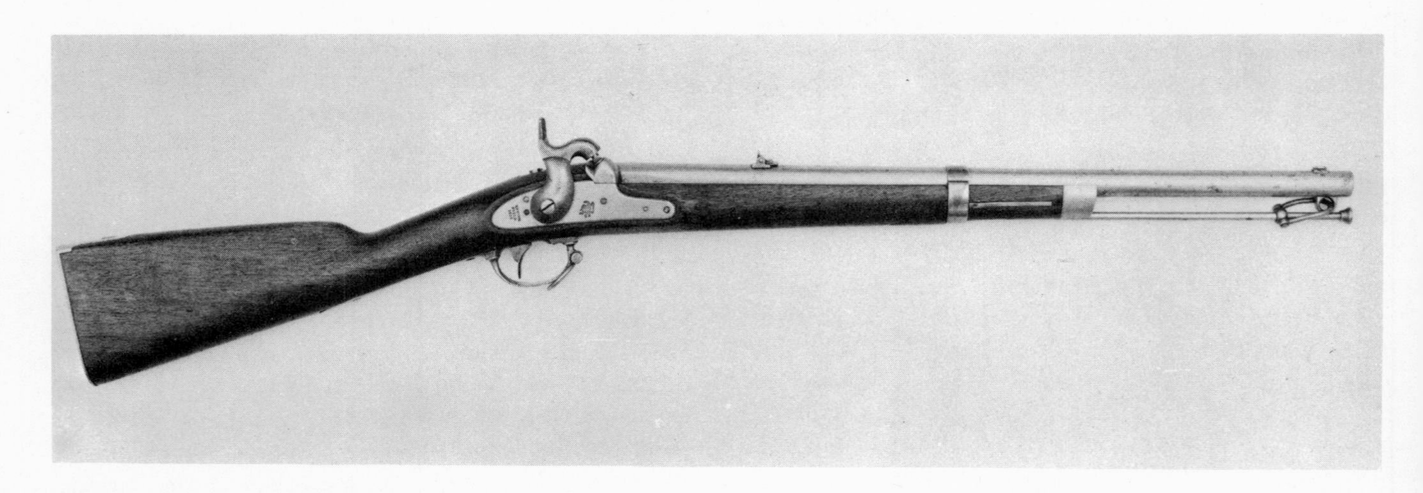

FIGURE 3-14 U.S. Model 1855 rifled carbine.

with a patched, round bullet used in all previous muzzle-loading firearms there was an airtight seal between the bullet and the bore, and all the air had to escape through the vent at the breech end of the barrel. Thus the Minié bullet could be rammed much faster and more easily.

Upon firing, the gas pressure acted within the hollow skirt of the Minié bullet flaring out the back end and providing an excellent seal between bullet and barrel. This design had another advantage in eliminating the rattling of the bullet from side to side as it traveled up the bore.

The cavalryman's next move was to withdraw the ramrod from the barrel and replace it in the channel in the stock. The final step was to fumble for a percussion cap and place it on the cone. If the carbine was to be fired immediately the hammer was drawn to full cock, the carbine aimed and fired. If the carbine was being loaded for later use, the general practice was to ease the hammer down gently onto the percussion cap, holding it solidly in position.

To put it mildly, the tiny, lightweight percussion caps were a royal pain in the neck to handle. The flared skirt on the cap helped somewhat in that the cap could be aligned by feel and the flared skirt provided something of a "lead in" to help align the cap with the cone. Many inventors worked on developing better systems to handle the small, fragile caps. Mechanical capping devices were developed which held a string of 10 to 50 caps in a straight or spiral track. These devices were far more successful for revolver caps which had no skirt and which were, incidentally, even more difficult to handle. The most successful systems for solving this problem were the Maynard tape priming system which was standardized on the Model 1855 rifles and rifle-muskets, and the Lawrence pellet priming system which was standardized on the Sharps carbines and rifles.

MODEL 1855 RIFLES AND RIFLE-MUSKETS

The 1840's and early 1850's saw a great change in the design of muzzle-loading firearms. The round ball either bare or with a patch had been the universal projectile for all firearms for 500 years. The rifle was much more accurate than the musket, but was a slow, cumbersome firearm to load and became more and more difficult as the barrel was fouled by powder residue. The percussion ignition system had reached the stage of military standardization in the 1840's and 1850's, and experiments with "elongated bullets" were being pressed in Europe and in the United States. All the experiments had two objectives. One was to develop a system which would be much easier to load — preferably with a bullet which was loose in the bore during the ramming process and then somehow expanded before or during the firing to provide a tight fit and a good gas seal as it was accelerated out the barrel. The second objective was to greatly increase the range and accuracy by developing smaller diameter bullets with reduced air resistance and greater weight due to their elongated shapes, thus maintaining velocity much better as they traveled through the air. These experiments were highly successful and bullet designs gradually evolved with a cylindrical body surmounted by an ogive nose. These were blunt, chunky bullets compared with the smooth curved shape and sharp nose of modern projectiles, but they represented a tremendous improvement in performance as shown in Figures 3-11 and 3-12.

The French proposed a system with a sharp stake screwed into the breech plug of the barrel which projected through the powder cavity into the area where the bullet was seated. As the bullet was rammed down the barrel it struck this sharp stake and a few sharp blows of the ramrod forced the bullet back onto the sharp surface displacing the lead outwards to seal the barrel surface. This French system allowed the use of plain based bullets which were easy to manufacture, but it was very difficult to keep the barrel clean, particularly in the chamber area. The expansion of the bullets was highly dependent on the force and number of blows from the ramrod.

A much better system was developed by a French Army Officer Captain C. E. Minié in which hollow-based projectiles were developed very similar to our modern rifled slug. (See Chapter 2).

The Ordnance Department of the United States was alert to these changes and watched the developments in Europe very carefully. Experiments were performed in the brand-new Washington Arsenal during the late 1840's and early 1850's under the direction of a very gifted officer, Major Alfred Mordecai, who made many important contributions to the development of the United States military firearms. As a result of these experiments a decision was reached in the mid-1850's to eliminate two separate calibers for the rifle and musket. Rifling was to be included in all firearms of the future and a single caliber of .580 of an inch was recommended by the Colonel of Ordnance on June 26, 1855, and this recommendation was approved by Jefferson Davis, Secretary of War in mid-1855.

Old patterns of thought die hard. Bullets had been referred to as "balls" for 500 years and so the new bullet designs were referred to as "elongated balls" during the 1850's and 1860's. Military officers and ordnance people could not quite give up the traditional distinction between muskets and rifles. It had been quite simple to separate the functions during the Revolution and War of 1812. The musket was used for close combat. It had a .69 caliber smoothbore barrel and a very long barrel of 42 to 46 inches. The rifle had a smaller diameter .54-inch bore, and a shorter barrel with thicker, heavier walls and a much lighter bullet. It was slower to load but was much more accurate. Each weapon had its corps of devoted boosters who disdained the merits of other types of firearms. The Army finally simplified the situation by settling firmly on a single caliber for all long arms. Even this decision was opposed by the Navy which said it had no need for the lighter ammunition and would insist on continuing the .69 caliber in Navy rifles, which were designed with relatively short barrels and fired the 740-grain Minié bullet. The Navy pointed out that it wasn't interested in lighter ammunition since their men needed firearms with tremendous punch for close combat in sailing ships that were locked together during a boarding engagement.

The Army at least agreed upon a single caliber, but to keep everyone happy settled on three different types of firearms in the new standard caliber. The first was the carbine with its 22-inch barrel. The second was a rifle which continued many of the features of the Model 1841 Mississippi rifle, including the 33-inch barrel and two barrel bands. The third model was called the rifle-musket. This had a long barrel of 40 inches and three barrel bands, and was considered the standard infantry weapon. All others were shorter, specialized firearms, manufactured in smaller quantities and considered suitable for special forces, such as Sharpshooters, Cavalry, Artillery or Engineers (Sappers). The specifications of these rifle and carbine models are shown in Figure 3-13, page 79.

Model 1855 Rifle-Musket

There were many, many innovations in this new firearm which is shown in Figure 3-15. The barrel had been shortened two inches compared with the Model 1842 smoothbore percussion musket and the over-all length was shortened to 56 inches. (The official length given in the 1861 Ordnance Manual is 55.85 inches.) Great attention was given to reducing the weight, and the Ordnance Manual lists the weight of the rifle-musket at only 9.18 pounds. This is a surprisingly low weight, for the rifle with only a 33-inch barrel is listed at 9.93 pounds. This weight reduction on the rifle-musket was accomplished by making a lightweight, thin-walled barrel which weighed only 4.28 pounds. The 33-inch heavy-walled barrel on the Model 1855 rifle weighed 4.8 pounds — a difference of ½ pound. A new, simplified style of forearm cap was fitted to the Model 1855 rifle-musket and the three flat barrel bands were retained by spring catches. A blade front sight was welded to the barrel. Several designs of rear sight were manufactured for mounting between the breech and first barrel band. The 1861 Ordnance Manual shows a sight with a short leaf for point-blank range and two longer leaves which could be raised for extended range. The rifle-musket shown in Figure 3-15 has a rear sight with a sliding elevator with graduations to 400 yards with the leaf in a relatively horizontal position and provision for extended range sighting with the leaf held vertically.

A major innovation in the Model 1855 rifles and rifle-muskets, was the use of the Maynard tape priming system. The tape primer was very similar to a modern child's cap pistol. Two narrow strips of paper were glued together with small pockets filled with fulminate priming compound at equal spacings along the strip. After gluing the paper was varnished to provide water resistance. This strip was then coiled and placed in a circular recess under the little pivoted door which was fitted between the hammer and the cone-seat in Figure 3-15. The strip was led up vertically in front of the hammer, and then arced over in a curved path so that the fulminate would be placed immediately over the cone. An ingenious ratchet mechanism within the lock moved the strip of paper upward each time the hammer was cocked, bringing a fresh spot of fulminate compound over the cone.

As the hammer fell the fulminate was ignited, cutting off the paper strip and sending a flame down through the cone and cone-seat to ignite the main charge as in a regular percussion system. Although the Ordnance Boards examining this system did not give it an unqualified recommendation, Jefferson Davis felt that it was an excellent improvement in eliminating the fussing around soldiers had to do with the individual percussion caps. He was an excellent and decisive Secretary of War, qualities which he later brought to his executive office as President of the Confederacy. After he reached this decision on the improved qualities of this new system, he insisted it be applied to all future rifles and rifle-muskets for the U. S. Service. Dr. Edward Maynard, the inventor of the system, was paid $4000 in 1845 for a trial installation on 4000 muskets. In 1854 the Government bought the rights outright for $50,000 and gave contracts to Remington for the conversion of 20,000 flintlock muskets to the Maynard system. Springfield Armory also converted many flintlock firearms to the Maynard-tape priming system.

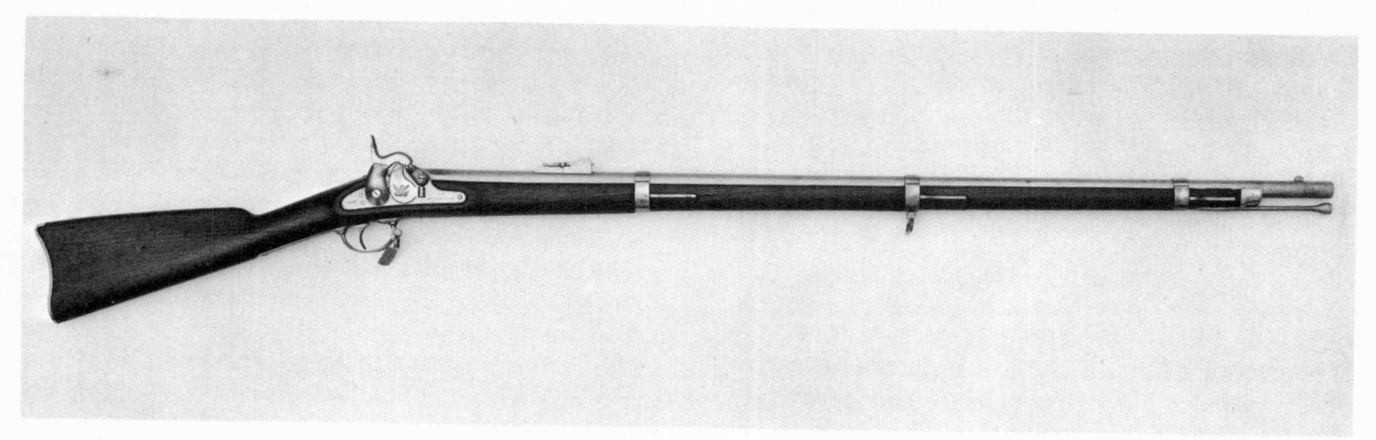

FIGURE 3-15 U.S. Model 1855 rifle–musket.

The Model 1855 rifle was very similar to the rifle-musket shown in Figure 3-15, except that the middle barrel band was eliminated and the barrel shortened to 33 inches. The over-all length was given as 49.3 inches in the 1861 Ordnance Manual. Even though the Model 1855 rifle fired exactly the same cartridge as the Model 1855 rifle-musket, the shorter barrel had such heavy walls that the over-all weight of the rifle was 9.93 pounds. Thus, much of the advantage of the shorter length and easier handling of the rifle was lost through the ¾-pound increase in weight.

There were a number of small changes in the percussion system. The cone-seat was still welded to the barrel at the breech end, but it was fitted with a "clean-out screw" which could be removed to allow the soldier access to the horizontal hole which carried the flame from the cone to the main powder charge in the barrel. The hammer shape was modified to make room for the fairly bulky tape priming mechanism. The lock plate was flat with beveled edges. The date of manufacture was stamped to the rear of the hammer. The United States eagle was stamped on the little steel cover of the priming mechanism and the manufacturer's name was stamped on the forward section of the lock plate. The rifle-musket of Figure 3-15 was manufactured at Springfield Armory which is stamped in two lines: U.S. on the upper line, and Springfield on the lower. The date of 1858 is on the lock plate to the rear of the hammer.

The barrel bands and butt plate were made of iron, but the early forearm tips were made of brass. In 1859 this was changed to iron to match the other components. The barrel was finished bright and was rifled with three grooves with one turn in 72 inches. The grooves were deeper at the breech and became shallower toward the muzzle since extensive experiments in the United States and Europe had established that this gave better accuracy. This is not to be confused with "gain twist" rifling. The pitch of the rifling was uniform with one turn in 72 inches, but the depth of the grooves was deeper at the breech than at the muzzle. Model 1855 rifle-muskets were made at both Harper's Ferry and Springfield Armories.

MODEL 1861 RIFLE-MUSKET

Basic specifications for the United States percussion rifles are given a complete rundown in Figure 3-14. The Model 1841 Mississippi rifle continued the .54 caliber design which had first been standardized in the Model 1803 rifle. The Model 1842 rifle-musket had a .69 caliber barrel — a size which went back to the French Charleville muskets of the American Revolution. The Model 1855 designs in three sizes, short, medium and long, established the common .58 caliber diameter and the basic sizes which were to be continued to the end of the percussion era. The Model 1855 rifles and rifle-muskets both contained the Maynard tape lock mechanism. The Ordnance Board had had reservations on recommending this tape lock mechanism when it was first presented to them in 1854. Jefferson Davis had enthusiastically endorsed it and it became standard for the latter part of the 1850's. Field experience was not very good. It was a fast priming system reducing the operations required by the soldier and worked satisfactorily under good condition in dry weather. The reports from field commanders and from the Inspector General were heavily against the Maynard priming system as unreliable for general service. The internal lock work to move the paper tape upward on each shot was more complex than the standard lock, and the paper strip of caps was susceptible to moisture. Many commanding officers insisted that their troops have regular percussion caps as a backup in case the Maynard priming system malfunctioned while the troops were in the field.

As the Civil War began the Ordnance Department realized that it would be necessary to greatly expand the production capacity at Springfield Armory and to encourage many private manufacturers to tool up for high rates of production to meet the needs of the war. They took a hard look at all military equipment from the standpoints of utility, function and ease of production. A Northern disaster was the loss of Harpers Ferry Armory in Northern Virginia to the Confederates in 1861, and the Federal troops did all they could to destroy the production capability, burning many of the buildings. Despite this, much of the Harpers Ferry equipment was repaired and did provide a substantial production asset to the Confederacy.

The rifle-musket standardized for large-scale production in 1861 is shown in Figure 3-16. This particular model was manufactured at Springfield Armory in 1862. It is shown with a triangular bayonet below the musket and with a wooden "tompion" in the end of the barrel to keep it free of dirt and water. The basic specifications were very similar to the Model 1855 rifle-musket — the same barrel length of 40 inches and an over-all length given in the Ordnance Manual of 55.85 inches. The lock was simplified by the elimination of the tape priming mechanism. The backward curving hammer was retained since the tooling was available, but the lower section of the hammer was made wider and thicker, apparently to reduce breakage in the field. The rear sight was redesigned and repositioned to 3 inches forward of the breech.

The extremely capable ballistician, Major Alfred Mordecai had been recognized as one of our leading ordnance experts and was president of the Ordnance Board convened in May 1860 to define the specifications for the Model 1861 rifle-musket. Elimination of the tape lock mechanism simplified the firearms, and also meant that the strength of the mainspring could be reduced to between 65 and 75 pounds. The Model 1855 lock was the first one in which the mainspring did not bear directly on the hammer tumbler but pulled downward on the tumbler through a small stirrup. This was a mechanical improvement which reduced the high friction force between the mainspring and the tumbler and made the power flow through the lock more efficiently. This feature was continued on the Model 1861 and all later rifle locks. The Ordnance Board had recommended that the rifle-musket contain a patch box similar to that on the Model 1855 rifle, but this patch box was not incorporated due to the pressure of war production. The 40-inch barrel was rifled with three grooves with a twist of one turn in 72 inches. It was finished bright and had the two-leaf rear sight attached 3 inches forward of the breech, and a blade front sight was welded to the muzzle. The three flat barrel bands were retained by springs and were also finished bright. The ramrod had a cup-shaped end to fit the Minié ball and was held in the stock by a spring retainer. The stocks were oil finished and made of walnut.

Contracts were given to a large number of manufacturers for Model 1861 rifle-muskets to build a broad production base and achieve high volume production as rapidly as possible. Some of the manufacturers were allowed to make variations in the design to take advantage of available tooling.

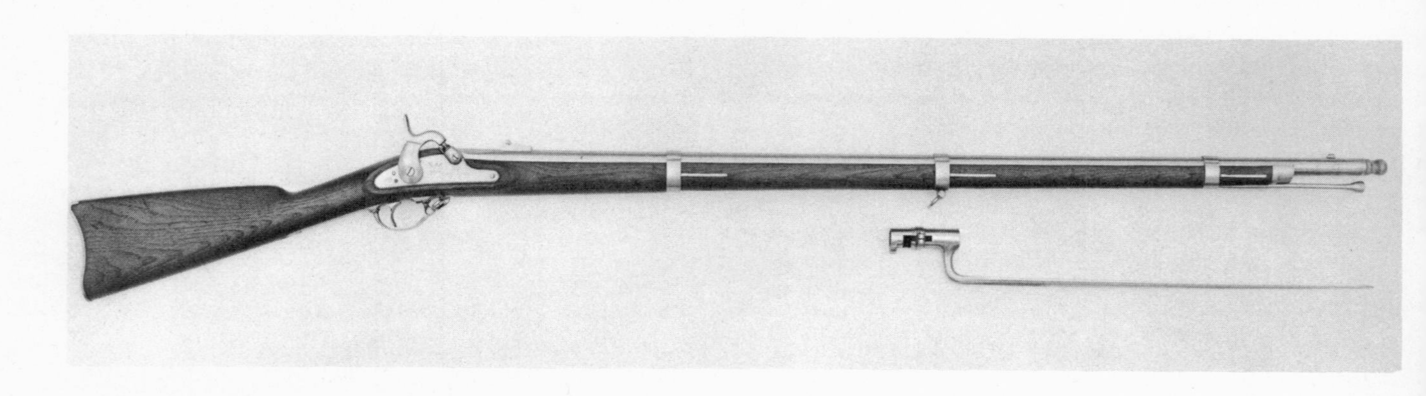

FIGURE 3-16 U.S. Model 1861 rifle–musket with triangular bayonet.

FIGURE 3-17 Model 1862 Remington 'Zouave" percussion rifle.

MODEL 1862 — REMINGTON ZOUAVE

Ordnance policy of allowing contractors latitude in the design of muskets and rifles to be manufactured for the war emergency led directly to the most colorful of all Civil War long arms — the Remington Zouave model shown in Figure 3-17. When the Civil War broke out Eliphalet Remington was a highly successful businessman in his late sixties with wide experience in the manufacture of sporting and military firearms. In addition to flintlock muzzle-loading rifles, which were manufactured in the early years, the company had broad experience in manufacturing percussion muzzle-loading rifles and shotguns, and had become increasingly active in the percussion revolver field during the late 1850's. When war broke out the Government negotiated with Remington for the production of 10,000 Model 1861 rifles and the contract was signed on July 30, 1861. The elderly Eliphalet Remington had been working extremely hard in the conversion of the factory from peacetime production of sporting firearms to the large-scale production of military rifles, and the effort proved too much for he died only a month after signing this first war contract. His sons were active in the business and took over the leadership. In order to make use of the extensive production machinery developed for manufacture of the Model 1841 Mississippi and the Model 1855 rifles, the Remington Company proposed a number of changes from the standard specifications. These changes were so extensive that a new contract was written on August 11, 1862, for large-scale production at $17.00 per rifle. The rifle differed so much from the other standardized Ordnance rifles that they have come to be known as the "U. S. Rifle Model 1862", although it was never given a formal Ordnance designation. These rifles were often issued to troops who wore colorful costumes including baggy red trousers, white leggings, and cut-away green jackets with red knapsacks and red or green fez hats. The costumes were inspired by the elite French troops known as Zouaves who were noted for their superb drill and discipline and who fought in campaigns in romantic, far away places such as Egypt. Other Zouave units, such as Ellsworth's Zouaves, had elegant white uniforms with baggy trousers and a short white jacket with light blue trim and a broad-brimmed white hat with one side of the brim turned up Australian style. In the United States the term Zouave came to mean élite troops with colorful uniforms.

The Remington Zouave rifle had a very elegant appearance as shown in Figure 3-17. The barrel was 33 inches long and was the standard .58 caliber. Early production models were rifled with the tooling from the Model 1841 Mississippi rifle and had seven narrow grooves. Later production models utilized newer tooling with the standard three-groove Civil War style rifling. The lock plate was flat with beveled edges and was inset into the stock to the height of the bevel. The hammer had a much more graceful shape than the standard 1861 rifle-musket and hammer and lock plate were finished with mottled case-hardened colors. The stock was of walnut about 44 inches long and had a dull oil finish. All of the accessories were brass which contrasted richly with the blued barrel, case-hardened lock, and dark walnut stock. A brass patch box was fitted to the butt of the stock with a spring hinge at the forward end. The two brass barrel bands and the brass forearm cap were more expensive as to material but they utilized

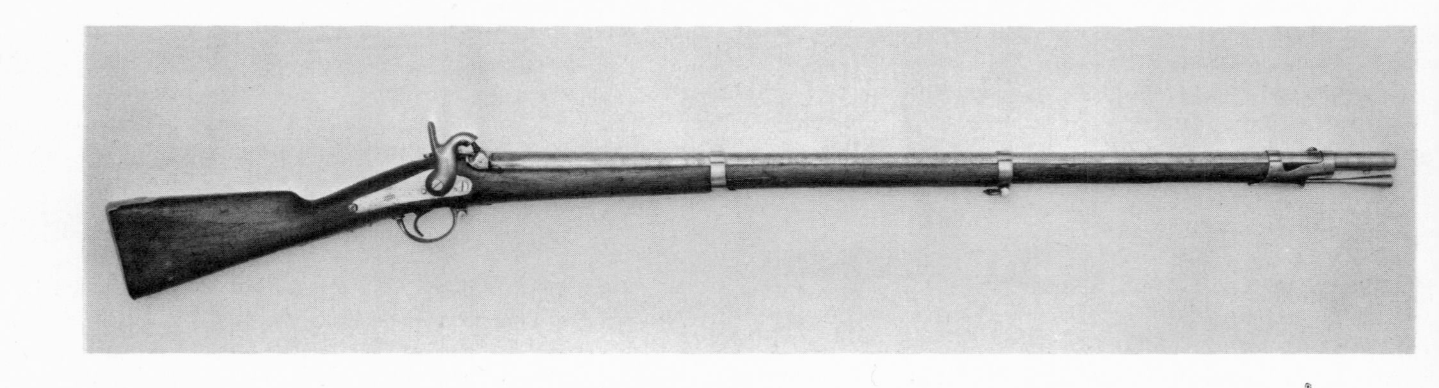

FIGURE 3-18 European .69 caliber rifle–musket with "back lock" action.

tooling from the Mississippi rifle and could be cast and polished more easily than forging and finishing iron parts.

This rifle had many characteristics in common with the earlier percussion rifles as shown in Figure 3-14. The barrel length of 33 inches was the same as the Model 1841 Mississippi rifles and the Model 1855 rifles. The over-all length was very similar at about 49 inches. The Remington rifle had one major advantage over the Model 1855 rifle in that the barrel was not quite so heavy and over half a pound had been saved, reducing the weight to 9.38 pounds. This weight was still a pound heavier than the Model 1861 rifle-muskets. Civil War experience with this rifle was excellent. It had the power, range and accuracy of the longer rifle-muskets, but the shorter length and lighter weight meant less fatigue for the soldier. The Civil War was an infantry war, and hundreds of thousands of young men spent day after day in constant marching as the fortunes of war swept north and south. Some of the southern units, particularly Stonewall Jackson's brigades, became known as "foot cavalry" for the men could literally keep up a relatively rapid march for 15 hours with short breaks, and could cover incredible distances. The saving of half a pound on the weight of the soldier's firearm was a very significant improvement, particularly when neither range nor accuracy was lost. It is only surprising that the rifle was not reduced in weight *below* the rifle-musket, for the thin rifle-musket barrel was obviously strong enough.

The design of the rifle with two bands and an over-all length in the range of 56 inches became the standard design after the Civil War, appearing in the Models 1868, 1870 and in all the .45 caliber "trapdoor" Springfield rifles starting with the 1873 and running through the late models of the 1880's.

MODEL 1863 RIFLE-MUSKET

One of the important manufacturing variations requested by the Colt's Manufacturing Company was the elimination of the barrel band springs and the substitution of barrel bands which were split and clamped to the stock by screws. This was felt to be a worthwhile simplification and a new rifle-musket was standardized in 1863 with it. There was also a design change in the cone-seat welded to the barrel which was shorter and more rounded. The clean-out screw was eliminated and the American eagle was stamped on the end of the cone seat. The hammer was redesigned to a much more graceful S shape and the ramrod was slightly redesigned to eliminate a swelling used to retain it in the stock. It was instead retained by a friction spring.

By the end of 1863 problems had shown up with this musket and a new design was standardized. Experience in the field had shown that as the rifle-musket was fired the clamped barrel bands slowly moved toward the muzzle due to recoil forces. What really happened from a scientific standpoint was that the three barrel bands had a certain amount of weight — and tended to stay fixed in space as the rifle recoiled shot after shot. As the gun fired it snapped to the rear and the barrel bands tried to stay in their fixed position until accelerated rearward by the friction force between the barrel band and the stock. This resulted in minute slippage shot after shot and eventually the bands had moved a considerable distance toward the muzzle and became loose. This proved to be a real annoyance to the soldier in the field who did not always have a screw driver to loosen the bands, push them back in position and retighten, and could be a major hazard if the barrel became loose in the stock due to band slippage, for this would change the sighting pattern. In December 1863 a revised model was specified requiring the use of solid bands with spring retainers.

Other very minor changes were made such as the elimination of the dovetail cut in the barrel to hold the rear sight and attachment of the sight by screws. These changes were not universal, for the author has a Model 1863 rifle-musket manufactured by Remington in 1865 which still has the clamped barrel bands with no spring retainers. The revised Model 1863 is often known as the "Model of 1864" for it did not go into production until that year, and with war production in full swing tremendous numbers were manufactured. Springfield Armory alone produced over a quarter million of the two models during 1864 and 1865.

EUROPEAN PERCUSSION RIFLES

Very large quantities of British, French, Belgian, and German muskets were purchased by both the Union and the Confederacy during the Civil War. The English Enfield percussion rifle of .577 caliber was particularly popular and purchased by both sides. One of its major advantages was that it differed in bore size from the standard American caliber by only .003 of an inch and the same Minié bullets could be used in either British or American percussion rifles. The French and Belgian firearms were often .69 caliber and a rifle-musket showing the typical Continental characteristics is shown in Figure 3-18. This rifle-musket is a curious blend of early and late features. It is .69 caliber with shallow rifling typical of the designs of the 1840's. It also has the early style of forearm assembly, including a forearm cap with a double barrel band and a flared opening to receive the ramrod. The front sight is welded to the top of the barrel and a bayonet lug is welded underneath the barrel close to the muzzle. Two flat barrel bands are fitted and a forward sling swivel is attached to the middle band. All three barrel bands are retained by spring catches.

The cone-seat appears to be forged integral with the barrel and is much closer to the center line than in American practice. This required that the hammer have considerable offset toward the center line of the rifle-musket, so that the hammer was not flat but had a very twisted appearance when viewed from any but a side angle. Another design feature characteristic of the French and Belgian firearms was the design of the hammer with the cocking surface sticking straight up. This apparently had been found to be useful to the soldier in cocking the hammer under stress, but it did not add to the beauty.

The trigger guard was iron and was bolted to a trigger guard plate. The rear sling swivel was attached to a vertical plate which passed through the trigger plate and was cross pinned in the stock of the rifle. This was a cheaper construction than that used in American military firearms. Two serrated grips for the finger were forged into the trigger plate at the small of the grip. The barrel bands, trigger guard, trigger plate and butt plate were all forged of iron. Ramrods were either the trumpet shape design shown in Figure 3-18 or had a parallel section with a cross hole which was particularly common on Belgian muskets.

A very significant feature shown in this illustration was a new type of lock known as the "back action" lock. Notice that the hammer is very near the front of the lock plate as compared with all the locks previously illustrated. This represented a significant improvement in design, for the mainspring was moved from the front of the lock to the rear and the delicate lock mechanism was moved away from the area where all the dirt, flash and flame occurred.

Details of this lock compared with a traditional lock are shown in Figure 3-19. If these two designs are compared with the lock from the Brown Bess flintlock in Figure 2-2, the design improvements over a 200-year span can readily be visualized. The Brown Bess flintlock mechanism had two subsystems. One was involved with the pan, battery, battery spring and pivots. This mechanism kept the powder in the pan dry and covered until the shot was fired — and the pan was snapped open by the flint striking the battery and sending a shower of sparks down into the pan. The second subsystem included the springs, pivots and sears that provided power to the hammer. The hammer had a movable jaw in order to clamp the flint which had to be replaced every 15 or 20 shots. The hammer also had surfaces designed to absorb the excess energy delivered by the mainspring, for the flint and battery could not be counted on to absorb all the hammer spring energy. There was a stopping surface forged onto the hammer and a matching flat surface on the lock plate to absorb the heavy blow.

The mainspring pushed down directly on the tumbler causing the tumbler and the hammer to rotate. The mainspring was extremely powerful, pushing downward with close to 100 pounds of force. The contact between the spring and the tumbler was a source of high friction and wear.

By the 1850's the American percussion locks had evolved into the design shown in the left-hand side of Figure 3-19. The entire mechanism comprising the pan, battery, battery spring and pivots had been eliminated by the substitution of the much simpler percussion ignition system. The arrangement of the mainspring and the hammer mechanism was similar to that shown in the Brown Bess lock of 150 years earlier. The one major area of improvement was the elimination of the heavy bearing contact between the mainspring and the tumbler. The hammer spring was reduced to 65 to 75 pounds of force, and this was transmitted to the tumbler through a little intermediate link which was known as the stirrup or swivel. The hammer spring had a slot cut in the middle of the end and two hook-shaped fingers machined into the very end of the spring. These slipped over a cross bar in the little stirrup which in turn could swing freely on a cross shaft in the tumbler. By this means the heavy bearing contact between the spring and tumbler was eliminated and a much lower friction of rotating shafts was substituted.

The remainder of the mechanism was quite similar. The hammer components were held in position by a bridle which was firmly fixed to the lock plate by two screws. The rear screw served as the pivot shaft for the sear. The surface on the bridle immediately above the sear pivot formed the stop surface to prevent excess hammer motion. This was only needed if the lock was removed from the rifle, or if the cone broke off and did not provide a proper stopping surface for the hammer. With a properly functioning arm all the hammer energy was absorbed by the percussion cap and cone. If the lock was removed from the rifle or the cone broken off, then a flat surface on the tumbler moved upward as the hammer rotated and slammed into fixed surface at top of bridle.

The sear was held in its proper position by the sear spring which was a small and delicate spring compared with the hammer spring. It provided a limited downward force rotating the sear in a clockwise direc-

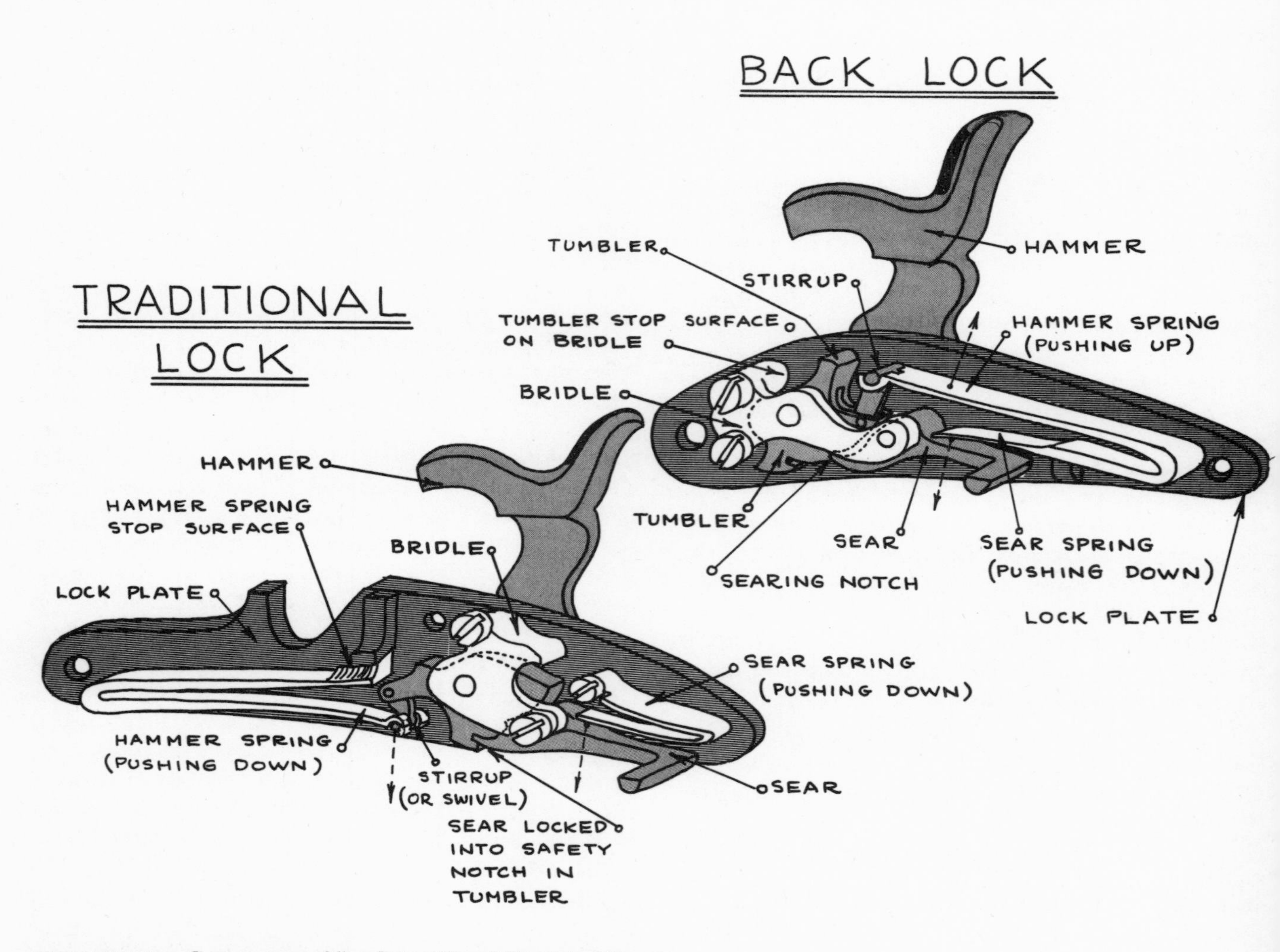

FIGURE 3-19 Comparison of "traditional" and "back lock" actions.

tion and holding it in proper engagement in the notches cut into the tumbler. The sear in Figure 3-19 is shown engaged in the safety notch which locked both the trigger and hammer in position.

The design of a "back lock" is shown in the right side of Figure 3-19. Here the percussion mechanism is reduced to its simplest terms. Where the lock for the Brown Bess flintlock had three separate springs, the back lock percussion mechanism generally had only one spring. The powerful hammer spring was mounted at the back of the lock plate and pulled upward rather than pushing downward. The tumbler was redesigned and the stirrup relocated so that this upward force still provided a powerful movement tending to rotate the hammer counterclockwise. There was a small triangular stop surface forged into the lower part of the lock plate which took the reaction of the hammer spring and then a thin section of hammer spring was extended forward to serve as the sear spring, pushing downward and holding the sear in proper engagement with the tumbler. This drawing shows the hammer seared up on the firing notch which is considerably shallower than the safety notch immediately forward. Care was taken to provide a stop surface to prevent the hammer from rotating too far. The vertical surface was forged onto the tumbler and this is shown in the illustration at the arrow point from the word "tumbler." If the lock were snapped outside of the gun mechanism or if the cone on the barrel had broken off, this tumbler would contact the tumbler stop surface on the bridle.

The back action lock represented the final design improvement in the percussion era. It was lighter in weight and cheaper to manufacture than the older type of locks. The lock mechanism was moved rearward in the stock so that there was less chance of dirt and debris working their way into the lock mechanism. These types of locks proved to be so satisfactory that their use has continued to the present day and some "hammerless shotguns" have mechanisms very similar to the back lock mechanism, but with a small internal hammer that is hidden from view.

Breech-Loading Ammunition

CHAPTER 4

Early in the 19th century the United States Army took the remarkably advanced step of experimenting seriously with breech-loading flintlock rifles. Considering the formidable problems of the very limited supplies of good metal in the United States, and the crude manufacturing techniques of the period — limited entirely to hand and water-powered machinery, this was a remarkable development. The invention and development of the Hall breech-loading flintlock rifle is described in Chapter 5, but it is important to realize that a climate of willingness to consider new ideas and to nurture them through the complex stages of development until a successful system could be devised was provided by the United States Government.

The idea started with an inventor, John Hancock Hall, who made some pistols using his ideas in 1811 and a military rifle model in 1812. The Government thought enough of the ideas to place Hall on the staff of the Harper's Ferry Armory, and offered to pay him a royalty of $1.00 per rifle if the rifle was standardized and manufactured. The experiments proceeded until a successful model was standardized in 1819. The paper cartridge for this remarkable rifle is shown in Figure 4-1. It was very similar to that used in the muzzle-loading flintlock muskets and rifles, consisting of a spherical lead ball contained in a paper cylinder which held the appropriate powder charge plus priming charge.

Loading sequence: The release catch in front of the trigger guard was pulled back and the breechblock pressed upward, raising the front of the chamber above the top of the barrel. The paper cartridge was removed from the pouch and the end bitten off. The hammer was cocked to the safety notch and the priming charge placed in the pan. The pan cover and the frizzen were snapped shut. The remainder of the powder charge was poured into the open end of the chamber with the rifle held vertically upward. The paper cartridge was usually wadded up and stuffed into the chamber together with the lead ball. The wadding was not essential and a bare ball could be loaded. The breech was snapped shut and latched. The rifle was normally carried this way in situations of danger. All that was required to fire was to draw the hammer back to full cock, aim and pull the trigger.

During the early 1800's the manufacture of paper cartridges was often left to the field forces as a "spare time" project. The result was that lead balls and loose powder carried in powder flasks was a more common form of ammunition. Special powder flasks were designed and manufactured for the Hall rifles.

An improvement in the Hall ammunition was made after 1830, when the paper for the cartridges was soaked in niter which made the paper combustible. This improvement was used with the percussion type Hall rifles and allowed the entire cartridge to be rammed into the chamber at one time.

The Hall rifle was truly a remarkable development

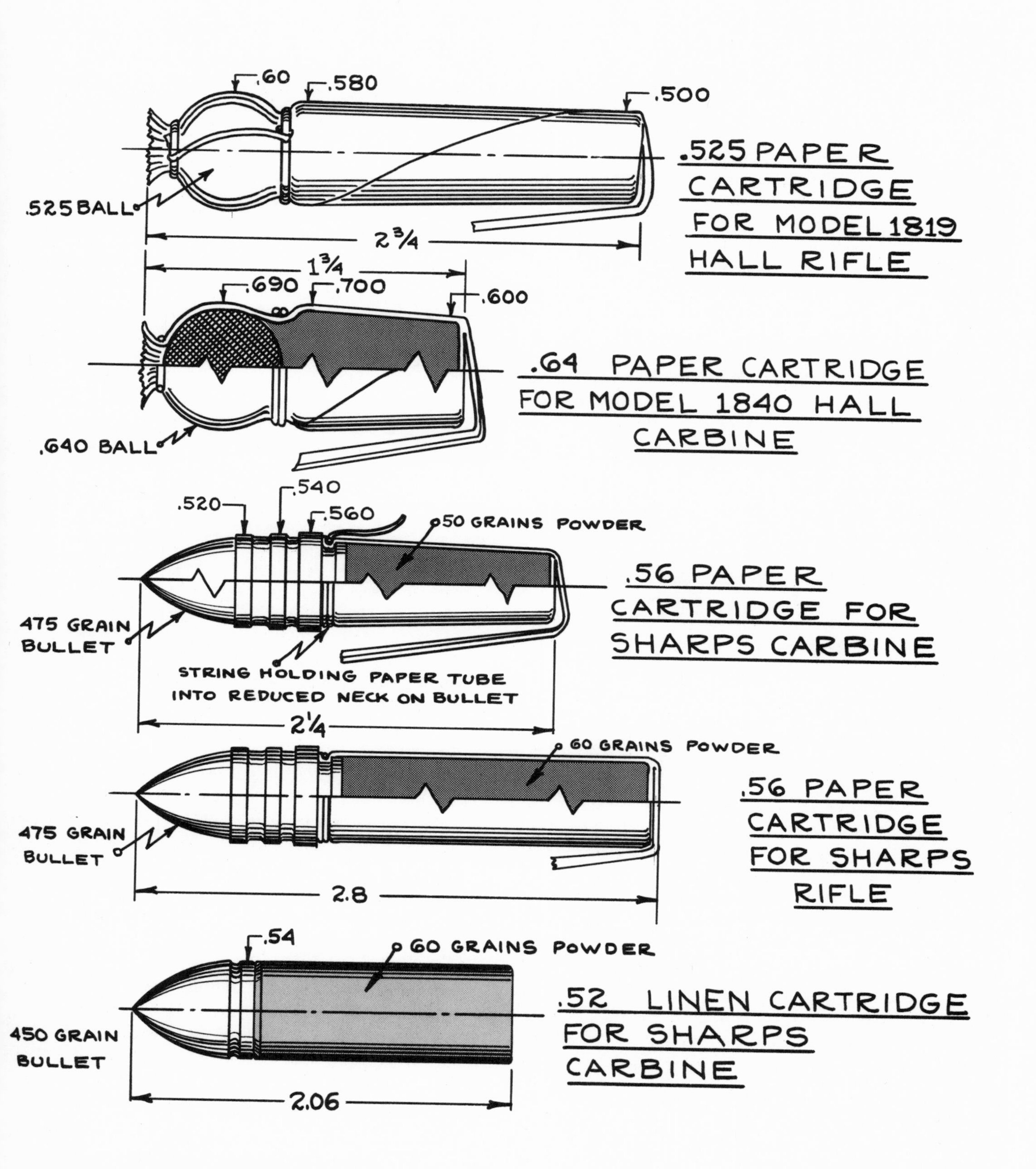

FIGURE 4-1 Early breechloading ammunition.

and was manufactured for 25 years, from 1819 into the 1840's. There was an extra advantage to the system in that only one cartridge could be loaded in the rifle at a time. This contrasted strongly with the muzzle-loading rifles where a soldier under the stress of combat could continue to ram additional charges into the gun, one on top of another, without ever firing the rifle. Eventually the Hall system was dropped because the crude manufacturing techniques of this early period resulted in considerable gas leakage at the breech, and the soldiers objected to the blast of smoke and flame so near their faces.

Two of the cartridges that were manufactured for the Hall rifles are shown in Figure 4-1. The upper illustration shows the standard ball cartridge for the Model 1819 Hall rifle. A .525-inch diameter lead ball was loaded in the front of the cartridge and retained by a loop of string. Two powder charges were used with this rifle, an 80-grain load and a 100-grain load. In each case about 10 grains were used to prime the pan and the net charge of 70 or 90 grains went into the chamber of the rifle. Some tests were made with this rifle at the Washington Arsenal in 1843 and 1844 using a ballistic pendulum. The rifle was a flintlock with a 32½-inch barrel forward of the chamber and an over-all barrel length of 35.1 inches, including the chamber. The net charge of 70 grains propelled the .525-inch diameter lead ball at 1490 feet per second. The ballistics of this rifle are shown in the top line of Figure 4-2. These ballistics are for an 80-grain cartridge with 10 grains of priming and a net charge of 70 grains in the chamber. The .525-inch diameter soft lead ball weighed 219 grains and had no lubrication. Measured on a ballistic pendulum, the muzzle velocity of 1490 feet per second corresponds to a muzzle energy of 1080 foot-pounds with a 219-grain bullet.

Considering the crude machining techniques available in the 1830's and the fact that the joint between the chamber and the barrel was located where the gas pressure was maximum, the efficiency was quite good at 15.4 foot-pounds of muzzle energy per grain of propellant.

Another measure of performance is the "muzzle impulse" which gives an indication of the amount of "kick" that can be expected in firing the rifle. Newton's principle of conservation of momentum states that the momentum of the bullet, powder gases and paper wads coming out the muzzle will be exactly balanced by the momentum of the gun moving to the rear against the shooter's shoulder. For the early Hall rifle the muzzle impulse works out to 1.9 pound-seconds, which is quite moderate for these early firearms. A modern comparison is the 5.56 mm (.22 caliber) M-16 rifle which has a muzzle impulse of 1.4 pound-seconds and a .30 caliber M-14 Army rifle which has a muzzle impulse of 2.7 pound-seconds. The M-16 is considered to have a light kick, and the M-14 a heavy kick by modern standards.

The ammunition for the Hall carbine is very similar in appearance but shorter in over-all length. The Hall carbine was the first percussion firearm to be standardized by the United States Army and was made in both .525 and .64 caliber. Tests of a Model 1840 Hall carbine manufactured by Simeon North were run at the Washington Arsenal in 1843. This carbine had a barrel length of 23.4 inches including the chamber and fired the same .525-inch diameter bullet and 70-grain powder charge as the rifle cartridge. In tests the carbine load with 70 grains of powder in the percussion carbine gave a muzzle velocity of only 1240 feet per second and a muzzle energy of 748 foot-pounds. The efficiency of this load is substantially less at only 10.7 foot-pounds of muzzle energy per grain of propellant. This efficiency is about equivalent to that of the flintlock musket of about 1800 which used a less powerful form of black powder. The efficiency of the Model 1841 muzzle-loading percussion rifle in this same series of tests was 19.8 foot-pounds of muzzle energy per grain of propellant. Interestingly enough, the Model 1844 Jenks carbine, firing the same cartridge with a .525-inch diameter ball and a 70-grain powder charge, gave a velocity of 1687 feet per second or an efficiency of 19.78 foot-pounds per grain of propellant. Even the 57 caliber Model 1830 Flintlock cadet musket (which incidentally fired the same .525-inch diameter ball) gave a muzzle velocity of 1690 feet per second with a 70-grain powder charge. The Hall carbines lost efficiency primarily due to the joint between the chamber and the barrel.[1]

Large caliber versions of the Hall carbines were made using the .640-inch diameter lead ball designed for the .69 caliber smoothbore muskets. One of these cartridges is shown in the second line of Figure 4-1. The powder charge for this cartridge varied over the years and loads of 110, 100, 86, and 75 grains are listed in various ordnance manuals. The front end of the paper tube was tied off with string, and then the .64 caliber round ball loaded into the tube. The string was led across the ball and two turns taken to secure the ball in the front of the cartridge. The black powder charge was then poured into the tube and in

[1] B. R. Lewis, *Small Arms and Ammunition in the U.S. Service*, Smithsonian, 1968, P 95.

the early cartridges the end was twisted around. After 1830 the construction shown in Figure 4-2 was used; that is, the paper tube was carefully folded into a flat configuration and then folded in two right angle turns so that the tail end lay alongside the powder cavity.

There are a number of comments in the literature of firing heavy 100-grain powder charges in the Hall carbines. There was a fearsome blast of flame out the muzzle, for such a heavy powder charge could not be burned in a carbine length barrel. If the carbines were slightly worn, there was another blast of gas leakage at the breech, adding up to a very unpleasant experience for the soldier.

The author vividly remembers cartridges which split at the rim and leaked gas like the Hall rifles. I started collecting old rifles as a teenager in the early 1940's. Teenagers' budgets are notoriously skimpy and particularly so when antique firearms only represent noise, danger, and mess to the older generation.

In the early 1940's Bannermans, located on lower Broadway in New York, still had a table in the back of the store which was loaded with "Unserviceable firearms — For Decoration Only." These ancient relics were too grimy for Bannerman's to bother cleaning up and placing in the regular gun inventory, but they represented a veritable gold mine to a youngster who had a great deal of time and very little money. Bannerman's also sold very old ammunition which was generally loaded in weak folded head cartridge cases. Ammunition for odd calibers such as the .43 Spanish was $1.75 for a pasteboard box of 20 cartridges. The ammunition was unreliable. Many misfires occurred and many that did fire split the brass cases. There are vivid recollections of breaking down the misfired cartridges with the forlorn hope of reloading the ammunition. The black powder had become a solid cake and in most cases had eaten into the brass case from the inside. The soft lead from the bullets was salvageable, but the caked powder and cases were rarely any good.

I clearly remember the occasions when a cartridge case split at the rim and a blast of gas shot upward out of the action. The event was accompanied by an ear-splitting noise. This was not the normal heavy boom of the powerful black powder cartridges. This was an extremely sharp and penetrating noise produced by the gases leaking from the chamber while the cartridge was still at peak chamber pressure, and it was generally such a piercing sound that my ears would ring for several minutes.

With a worn Hall carbine or rifle the poor soldier would be exposed to this situation on every shot, for as soon as the ball jumped from the front end of the chamber into the conical opening in the barrel, powder gases at 10,000 to 15,000 pounds per square inch breech pressure would start pouring out of the imperfect joint between the chamber and barrel, producing a painful and penetrating noise. I can well understand the reluctance of troops to subject themselves to this punishment, and their preference for the slower, clumsier but quieter muzzle-loading rifles and muskets.

Breech-Loading Experiments

What if we had a breech-loading rifle or carbine that only required that the action be thrown open, a "cartridge" thrown into the breech and the action closed and be ready to fire? It would represent a tremendous improvement for all of the troops and most particularly the cavalry. The need felt by the cavalry was so great and so obvious that the great majority of the early breech-loading systems were adopted for cavalry use. Most of the inventors were dreaming of inventing the perfect rifle which would be adopted first by the cavalry and then by the entire Army as the golden road to fame, riches and success. Many expended their lives and fortunes in this effort, and the patent records of the 1850's and 1860's show literally hundreds of patent designs on which inventors had lavished their skill and effort.

One of the very important constraints on inventors of the 1840's and 1850's were the very limited techniques for manufacturing ammunition. The simple, direct methods are in sharp contrast to the complex manufacturing processes of today.

MAKING PAPER CARTRIDGES

The Ordnance Manual of 1850 describes the current processes developed for the manufacture of paper cartridges. Sheets of paper 16½ inches long by 13 inches wide were used for the musket cartridges and these sheets were cut up into trapezoids with a long side 5¼ inches, a short side 3 inches long, and a height of 4.33 inches. Paper-cutting machines were used at the arsenals which cut the paper into strips 4.33 inches wide and then cut 12 at a time into the trapezoidal shape. To make the cylinders a crew of one master and 19 men was recommended. There is an interesting comment that "boys or girls from 12 to 18 years of age may be advantageously employed." The crew consisted of 10 men to roll the cylinders. Each took the paper in his left hand and a wooden cylinder or former in his right. The paper was rolled up onto the cylinder and then choked off with a piece of string wrapped around the paper about ½ inch from one end.

The wooden former was withdrawn and the choking string drawn up to compress that end of the cylinder. Two and a half additional turns of string were taken around the choked portion. The ball was then dropped into the open end of the cylinder and pushed to the end with the wooden stick. The thread was then carried around the ball two more turns taken to hold the ball in place. These turns were retained with two half hitches. The thread was then cut and the subassembly placed in a box.

The boxes of cylinders were then given to a second crew. The powder charges were added by pouring from a conical copper charger with a handle at the top. Various size chargers were used corresponding with the powder charge. In 1850, for example, the standard musket cartridge contained 110 grains of powder and this required a charger .80 of an inch in diameter at the top and .60 of an inch in diameter at the bottom with a height of 1.35 inches. One man was employed filling the cartridges with powder and then he passed filled cartridges to a folding crew of four men. The paper was neatly folded down over the powder with two rectangular folds and passed along to the next crew of four men for bundling. The cartridges were packaged two tiers of five cartridges each parallel to each other with wrappers in between. A package of 12 percussion caps was placed in each box of 10 cartridges. A finished box of musket cartridges was 2.6 inches long, 3.1 inches wide and 1.35 inches thick. These packages in turn were placed in wooden boxes made of pine, 6¾ inches by 15½ inches by 11¾ inches which held 1000 musket cartridges. The Army even specified that the box was to weigh 12 pounds empty and 107 pounds loaded.

MANUFACTURING BULLETS

Up until the late 1830's bullets were made in the United States by the casting process. Experiments with rolling or swaging processes, at factories and the arsenals showed that these processes had promise for making bullets of more uniform density and closer dimensions. By the early 1840's these experiments were successful and the ballistics tests by Captain Alfred Mordecai at Washington Arsenal in 1843 and 1844 led to the recommendation of use of swaged balls. These experiments found that the greater uniformity of the swaged balls allowed the diameter of the ball to be increased by .010 of an inch. In the .69 caliber musket this was a change from .640 of an inch to .650 of an inch and the reduced area for gas leakage between the ball and barrel was equivalent to increasing the charge by 10 grains of powder. During the 1840's more accurate molds were developed so that the 1850 Ordnance Manual specified .650-inch balls whether swaged or cast. The description of casting the balls specified use of a large iron kettle on top of a furnace. Six men were required for each furnace. The lead was weighed and dumped into the kettle and covered with a 1-inch layer of powdered charcoal. Everyone turned to and fueled the furnace furiously for several hours until all the lead was melted and the heat was sufficient to set a piece of paper on fire when pushed into the melted lead. With a good crew this required one to two hours.

Two iron ladles, 3½ inches in diameter were used. These were filled ¾ full of lead, and as they were withdrawn from the tank some of the powdered charcoal would remain on top of the lead, protecting it from oxidation.

Six brass molds, known as "gang molds", were used. They had a double row of cavities, one on the top, and the other on the bottom. Some molds were designed to cast 12 or 16 musket balls at each filling. Others were designed with a row of 8 musket balls on one side and 15 buckshot in the other row.

The Army even specified gauges to be used. One, a ring gauge .002 of an inch greater than the nominal size of the ball and the other .0015 of an inch less than the size of the ball. This meant that with a nominal musket ball of .650 of an inch any balls larger than .670 of an inch, or smaller than .635 of an inch were thrown back into the pot for recasting. The balls were cast by filling the cavities on one side then turning the mold over and filling the cavities on the other side. As with any mold the bullets were ragged, partially filled and rough until the mold got very hot.

Two men were required to cast the balls. The molds were then passed to another man who opened the molds and extracted the bullets and sprues (waste lead left in the runners of molds). The bullets were passed to a crew of three men who used nippers, powerful metal cutters something like a pair of pliers. One handle was attached to the work bench and the other was about 5 inches longer and had a wooden handle. The 2-inch jaws were of steel 2 inches, tempered and ground sharp. The bullet was placed with the sprue in the jaws of the nipper, and the handle pressed down. The Ordnance Manual specified that a hole be bored in the bench under the jaw of the nippers so that the balls fell through the hole into storage boxes. The runners or sprues were dumped back into the melting pot.

The next step in the process was to place the balls

in a hard wood rolling barrel 2 feet long and 1 foot in diameter. The rolling barrel had a shaft sticking out each end which was set into a frame and a crank attached. About 100 pounds of balls were put into the rolling barrel and rotated for several minutes. When this equipment was not available 50 pounds of balls were put into a strong canvas bag about 5 feet long and 16 inches in diameter. The canvas bag would then be shaken for about 5 minutes to round the balls.

A large iron screen was also used with holes the size of the large ring gauge (.670 of an inch). The balls were then dumped from the tumbling barrel or canvas bag onto the screen. All those remaining on the screen were dumped back in the pot for recasting, while those passing through the screen were packed for use.

The 1850 Ordnance Manual glibly states: ". . . with the above force 30,000 to 35,000 musket balls are made in 11 to 12 hours." Such a comment can lead one to suspect that the "old Army" was truly composed of iron men of Herculean physical strength and whose physical conditioning was such that they never tired. Anyone who has molded bullets for hand loading is well aware that this is very hard work and that two hours is a long casting session.

During the 1840's more and more ammunition was manufactured at the Arsenals and less by troops in the field. The Ordnance Manual states ". . . lead balls are now generally made by compression, by means of machinery; either at the arsenals or at private establishments. These balls are more uniform in size, smoother and more solid than the cast balls. Compressed buckshot are also readily obtained from private shot works."

Balls made by either process were generally packed in boxes 9 inches square inside and 5 inches deep containing 100 pounds of balls or buckshot.

Bullets of our familiar modern shape are technically known as cylindro-conoidal bullets (a cylindrical body with a curved, pointed nose.) During the 1840's and 1850's all bullets were composed of pure lead, or lead slightly hardened with addition of tin or other elements.

In the manufacture of large quantities of cylindro-conoidal bullets it was customary to utilize the swaging process which gave greater uniformity and much more rapid production rates. The lead was cast into long round bars which were rolled to the approximate diameter of the finished bullet. They were cut by machine into short lengths which gave a short cylindrical slug of the proper weight. These short sections were fed into powerful bullet swaging presses which formed the lead in closed dies under intense pressure to the final bullet shape — a process that is the basic method of manufacturing lead bullets today.

SHARPS AMMUNITION

The most successful breech-loading design to come along in the 1850's was the Sharps which is described in Chapter 5. The Sharps design was the essence of simplicity and, in fact, is still commonly used today in artillery up to 105 mm. This type of action is also the standard used by leading commercial firms and the Government for ballistics development of cartridges where pressures may greatly exceed those the designer anticipates! The Sharps action consists of a rectangular breechblock which slides vertically to close off the exposed end of the chamber. The Sharps designs have the same problem as the Hall in trying to minimize gas leakage at peak chamber pressure. Many experiments were performed, including the design of *platinum* rings and complex gas checks which use the gas pressure to drive the seal forward against the fact of the chamber. The experiments were successful, and Sharps developed in his 1859 model a rifle and carbine which leaked very little. This became the most popular breech-loader in the early years of the Civil War. A total of 9141 rifles were purchased during the war and 80,512 carbines.

The ammunition for the Sharps rifles and carbines is shown in the lower three illustrations of Figure 4-1. They typify the cartridges in which the lead bullet was exposed and the powder chamber attached to the bullet by various means. The top illustration shows the standard Sharps carbine cartridge specified in the 1861 Ordnance Manual. A paper tube was rolled up with a diagonal seam very similar to that used in the earlier muzzle-loading and Hall paper cartridges. A soft lead bullet was made by either a casting or swaging process.

Paper tubes for the Sharps cartridges were made by a process very similar to that for the standard Army loads. A trapezoidal sheet of paper was cut and rolled up on a stick about ½ inch in diameter. The front end of the tube was slid gently over the extension at the rear of the Sharps bullet and two turns of string were taken around the paper to hold it firmly in the groove. The paper cartridge was then loaded with a 50-grain powder charge if for the carbine or a 60-grain powder charge for the rifle. The construction of the specimens used for the illustrations shown in Figure 4-1 indicate that sometimes the same tube was used. With a larger powder charge the folded tail simply was shorter.

Firing the Sharps Cartridge

The Sharps carbine and cartridge were improvements, particularly for cavalrymen. They were so successful that the Northern Cavalry clamored for them and 80,152 were purchased for the mounted troops. Other elite troops such as Berdan's Sharpshooters were armed with the Sharps rifles and 9141 were purchased. It must be remembered that these rifles and carbines cost approximately twice as much as the standard muzzle-loading weapon and the Federal Government under Congress' watchful scrutiny had always been quite conservative in allocating money for more expensive weapons. The Sharps carbines and rifles were purchased in the face of adamant opposition from many Ordnance officers including the Chief of Ordnance, General Ripley, who was extremely concerned with problems of supplying vast quantities of odd-sized ammunition for the different models of firearms being purchased. General Ripley had some justification for his position; if troops armed with .58 caliber muzzle-loading rifles were delivered .54 caliber Sharps cartridges in the thick of battle, heavy casualties would certainly result. It is a tribute to the Union supply system that ammunition shortages were extremely rare and, in general, the Northern troops were abundantly supplied with the proper ammunition even when operating far afield. The Ordnance Department was also very much concerned with the increased firepower of breech-loading weapons which, it was felt, must inevitably lead to the soldier shooting using up all his ammunition early in a battle and being without ammunition at the height of the conflict. These fears were ungrounded. The performance of the breech-loading rifles and carbines in the Civil War gave the Northern troops a substantial edge over their Southern opposition.

Imagine you are a Northern cavalryman jogging along on a strong and well-fed charger. The horse needed to be strong and well-fed to carry the cavalryman with his heavy boots and coat, bedroll, canteen, mess kit, saddle and blanket, large sabre and often two .44 caliber Colt's revolvers in saddle holsters plus a Sharps carbine, and ammunition boxes for both carbine and revolvers. The cavalryman of 1863 was almost a travelling fortress!

While many cavalry actions were fought with the troopers dismounted and the horses led to the rear, it was perfectly possible to load and fire effectively while mounted. With breech-loading weapons, all the trooper had to do was loop the reins over his left arm, hold the carbine with his left hand and depress the lever to flip the breech open with his right hand, withdraw a cartridge from the cartridge box and push it into the chamber. As the breechblock was slammed shut the sharp edge on the upper surface of the block cut off the back of the paper cartridge, exposing the raw powder in the rear of the chamber. The hammer was then cocked and a percussion cap placed on the nipple and the carbine was ready to fire. The whole process was much simpler and at least twice as fast as trying to manipulate a muzzle-loading carbine while on horseback. (See Chapter 3.)

Sharps Linen Cartridges

Now we move on to a second style of Sharps cartridge, shown in the bottom illustration of Figure 4-1, is typical of a large number of different ammunition designs for many breech-loading carbines. It is also similar in appearance to the cartridges for the Colt's revolvers with the exception that the Colt's had a slightly conical shape to the powder cavity. In this design the linen tube was formed up and then glued to the back of the soft 450-grain lead bullet. The cloth was often "nitrated" or soaked in saltpeter which made it burn readily. With this design the cartridge was placed in the chamber of the rifle or carbine and did not have to be cut off by the breechblock. The flame from the percussion cap traveled down three passages in the breechblock and struck the center of the rear of the cartridge with sufficient energy to ignite the linen cloth and the powder inside.

Many experiments were performed to develop the best form of cloth covering. Almost everything was tried, and the most successful were linen or thin skin membranes from animals.

Ballistics of the Sharps Cartridges

The ballistics of the early Sharps are difficult to pin down. Since accurate velocity-measuring equipment was quite rare almost all early tests were performed by measuring the penetration through pine boards. The usual test was to set up a series of one-ince pine boards with a one- or two-inch air space between each board. The rifles under test were fired at ranges from 30 to 500 yards at the target, and measurements made of the number of planks penetrated. This was a practical method of measurement which answered the needs of the day, but the results cannot be easily correlated to velocity measurements, since so many factors such as bullet shape, hardness, and the characteristics of the wood enter into the tests. The ballistics of the early Sharps firearms have been estimated in Figure 4-2. Experiments with gas seals had been successful by the late 1850's and the Conant seal in particular minimized

Rifle	Bullet Diameter	Bullet Weight	Net Powder Charge	Muzzle Velocity Ft/Sec	Muzzle Energy Ft-Lbs	Efficiency
Model 1819 Hall Rifle	.525	219	70	1490	1080	15.4
Model 1840 Hall-North Carbine	.525	219	70	1240	748	10.7
Hall .64 Carbine	.640	397.5	75	966*	825*	11.0*
Sharps Paper	.56	475	50	949*	950*	19.0*
Sharps Linen	.54	450	60	1068*	1140*	19.0*
Maynard	.50	343	40	1000*	760*	19.0*
Burnside	.54	400	45	981*	855*	19.0*
Spencer	.56	450	40	900*	809*	20.3*
Henry	.44	200	28	1125	568	20.3

*Calculated Figures

FIGURE 4-2 Ballistics of early breechloading ammunition.

gas leakage. The efficiency of the Sharps system has been estimated at 19 foot-pounds of muzzle energy per grain of propellant. This is higher than the Hall rifle of 1819 which gave 15.4 and much higher than the Hall-North carbine which gave only 10.7. It is in the range of instrumented tests with the Jenks carbine of the 1840's which delivered just under 20 foot-pounds of muzzle energy per grain of powder despite some leakage at the breech.

The ballistics of the standard Sharps carbine cartridge have been calculated out at a muzzle velocity of 950 feet per second for the 475-grain bullet and a muzzle energy of 952 foot-pounds.

The Sharps rifle cartridges were generally loaded with 60 grains of powder. The later bullets such as that shown in the lowest illustration of Figure 4-1, weighed only 450 grains. The ballistics of this combination calculate out at a muzzle velocity of 1070 feet per second and a muzzle energy of 1144 foot-pounds.

The Sharps represented a very outstanding step forward in firearms technology and may be considered the most successful of the breech-loading rifles and carbines firing caseless ammunition. The ammunition, while very fragile by modern standards, was simple to make and highly effective for the needs of the day.

METALLIC AMMUNITION

During the 1840's and 1850's hundreds of inventors throughout the world were working on the problem of developing breech-loading rifles and ammunition. Most of the inventors were pursuing unsuccessful lines of approach. Many had very advanced ideas which were simply not proctical with the manufacturing processes available. Some of these inventions formed very important links in the chain of development of our modern day ammunition.

One of these very significant inventors was Walter Hunt of New York City who was born in 1796 and made inventions in many different fields. Two of his most significant inventions were the "rocket ball' cartridge, which was patented in 1848, and a .54 caliber repeating rifle on which patent No. 6663 was issued in 1849.

The patent for the rocket ball cartridge is shown in Figure 4-3. Most of us find patent drawings and descriptions extremely difficult to follow. This figure has been prepared with the illustration magnified several times its original size in the patent drawing and printed next to the text so that it is a little easier to follow. The essential elements are most clearly shown

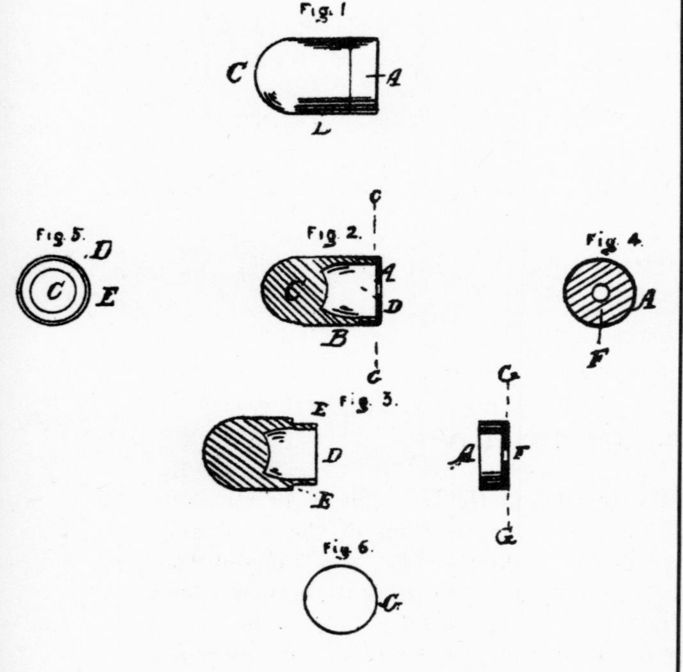

UNITED STATES PATENT OFFICE.

WALTER HUNT, OF NEW YORK, N. Y., ASSIGNOR TO GEO. A. ARROWSMITH.

METALLIC CARTRIDGE.

Specification forming part of Letters Patent No. 5,701, dated August 10, 1848; Reissue No. **164**, dated February 26, 1850

To all whom it may concern:

Be it known that I, WALTER HUNT, of the city, county, and State of New York, have invented a new and useful improvement in the construction of a metallic cartridge made entire with the ball, for fire-arms, which I term a "rocket-ball"; and I do hereby declare that the following is a true and faithful description of the same.

The nature of my invention consists in making balls of metal for fire-arms with the rear part thereof cylindrical and with a cavity of sufficient capacity to receive the entire charge of gunpowder, which is therein confined by a cap, or the equivalent thereof, having a central hole, through which the charge is inflamed.

Figure 1 in the annexed drawings is an external longitudinal view of said rocket-ball, which is charged ready for use. Upon the open end of the cartridge is fitted a thin sheet-metal cap, A. Upon the opposite front end of B (the cartridge) projects one-half of the ball C, which all together resemble the ordinary top thimble. Fig. 2 gives a longitudinal cut sectional view of the same, showing the internal structure of the cap A, cavity D in the cartridge B, and its junction with the ball C. The dissected longitudinal cut section, Fig. 3, shows the cap A separated from the flange or neck formed by the shoulder at the dotted line E upon the rear end of B. Fig. 4 is an end or face view of A, which in form resembles the Chinese gong, with a central perforation, F, in its discous head, which is the point of ignition from the priming. Over this perforation upon the inside face of said cap is placed a thin waterproof tissue or seal (see Fig. 2) at the dotted line G and face view, Fig. 6. This seal may be made of any thin material through which the fire from the priming may penetrate, and which will at the same time secure the powder in the cartridge from escape or accidental injury. This ball and thimble should be formed in molds by pressure. The powder being well packed in the cavity D, the cap A lined, with the seal G being fixed upon the flange, and pressed up to the shoulder E, should then be subjected to a second pressure, in order to fix the cap firmly and produce a uniformity in the size of the cartridges.

It will be readily perceived that this plan of a combined ball and cartridge is well adapted to fire-arms made to be charged at the breech, from the fact that in firing this ball the cap A is left in the breech, with its head or disk pressed firm against the breech-plug, and its rim or flange forced outward against the inner periphery of the caliber of the barrel, forming an air-tight stopper, which effectually prevents all backward escape of the powder, notwithstanding the breech-plug may be loosely fitted in the breech of the barrel behind the charge, which must necessarily be the case in all reciprocating breech-pins, in order to prevent their binding from heat, deposits, &c., in rapid firing. It is also obvious that in guns made with piston breech-pins the cap A in my plan would be carried out forward of each succeeding ball, operating as an effectual wiper to the barrel at each discharge of the piece.

I am aware that balls have been made with a small cavity in the rear end thereof, to contain a charge of fulminating powder, or of fulminating-powder mixed with a small portion of common gunpowder; and I am also aware that a metal cap with a hole in the center has been used to retain the charge in a cylindrical paper cartridge attached to an ordinary ball, the cap being left, by the discharge, in the barrel, and pushed out by the succeeding charge. I do not therefore claim either of these as of my invention; but

What I do claim as my invention, and desire to secure by Letters Patent, is—

Making metallic balls for fire-arms with the rear part thereof cylindrical, and a cavity in the said cylindrical part of sufficient capacity to receive the entire charge of gunpowder, substantially as herein described, when the said charge is retained in the ball by a cap or the equivalent thereof, having a central hole through which the charge can be inflamed, substantially as described.

WALTER HUNT.

Witnesses:
ROBT. D. HOLMES,
WILLIAM H. MARSAE.

FIGURE 4-3 Walter Hunt ammunition patent.

in the third line down in the illustration. What Hunt visualized was not so much a "hollow bullet" as a spherical ball with a metallic skirt attached to hold the powder. The left-hand illustration in the third line down shows this rocket ball before any other components have been added. Hunt's idea was to pack the cavity D with a compressed load of black powder. The small metallic cup on the right-hand side of the third row of illustrations was then slid over the back end of the bullet sealing it off. There was a small hole F which allowed the flash from an external priming system, such as a percussion cap, to penetrate the cartridge and set off the charge of powder.

When the Hunt cartridge was fired in a rifle the blast of flame from a separate percussion cap or priming passed through the center hole F and ignited the charge. The metallic cap A did not go out the barrel but instead acted as a short-cartridge case expanding against the walls of the chamber and serving to partially seal the breech of the action. While this rocket ball was a very important concept, Walter Hunt did not have the temperament or financial resources to drive through the years of patient experimentation required to develop a successful system. It was for later inventors to take these ideas and build the foundation of the Winchester Repeating Arms Company.

Maynard Ammunition

The next significant step in the chain of progress may be seen in the Maynard patent No. 15,141 of 1856. This patent is shown in Figure 4-4. The illustration has been magnified several times over that shown in the patent drawing, but it is still not completely clear. A cross section through the cartridge is shown in Fig. 1 on the left side. The lead bullet had a flat base and was pressed into a "cylindrical shaped shell A of brass, or some other tough and stiff metal, having a centrally perforated bottom." The hole through the bottom of the cartridge case is shown in the right side illustration. The hole was sealed off by "internal packing" and then the cavity was charged with powder. The two grease grooves in the bullet, which are shown faintly, were packed with grease before the bullet was pressed into the case.

The Maynard approach represented a substantial improvement over the Hunt design since the powder cavity could be made as large as desired. Dr. Maynard did pursue this invention and developed a very successful carbine and ammunition that was used during the Civil War. The ammunition design of 1860 is shown in Figure 4-5. This was still an externally primed system, that is the cartridge itself contained no priming. The cartridge consisted of a hollow drawn copper or brass cup to which a heavier flange was soldered, thus forming a rim on the head. A hole through the flange and through the copper cartridge case allowed the flame from the percussion cap to penetrate the head of the cartridge and ignite the 40-grain powder charge inside the case.

The bullet was of an improved design with a cylindrical section into which the grease groove had been swaged and had a rounded ogive point with a flat at the forward end. This type of bullet design is known as "inside lubricated" since the grease in the groove is inside the case and not subject to being wiped off during handling.

This illustration is contained in the Ordnance Memoranda Number 14 entitled "Metallic Ammunition" which the Government published in 1872. The comments on "externally primed" ammunition are significant.

> In the earlier varieties of the metal cartridge, the primer or cap by which it was fired was detached from the cartridge, as in the Burnside, and Maynard, and etc., the cap being applied to a cone, as in muzzle-loaders, and the flame of it having to penetrate through the devious channel of the vent of the arm to the vent in the rear end of the cartridge, causing a considerable percentage of *failures to ignite, due to fouling the vents, etc.*

This was a valid criticism for the flame from the percussion cap in many of these early arms had to pass a considerable distance before igniting the cartridge. For example, in the Sharps the hammer struck the percussion cap high up on the breechblock on the right-hand side. The flame had to pass down a diagonal passage to the center line of the breechblock, travel through a horizontal passage across to the center line of the action, and then make another right-hand turn into a third passage located along the axis of the barrel. The flame burst out of the third passage, penetrated head of linen cartridge, and ignited charge.

During the 1850's, the Government experimented with many different designs of breech-loading carbines. Four hundred of the Maynard carbines were purchased in 1857 using a tape priming system. This eliminated the need for putting a separate percussion cap on the cone or nipple on for each shot.

The ballistics of the Maynard ammunition of 1860 are estimated in Figure 4-2. The powder charge was quite low at 40 grains but it propelled the relatively light 343-grain bullet at about 1000 feet per second. This velocity has been calculated based on an estimated efficiency of 19 foot-pounds of muzzle energy per grain of propellant.

Tests were fired with the Maynard at an extreme range of 1300 yards. The target, 10 feet high by 30 feet wide, was built of 1-inch boards, and 14 out of 43 shots actually penetrated through the target at this range. In further tests 12 rounds were fired in 1 minute and a total of 562 roúnds were fired before the gun required cleaning. Two of the cartridge cases were used to fire 100 rounds apiece by reloading, and these remained in good condition.

During the Civil War, the Government purchased 2,157,000 Maynard cartridges in .50 caliber — actually not a significant number. One of our leading commercial manufacturers at the present time loads 2 million .22 caliber rimfire cartridges *a day strictly for commercial use.* There were 20,002 Maynard carbines purchased during the Civil War compared with 55,567 Burnsides, 80,512 Sharps and 94,196 Spencers. The quantity of Maynard ammunition seems extremely small, averaging 100 rounds per carbine.[2]

[2] *Ibid.* P 157

UNITED STATES PATENT OFFICE.

EDWARD MAYNARD, OF WASHINGTON, DISTRICT OF COLUMBIA.

IMPROVEMENT IN CARTRIDGES.

Specification forming part of Letters Patent No. 15,141, *dated June* 17, 1856.

To all whom it may concern:

Be it known that I, EDWARD MAYNARD, of the city and county of Washington, in the District of Columbia, have invented and constructed a new manufacture in the shape of an Improved Article of Fixed Ammunition for Breech-Loading Fire-Arms; and I do hereby declare that the following is a full and exact description thereof, reference being had to the accompanying drawings, making a part of this specification—

Figure 1 being a longitudinal section in a line passing through the center of a piece of my improved fixed ammunition, and Fig. 2 a rear-end view of a piece of said ammunition.

Each piece or cartridge of my said improved fixed ammunition consists of a cylindrical-shaped shell, *a*, of brass, or some other tough and stiff metal, having a centrally-perforated bottom, rendered impervious to air and water by internal packing, then charged with powder, and then combined with a projectile, *b*, of the shape and in the manner substantially as hereinafter set forth.

The exposed portion of the projectile *b* is of a pointed or semi-oval shape, and the portion of said projectile that enters the shell is of a cylindrical shape, of such a size as to closely fit within the shell, and having a sufficient length of bearing-surface to insure the point of the projectile being retained in a line with the axis of the shell. To insure a perfectly tight joint between the outer periphery of the projectile and the inner periphery of the shell, annular grooves are formed in the cylindrical portion of the projectile, and filled with any suitable greasy composition. The peripheries of the ledges between the grooves in the cylindrical portion of the projectile, fitting closely against the inner periphery of the shell, will prevent the grease working inwardly to injure the powder, or outwardly to soil anything that the ammunition may be brought in contact with. The said greasy composition serves the purpose of rendering the joint between the projectile and the shell perfectly tight while the ammunition is in a fixed state; and when the ammunition is discharged, the said greasy composition serves to lubricate the bore of the gun.

The perforated back end of the shell may be closed and made perfectly impervious to air or water by placing one or more disks of waxed or gummed paper against its inner surface before placing the powder within the shell.

The projectile should be pressed into the shell with a sufficient degree of force to insure close contact between the inner end of the projectile and the powder, care being taken in so doing not to turn the point of the projectile out of line with the axis of the shell.

After a cartridge has been discharged, the shell *a* should be removed from the chamber of the gun.

In using my improved fixed ammunition, the projectile is set more accurately within the chamber of the fire-arm than it is possible to set it in the best muzzle-loading target-rifles. The cartridges may be exposed with impunity in any weather, and may be handled roughly with less liability to injury or accident than would be likely to occur from such usage of any other fixed ammunition for small-arms known to me.

The shells may be charged a great number of times, with less apparatus and at less cost than that of the ordinary cartridges, and the expense of the shells is so small as to be quite insignificant when taking into account the great advantages possessed by this ammunition.

As a matter of course, the shells of my improved cartridges must be of such a size as to fit accurately within the chamber of the gun the said cartridges are prepared for.

I am aware that cartridge-cases of a tapering shape have been made of sheet-copper or other hard metal, combined with soft-metal rings, as described and represented in a patent granted to A. E. Burnside, March 25, 1856; and I am also aware that the said cartridge can only be used in a movable breech-piece, and that it does not possess in other particulars the peculiar advantages which distinguish my improved cartridge for breech-loading fire-arms; therefore,

What I claim as my invention, and desire to secure by Letters Patent, as a new manufacture, is—

My improved cartridge for breech-loading fire-arms, composed of a hard-metal cylindrical case, charged with powder and combined with a projectile of such a shape that, whether the case receive a large or a small charge of powder, the said projectile is self-retained in contact with the powder, in such a position that its point must be coincident with the axis of said case, and a perfectly tight joint formed between said projectile and case, by filling the grooves in the former with greasy matter, substantially as herein set forth.

The above specification of my improved fixed ammunition for breech-loading fire-arms signed this 16th day of April, 1856.

EDWARD MAYNARD.

Witnesses:
Z. C. ROBBINS,
M. H. MANSFIELD.

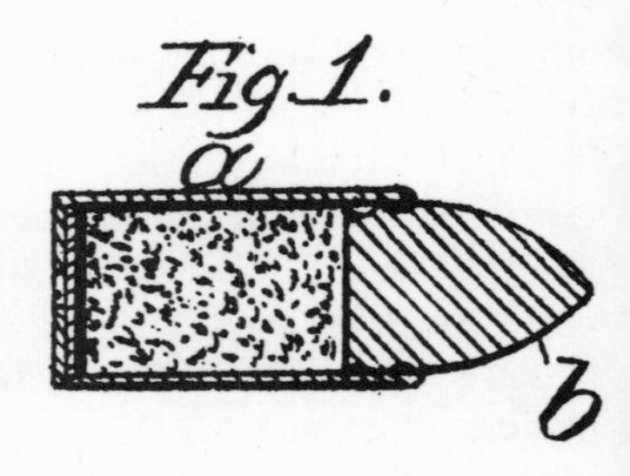

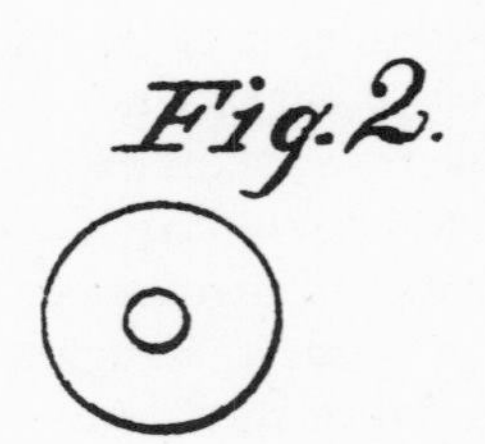

FIGURE 4-4 Edward Maynard ammunition patent.

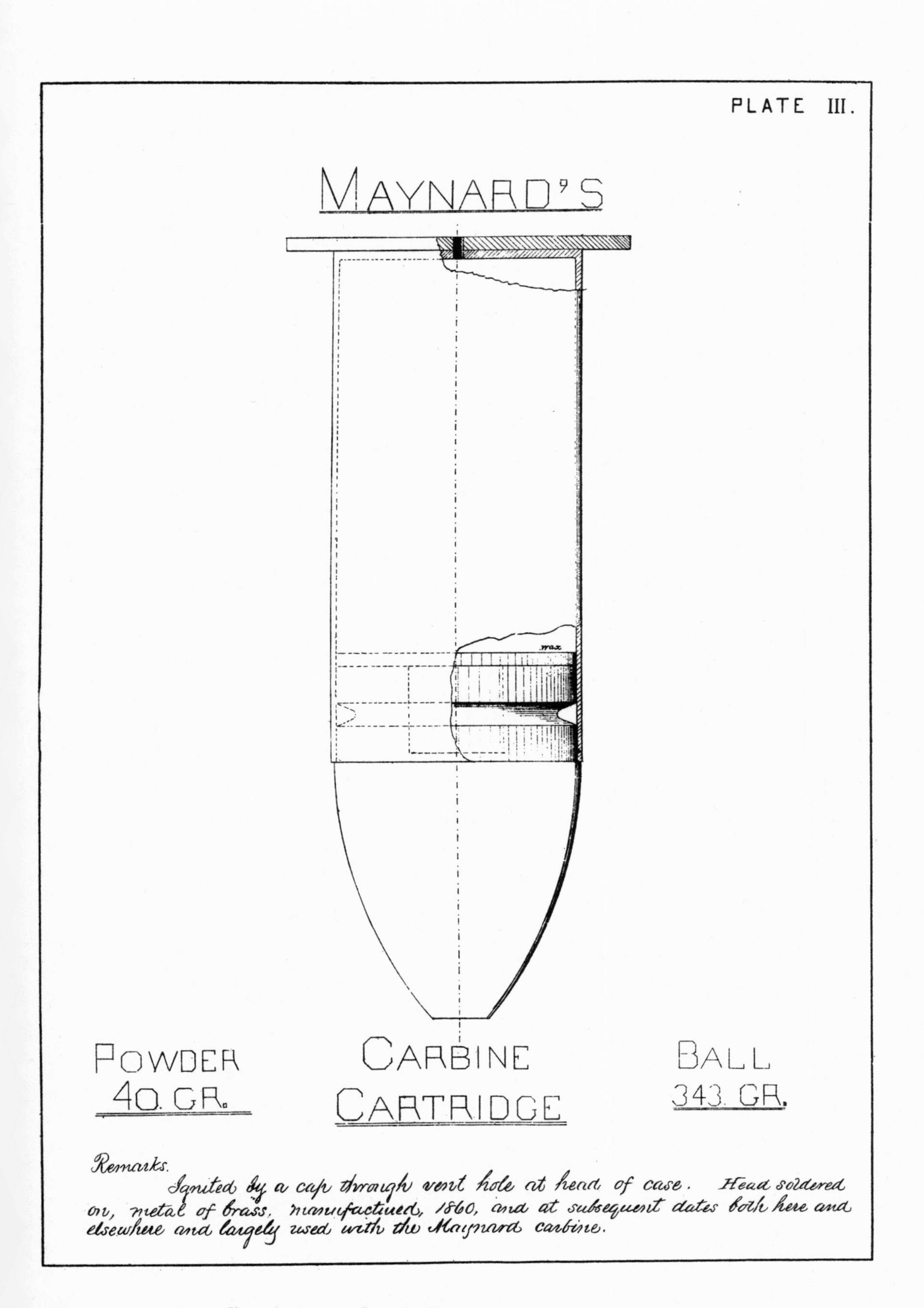

FIGURE 4-5 Maynard's carbine cartridge of 1860.

So many inventors had created improved breech-loading firearms and ammunition that by late 1863 the supply situation in the Union armies was becoming very serious. An Ordnance Board was convened September 24, 1863, and after studying the problem recommended changes to reduce the number of types of ammunition required for carbines. The board suggested that a minimum charge be established at 1/10 the weight of the bullet. They also recommended that the Sharps, Gibbs, and Starr carbines be manufactured so as to use .52 caliber Sharps paper or linen cartridges. They recommended that the Spencer, Joslyn, Sharps and Hankins and Ballard carbines also be made in .52 caliber and all be chambered for the Spencer 56/52 caliber rimfire cartridges. No changes were recommended in the cases of several carbines "using peculiar cartridges not adopted to interchangeability." The Maynard came under this specialized category for it fell between the Sharps cartridge, which was externally primed and used a combustible case, and the Spencer cartridge, which was very similar to our modern rimfire cartridges with a metallic cartridge case containing the priming in a rim cavity. The commonest Maynard cartridge of the Civil War was a .50 caliber design with a case .76 of an inch long and a 335-grain bullet.

Burnside Cartridges

Two important links leading to modern metallic ammunition were the Burnside carbines and ammunition developed in the 1850's. The Burnside fired a unique cartridge which is shown in Figure 4-6. This illustration of the Burnside cartridge is from the Ordnance Memorandum Number 14, "Metallic Ammunition," published in 1873. In describing the Maynard ammunition, Major T. J. Treadwell, commanding officer of Frankford Arsenal in Philadelphia, wrote of the developments of the 1850's:

> About the same time the Burnside, Maynard, and a few others, were produced, some of which were good in their day, and for the arms for which they were designed, but were fired by means of a cap (percussion cap) through a vent, at some distance from the cartridge, and were extracted by the fingers. With them there was not that necessary nicety of fit to the chamber of the gun, the joint was not absolutely closed, and failures to explode were as frequent as with the old-fashioned paper cartridge and percussion caps. Such failures would, nowadays, be considered a most unwarranted percentage in any metallic ammunition laying claim to excellence, and, in the best known varieties, do not occur to the extent of one in one thousand rounds; in fact, many attain a much higher standard of surety than indicated by this figure. The records of the testing-ground show long-continued firing and consumption of thousands of rounds without failure at all from any cause, and the summation of a year's practice and tests, in proof of manufacture, exhibiting an exceedingly small percentage of such failures.

Major Treadwell's comments are highly optimistic to say the least. A series of field tests performed just the previous year by the Army Ordnance Department had, in fact, showed an average misfire rate of 2½ percent for the center-fire metallic cartridges which were considered the most reliable type at that time. In light of these statistics it appears probable that the externally primed rifles and cartridges such as the Sharps, Maynard and Burnside probably had misfire rates in field service of between 5 and 10 percent. This meant that the soldier had to be very careful to keep his carbine clean, particularly in the area of the ignition system, in order to have a reliable firearm.

The Burnside carbine and ammunition were very interesting for in many ways they were a development of the old Hall flintlock and percussion rifles. In the Burnside system, as in the Hall, the chamber was separate from the barrel. The cartridge was loaded into the front of the chamber and in each case was ignited by a flame striking the rear of the cartridge. There was a sealing ring at the front of the Burnside cartridge case which was intended to provide gas sealing during the peak chamber pressure. In fact, it was a common experience for the Burnside cartridge case to tear in half at this ring and for the front portion of the cartridge case to be permanently swaged to the bullet and travel with the bullet down the barrel of the rifle. Many Burnside bullets recovered from Civil War battlefields show the front section of the cartridge case with the rifling grooves engraved in it and a torn section to the rear where the cartridge case gave way under peak firing pressure.

A total of 55,567 Burnside .54 caliber carbines were purchased during the Civil War and 21,819,200 rounds of ammunition, an average of 410 rounds of ammunition per carbine, were also purchased. The metallic cartridge case sealed the chamber pretty well so that an efficiency of 19 foot-pounds of muzzle energy per grain of propellant has been estimated. With a joint between the chamber and barrel allowing leakage at the highest chamber pressure, it was necessary to use a fairly conservative powder charge of 45 grains. This tended to keep the chamber pressure down so that leakage did not become too severe. The performances

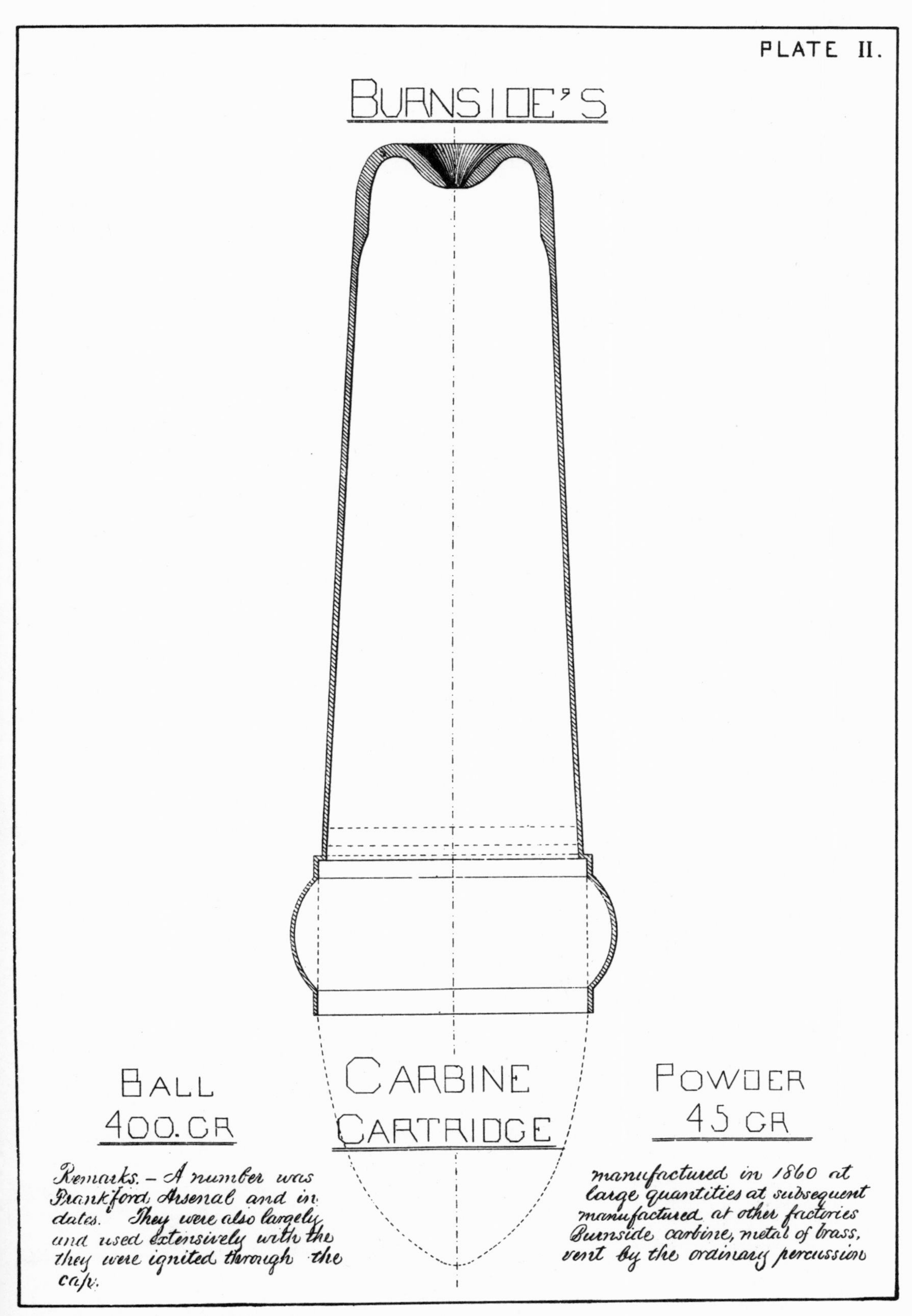

FIGURE 4-6 Burnside's carbine cartridge of 1860.

UNITED STATES PATENT OFFICE.

HORACE SMITH, OF NORWICH, AND DANIEL B. WESSON, OF NEW HAVEN, CONN., ASSIGNORS TO THE VOLCANIC REPEATING ARMS COMPANY.

IMPROVED PRIMERS FOR CARTRIDGES OF FIRE-ARMS.

Specification forming part of Letters Patent No. 14,147, *dated January* 22, 1856.

To all whom it may concern:

Be it known that we, HORACE SMITH, of Norwich, in the county of New London and State of Connecticut, and DANIEL B. WESSON, of New Haven, in the county of New Haven and State of Connecticut, have invented a new and useful Improvement in Primers for Fire-Arm Cartridges, of which the following is a full and exact description, reference being made to the annexed drawing, the same making part of this specification.

Figure 1 shows a side view of the primer, made in a cylindrical form with a convex projection at one end, composed of four materials, combined: First, copper or brass; second, iron or steel; third, cork or its equivalent; and, fourth, fulminating-powder.

Fig. 2 shows a section of the iron or steel disk, made in the form of a cross, with the arms bent upward sufficiently to allow them to bear firmly on the copper case which covers it. (See Fig. 4.) This disk has also an indentation, concave on the inside and in the center, forming a proper cavity for the fulminating-powder *x*, which is placed in it.

Fig. 3 shows a section of the cork, made cylindrical. This cork is placed in the disk upon the fulminating-powder *x*, serving to secure it in its position, and affording for it an elastic protection from any blow the primer may receive on its exterior surface. It also serves as a means for withdrawing the primer from the arm after it has been discharged.

Fig. 4 shows the copper case or covering, made in the form of a cylinder, with one end closed, except a small circular hole, *m*, Fig. 5, through the center.

Fig. 5 shows rear end of primer and disk. This primer is more particularly designed for a loaded ball, made solid, except a cavity, C, Fig. 7, which contains the powder and primer, both pressed into it by power, the primer closing the rear end water-tight and resting firmly on the powder.

Operation: The ball being placed in the arm, a blunt projecting piece is pressed through the cork until it bears on the fulminating-powder and disk. A smart blow from a hammer will then ignite the percussion, and by forcing the fire through the openings *a a a a*, Fig. 6, will explode the powder in the ball.

We do not claim the steel disk; nor placing the percussion-powder on it in the rear of the powder; nor the method of exploding the same, as a patent has already been granted to us for that; but

What we do claim as our invention, and desire to secure by Letters Patent, is—

The combination of a copper or brass case, an iron or steel disk, with cork or its equivalent, and fulminating-powder, substantially as herein set forth and specified.

HORACE SMITH.
DANIEL B. WESSON.

Witnesses for Horace Smith:
WM. C. HICKS,
HENRY B. HARRISON.

Witnesses for Daniel B. Wesson:
HENRY B. HARRISON,
WM. C. HICKS.

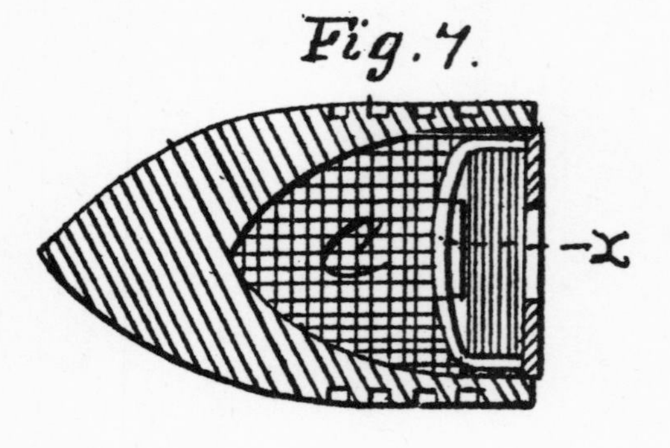

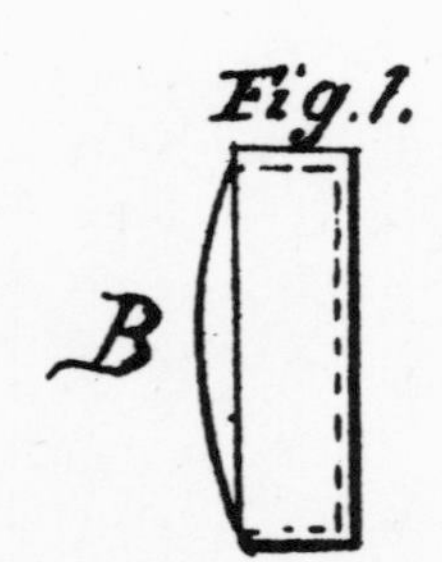

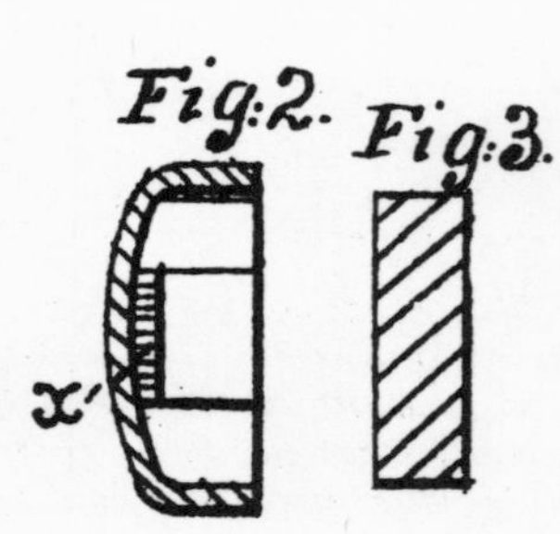

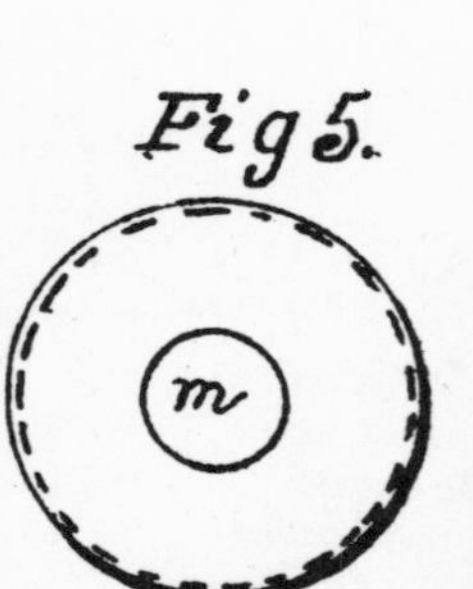

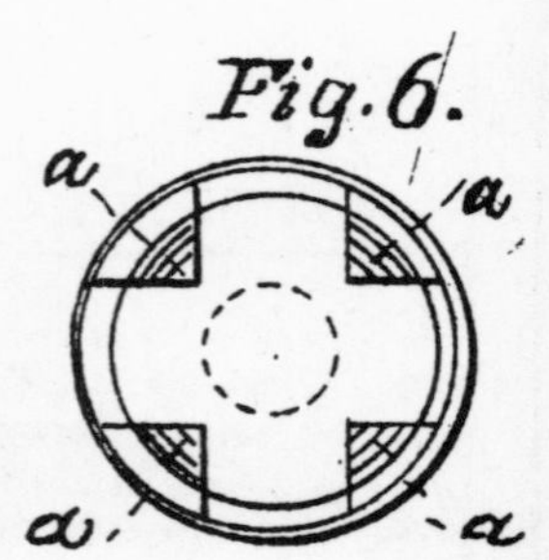

FIGURE 4-7 Smith and Wesson "Volcanic" ammunition patent.

has been calculated as a muzzle velocity of 980 feet per second and a moderate muzzle energy of 855 foot-pounds.[3]

Self-Primed Cartridges

The final step in the evolution of modern ammunition was placing the priming material within the cartridge assembly. This step eliminated the need for the soldier to place the percussion cap on the rifle for each shot or for a separate tape priming mechanism. There were many experiments before the best combination was achieved. One of the very significant experiments was a design by Horace Smith and Daniel Wesson. Smith and Wesson ultimately formed the pistol manufacturing company which bears their name. During the 1850's they worked for the Volcanic Repeating Arms Company in New Haven, Connecticut, which was a predecessor to the Winchester Repeating Arms Company. Smith and Wesson served as extremely important links in the chain for they took the ideas of Walter Hunt and developed his rocket ball cartridge into the Volcanic cartridge shown in Figure 4-7. The patent was dated 1856 and combined many elements into an ingenious assembly. In this illustration, prepared by the Winchester Photographic Laboratory, the illustration is about three times normal size and for clarity is placed immediately under the written description of the patent. The basic elements were a hollow lead bullet with a deep cavity similar to that of a Minié ball. The cavity "C" was packed with a compressed charge of black powder. An assembly of two copper cups was inserted. The front cup is shown in Fig. 6 and contained four arms. The pellet of priming material (X in Fig. 2) was placed within the copper cup. This was covered by a cork disc (Fig. 3). The whole assembly was then enclosed in the copper cup shown in Figs. 4 and 5. Then the assembly was pressed into the rear of the bullet.

The cartridges were loaded into a lever action repeating rifle or pistol mechanism which contained many elements of the Winchester Model 1866 rifle. The Volcanic bullets were contained in a tubular magazine below the barrel. They fed into a brass carrier and were raised by a lifter mechanism up to the center line of the barrel. As the breech bolt moved forward, it pushed the Volcanic bullet into the chamber. When the trigger was pulled the hammer drove a firing pin forward which penetrated through the opening in the copper cup and through the cork disc, and then crushed the fulminate compound against the iron cup. This ignited the fulminate which caused a flash of flame to go through the passages shown in Fig. 6 as a-a, in igniting the powder charge in the cavity C. The entire assembly was very ingenious and brought together in a compact package all the elements required for self-primed ammunition. There was, however, a very serious problem with the system — manufacturing techniques were not sufficiently advanced to provide an adequate seal at the breech of the rifle. As a result a large percentage of the gas leaked out the breech and the ballistic performance was poor. The sealing system used was a cylindrical seal only 1/10 of an inch long. With the very low powder charge that could be crammed into the hollow cavity in the bullet, the leakage was too high a percentage of the energy available and the exterior ballistics were unsatisfactory.

Smith and Wesson Cartridge

The road to successful ammunition was advanced by another invention of Horace Smith and Daniel Wesson shown in patent No. 11,496 issued in 1854. Those cartridges are significant in that all the elements required for successful ammunition were specified. The patent is shown in Figure 4-8. The right-hand figure shows a cross section through the cartridge. The assembly consisted of a thin cylindrical copper cartridge case with a slight flange at the base. Immediately inside the cartridge case was placed a pellet or priming material or fulminate, and this was held in position by a perforated disc or partition pressed down close to the head of the cartridge case. The space above this partition was filled with powder and then another partition was pressed into the cartridge case. The space above the second partion was filled with tallow or other lubricant and then a spherical lead ball d was pressed into the mouth of the cartridge case.

This important patent defined all the elements required in successful ammunition. When the cartridge was placed in a firearm the firing pin struck the cartridge case in the middle of the head, crushing the priming material against the perforated partition. The flame from the fulminate passed through the partition, igniting the powder and ejecting the lead bullet, lubricant, and the second partition from the muzzle of the rifle.

The experiments continued in the late 1850's and the final breakthrough in rimfire ammunition occurred in 1860. The experiments were tremendously competitive for Smith & Wesson was issued patent No. 27,933 April 17, 1860. This patent defined fulminate priming in the rim of the cartridge with a perforated base wad

[3] *Ibid.* P 157

UNITED STATES PATENT OFFICE.

HORACE SMITH AND DANIEL B. WESSON, OF NORWICH, CONNECTICUT.

IMPROVEMENT IN CARTRIDGES.

Specification forming part of Letters Patent No. 11,496, *dated August* 8, 1854.

To all whom it may concern:

Be it known that we, HORACE SMITH and DANIEL B. WESSON, of Norwich, in the county of New London and State of Connecticut, have invented a new or Improved Cartridge for Pistols, Rifles, or other Fire-Arms; and we do hereby declare that the same is fully described and represented in the following specification and the accompanying drawings, letters, figures, and references thereof.

Of the said drawings, Figure 1 denotes an external view, and Fig. 2 a longitudinal section, of our improved cartridge.

In Fig. 2, *a* represents the cylindrical case of the cartridge, which may be made of thin plate-copper or any other suitable material. It is formed with a partition, *b*, across it and near to the ball *d*, which is to be fixed in one end of the cartridge, such partition forming a chamber, *c*, between itself and the ball. Such chamber is to be filled with tallow or other equivalent. The powder is shown at *e* as placed in that part of the cartridge which is in rear of the partition *b*. A metallic perforated disk or plate, *f*, is placed on the powder after it has been suitably filled into the cartridge, and between such disk (which, however, may be made of any other material having a suitable degree of induration) and the closed end *h* of the cartridge the percussion-pellet or priming *g* is placed, it being made to rest against the disk. The end *h* should either be made very thin and yielding, or of some substance easily punctured by a blunt point or needle driven against it, and this for the purpose of causing priming to be inflamed either by the effect of a smart blow given on such end of the cartridge by the cock of a gun, or by a blunt needle driven smartly through the end of the cartridge and against the priming while the latter is resting on the seat-piece or disk *f*.

The tallow used with a cartridge has been generally placed on the outside of the ball, but never to our knowledge in a chamber within the cartridge.

Our improvement, therefore, and what we claim, is the arranging of the tallow within the cartridge and between the ball and charge of powder, or in a chamber, *c*, suitably made in rear of the ball of the cartridge, whereby the necessary amount of tallow for a discharge is preserved with the charge in a convenient and compact form.

We are aware that in the construction of a cartridge it has been customary to use in the same a metallic plate or disk carrying a capsule for containing the percussion-powder, and having the mouth of such capsule opening directly against the gunpowder in front of the said plate; we therefore do not claim such; but

What we do claim as our invention is—

The employment, in the cartridge, of the metallic or indurated disk or seat-plate, so that it shall rest directly on the powder, in combination with arranging the priming or percussion-powder in rear of said disk, or on that side of it opposite to that which rests against the powder, our said arrangement of the disk and priming affording an excellent opportunity for applying the force of the blow by which the priming is inflamed, such force being applied in the line of the axis of the cartridge.

In testimony whereof we have hereto set our signatures this 10th day of May, A. D. 1853.

HORACE SMITH. [L. S.]
DANIEL B. WESSON. [L. S.]

Witnesses:
C. D. RICE,
JOHN D. PARKE.

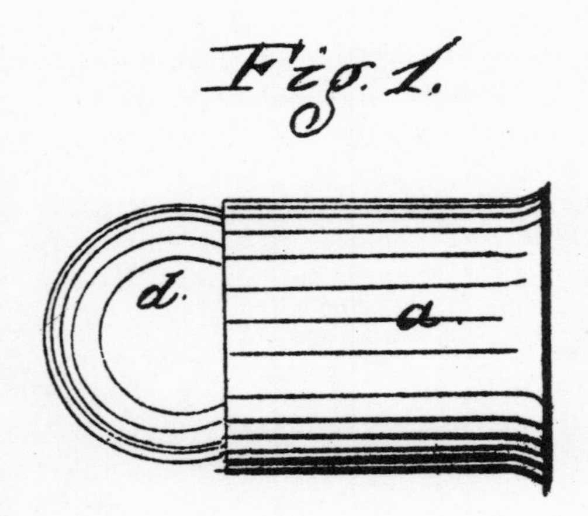

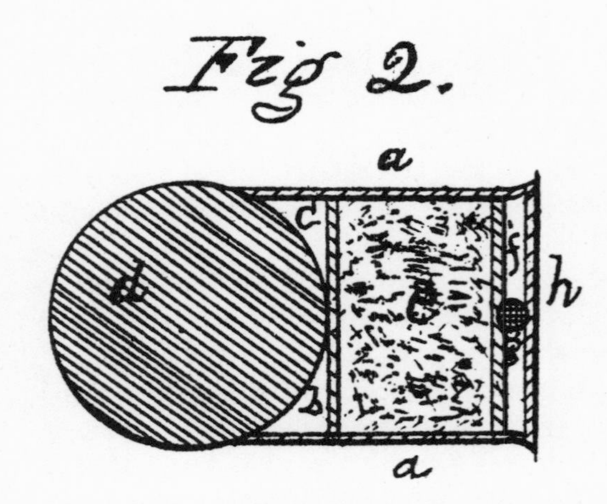

FIGURE 4-8 Smith and Wesson center-fire ammunition of 1865.

which held the priming material out in the rim but allowed the flame to pass into the powder cavity. By this time Smith & Wesson had left the Volcanic Arms Company, but the experiments in rimfire ammunition had continued at a furious pace under direction of B. Tyler Henry, the new Volcanic plant superintendent. Under the agreement between Smith & Wesson and Oliver Winchester, President of Volcanic, Henry was allowed to use the ammunition improvements developed by Smith & Wesson. Thus in the same year as the Smith and Wesson patent was issued the .44 Henry rimfire cartridge was developed, and the lever action Henry repeating rifle introduced. The Henry rifles and ammunition, important links between the Volcanic lever action rifle and the Winchester Model 1866, are discussed in Chapter 8. The Henry .44 caliber lever action rifles, and the Spencer .56 caliber lever action rifles were the only successful repeating rifles used in the Civil War.

The pace of development was such that Christian Sharps procured patent No. 29,108 on July 10, 1860, for a slightly different design of rimfire cartridge in which the priming material was held out into the rim by a shallow copper cup pressed in from the mouth of the cartridge case.

Spencer Rimfire Cartridge

There is no doubt that the most popular rimfire cartridge of the Civil War was the Spencer, shown in Figure 4-9. This illustration is from the Ordnance Memorandum No. 14 published in 1873 and shows the configuration of the Spencer cartridge as loaded by Frankford Arsenal in 1864 and 1865. The fulminate priming compound was contained in the small pocket formed within the rim. The rim was .647 of an inch in diameter so there was a relatively large area for the gas pressure to act upon, tending to expand the rim and fracture the material. With the cartridge-making machinery and materials available in the early 1860's it was not practical to make the cartridge case out of brass and the powder charge had to be held to 40 grains so as not to exceed the pressure which the relatively weak case could stand.

The standard cartridge for the .58 caliber muzzle-loading rifle had a 60-grain powder charge and a 520-grain bullet. The Sharps rifles used a 450- or 475-grain bullet with a 60-grain powder charge for the rifle and a 50-grain powder charge for the carbine. With the Spencer cartridges for both rifle and carbine limited to a 40-grain powder charge, the muzzle velocity of the bullet was pretty low. The ballistics have been calculated in Figure 4-2 using a predictive computer program which takes seven factors into account. The Spencer had slightly higher efficiency than the externally primed cartridges since the Spencer design insured that all the powder gases were sealed at the breech by the cartridge case. The ballistics calculate out to a muzzle velocity of 960 feet per second and a muzzle energy of 921 foot-pounds. Despite the ballistic limitations, the Spencer was generally considered the best breech-loading repeating rifle of the Civil War. A total of 94,196 Spencer carbines were purchased and 12,471 rifles. A total of 58,238,924 rounds of Spencer rimfire ammunition was purchased making Spencer the most popular metallic ammunition of the Civil War.[4]

The Spencer carbine and ammunition provided a tremendous increase in firepower for the Northern Cavalry. Imagine yourself a veteran cavalryman who had been armed with a muzzle-loading carbine in the Army of 1860 and who, as an elite trooper, had received one of the "newfangled" Sharps carbines in 1862. Now as you ride into a skirmish with your new Spencer the problem of reloading is greatly simplified. The only operations required are to cock the hammer and swing down the finger lever opening the breech, and then slam the finger lever shut again. These motions carry a cartridge from the tubular magazine in the butt stock into the chamber of the carbine which was then ready to fire. Every seven shots the magazine tube had to be removed and seven fresh cartridges dropped into the butt stock and the magazine tube replaced. The Spencer represented a tremendous increase in firepower since the Northern Cavalry could empty a magazine in about the same time it took their Southern foe to get off two shots with his muzzle-loader. It is no wonder that the Southerners referred to the Spencer as "the damn Yankee rifle which you load on Sunday and fire all week."

Late in the war a still further improvement was made consisting of a cartridge box containing preloaded tubes with seven cartridges each. With this arrangement the cavalryman did not even have to fumble with individual cartridges but in one motion could slide a fresh magazine load into the butt of the rifle.

The Spencer represented an outstanding solution to the needs of the Cavalry and late in the war a number of infantry units were being re-equipped with this vastly improved rifle. Yet, by 1870 the Spencers were being discarded in favor of a .50/70 caliber single-shot Springfield carbine. The Spencer was so ideally suited to the needs of the frontier garrisons of the

[4] *Ibid.* P 157

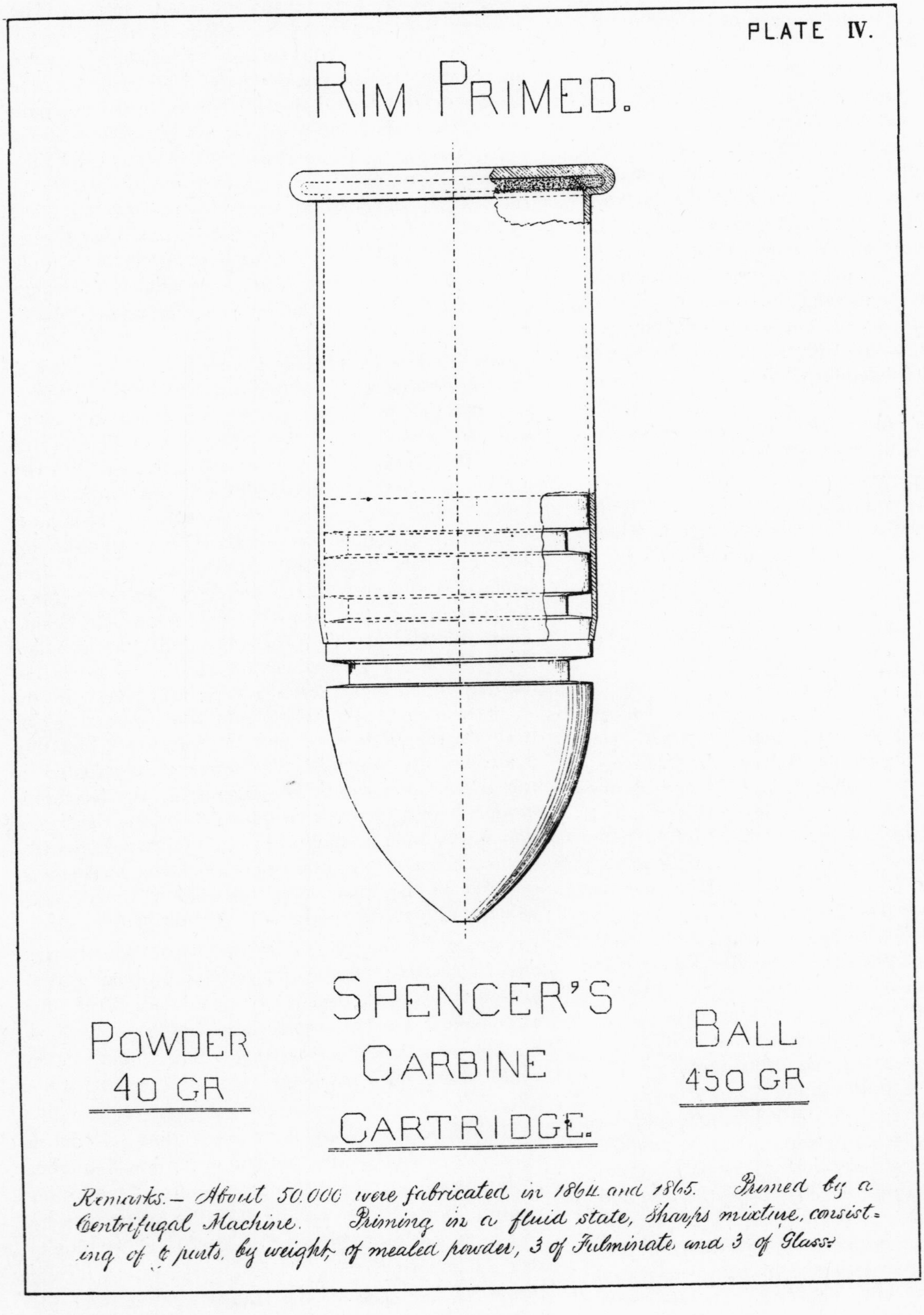

PLATE IV.

RIM PRIMED.

SPENCER'S CARBINE CARTRIDGE.

POWDER 40 GR

BALL 450 GR

Remarks.— About 50.000 were fabricated in 1864 and 1865. Primed by a Centrifugal Machine. Priming in a fluid state, Sharps mixture, consisting of 6 parts, by weight, of mealed powder, 3 of Fulminate and 3 of Glass.

FIGURE 4-9 Spencer's .56/.56 Civil War rim-fire cartridge.

Western outposts that it is very hard to understand why it was dumped in favor of a much slower firing single-shot Springfield.

Apparently the Cavalry fought hard to retain their Spencer carbines and were successful through the late 1860's. Even the report of the Chief of Ordance in 1872 notes the issuance of 180 Spencer carbines and 339,000 rounds of Spencer ammunition to the regular Army and to frontier posts during the previous year.

Rimfire cartridges were becoming tremendously popular in commercial firearms such as the Winchester Model 1866 and had been adopted by the Swiss Army for their .41 caliber Vetterli rifle. The United States Army was definitely turning sour on rimfire cartridges, and the reasons are contained in Ordnance Memorandum No. 14 published in 1873:

> For some time the idea of combining the primer and cartridge did not assert itself, but some inventions were pushed in this direction, and the rim-primed cartridge case was produced. In this the fulminate composition was placed in the folded head of the case. This mode of priming requires a large charge of the priming composition, which, being thrown into the fold by swiveling, the entire circumference of the head was not always primed thoroughly, and as the cartridge is exploded by striking the rim at a part of the head under the hammer, it not infrequently happened that it failed from the point struck not having any priming. The large charge required (about 5 grains against ½ grain for the center-fire), was a further objection to rim priming. The exploding of so large a quantity of quick powder (priming) in the folded-head, the weak part of the cartridge, tended to strain and open the fold to bursting as it frequently did. Another objection to rim-primed cartridges is that they are more liable to accident in handling, and in shocks of transportation, and those incident to service.

Experiments had been performed at Springfield Armory to develop improved types of Spencer ammunition which would give higher muzzle velocities. Late in the Civil War, Springfield developed a .56/.50 caliber cartridge for the Spencer in which the bullet weight had been reduced to 350 grains and the powder charge increased to 45 grains. While this gave improved performance, it was not sufficient to justify rebarreling all the Spencer rifles and carbines to the new cartridge.

Springfield Armory also experimented with a .58 caliber rimfire cartridge for use in the first trapdoor Springfield rifle (the Model 1865). The .58 rimfire cartridge fired a 500-grain bullet with a 60-grain powder charge. The ballistics of this cartridge have been calculated by the author as a muzzle velocity of 1040 feet per second and a muzzle energy of 1200 foot-pounds. This cartridge was in service only a short time and specimens are quite rare.

In 1866 new .50 caliber rimfire and center-fire cartridges were designed to hold 70 grains of powder and a 450-grain bullet. Even at this early date great pressure was put on Springfield Armory and Frankford Arsenal to adopt a center-fire cartridge design. The result was the selection of the .50/70/450 center-fire cartridge.

Rimfire cartridges were successful in the .56 Spencer rifles, and .44 caliber Henry rifles used in the Civil War and were very successful on a commercial market in the decades following the war. The great majority of cartridges made and sold during the 1870's were rimfire designs. Many of the commercial cartridges were similar to the .44 Henry rimfire cartridge adopted to the Henry rifle and later to the Winchester Model 1866. The ballistics of this cartridge are shown in Figure 4-2. It was a much smaller cartridge than the Spencer, with a 200-grain bullet and a 28-grain powder charge. The efficiency was very similar at 20.3 foot-pounds of muzzle energy per grain of propellant, which provided a muzzle velocity of 1125 feet per second and a muzzle energy of 568 foot-pounds. This was a relatively high muzzle velocity for its day, and the cartridge was lightweight and fairly inexpensive. Accuracy was good and the 200-grain soft lead bullet provided excellent stopping power at the short- to medium-hunting ranges of that day. The effectiveness of the Henry and Model 1866 rifles in the hands of frontiersmen hunting dangerous game or resisting Indian attacks attest to the reliability of the early rimfire rifles and ammunition.

Experiments with Center-Fire Ammunition

The late 1860's saw intensive experimentation at Springfield and Frankford Arsenals. The results of the ammunition experiments were published as Ordnance Memorandum No. 14 dated 1873 and written by Major T. J. Treadwell, commanding Frankford Arsenal. Major Treadwell's comments on the deficiencies of rimfire ammunition were quoted above. The objectives Frankford pursued in studying center-fire cartridges give a picture of the official thinking at that time:

> Hence, efforts to produce still more reliable and satisfactory cartridges, and the development, production, and general adoption for service of what is now so well known as *center-primed metallic ammunition,* its advantages being sure explosion when

struck by the point of the firing-pin; less of fulminate and less strain on the head of the cartridge; greater security in handling and using under all exigencies of service. These cartridges have been subjected to the severest tests, to determine their capability to resist all accidents such as mashing up boxes of ammunition, and even firing into them with bullets. Only the cartridges actually impinged upon exploded under such tests, their neighbors being only blackened and not otherwise damaged. The safety of handling and transporting this ammunition and comparison with that of the old fashioned kind is vastly in its favor, and the risk attending its carriage is almost nothing. Its greatly superior quality to resist exposure of climate, moisture, etc. has also been proven by such severe tests that it may be asserted to be practically waterproof. A central and direct blow on the point primed is an essential and highly important feature of the center primed cartridge; its general adoption, and the adoption of all breech loading service small-arms to its use is the best proof of its acknowledged superiority.

There were literally hundreds of center-fire ammunition assemblies designed and experimented with by private inventors and at the national arsenals in the United States and Europe. This is discouraging to the modern inventor, for when he rushes up to a manufacturer with a "new" idea in ammunition on which he has lavished much time and care it is usually found that his concept and many close variations are already cited in the patent literature from the great period of ferment in the 1860's and 1870's.

The experiments at Frankford Arsenal in 1864 and 1865 started with conventional rimfire cartridges without priming. A flat plate was stamped out which had an anvil at one end. A conventional percussion cap was placed over this anvil and the plate slid into the copper cartridge case forming a longitudinal partition in the case. After the powder was charged the bullet was pushed into the case and crimped in, holding the center-line partition firmly up against the head of the cartridge case. When the firing pin struck the head of the copper case in the center the copper was driven in, deforming the percussion cap against the anvil and igniting the cartridge.

Other experiments used a shortened center partition which was retained by crimping the sides of the cartridge case inward into detents in the center-line partition.

Other experiments included dimpling the cartridge case head outward at the center, thus forming a pocket into which priming could be poured from the inside. The priming was then retained by perforated plates pushed in from the mouth of the cartridge case, forming an inner partition to retain the priming just like that shown in the Smith & Wesson patent in Figure 4-8.

The ideas built on each other in a freewheeling, creative kind of way. One of the Frankford Arsenal ideas is shown in Figure 4-10. Here only the top portion of the center-line partition has been cut off, forming an anvil for the primer. This has been slid inside the slightly modified percussion cap and this assembly in turn has been press-fitted into a "blank punched out like a star and then formed into a cup holding the anvil and percussion cap." Thus the primer consists of modified percussion cap, containing the fulminate priming compound, and an anvil. These parts were pressed into the cup which had the four "wings". The wings were bent forward at about a 45-degree angle so that the distance across the wings was less than the inside diameter of the cartridge case. As this assembly was press-fitted into a conventional rimfire case, the wings struck the head of the case and, as the assembly was pushed farther toward the rim, they spread out and locked in place within the rim cavity. Fifty such cartridges were made up and fired without failure.

This design was developed by Colonel S. V. Benét, commanding Frankford Arsenal in 1865. When this cartridge was fired the firing pin had to indent the flat head of the cartridge case plus the thin material forming the primer pocket and crush the fulminate material against the anvil. Advantages to the design were the excellent seal of the head of the case. The disadvantages were the lack of sensitivity due to the double thickness of material to be deformed by the firing pin plus a tendency for the inner cup held by its four arms to deflect away from the firing pin blow.

The short step from this experimental ammunition to the primer construction which in use today is shown in Figure 4-11. This ammunition is titled Benét's center primed experimental Frankford Arsenal ammunition. The design of this ammunition is generally credited to Colonel Hiram Berdan of Civil War Berdan's Sharpshooters fame. There is an annoyed note at the bottom of Figure 4-11, stating:

> The principal feature of this cartridge is the forming of the pocket of one continuous piece of metal. It is believed to have been invented and successfully carried out at the Frankford Arsenal by Colonel S. V. Benét, Commanding in 1866. It is now one of the principle features of Berdan's cartridge, he having come to the Arsenal and obtained the necessary information taking with him samples and sizes of tools and afterwards applying it to his cartridges, which previously had a separate cup inserted at the head.

Whether or not the statement is accurate, the idea of a separate primer assembly pressed into a pocket formed in the head of the cartridge case is the basic principle

PLATE VI.

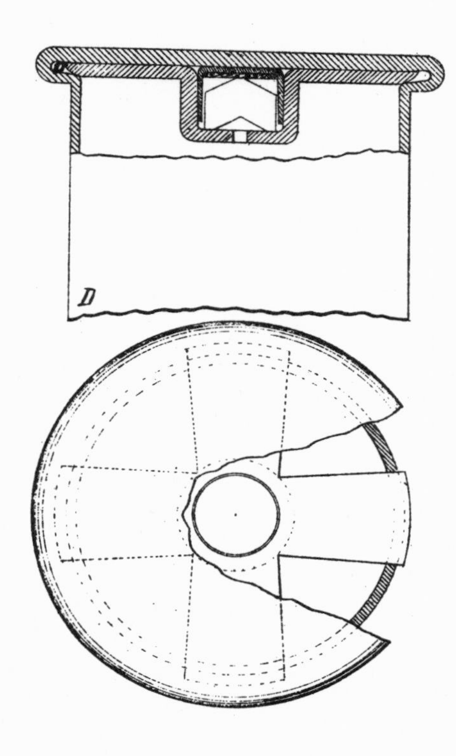

Previous to the year 1866 experience in the manufacture of metallic cartridges at this Arsenal was limited to making a few of the Morse, Burnsides, Maynards and rim-fire cartridges for experimental purposes. In the early part of 1864, Col. Laidley comdg., special machinery, (Draw Presses) was introduced preparatory to making cartridges. In 1865, Col. Benét comdg., a few experimental "Gatling" 1 in. calibre rim-fire cartridges were made to test the Gatling Gun. In 1866, it being evident that the rim-fire would be superseded by centre-fire, considerable attention was given to the production of a reliable centre-fire cartridge. Samples of the first attempts to make centre-fire cartridges are shown at A, B, C, D; the case at C has a small cap containing the composition set on the bottom of case without anvil and has the metal pressed over on the cap to hold it in place; it was difficult to make a gas check with it. The case at D was an attempt to make an inside primer by a blank punched out like a star and then formed into a cup holding the anvil and cap with wings which were forced into place by stretching out the wings and securing them in the flange at O. 50 were fired without failure.

FIGURE 4-10 Col. Benet's experimental center-fire ammunition of 1865.

PLATE XVI.

CENTRE BENET'S. PRIMED.

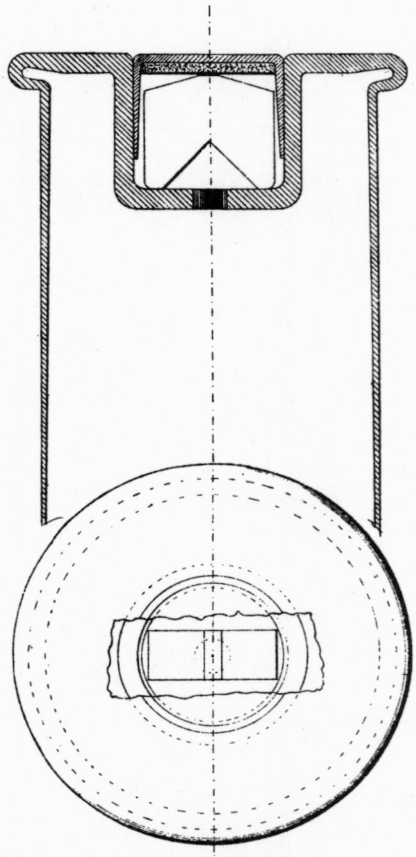

EXPERIMENTAL.

FRANKFORD ARSENAL

JAN 1866 APR

Remarks.

The principal feature of this cartridge is the forming of the pocket of one continuous piece of metal. It is believed to have been invented and successfully carried out at the Frankford Arsenal by Col. S. V. Benét, comdg. in 1866. It is now one of the principal features of Berdans Cartridge, he having come to the Arsenal and obtained the necessary information, taking with him samples & sizes of tools and afterwards applying it to his cartridge, which previously had a separate cup inserted at the head.

FIGURE 4-11 Col. Benet's experimental center-fire ammunition of 1866.

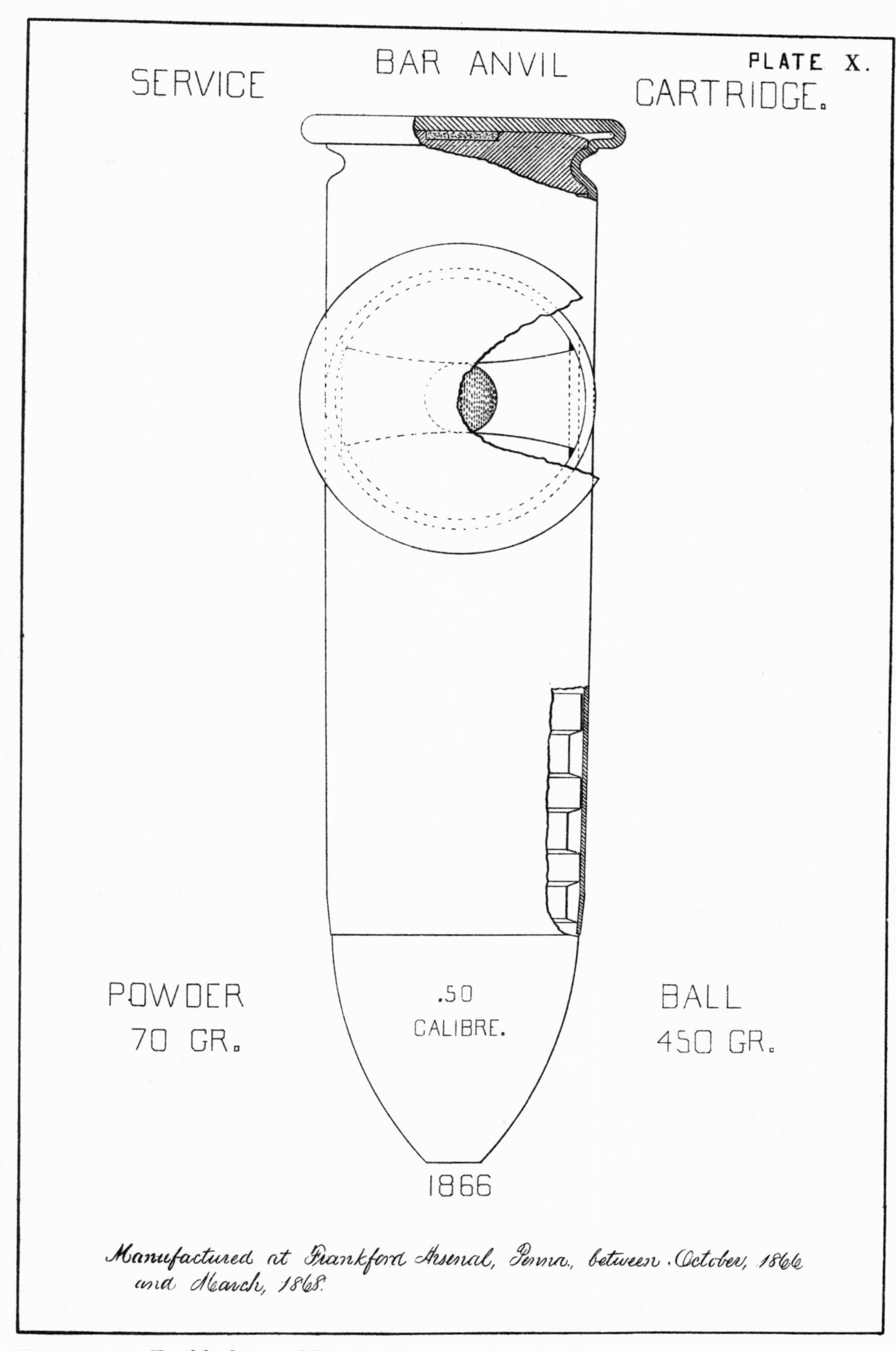

FIGURE 4-12 Frankford Arsenal "Bar Anvil" ammunition of 1866.

used on United States center fire ammunition for the past 90 years.

There were many other experiments with ammunition designs during the late 1860's and early 1870's. The preferred design from 1866 to 1868 is shown in Figure 4-12. The design shown was the .50/70/450 cartridge. In this design the cavity was formed in a bar of metal. Priming compound was placed into the cavity and the assembly was then pressed into the cartridge case from the mouth up to the head. The bar anvil was held in place by detents which were swaged in just forward of the rim during assembly. The cartridge was loaded with powder and a 450-grain "inside lubricated lead bullet" pressed into the mouth of the case. The bullet is shown in partial section in Figure 4-12. It had three grooves swaged into the cylindrical section of the bullet which were filled with grease prior to assembly into the cartridge. The bullet was retained in the cartridge by swaging, which can be seen as a slight conical shape toward the mouth of the case. A close examination of this illustration shows the intermixing of ideas of the previous decade. The priming concept is somewhat similar to the Smith & Wesson patent of 1854 in which the fulminate compound is shown as a ball between the head of the cartridge case and an internal partition. This design is a much improved concept with the fulminate being placed in a cavity in the center of the bar and the bar being clearly retained in place by crimping grooves swaged into the case just forward of the rim. The relationship of this design to that experimental design shown in Figure 4-10 is also close.

The designs further evolved into "Benét's cup anvil" which became the standard service cartridge in 1868. This design is illustrated in this book in Figure 4-13 in .50/70/450 configuration. The bar anvil has been replaced by a cup of copper. The head of the cup has been dimpled to provide a recess for the priming compound and two holes have been punched through the cup to allow the flame to reach the powder. Priming compound was placed into the cup which was then pressed into the cartridge from the mouth. When the cup anvil was firmly seated on the cartridge head, two grooves were swaged into the cartridge case to retain the anvil solidly against the cartridge head.

This became a very popular type of cartridge, widely used in the 1870's and 1880's. They may easily be identified on cartridge boards and in cartridge collections for they look like rimfire cartridges except for the two swaged sections just forward of the rim. They became the Service cartridge in 1868 and remained the standard design well into the 1870's. They proved to be sturdy serviceable rounds of ammunition and were relatively economical and easy to manufacture. The major disadvantage of this ammunition was that it could not be reloaded and the design was limited to relatively weak copper for the case material. These problems are discussed in Ordnance Memorandum No. 14 as follows:

> The copper cartridge case, from its expansion and comparatively small elasticity, does not return to its shape after firing, and could not be used as a reloader without reduction.
>
> The brass case expands sufficiently to act as a perfect gas check, and by its superior elasticity regains sufficiently its shape to be used as a reloader without reducing, if properly made. For the same reason the brass extracts more easily than the copper. The wrapped-metal case (Martini-Henry style) expands by unfolding, and from its somewhat yielding nature extracts easily and can also be reloaded and used without reduction.
>
> All experience shows that the fulminate composition for priming should not be in contact with any easily corroding metal, or so deposited in the primer or in assembling the parts as to render any galvanic action possible for its deterioration and eventual destruction.
>
> It is not believed that the service fulminate composition for priming in contact with pure copper undergoes any such deleterious change, as our percussion caps of 20 years ago are now prompt and perfectly reliable. It (the priming) should not be in immediate contact with brass, however, where brass is used in construction.

The fact that copper cartridge cases were relatively weak and that the 19th century priming composition attacked brass made it very important that the priming be contained in a separate priming container. Collectors of old cartridges are well aware that most center-fire brass cartridges of the 19th century and early 20th century had copper primers. The priming compositions of the late 1860's were of two formulations:

1. 35 parts fulminate of mercury, 15 chlorate of potash, 45 glass-dust, 4 gummed water.
2. 35 parts fulminate of mercury, 15 niter (saltpeter), 45 glass-dust, 4 gummed water.

Copper as a cartridge case material was weak but it provided many advantages. One of the weird and wonderful center-fire cartridge designs which took advantage of the extreme malleability of copper is the Martin primer shown in Figure 4-14. The fact that copper could survive this kind of treatment is a tribute to its ductile nature. Starting at the upper left a deep drawn cup of soft copper is placed in the die. An upper punch comes down forming a recess in the head and in the top right illustration this punch has bottomed forming a deep cavity and driving the folded loop of copper outward to form a rim. In the second row of illustrations the cartridge case has been placed in a second series of dies which contained a fixed punch on the

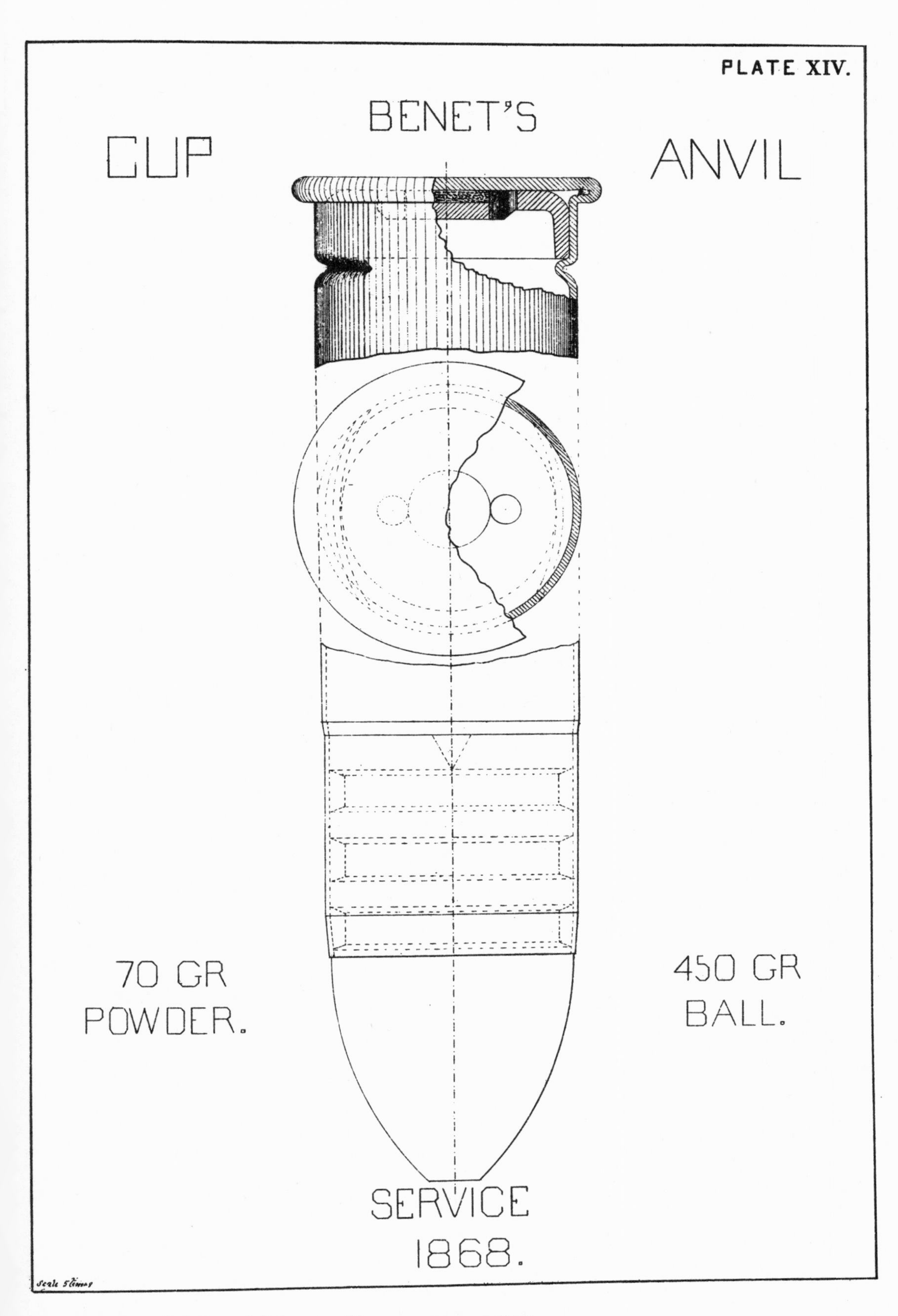

FIGURE 4-13 Col. Benet's "Cup Anvil" ammunition of 1868.

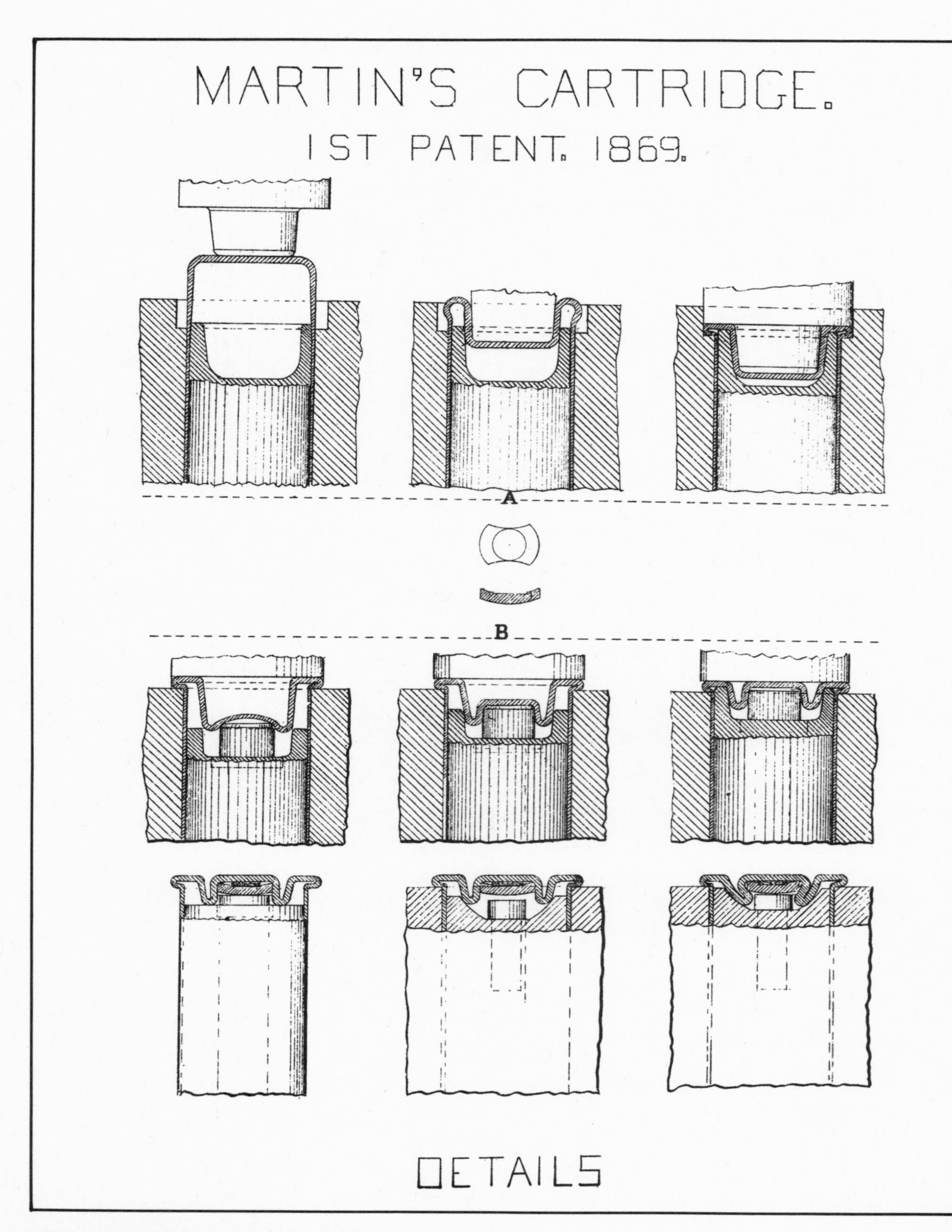

FIGURE 4-14 Martin center-fire cartridge construction of 1869.

upper surface and a movable lower punch which drove upward to form an inner recess within the cartridge head. In the lowest left illustration a primer sub-assembly consisting of a dished cup with a fulminate pellet inside has been pressed into place by a third set of dies. The cartridge case was then placed in a fourth series of dies shown in the lowest center illustration and as these dies were closed the walls of the cylindrical cavity were driven inward to retain the dished primer cup. Believe it or not, this cartridge became a very popular design and the cartridges are commonly found in early cartridge collections.

The Smithsonian Institution in Washington has a cartridge board on display made by the Union Metallic Cartridge Company in 1875 and this clearly shows "Martin's Patent Central Fire" U.S. Government cartridge .50/70. It may be hard to identify a Martin's center-fire cartridge for it looks like a standard center-fire cartridge with a large gap between the primer and the primer pocket. Ordance Memorandum No. 14 describes tests and development of the Martin cartridge in the 1870's, and shows pressure tests in which the cartridge case has fractured at the underside of the rim, or at the edge of the rim. Surprisingly few failures occurred at the primer folds despite extreme working of the material during the manufacturing process.

Another unusual cartridge design was the Boxer-Henry cartridge shown in Figure 4-15. The cartridge assembly consisted of a "thin metal wrapped cartridge case made with cages not united, in combination with an internal or external strengthening disc or cup made of paper, metal, or elastic material." The fact that it would work for a powerful center-fire cartridge is a miracle. The general process used for constructing this cartridge case was very similar to that of making the early paper cartridges for muzzle-loading muskets. A sheet of thin brass was cut in a trapezoidal shape and rolled up into a cylinder. This meant that there were more thicknesses of brass at the base than at the mouth of the case. The brass cylinder was then placed in a press which formed the brass inward at the more heavily wrapped end to form a bottom or cup to the case. Other components were assembled, including a stamped disk or flange which served as a rim of the case, reinforcing copper or brass cups for the base, and an internal thick washer made of cardboard or fiber with a large hole punched in the center. This weird and wonderful assembly was held together by a copper primer cup very similar to the battery cup primer used on modern shotshells. The primer cup was forced through the center of the cartridge rim and expanded on the inside to lock the entire head assembly together.

A process was even developed to place this fragile assembly into another press and to neck down the front of the cartridge case from .577 caliber to .45 caliber. This cartridge became known as the .577/.450 Martini-Henry cartridge since it was basically a .577 caliber cartridge but was necked down to hold a .45 caliber bullet. These are the most disreputable looking cartridges imaginable. The area where the cartridge is necked down is covered with wrinkles and the whole cartridge looks as if it would fall apart if dropped on the floor. The reason it works is because of the extreme resiliency of the thin brass sheet. When the cartridge is fired the case expands against the walls of the chamber and obdurates the powder gases very well. Cartridges can be made cheaply with low cost materials and relatively crude machinery. This cartridge became the standard throughout the British Empire in the 1870's and 1880's and remained a secondary standard well into the 20th century. The cartridge is still manufactured in large quantities today for sale to the former colonies of the British Empire in Africa and India. It provides a low cost and reliable cartridge even though a mediocre performer by modern standards.

Berdan Cartridge Design

Another cartridge design which became popular is shown in Figure 4-16. The cartridge was made by extensively working a sheet of brass. The cartridge head was formed by drawing and then swaging the brass cup to form a hollow rim. The center of the head of the case was formed inward to provide a primer pocket. The center of the primer pocket was bumped by a conical punch running in from the mouth of the cartridge case which formed an anvil in the bottom of the primer pocket. Two flash holes c-c were punched through the bottom of the primer pocket. A primer assembly consisting of a shallow copper cup (b) was charged with fulminate priming compound and pressed into the primer pocket.

This particular patent by Berdan relates to a re-inforcement to the head of the cartridge case consisting of a second brass cup (d) which is pushed in from the mouth of the cartridge case and serves to reinforce the inside surface of the head against the gas pressure. The cartridge case was then slightly swaged down with the neck being shown as (a) in the patent illustration. The patent defined the use of a paper patched bullet made of "bank note paper" which was cut into a trapezoidal shape and rolled around the bullet to form a lubricating shield between the lead and the steel of the barrel. Note that the bullet has no grease grooves swaged into the cylindrical part of the bullet. The paper patched bullet was

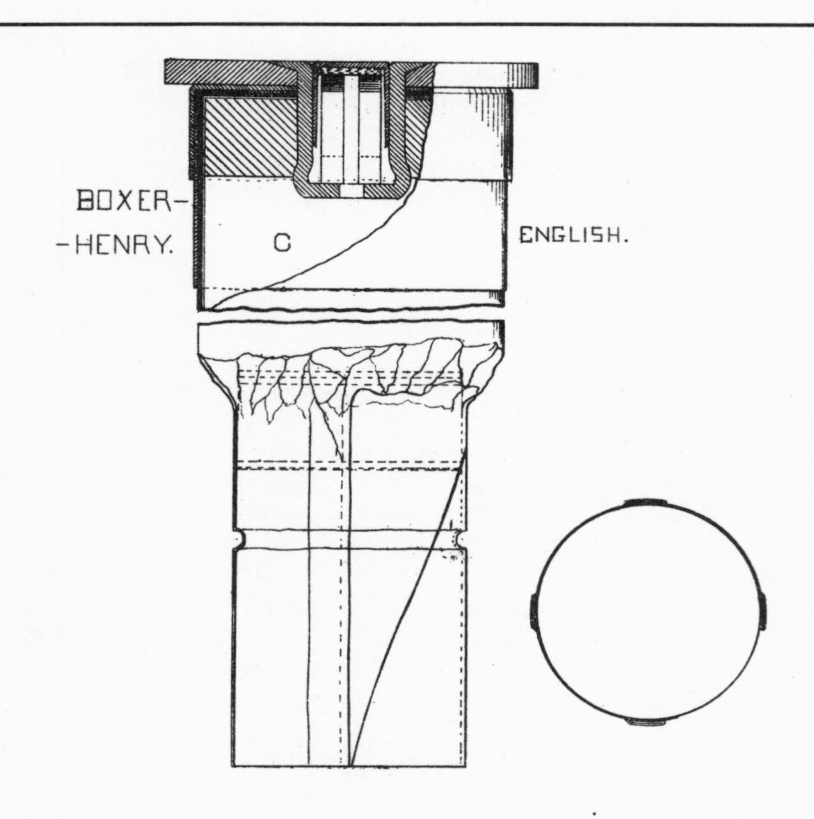

The late Gen'l. Rodman and Col. Crispin, Ord. Dep'nt. patented a wrapped metal cartridge in 1863, No. 40.988, Pat. Off. Report of 1863. Claim.—The thin metal wrapped cartridge case made with edges not united, in combination with an internal or external strengthening disc or cup, made of paper, metal or elastic material, substantially as set forth. The case, Fig. A, is made on the above plan; blank forms, Fig. B, cut from strips of sheet metal made of required width and about .005 to .006 in thickness or less are wrapped by hand on formers; the end is folded over on the former to hold the case to the base; a paper washer is used in connection with a rivet priming cup and metal flange or head; a strengthening cup O prevents the unfolding of the metal and the cutting through at the extractor seat in firing.

The advantages claimed for the above case are strength of base, ease of extraction and cost.

In the manufacture of about 12.000 in January and February, 1872, Col. Treadwell dispensed with the paper washer, iron head and rivet cup, substituting a strengthening cup with a folded head and priming pocket made from continuous metal fastened to the case by solder. It is not proof against dampness; a number were packed in varnished paper boxes (service) and put into a damp cave for six months and were found to have lost about ten per cent. initial velocity. A number of experiments have been made with these cartridges variously made, and with good results, and a considerable number issued for test in service and climate exposure.

A large number like those described, Fig. A, were made by Leet of Springfield, Mass. during the Franco-Prussian war. The case, Fig. C, is the celebrated English service Boxer-Henry cartridge case, made precisely on the same principle as the Rodman & Crispin, differing only in having two strengthening cups and anvils instead of one and a strip of tin about (a copper strip has been substituted for this) 7 in. wide enclosed in the case below the first cup, as if for additional strength; the case is .65 in. diameter and reduced for a .45 calibre ball on end by folding in and lapping the metal. A groove is made in the ball to secure it to the case. The cartridge has a rough and ungainly exterior and seems to be the product of unskilled mechanism, costing however in England (See Report of Committee on Breech Loading Rifles, testimony of Col. Boxer, page 82,) 4£. 7s. 5d. per 1000 rounds. Considering the difference in price of labor and material in England as compared with the United States it would cost here about 40 dollars per 1000, whereas a plain folded reinforced head made from drawn metal can be produced by the modern appliances for a much less sum and it is believed to be a more reliable cartridge in all respects.

FIGURE 4-15 English Boxer—Henry "Built Up" cartridge construction.

UNITED STATES PATENT OFFICE.

HIRAM BERDAN, OF NEW YORK, N. Y., ASSIGNOR TO THE BERDAN FIRE-ARMS MANUFACTURING COMPANY, OF SAME PLACE.

IMPROVEMENT IN METALLIC CARTRIDGES.

Specification forming part of Letters Patent No. 82,587, dated September 29, 1868; reissue No. 4,491, dated August 1, 1871.

To all whom it may concern:

Be it known that I, HIRAM BERDAN, of New York, in the county of New York and State of New York, have invented certain new and useful Improvements in Cartridges; and I do hereby declare that the following is a full, clear, and exact description thereof, reference being had to the accompanying drawing making part of this specification and to the letters of reference marked thereon, like letters indicating like parts wherever they occur.

To enable others skilled in the art to construct and use my invention, I will proceed to describe it.

My invention relates to metallic cartridges; and it consists in combining in a cartridge certain features whereby a better and more efficient cartridge is produced than has heretofore been made, as hereinafter more fully explained.

Figure 1 is a side view on an enlarged scale of my improved cartridge; Fig. 2, a longitudinal section of the same; and Fig. 3 is a plan of the patch before it is applied.

The object of my invention is to produce a superior cartridge for military arms, one which shall fulfill all the required conditions to a greater degree than any heretofore produced. In cartridges of this kind the following conditions are to be complied with: First, the ball must have great range, with a flat trajectory, and to obtain this it must have a large propelling charge. To withstand the explosive effect of this heavy charge the head of the shell must be made unusually strong. Second, in order to reduce the resistance of the atmosphere to the passage through it of the bullet it is necessary to reduce the diameter of the latter; and in order to retain its momentum it is necessary that the weight of the bullet shall not be lessened. To do this I make the bullet of less diameter, but of greater length, it being preferably two and a half or three diameters long. Third, as this elongated bullet will have a long bearing on the walls of the barrel it is necessary that it shall be patched in such a manner as to prevent leading, and at the same time pass through the barrel with the minimum of friction consistent with the insuring of its rotation; and, fourth, the body of the shell must be made of some material that will admit of the insertion of the patched bullet without bulging or misshaping the shell, and which shall, at the same time, hold the bullet firmly and accurately in place.

To make a cartridge which shall comply with these requirements I proceed as follows: In the first place I select a good quality of sheet-brass, from which I draw the shell by means of dies and punches in the usual manner. This material forms a shell that is more springy or elastic than the copper heretofore and generally used, and, being stronger and not so easily set, it permits the patched bullet to be shoved in with sufficient force to retain it securely in place and, at the same time, not bulge or swell out the front portion of the cartridge. I then form the head of the shell as represented in Fig. 2, by which a recess is produced on its exterior, with a point therein to act as an anvil for exploding a cap applied exteriorily—this feature being more fully described in a previous patent granted to me. I then form a cup, B, which has a hole at its center of such a size as to fit over or around the inwardly-projecting part of the head of the shell, this cup being inserted at the mouth or open end of the shell and pressed firmly down upon the base, as shown in Fig. 2. I then compress the front end of the shell A to a diameter corresponding with that of the bullet B, the compression extending back as far as the bullet is to be inserted, and as indicated between the letters *a i*, Fig. 2. I then make a bullet, which is of the form represented in Fig. 2, the same being from two and a half to three diameters in length. I next prepare a patch by cutting sheets of tough thin paper—bank-note paper being preferred—into strips of the form represented in Fig. 3. These strips I apply to the bullet by first moistening the paper and then rolling it smoothly and snugly around the bullet so as to cover the latter for nearly its entire length, and fold or twist its rear portion down over the rear end of the bullet, the end being secured by a little paste, if desired. This patch C should be of such a length as to make one or more complete turns around the bullet so as to envelop the latter on all sides with a uniform thickness, and thus insure its being perfectly centered in the bore of the gun when inserted therein. After the patch has dried, by which means the paper is contracted and made to fit the bullet smoothly and snugly, I then insert this patched bullet securely into the front end of the shell A, taking care to insert it far enough to hold it true and firmly in place, the shell, of course, having been previously filled with powder. A cap, *b*, is then applied to rear end of the shell, as shown in Fig. 2, and the cartridge is complete.

It is obvious that in case it be desired to make this style of cartridge of a smaller size for use in pistols or other smaller arms, then the cup B may be omitted; and it is also obvious that the brass shell and patched bullet may be used with the fulminate arranged within the shell; but in such case the shell cannot be refired, which I consider a great object, because in case of necessity, where, for instance, a new supply cannot be readily obtained, these shells can be reloaded and used many times over. By this method of constructing a cartridge I am enabled to produce an article much superior to anything of its kind heretofore known. The paper patch is the only thing that can be relied upon to adhere to the bullet and pass with it through the bore of the gun, and thus prevent leading. A cartridge made on this plan has sufficient strength to withstand the effect of a large charge, thus insuring great range, a flat trajectory and consequent accuracy of flight of bullet. By reduction of the diameter and lengthening the bullet its momentum is preserved, while its resistance in passing through the air is lessened, and by means of the paper patch the leading of the barrel is prevented and the friction thereby kept at its minimum, thus fulfilling all the required conditions for success.

Having thus described my invention, what I claim is—

1. The combination of the drawn brass shell with the patched bullet, substantially as described.

2. The combination of the metallic shell with a paper-patched bullet and a re-enforce cup, all constructed and arranged to operate as set forth.

3. The combination of the metallic shell A with the paper-patched bullet, and a cap or primer applied exteriorly, substantially as described, whereby the same shell may be repeatedly used, as set forth.

HIRAM BERDAN.

Witnesses:
HENRY MARVAL,
ISAAC BRADLEY.

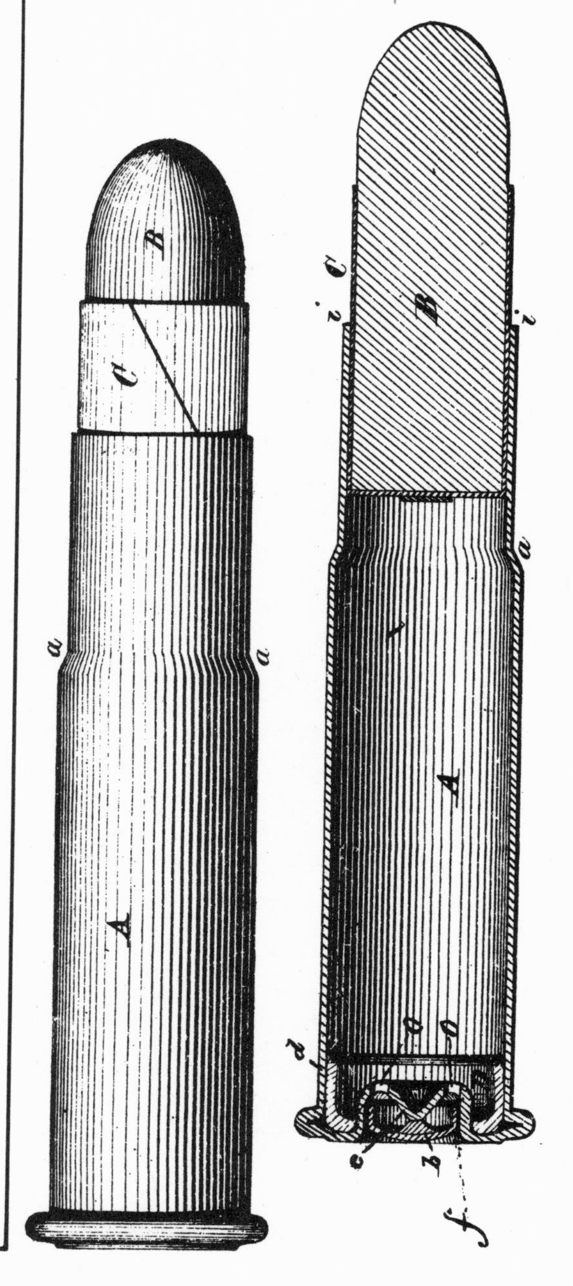

FIGURE 4-16 Hiram Berdan reinforced center-fire cartridge patent.

a very popular design particularly in the heavy Sharps rifles used for long-range buffalo shooting and it was found widely in sporting and target ammunition during the 19th century. The use of paper patched bullets gradually disappeared as sportsmen found that the bullets with lubricant in the grooves were just as effective and were considerably cheaper. One of the interesting twists of fate is that the Berdan primer design, as shown in Figure 4-16 has become the standard cartridge construction used in Europe and throughout the rest of the world. The cartridge construction shown in Figure 4-11 is generally credited to Colonel Boxer of England, and it has become the standard cartridge and primer construction in the United States.

Very thorough tests of a wide variety of ammunition designs were performed during 1872 and the results of the tests were summarized in a "Report Of A Board Of Ordnance Officers... For The Purpose Of Determining The Proper Caliber For Small-Arms." The Board studied a number of cartridge designs from .40 to .50 caliber of both straight and bottle necked design. The report is difficult to plow through, but the conclusions were that the Martini-Henry .577/.450 cartridge was too powerful and gave excessive recoil and that of all the designs studied the best was "Ammunition No. 58" which was the famous .45/70/405 cartridge. Few people today realize that this was the cartridge defined by the Ordance Board and that the .45/70/500 cartridge with its 500-grain bullet was strictly an afterthought in the 1880's. The facts are that the .45/70/500 cartridge went against many of the recommendations of the Ordnance Board (Such as the excessive recoil on which the Martini-Henry was rejected).

The selected .45/70/405 ammunition was specified in extreme detail, including the length and diameter of the chamber; the length, diameter, and exact shape of the bullet and each of its grease grooves; and the length, diameter and specifications of the cartridge case in detail. The bullet, for example, was specified as

> 12 parts by weight of lead, and 1 part by weight of tin, compressed (this means a swaged bullet not a cast bullet). The form (disregarding for the moment the cannelures) is a cylinder, surmounted by a conical frustrum, which is surmounted by a spherical segment. Length of cylinder, 55/100 of an inch, diameter of cylinder 458/1000 of an inch, length of frustrum 35/100 of an inch....

The other components were specified in equal detail. The result was a cartridge using the construction shown in Figure 4-13, but with extremely high efficiency for its day. The 70-grain powder charge drove the bullet 1330 feet per second for an efficiency of 22.5 foot-pounds per grain of propellant. The normal efficiency for this period of development was about 20 foot-pounds per grain of propellant, and the .45/70/405 represented an outstanding ammunition design for the 1870's.

The design of some of the most significant early cartridges is shown on the left side of Figure 4-17. Metallic ammunition technology was in its infancy during the Civil War, and the short, large-diameter Spencer cartridge represented the easiest type of self-primed cartridge case to manufacture. The copper case material and manufacturing process limited the powder charge to 40 grains to drive a 450-grain bullet. This ratio provided a muzzle velocity of about 960 feet per second, with a very curved trajectory. Despite these limitations, Northern Cavalry were able to drive Southern sharpshooters out of prepared positions across a river 500 yards wide! Although Spencer firearms gave excellent service there was an obvious need for higher velocity and flatter trajectory.

By late 1866 Frankford Arsenal had developed the .50/70/450 center-fire cartridge shown as the second from the left in Figure 4-17. This cartridge represented a technical advance over the Spencer for many more drawing operations were required to create a taller case, and the center-fire construction required more powerful machinery to form the head. The ballistics were substantially improved with a 300-foot per second rise in velocity and a 65 percent increase in muzzle energy as shown in Figure 4-18.

In 1873 the Army went to a still longer, smaller diameter case in the .45/70. The cartridge was originally adopted with a 405-grain bullet driven by 70 grains of powder. A more powerful cartridge loaded with a 500-grain bullet was standarized in the 1880's and this is shown as the third cartridge from the left in Figure 4-17. This particular cartridge was manufactured at Frankford Arsenal in 1886 and used a copper-colored, gilding metal for the case material.

As Americans became seriously interested in long-range target shooting during the early 1870's a search was started for the very best cartridges for shooting at 800 to 1000 yards. What finally evolved was a family of cartridges typified by the two center cartridges in Figure 4-17. The fourth cartridge from the left is a .45/100 Sharps straight case loaded with a paper patched bullet of 485 to 550 grains of weight. While the Government .45/70 cartridge of the 1880's drove a 500-grain bullet at about 1200 feet per second, the Sharps .45/100 could drive a 550-grain bullet at 1360

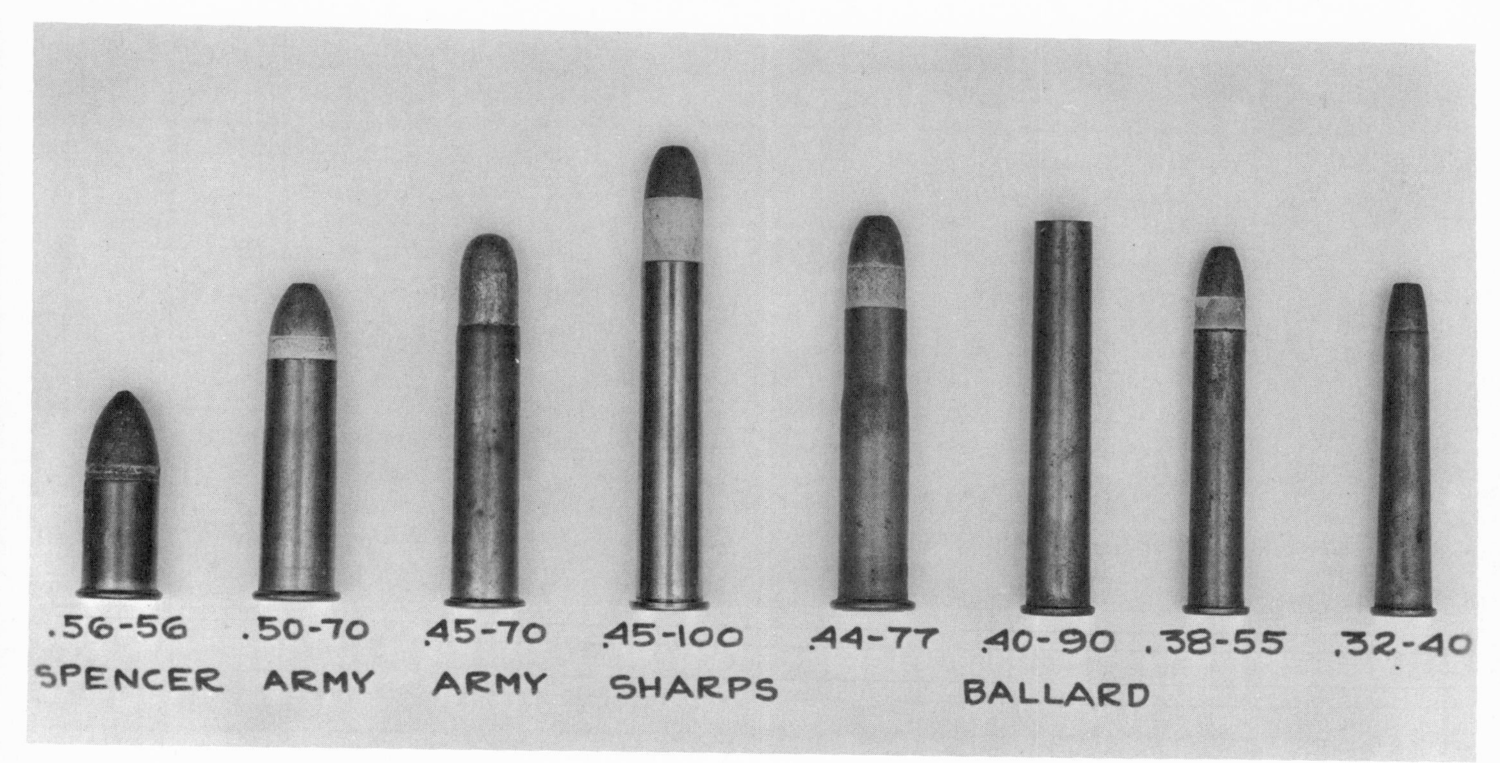

FIGURE 4-17 Early single-shot rifle cartridges.

feet per second. To modern shooters both these velocities are extremely low, but to be a skilled shooter at 1000 yards, the reduced time of flight of the heavier bullet at a higher velocity could make a substantial difference in winning a match, particularly if a cross-wind was present.

The most famous long-range rifle match in American history was fired at the Creedmoor, New York, range in 1874. This match reflected a challenge to the Americans from the Irish team who had won the Championship of the British Empire with very accurate muzzle-loading rifles. The match was held at 800, 900 and 1000 yards. The Americans selected specially developed Sharps and Remington rifles chambered for powerful .44/90 caliber slightly bottle-necked cartridges. A paper patched .44-77 Sharps or Remington cartridge is shown in Figure 4-17. This is typical of the family of slightly bottle-necked .44 caliber cartridges used for long-range target shooting. The most popular of all long-range cartridges was the .44/90 which was very similar in appearance to the .44/77 illustrated. The .44/90 Remington cartridge was loaded with a 550-grain bullet launched at a muzzle velocity of 1250 feet per second. The .44 Sharps cartridge was often loaded with a 520-grain bullet at 1270 feet per second. The muzzle energy of both cartridges was about 1850 foot-pounds compared with 1600 foot-pounds for the standard .45/70 Army cartridge. Neither of these approached the power level of the .44/100 Remington, or .45/100 Sharps as shown in Figure 4-18.

The trend toward smaller calibers continued with the development of .40 caliber target cartridges. An outstanding example is the .40/90 Ballard shown in Figure 4-17. This particular cartridge was an "ever-lasting" type of case with a very heavy head section. A piece of paper hidden in the case notes that it has been reloaded ten times with maximum charges and the case shows only a slight flattening of the head stamp. Cartridges of such long slender sections were very difficult to draw and reflected the tremendous improvement in ammunition technology in the 15 years since the introduction of the .56/.56 Spencer.

Cartridges which became popular for the shorter range "Schuetzen" shooting are shown in the right-hand side of the figure. The trend toward smaller caliber was continued and lighter powder charges were perfectly satisfactory for medium-range shooting. The .38/55 cartridge was normally loaded with a 255-grain bullet and provided a muzzle velocity of

CARTRIDGE	BULLET WEIGHT GRAINS	APPROXIMATE POWDER CHARGE GRAINS	MUZZLE VELOCITY FT/SEC	MUZZLE ENERGY FOOT/POUNDS
56-56 Spencer	450	40	960[1]	921[1]
50-70 Army	450	70	1240	1440[2]
45-70 Army	500	70	1201	1602[3]
45-100 Sharps	550	100	1360	2240[4]
44-77 Sharps and Remington	365	77	1460	1730[4]
44-90 Sharps	520	90	1270	1860[4]
44-100 Remington	550	100	1380	2338[4]
40-90 Ballard	370	90	1427	1672[4]
38-55 Winchester	255	55	1320	985[3]
32-40 Winchester	165	40	1440	760[3]

[1]Calculated by an accurate predictive computer program.
[2]Ordance Bureau Tests 1870's.
[3]Winchester tested ballistics 1916.
[4]From early manufacturers' catalogs.

FIGURE 4-18 Ballistics of early military and target cartridges.

1321 feet per second. The muzzle energy was slightly under 1000 foot-pounds.

The .32/40 shown on the right side of the figure was an extremely popular cartridge providing excellent accuracy and mild recoil. This was normally loaded with a 165-grain bullet which was launched at 1428 feet per second muzzle velocity. The cartridge provided a muzzle energy of 747 foot-pounds and had a history of superb accuracy in the carefully constructed single-shot target rifles of the late 19th century.

By endless experimentation European shooters had developed muzzle-loading target rifles to a very high level of perfection. Americans had shifted to breech-loading firearms during the Civil War and the drive to perfect these radically new firearms continued in the 1870's. Accurate target shooting at ranges of over half a mile provided a very demanding testing ground for new ideas. Through great experimentation shooters found that very powerful cartridges firing heavy bullets at moderate velocities were the most accurate possible combination for black powder technology. This runs counter to the impression of most shooters. For example, if you had to choose between a 300-grain bullet at 1500 feet per second or a 500-grain bullet at 1200 feet per second most shooters would say that the 300-grain bullet would have a shorter time of flight and would, therefore, have less wind deflection. It turns out that this is not the case. The wind deflection is strongly influenced by a factor known as "lag time." Lag time may be defined as the difference between the actual time of flight of the bullet and the time of flight if the bullet traveled the entire distance at its muzzle velocity. The 500-grain bullet would lose a much smaller percentage of its velocity than would the 300-grain bullets launched at a higher velocity. The 300-grain bullet would, therefore, have more lag time, and would be more deflected by the wind.

The exterior ballistics of several cartridges for 1000-yard target shooting have been calculated with a 10-mile crosswind. For comparison, the ballistics of one of our finest 1000-yard modern match cartridges has also been calculated. The modern cartridge is the powerful .300 Winchester magnum loaded with a 180-grain boat-tailed bullet. This is launched at a muzzle velocity of 3070 feet per second, and a muzzle energy of 3766 foot-pounds. The time of flight over 1000 yards is only 1.42 seconds and the wind deflection due to a 10-mile per hour crosswind is 6.45 feet.

The performance of the standard service cartridge of

a century ago is shown in the second line of Figure 4-19. The .50/70 cartridge was launched at 1260 feet per second and had a remaining velocity at 1000 yards of 670 feet per second. The real time of flight would be 3.52 seconds and the lag time 1.42 seconds, resulting in a fairly high wind deflection of 16.7 feet.

The .45/70 cartridge, adopted in 1873, did not do much better. The same 70-grain powder charge drove the 405 grain bullet at 1318 feet per second, but it took 3.4 seconds for the bullet to travel 1000 yards and the wind drift was 16.5 feet.

The ballistics of the .44/77 target cartridge were not much better with a time of flight of 3.2 seconds but an increased wind drift of 17.4 feet due to the lighter 365-grain bullet. The real performance improvement required the very powerful target cartridges such as the .45/100 and the .44/90. The performance of the .45/100 is shown on the fourth line of Figure 4-19. It was loaded with a heavy 550-grain bullet which was driven to 1360 feet per second by the powerful 100-grain powder charge. This velocity was only 40 feet per second higher than the .45/70 cartridge and yet the long, heavy paper patched bullet had almost 100 feet per second higher velocity remaining at 1000 yards. The time of flight had been cut to 3.1 seconds and the wind drift reduced to 13.1 feet. This may not seem like much of an improvement compared with the 6.45 feet of the modern high velocity match cartridge, but it could make the difference between a 10 or a 9 in a crucial match.

After endless experimentation shooters selected the .44/90 long-range cartridge as their favorite, and this was used in the famous Creedmoor matches in the fall of 1874. Analysis of the long-range ballistics of this cartridge show why it was such an excellent choice. There were two variations, one designed by Remington and one by Sharps. The ballistics were very similar and the Sharps cartridge, loaded with a 520-grain bullet, is shown in the lowest line of Figure 4-19. The 90-grain black powder charge drove the heavy bullet at 1270 feet per second — almost the same muzzle velocity as the .50/70 government cartridge. The heavy .44 caliber bullet with its smaller cross sectional area and increased weight had over 110 feet per second higher retained velocity at 1000 yards than the .50/70 government cartridge and the time of flight was 3.18 seconds. The heavy bullet at its moderate velocity lost a smaller percentage of velocity than any of the contemporary cartridges and this resulted in a very low wind deflection of 12 feet.

Modern long-range target rifles can substantially outperform the firearms of a century ago. The powerful modern .30 caliber magnum cartridges provide much flatter trajectory and almost half of the wind deflection of the best cartridges of a century ago. Modern ammunition has eliminated the need for the elaborate procedures of the early shooters which often included swabbing the bore between shots. The elaborate sights of a century ago often included a micrometer adjustment for windage on the front sight together with a leveling bubble to insure that the shooter held the rifle exactly vertical. Tall tang peep sights with fine screw adjustments were developed to offset the arced trajectory and wind sensitivity of the early cartridges. Careful reading of the old catalogues and records shows that the remarkable performance of the target rifles of the 1870's and 1880's reflects great ingenuity, patience and skill on the part of the manufacturers and skilled marksmen of a century ago.

LONG-RANGE ACCURACY

It is difficult to locate carefully documented information which defines the real accuracy potential of the early black powder single-shot rifles. One good source is the series of government tests to determine the "Proper Caliber For Small Arms" performed in 1873. The report includes well-documented experiments with .40, .42, and .45 caliber cartridges at ranges of 500, 800, and 1050 yards. The tests were fired by skilled shooters from the prone position with a rest for the forearm of the rifle, and were also fired from machine tests. The accuracy was measured by a procedure called "mean absolute deviation." The tests were fired with 20-shot targets and the center of impact for each group was determined. The vertical and horizontal distance of each shot from the center of impact was calculated and averaged to give the "mean vertical deviation" and the "mean horizontal deviation." The "mean absolute deviation" was calculated as the square root of the sum of the squares of the mean vertical and horizontal deviations. The "mean absolute deviation" is similar to the "mean radius," or the *average* distance from the center of impact to the bullet holes. The two measurements would very rarely differ by more than 5 percent.

Tests of the .40 caliber cartridges were performed with three ammunition designs and the best design gave a mean absolute deviation of 10.4 inches at 500 yards. The figure for 800 yards was 24.5 inches, and at 1050 yards, 49 inches. The 340-grain bullet was launched at a muzzle velocity of 1388 feet per second and had a muzzle energy of 1454 foot-pounds.

Forty-two caliber cartridges provided much better accuracy levels. A series of trials was made with 370-

CARTRIDGE	BULLET WEIGHT GRAINS	MUZZLE VELOCITY	VELOCITY AT 1000 YARDS	ACTUAL TIME OF FLIGHT	LAG TIME	WIND DEFLECTION FEET
300 Winchester Magnum	180	3070	1478	1.42	.44	6.45
50-70 Government	450	1260	670	3.52	1.14	16.7
45-70 Government	405	1318	696	3.40	1.12	16.5
45-100 Sharps	550	1360	789	3.10	.90	13.1
44-90 Sharps	520	1270	783	3.18	.82	12.0

FIGURE 4-19 Wind deflection of long-range cartridges (1000-yd. shooting in 10mph crosswind).

grain bullets with powder charges of 60 to 80 grains. Surprisingly, the accuracy at 500 yards was very dependent on powder charge. The 60-grain load gave a mean absolute deviation of 6.9 inches. At 65 grains the group opened up to 9.07 inches, at 75 grains to 19.2 inches, and at 80 grains to 26.5 inches with three bullets completely off the target. The 60-grain charge was considered too low in power level and the 65-grain load was selected for continued development, providing accuracy levels of 9.96 inches, 12.1 inches, and 14.6 inches in further tests. The real advantage of the .42 caliber cartridge showed up in a series of tests fired at 1050 yards where mean absolute deviations of 32.7, 41.9, and 47.4 inches were recorded. Each of these figures represented the average "mean absolute deviation" for five 20-shot targets.

The famous .45/70 cartridge was developed during these trials. Most of the tests were performed with a 400-grain hardened lead bullet with four grease grooves. The tests were performed with powder charges of 60, 65, 70, 75, and 80 grains. The cartridges with the 70-grain powder charge gave the best over-all balance and a mean absolute deviation of only 10.6 inches at 500 yards. The bullet was launched at a velocity of 1300 feet per second and a maximum pressure of 16,300. At 800 yards the accuracy was 24.2 inches and opened up to 57 inches at 1050 yards. The final .45/70 cartridge improvement was made during this series of tests by a design change to a five-groove bullet which brought the weight up to 405 grains but cut the mean absolute deviation to a remarkably low 35.2 inches at 1050 yards.

These figures may be roughly visualized as reflecting the radius of a circle out to the *average* bullet impact point. With this thought in mind a circle of 35-inch radius or 6-foot diameter is rather small for a range of 1050 yards with the long looping trajectories of the single-shot rifles and ammunition of a century ago.

Early Breech-Loading Rifles

CHAPTER 5

Inventors have been experimenting with breech-loading firearms since the 14th century. Some early cannons were made up with separate breech-blocks into which the powder and cannon ball were loaded. The breech-blocks were then aligned with the main barrel and wedged tightly into place. When the cannon fired, most of the powder gas and the ball came out the muzzle, but with the soft materials and crude machining techniques of the Renaissance period there was a great deal of gas leakage at the joint. The experiments continued with cannon, matchlock muskets and pistols. All these early firearms were dangerous to the users, and the breech-loaders were generally weaker than the muzzle-loading designs.

Seventeenth Century inventors even developed repeating breech-loading flintlocks. Michele Lorenzoni, one of the leading gunsmiths of Florence, Italy, developed a rifle with two magazines in the buttstock. One magazine held powder and the other round lead balls. The gun had a rotating breechblock controlled by a lever on the side. Loading was accomplished by dropping the muzzle toward the ground and rotating the lever. As the cavity in the breechblock passed the two magazines a measured charge of powder and a lead ball fell into the cavity. When the lever was returned to its original position, the breechblock was properly aligned with the barrel. The gun was very ingenious for it also featured a small magazine containing very fine powder in the lock mechanism. A small charge of priming powder was automatically placed in the pan and the hammer cocked by the motion of the breech-block lever.

Many inventors worked on this approach to develop a fast firing repeating rifle. A similar layout was utilized by John Cookson, a British gunmaker. A slightly different system with the powder chamber in the buttstock and a magazine for bullets under the barrel was developed on the Continent by a family named Kalthoff and manufactured in several countries. This basic system was later picked up by American inventors and became the basis for a series of experiments that eventually led to the Winchester repeating rifle. By their time the American inventors, Lewis Jennings and Walter Hunt, had better steels and more accurate machinery to work with, but their rifles were still not successful. Some of the European breechloading repeaters were issued in very limited quantities to élite military troops during the 17th century, but all were characterized by three serious problems:

1. The mechanism required to safely store the powder and meter a charge for each shot plus a separate magazine to handle the bullets was far too complex and delicate. This was particularly

true because the inventors were limited to relatively soft and weak materials such as iron and mild steel.

2. Machinery prior to the 19th century was quite crude. This meant that each of these repeaters was a handmade "work of art" depending on extreme skill of the craftsman for its success. If the tolerances were excessive, or if the parts wore enough for the flame to get back into the powder magazine in the buttstock, the result was disastrous.
3. When black powder is fired, only half the ingredients turn into gas. The other half are left in the gun mechanism or are ejected out the barrel as solid particles. These complex breech-loading repeaters had many crevices into which powder residue could pack and accumulate, making the action more and more difficult to operate. Disassembly and cleaning were complex and time consuming, and corrosion of the interior parts due to black powder fouling was a serious problem.

BREECH-LOADERS WITH SEPARATE CHAMBERS

The idea of a heavy iron cartridge case was developed by leading gunmakers in England and on the Continent. A remarkable example is a breech-loading match lock dated 1536 in the collection of the Tower of London. This breech-loading hand gun was an Arquebus, built for Henry VIII, and it had a breechblock which was pivoted on the left-hand side. When it was flipped open a heavy steel cup loaded with powder and ball could be dropped into the breech and the breechblock closed again. The separate chamber had its own flash pan containing the priming charge.

Most of the later breech-loading pistols and long arms developed in the 17th and 18th centuries utilized a break open type of action much like a modern double-barreled shotgun. Some had a similar system but with a barrel that pivoted open to one side. The hollow iron or steel chambers were generally fitted with a handle at the breech end or with a large flange

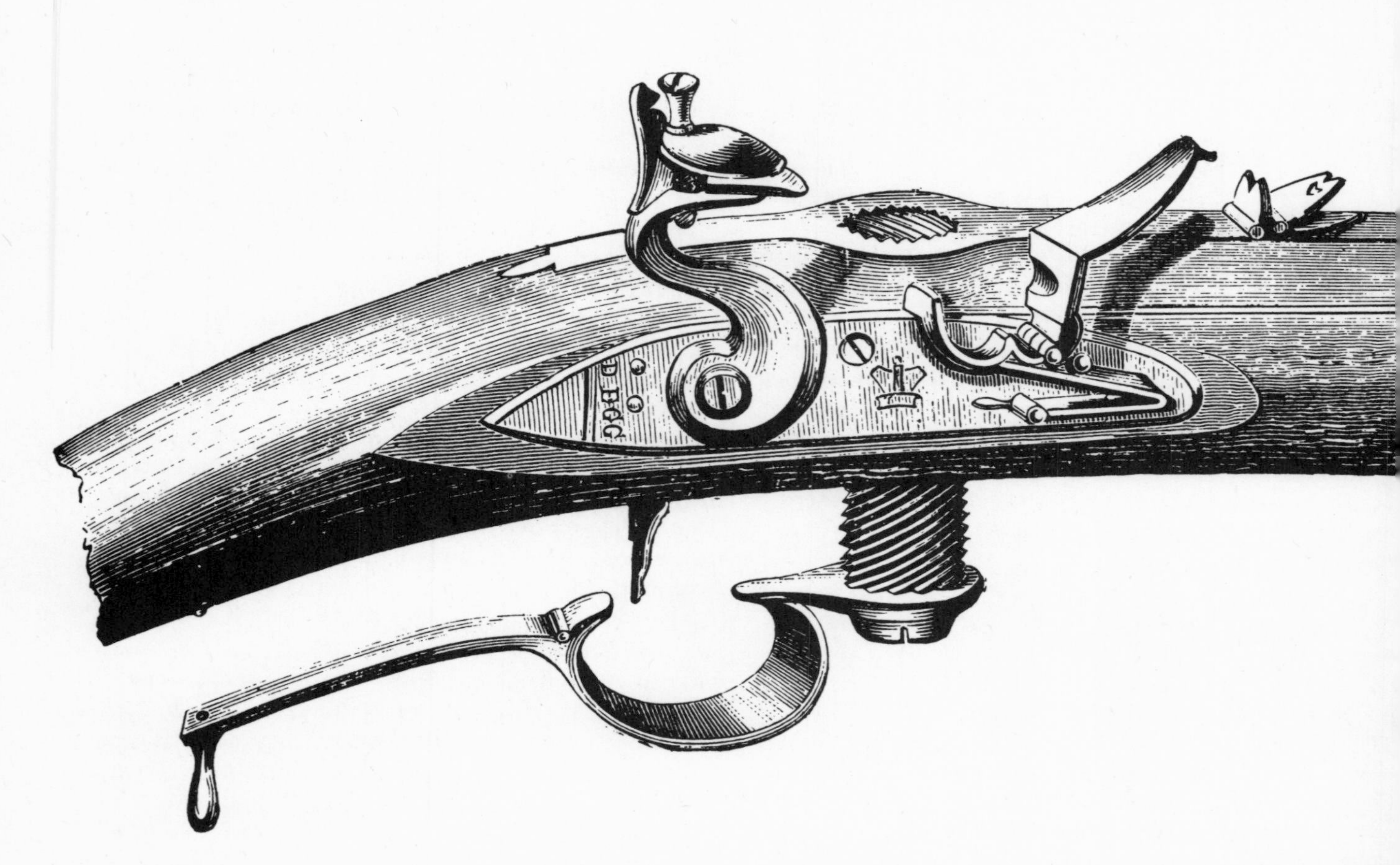

FIGURE 5-1 Ferguson breech-loading flintlock rifle.

to insure proper alignment when placed in the breech of the gun.

The designs all required very high standards of craftsmanship for success and were, therefore, quite expensive and manufactured in limited numbers. All shared the problems of gas leakage at the breech, powder fouling, and corrosion of the internal mechanism.

THE FERGUSON BREECH-LOADING FLINTLOCK RIFLE

The most successful 18th century breech-loader was the Ferguson rifle shown in Figure 5-1. This was the invention of a remarkable British officer, Major Patrick Ferguson, born in 1744. Ferguson was one of the able and highly dedicated military officers who did much to expand the British colonial empire around the world. At the age of 14 he was serving with a Scotch regiment in Germany as a bugler. He returned to England in 1762 due to ill heath but six years later he was off on another campaign to the British West Indies with the 70th Infantry Regiment. In 1774 he was again invalided home to England. A skilled marksman and with extensive military service, he was keenly aware of the needs of the soldier in the field. As a member of the Scotch aristocracy he had funds for experiments and contacts which allowed him access to the highest levels of the British Government. Ferguson was aware of the many difficulties in the previous breech-loading experiments and felt that a system invented by a Frenchman, LaChaumette, offered the best promise of success. LaChaumette had invented his breech-loader in 1704 and had had limited success in having his gun issued to French Dragoons and naval units. He fled to England in 1721 to escape religious persecution in France. LaChaumette obtained British patents on his gun and made up at least one for King George I during the 1720's.

Fifty years later Patrick Ferguson seriously studied this early mechanism and made substantial improvements which led to the creation of the most advanced 18th century military rifle. Ferguson modified the design of the breechblock so that when the breech was closed, it formed a flat breech face at the rear of the barrel, minimizing the build up of fouling. He also modified the design of the screw threads and provided recesses at critical places aroud the breech plug where fouling could accumulate rather than remaining on the threads and making the action very difficult to operate.

The Ferguson rifle is shown in a 19th century illustration in Figure 5-1. The barrel had an enlarged section at the breech with a large vertical hole which intersected the axis of the barrel. A multi-lead thread was cut into this vertical hole and a close fitting breechblock was machined with a matching thread. The breechblock was rigidly attached to the forward section of the trigger guard and an operating handle was riveted to the trigger guard extension. The design had many advantages. The fast pitch thread dropped the breechblock to a fully open position with one turn. The long tang on the trigger guard gave excellent leverage to overcome the friction due to powder build up in the mechanism. The close fitting thread gave excellent gas sealing in comparison with the other crude systems of the 18th century.[1]

The loading procedure was quite simple. The soldier spun the trigger guard lever one complete turn, dropping the breechblock to its lowest position. He pointed the muzzle of the rifle downward and dropped a naked lead ball in the breech. The ball rolled forward in the chamber until stopped by the rifling. A measured loose powder charge was poured in the breech and the trigger guard lever rotated one turn in a counterclockwise direction to close and seal the breech. A small amount of powder was poured in the pan and the frizzen snapped shut. The final operation was to cock the hammer, and the rifle was ready to fire. This was a far simpler loading procedure than for a standard musket, since no handling of the ramrod or ramming the charge the full length of the barrel was required.

The British military authorities were highly skeptical of the "newfangled invention," but the gifted Patrick Ferguson gave a breathtakingly successful demonstration in the rain that swept away all official doubts. On April 27, 1776, he set up a target in the marshes near Woolwich Arsenal at the very respectable range of 200 yards. In addition to the hard rain there was a high wind, a combination which made the standard military musket almost useless. Ferguson started continuous firing at the rate of four shots per minute — an unheard of rate for a military rifle. He performed a second demonstration at six shots per minute and then performed a "walking fire" demonstration, firing at a steady rate of four shots per minute while marching toward the target. His rifle was carefully made and fitted with sights. Ferguson was an excellent marksman and missed the target *only three times* during the entire demonstration.

British officialdom was very impressed and ordered

[1] D. F. Butler "Early Breech-Loading Rifles." *The Gun Report,* October 1970. Page 33

production of 100 rifles of Ferguson's design and asked the inventor to personally supervise production. They were finished in September 1776. During the following winter a special regiment of 100 riflemen was raised and in March 1777 they sailed for America to fight in the Revolution. In a minor engagement with the American forces at Chadd's Ford, Pennsylvania, on September 11, 1777, Captain Ferguson was struck in the right arm and seriously wounded. Without his strong leadership the rifle company was disbanded and the men returned to their original units. Although other Ferguson breech-loading rifles were made for the East India Company and for private purchasers, very few have survived to the present day.

The incredible will and tenacity of Ferguson continued to show itself. His right arm never fully recovered from the wound, but he taught himself to write and to shoot left handed and rose in the British service until by 1780 he was Inspector General of Militia in Georgia and the Carolinas. His career ended at the Battle of King's Mountain in October 1780 when the British became heavily engaged with skilled American backwoods troops armed with flintlock rifles. General Ferguson, on horseback, was too conspicuous a target to survive and was picked off by American sharpshooters.

HALL FLINTLOCK RIFLES

The search for a breech-loading rifle continued in Europe and in the United States. The next major step was development of the most successful of all breech-loading flintlock rifles during the first decade of the 19th century. This was the invention of an American mechanical genius, John Hancock Hall, born January 21, 1778. Hall was actively interested in many mechanical devices and apparently develope his breech-loading rifle without being aware of the tip-up chamber designs in Europe. He developed his ideas for a very ingenious mechanism and secured a patent on May 21, 1811. A William Thornton of Washington, D.C., made minor contributions and a joint patent was issued covering both Hall's and Thornton's designs. John Hall's description of his invention as given on his patent expresses the philosophy and the ingenuity of the design:

> The barrel is in two pieces. That which forms the breech rises at its forend upon touching a spring, or by any other method which may be found more convenient. The charge is then put into the receiver — viz., the breech part of the gun — without a ramrod, taking care to press the ball or shot to the powder with the finger. By this construction of the gun it may be loaded in less time and with less trouble than is necessary in loading common guns, in every situation, either standing, sitting, or lying. The ball goes with more certainty and force, because the chamber, being made where it receives a ball a little larger than the other parts of the bore, admits with ease a ball which completely fills the barrel in front, thus insuring its course in the direction of the bore, and preventing the elastic fluid (powder gas) from escaping by the side of the ball. The frequent cleaning of the barrel inside is avoided, for the ball, going tightly, drives out all before it, and also the danger of bursting, an accident which frequently happens by putting in two cartridges, for in this gun you can put but one.
>
> The peculiar construction of the lock, its simplicity, and its being attached to the barrel instead of the stock present the advantages of cheapness in construction and of durability. The parts are less in number than the parts of other locks, and consequently the chances of disorder are lessened. That part of the stock which with the locks now used is cut in every direction by the holes for screws, triggers, etc. and thereby much weakened, is left uninjured by this, and is strong as any other part of the stock in proportion to its size.
>
> I refer to the particular description with drawings, given under my hand and seal at Portland, March 16, 1811.

Two views of the breech mechanism of the Hall rifles are shown in Figure 5-2. Both are shown with the action open ready for loading. These illustrations show the Hall rifle of 1819 and it differs substantially from the patent drawings of 1811. Just to the rear of the breech face is a flange on the movable chamber. A vertical key was fitted into a recess in the receiver and held in with a horizontal screw. The top of this vertical key is apparent in both illustrations. The flange on the breechblock and the vertical key in the receiver constituted Hall's locking system. It was an excellent locking system for its day for two reasons.

1. The locking members were located very close to the joint between the breechlock and barrel. This meant that much less "springing" of the metal would occur than if the firing forces were taken on the hinge at the rear of the breechblock. In this latter case the entire receiver could stretch so that the "dynamic head space" would be much greater than with Hall's design.

2. The use of a separate key fitting into a recess in the receiver allowed very accurate head space adjustments by changing the relatively simple and inexpensive keys.

The Hall patent drawings of 1811 showed a much cruder locking system with a key that was screwed to

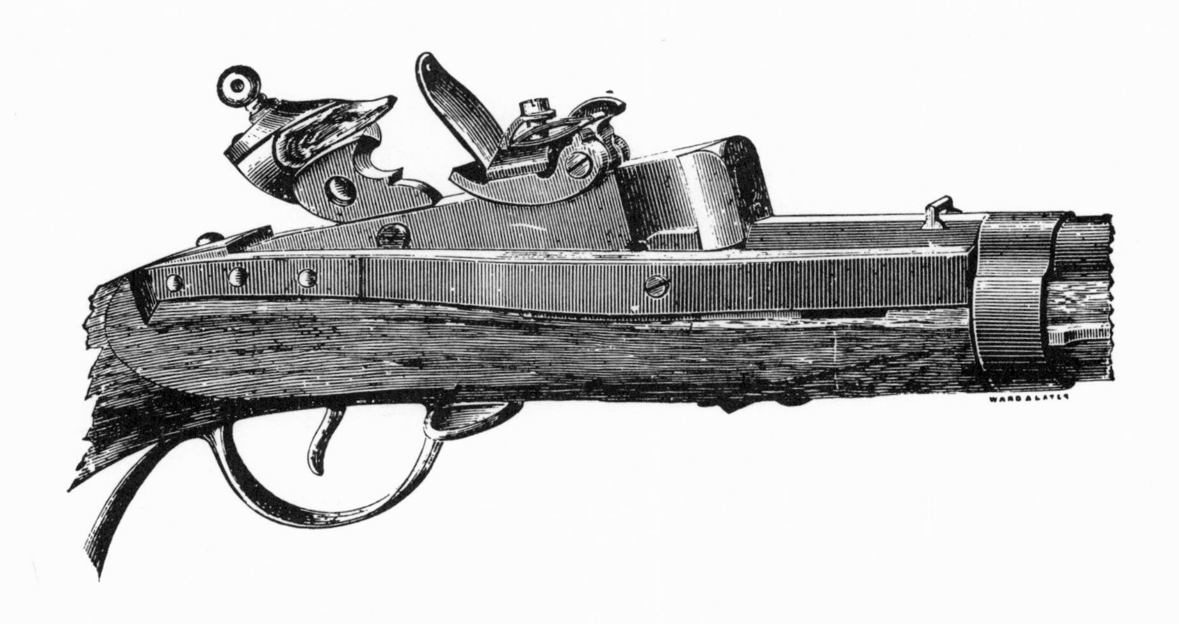

FIGURE 5-2 ABOVE: engraving of "John H. Hall's Amercian Breech-loading Carbine"; BELOW: action of Model 1819 Hall flintlock rifle with breech bolt tipped upward.

the side of the breechblock. The arrangement shown in Figure 5-2 represented a substantial improvement that has been developed over the intervening years. The patent drawings differed in many other respects such as the placement of the frizzen and pan on the side of the movable breechblock instead of on the top as shown in Figure 5-2.

Hall first applied his design ideas to a small number of pistols, but his eye was on the acceptance of his design as a United States military firearm.

Inventors have always been greeted with considerable skepticism by military authorities. Most inventors show up with half-developed ideas and wildly exaggerated claims. If an "improved" firearm is to be given to troops whose lives will depend on its performance, the military authorities have every reason to insist that the mechanism be well developed and thoroughly reliable. John Hall did not have an easy path for acceptance, but it is a great credit to the Ordnance Department of the infant United States that it was willing to have an open attitude toward new inventions and to allocate resources for tests and to actively assist in the development of some very advanced ideas. Hall's rifles were successfully tested in 1813 and 1816, and in January 1817, 100 rifles were ordered for field trials at a cost of $25.00 each. Hall had spent the intervening six years working hard on his designs, but he realized that there was much more to do. He asked for the opportunity to work at Harpers Ferry Armory where he continued his development efforts. This first 100 rifles were tested and reported on favorably in March 1819 and Hall was given an order for 1000 additional rifles. An agreement was reached between the Ordnance Department and the inventor reflecting great confidence on the part of the Ordnance Department in John Hall's skill and in awareness that the eventual success of the design would depend on extreme care in manufacturing. Hall was given a position as an assistant armorer at Harpers Ferry Armory at a pay of $60 per month plus a royalty of $1.00 per rifle. This appears to be a very generous arrangement for the early nineteenth century, and Hall continued to work at Harpers Ferry Amory until the 1840's.

A cross section drawing of the Hall rifle design is shown in Figure 5-3. This shows the Model 1819 mechanism in a locked position ready to fire. The 32¾-inch barrel had a bore diameter of .515 of an inch and was rifled with 16 narrow grooves. The barrel was bored out smooth to a diameter of .540 of an inch

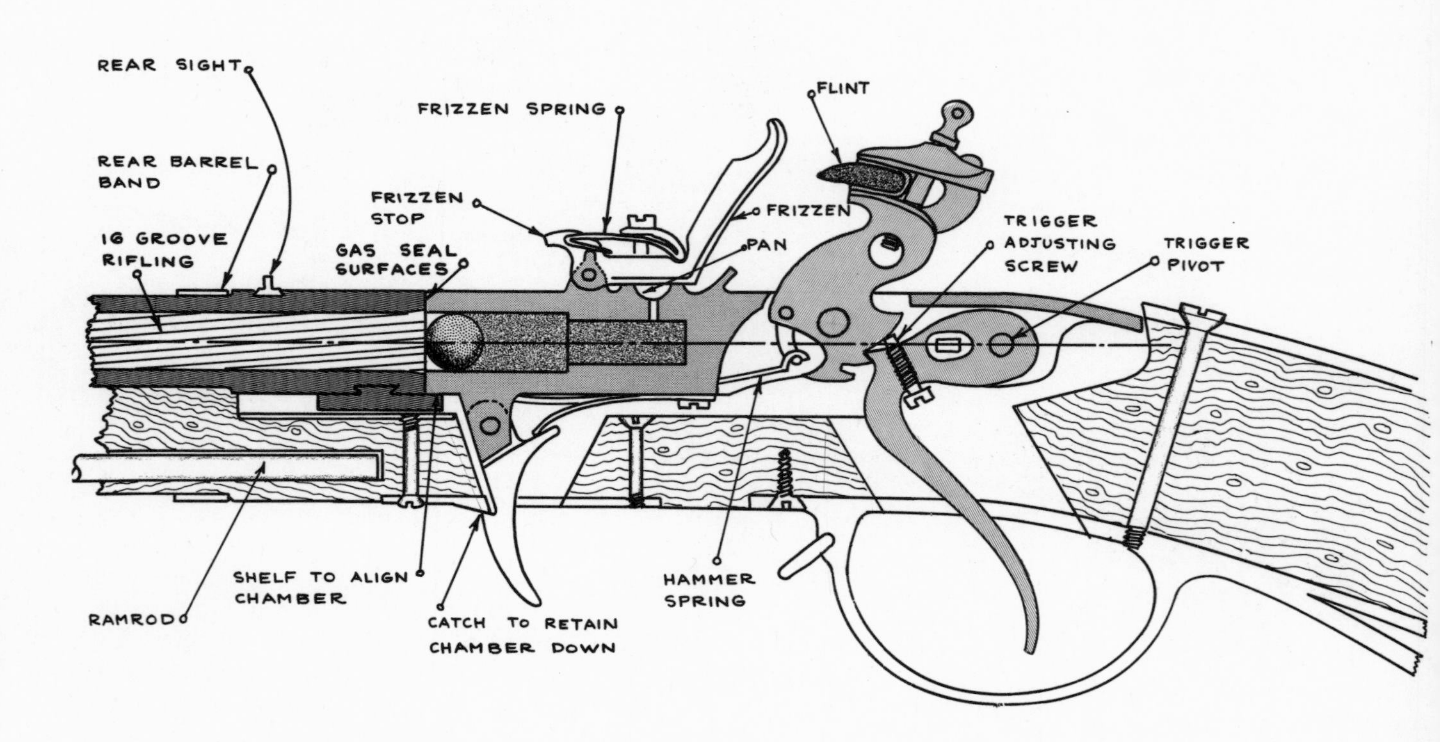

FIGURE 5-3 Cross-section of Hall Model 1819 breech-loading flintlock rifle.

FIGURE 5-4 Hall Model 1819 rifle with triangular bayonet.

at the muzzle to facilitate muzzle-loading in an emergency. A small plate was dovetailed to the bottom of the barrel, forming a shelf on which the chamber rested. The chamber was bored out with a slightly larger diameter at the front end so that a .525-inch rifle ball could be pressed in with the thumb. A smaller reduced chamber section was located to the rear into which a vertical hole was drilled up to the pan. A Model 1819 Hall rifle manufactured at Harper's Ferry in 1838 was examined and the forward section of the chamber was quite uniform, measuring .540 to .542-inch diameter along its length. The rear section of the chamber measured .405 of an inch.[2]

The pan and frizzen mechanism were located on top of the breechblock and an ingenious frizzen spring was designed whch kept the frizzen either in a fully shut or fully open position. After firing, the components were in the position shown in the lower illustration of Figure 5-2. The frizzen has snapped all the way open and a tail was resting on the top of the breechblock. The hammer has slammed forward and the lower jaw of the hammer was stopped on the fence at the rear of the pan.

The hammer spring was mounted on the underside of the breech block in a slot and it pulled downward on a stirrup at the front of the hammer. The trigger mechanism was quite ingenious. The trigger was pivoted at the rear and the design included a trigger adjusting screw so that the sear engagement could be carefully set. This is a design feature often utilized on high quality modern firearms, and was quite rare on flintlock weapons which generally had very rough and heavy trigger pulls.

The chamber was aligned with the barrel by use of a small shelf dovetailed to the underside of the barrel. The chamber was held down on the shelf by a spring loaded catch which engaged a plate inletted into the bottom of the stock. Two Hall rifles in the Winchester Gun Museum were measured and had .070 of an inch clearance on the catch although both were in excellent condition.

[2] *Ibid.* P 33

Loading the Hall Rifle

Loading the Hall was relatively simple. The soldier first cocked the hammer into the safety position which dropped the sear into the deep notch in the hammer. Holding the forearm with his left hand he reached under the stock with his right hand, pulling the catch to the rear and pushing upward on it at the same time. This was a smooth and natural motion and flipped the breechblock into the upward position shown in Figure 5-2. A standard rifle cartridge with a .525-inch diameter lead ball and 70 grains of black powder was withdrawn from the cartridge box. The folded end of the paper cartridge was torn open with the teeth. A small charge was poured into the pan on top of the breechblock and the frizzen snapped shut into the position shown in Figure 5-3. The remainder of the charge was poured into the open end of the chamber. The lead ball was then shaken out of the paper cartridge or the cartridge was torn to remove it and it was pressed into the open end of the chamber by the thumb. If the ball was undersize or the chamber worn, the paper from the cartridge case was often wadded up and stuffed in on top of the ball to hold it in position. The chamber was then pushed down into the aligned position shown in Figure 5-3, and the spring catch automatically locked it down into proper alignment. In this position the rifle was fully loaded and perfectly safe. To fire, the hammer was withdrawn to the full cocked position shown in Figure 5-3, the rifle aimed at the target and fired.

Model 1819 Hall Flintlock Rifle

The first breech-loading rifle to be a standard United States firearm was the Hall flintlock model of 1819. The breech design is shown in Figures 5-2 and 5-3. A full-length illustration is shown in Figure 5-4. The rifle weighed about 10 pounds and had a barrel 32⅝ inches long. Over-all length of the rifle was about 56⅝ inches. There was a post front sight welded to the barrel near the muzzle and a small open rear sight mounted in a dovetail slot in the barrel near the breech. The rifle had three flat barrel bands and both barrel bands and barrel were finished with a rich brown lacquer coating. The ramrod was mounted in guides beneath the barrel and was finished bright. The ramrod would normally be used only to clean the rifle, but in emergencies it could be used to clear an obstruction from the barrel or to load the rifles from the muzzle.

One of Hall's major patent claims was the fact that the chamber could be larger in diameter than the barrel affording an excellent seal between the bullet and barrel. For this reason the barrels were slightly smaller in diameter than for the Common Rifle and it would be quite difficult to muzzle-load the Hall rifle with the normal bullet. In order to help this situation the first 1½ inches of the muzzle was reamed out smooth to .540 inch diameter to give a "lead in" before the rifleman had to pound the bullet down the remaining length of the barrel.

The flintlock mechanism was located on top of the breechblock and was offset to the right side. This is shown in the illustrations in Figure 5-2, showing the pan slightly overhanging the right side of the breechblock. This offset was quite necessary so that there would be a smooth top line for the sights which were offset to the left.

The trigger guard was formed with a boss at the front end to which the sling swivel was attached on the rifle models. On the carbines this was generally left plain. To the rear of the trigger guard an ornate brass extension was formed to provide something of a pistol grip for the soldier.

John Hall was keenly aware that acceptance of his rifle by the Army troops would depend on reliable performance under field conditions. This meant that the ignition system must be at least as reliable as the standard flintlock muskets and that leakage of gas at the joint between the chamber and barrel must be minimized.

Hall and the staff at Harpers Ferry Armory spent five years developing the design and the specialized machinery required to successfully manufacture this "complex" new design. It is easy to look at the finished design and see that the parts are not too intricate. Careful examination of the parts of a Hall rifle reveals the many, many problems that were solved before the design was successfully put into production. Some of these are apparent in the lower illustration of Figure 5-2. For example, the design of the frizzen spring is quite tricky for the manufacturing methods available. This frizzen spring has two sharp bends and the flexible small end is split into two halves which surround the frizzen stops. To make these springs, for example, would be quite difficult by modern manufacturing methods and they undoubtedly gave many headaches in the early 19th century. A second problem was solved by having the excess hammer energy absorbed by the fence to the rear of the pan. The lower jaw of the hammer was designed with a broad flat surface which slammed into the fence to absorb the extra energy. It is the author's opinion that this rapid stopping caused the flints to slide in the hammer jaw, and this was solved by cutting into the lower jaw of the hammer sharp teeth which tended to grip tightly the leather in which the flint was clamped.

Other neat design details included the adjusting screw on the trigger mechanism which gives a very smooth, clean trigger pull on the Hall rifle in the Winchester Gun Museum. The nesting of springs on the underside of the breechblock is also very carefully worked out so that there is ample space for the springs, good power to the hammer, but very smooth hammer action.

Developing all these design refinements took a great deal of time and it was not until 1823 that the design work and machinery were completed. Production started with 22 rifles in 1823 and 980 manufactured in 1824. Hall found that it was necessary to manufacture the components to very accurate dimensions, and Harpers Ferry achieved a higher level of component interchangeability than on any previous rifle.

By the late 1820's steady production was achieved at Harpers Ferry Armory and the rifles were in great demand by the Regular Army. The Ordnance Department desired to increase production in order to provide firearms for the militia and so entered into contracts with Simeon North of Middletown, Connecticut, on December 15, 1828, for the manufacture of 5000 rifles at $17.50 each, including all necessary components, such as bullet molds, screwdrivers, cleaning tools and bayonets. The contract specified production at the rate of 1000 firearms per year. North received additional contracts for more rifles in 1829 and through the 1830's and early 1840's. North was one of the most skilled 19th century contractors with a record of production for the Government dating back to the turn of the century. He developed machinery to successfully manufacture these difficult firearms and showed considerable imagination in suggesting design improvements.

Hall Carbine-Model 1833

The Hall breech-loading system had advantages for mounted troops and the next model was specifically oriented for Cavalry needs. The Model of 1833 differed in three major respects. First it was primarily designed as a carbine with a barrel length of slightly over 26 inches and an over-all length of 45 inches. The weight was reduced to about 8¼ pounds and the cleaning rod was changed into a rod type bayonet with a triangular cross section.

The Model 1833 Hall carbine has the distinction of being the first United States firearm with percussion ignition. The third major change was that a .69 caliber smoothbore barrel was fitted. This was a remarkable change for the major disadvantage to rifling had been the slow loading required to pound the bullet down the length of the barrel. The Hall breech-loading system completely eliminated this disadvantage and it really made very little difference whether the bullet went whistling down a smooth barrel or spun by rifling. Apparently there was great conviction in the Cavalry that a large diameter smoothbore barrel was actually preferable to a rifled barrel, and a long series of Hall models were made with smooth barrels. The carbines were manufactured by North and were similar in their general arrangement to the Model of 1819. The cone of the percussion ignition system was offset to the right side of the block and the percussion hammer and trigger mechanism were located in the same position as on the Model 1819. The hammer was considerably simplified for the percussion design, and the pan, frizzen and frizzen spring were replaced by the cone and cone-seat. The hammer spring, lower section of the hammer, trigger mechanism, and breech-latching mechanism were very similar to that shown in Figure 5-3.

The breechblock, hammer, latch plate, trigger and the latch were all case-hardened in mottled colors as on the Model 1819 flintlock rifles. The barrel and barrel bands were finished in a brown lacquer, and the stock was oiled walnut. Recesses were cut in the underside of the stock near the butt plate for storage of ramrod and cleaning equipment, and these recesses were covered by a small hinged trap door and latch.

Hall Carbines of 1836 and 1838

In the late 1830's a new series of percussion carbines were manufactured with rifled .54 caliber barrels and with smoothbore .69 caliber barrels. The rifle barrels were actually .515-inch bore diameter with groove diameters slightly over .520 of an inch. The .54 caliber designation comes from the short reamed section at the muzzle which was opened up to .540 of an inch to assist in muzzle-loading in an emergency if the breechblock became jammed in a down position. The correct barrel designation should be .52 caliber.

The general design features of the Model 1836 breech action are shown in Figure 5-5. It is one of the Model 1819 Hall rifles which were converted during this time period into very effective percussion .52 caliber rifles. The way to identify the Model 1836 action is the fence to the rear of the percussion cone in the breechblock.

The carbine models were much more common and

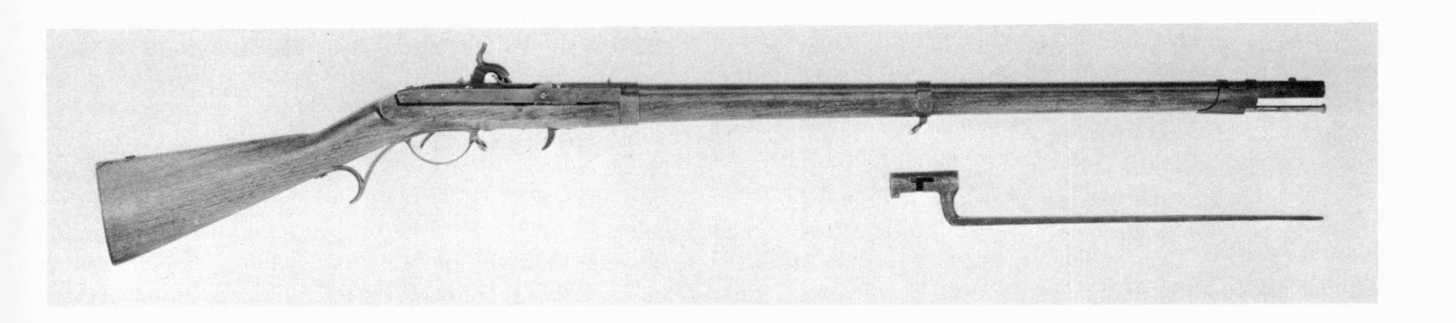

FIGURE 5-5 Hall Model 1836 percussion rifle with triangular bayonet.

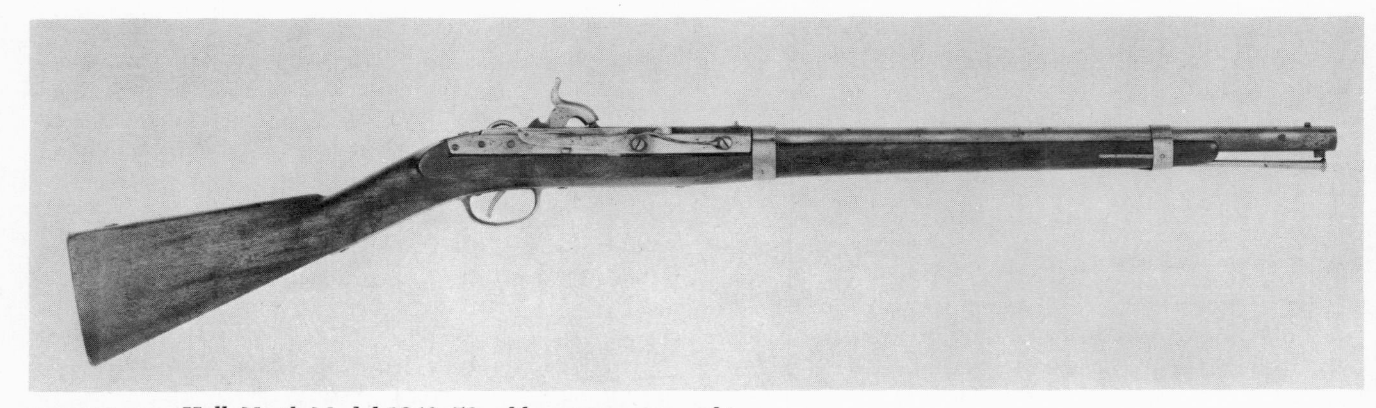

FIGURE 5-6 Hall–North Model 1843 .52 caliber percussion carbine.

usually were fitted with six-grooved rifled barrels 21 to 23 inches long. The carbines had an overall length of about 43 inches. The carbines were manufactured with two barrel bands and a triangular rod bayonet replacing the ramrod beneath the barrel. The rod bayonet was retained by a double loop bracket near the muzzle. When drawn forward it was held by spring catches to form an extended bayonet.

Cavities were machined in the underside of the butt stock near the butt plate. These cavities were covered by a hinged metal plate and were apparently designed for the storage of cleaning equipment.

Hall Carbine Model of 1840

Experimentation with Hall carbines continued in the late 1830's and several designs were manufactured in the early 1840's. The problem seems to have centered around the breech release mechanism. The vertical curved catch extending downward was a big nuisance to the soldiers who found that it dug into their shoulders in normal marching position and that it was also prone to accidental release when they were crawling along the ground or going through brushy country. It was rather disconcerting in a dangerous situation to find that your rifle had accidentally come open. The experiments led to a series of designs intended to be easier to open under combat conditions but still not prone to accidental opening.

One of the designs standardized in 1840 was a so-called "fishtail" lever design in which two wings extended out laterally on each side in front of the trigger guard. The soldier pushed down on these wings, which operated through a series of levers, to release an internal catch which held the breechblock in the down position. The fishtail lever designs were always used with the percussion mechanism.

There is great confusion over the Hall firearms of the early 1840's for they were made in carbine models with .52 caliber rifled barrels and .64 caliber smoothbore barrels. They were made with fishtail lever release mechanisms, and "elbow lever" release mechanisms. The latter were an L-shaped design that folded back along the front of the trigger guard when not in use.

No matter what the design of the release mechanism, the very practical American soldiers found that these Hall percussion firearms had one great advantage that was not in the Army Regulations. This was the fact that the entire breechblock could easily be removed from the firearm and carried around as a very crude pistol for self-protection. Although it was not an accurate firearm, since the bullet essentially was right in the end of the chamber, the .69 caliber or .52 caliber ball provided a very lethal pocket weapon at close range. It was common practice among soldiers in the Mexican War to carry this chamber in their pocket while on leave to give themselves a little added backup protection against unfriendly encounters.

Hall-North Carbine Model of 1843

The last Hall carbine was the Model of 1843, a smoothbore .52 caliber carbine with a 21-inch barrel and an over-all length of about 40 inches; it weighed about 8 pounds. The appearance of the carbine is shown in Figure 5-6. The design had been considerably simplified by the use of the percussion ignition system, and the cast brass tail on the trigger guard had been eliminated on all carbines. The key operating elements including the breechblock, hammer, lock plate and trigger were all case-hardened in mottled colors. The barrel and barrel bands were finished with a brown lacquer coating. There was a major change in the locking mechanism which held the breechblock in the down position. Simeon North had developed a rotary cam which locked the breechblock down on a beveled surface. The can in turn was controlled by a "side lever" which may be seen in Figure 5-6 lying along the right side of the breechblock. A screw was fastened at the pivot point and the arm of the lever lies to the rear. A control spring tending to hold the lever in a shut position extends forward of the lever and is anchored with a forward screw near the rear sight. This new breechblock hold-down mechanism was quiet compact and eliminated the soldiers' objections to bars or rods projecting from the gun mechanism. It did not, however, solve the serious problem of gas leakage between the breechblock and the barrel. One early test was to see if a piece of paper could be placed between the breechblock and the barrel. A piece of paper is generally .004 of an inch thick and even this much clearance extending all the way around the mouth of the chamber would result in significant gas leakage during firing, particularly since the breechblock would slam to the rear against the locking surfaces, increasing the clearance during firing. Hall rifles in the Winchester Gun Museum in "new" condition have gaps of .002 to .006 of an inch between breechblock and barrel.

By the 1840's most of the Hall rifles and carbines in service were somewhat worn and the problems of gas leakage had become a source of widespread complaints. This is not difficult to understand. Any gas leakage at the joint between the chamber and barrel would allow gas at the very highest pressure to escape. This leakage would occur all during the time the bullet was being accelerated through the barrel. As a result, even with small clearance, substantial quantities of gas could escape. Another factor was that the escaping gas at the high chamber pressure tended to produce an unpleasant shock wave that caused extreme discomfort to the soldier. The author vividly remembers shooting old black powder rifles with folded head ammunition. On occasion the old brittle heads would split at the rim allowing high pressure gas at full chamber pressure to escape into the atmosphere. The usual result was a sharp earsplitting sound superimposed on the normal boom of the cartridge. The secondary result was a severe ringing in the ears which was an indication that the safe threshold of noise had been exceeded and hearing had been damaged temporarily.

There was no question that the Hall rifles could be loaded much faster than conventional muzzle-loading rifles if you were on horseback, and this was a significant improvement for the Cavalry. It seems strange that the majority of the Hall firearms were fitted with smooth barrels, when the breech-loading system allowed the use of rifled barrels with no loading time penalty at all. It was probably due to the conviction that the Cavalry generally fought at short range, and the large .64 caliber smoothbore barrel could handle ball, buck and ball, and buckshot loads, providing flexibility and tremendous short-range power rather than long-range accuracy.

The Hall .64 caliber carbines had a chamber about 2.440 inches long with a diameter of .675 of an inch at the mouth tapering down to .610 inches at the rear. One bad side effect of this large chamber and barrel diameter was that the area of the sealing surfaces was substantially reduced. The chamber mouth was 1/16 inch larger all around than on the .52 caliber Hall rifles, and the result was a greater tendency for gas leakage.

Ammunition for the Hall Rifles

The ammunition for the Hall rifles has been described in Chapter 4. The two standard cartridges in .52 and .64 caliber are shown in Figure 4-1. Although paper cartridges were used in the early nineteenth century, it was far more common for the Hall rifles to be loaded with loose balls and powder from a special Hall powder flask. By the 1830's paper cartridges were coming into wider use in the American Army, and improved designs were developed in which the outer paper had been soaked in saltpeter so that it was readily ignited. With this design, the entire cartridge could be stuffed in the mouth of the chamber and the hot flame from the percussion cap would blast through the saltpeter-coated paper and ignite the main powder charge.

At the time the Hall rifle was adopted in 1819, there were virtually no instruments in the United States capable of accurately measuring force or velocity. As a result, comparative tests had to be made by pretty "rough and ready" methods. Tests performed in 1826 when the Hall rifles were first issued to troops gave the following rates of fire:

Hall Model 1819	100 shots
Model 1817 Common Rifle	43 shots
.69 Caliber flintlock musket	37 shots

A second series of tests were fired in the spring of 1837 at West Point, which was then a Government Arsenal. These tests gave slightly different results: [3]

Hall flintlock musket (100-grain charge): 5 shots per minute

[3] B. R. Lewis, *Small Arms and Ammunition in the U.S. Service,* Smithsonian, 1968, P 93

Model	Type	Powder: Grains	Bullet Weight: Grains	Muzzle Velocity: Feet/ Second	Muzzle Energy: Foot-Pounds	Efficiency: Energy Per Grain Of Propellant
Model 1817 Rifle "Common Rifle" 36 Inch Barrel	Flintlock, Rifled	70	218.5	1755	1495	21.4
Model 1830 Cadet Musket 36 Inch Barrel	Flintlock, Smoothbore	70	218.5	1690	1386	19.8
Model 1841 "Mississippi Rifle" 36 Inch Barrel	Percussion Rifled	100 70	218.5 218.5	2018 1750	1976 1488	19.8 21.25*
Jenks Carbine 24¼ Inch Barrel	Percussion Rifled	70	218.5	1687	1381	19.7
Hall Model 1826 Rifle 35 Inch Barrel	Flintlock Rifled	70	218.5	1490	1077	15.4
Model 1840 Hall-North Carbine 23.4 Inch Barrel	Percussion Smoothbore	70	218.5	1240	746	10.7

FIGURE 5-7 1843-1844 comparative tests of .52 and .54 caliber firearms.

Hall percussion rifle (70-grain charge). 3.56 shots per minute
Flintlock musket with solid ball: 2.53 shots per minute
Flintlock musket with buck and ball cartridge: 3 shots per minute

The power of these early firearms, as measured by penetration in white oak planks, is shown in the table below:

	100 Yds	200 Yds.	300 Yds
.69 Caliber Flintlock Musket	1 In.	.55 In.	"Shallow Dent"
Model 1817 Rifle .54 Caliber "Common Rifle"	.94 In.	.29 In.	".2 In. Dent"
.64 Caliber Hall Musket (86 Grain Charge)	.34 In.	Zero	
.52 Caliber Hall Rifle (70 Grain Charge)	.93 In.	Zero	

FIGURE 5-7a Penetration of white oak.

COMPARATIVE TESTS OF BREECH-LOADING AND MUZZLE-LOADING FIREARMS 1843-1844

In the late 1830's a rival inventor named William Jenks had developed a competitive breech-loading carbine which he felt was far superior to the Hall design. Jenks kept up an effective public relations campaign and eventually in 1843 and 1844 the very competent Army ballistician, Major Alfred Mordecai was asked to run a series of tests comparing the Hall and Jenks carbines with the standard muzzle-loading rifles. What is very interesting about these tests, is that five different weapons were fired with the standard rifle cartridge shown in the upper illustration of Figure 4-1. The ammunition was loaded with a round ball .525 of an inch in diameter, weighing 218.5 grains. The loads all had 70 grains of power except for the 100-grain load for the Model 1841 rifle. A later test of the Model 1841 with a 70-grain charge has been added for comparison. These tests then give a side by side comparison of the performance of the muzzle-loading rifles and two different design of breech-loaders. The oldest rifle tested was the Model 1817 Common Rifle, which was remarkably efficient. It ejected the 218.5-grain ball at a velocity of 1755 feet per second for a muzzle energy of about 1500 foot-pounds and a remarkably high efficiency of 21.4 foot-pounds of muzzle energy per grain of propellant. This is about the highest efficiency of any muzzle-loading rifle and it is particularly remarkable for a flintlock where gas leakage out the vent hole occurs all the time there is pressure in the barrel.

The Model 1830 Cadet smoothbore flintlock musket was designed to fire exactly the same cartridge. While the Model 1817 rifle had a bore diameter of .540 of an inch and a clearance between the bore and the barrel of only .015 of an inch the clearance in the musket between the bullet and barrel was three times as great or .045 inch. The diameter of the smoothbore Cadet musket barrel was .570 of an inch. The .525-inch diameter ball with its paper wadding was ejected from the muzzle at 1690 feet per second with a calculated muzzle energy of 1386 foot-pounds and a still remarkably high efficiency of 19.8 foot-pounds of muzzle energy per grain of propellant. The ballistic performance is compared in Figure 5-7.

In these 1844 tests the model 1841 percussion rifle (which also had a .540 of an inch bore) was fired with a 100-grain powder charge. This sent the ball whistling out the muzzle at 2018 feet per second and almost 2000 foot-pounds of muzzle energy. The efficiency was almost identical to that of the Cadet flintlock rifle at 19.8 foot-pounds per grain of propellant. A later test was fired at Washington Arsenal in 1855 with the Model 1841 rifle and the 70-grain powder charge. These tests gave an average measured muzzle velocity of 1750 feet per second and a calculated efficiency of 21.25 foot-pounds of muzzle energy per grain of propellant. This performance was identical to that of the Model 1817 Common Rifle.

These tests of the Model 1817 Flintlock Rifle, Model 1830 Cadet Flintlock musket, and Model 1841 Percussion rifle, all with barrels about three feet long could be said to define the efficiency of the muzzle-loading rifles and muskets firing the .525 of an inch ball, with very small amounts of leakage at the breech, at 20 to 21 foot-pounds of muzzle energy per grain of propellant. This was a very high efficiency for black powder firearms.

The Jenks Percussion Carbine

The performance of the Jenks breech-loading carbine in the series of tests was really impressive. The Jenks had a barrel only 24¼ inches long compared with the 36-inch barrels of the Model 1817 and 1841 rifles and Model 1830 Cadet Musket. The barrel length is rather important in determining the efficiency of a firearm for a longer barrel allows the same quantity of gas to do more work in accelerating the musket ball and expand further before being released to the atmosphere. A Jenks carbine with its 24-inch barrel delivered a muzzle velocity of 1687 feet per second with a muzble energy of 1381 foot-pounds. This performance was identical to that of the Cadet Flintlock Musket and calculates out to an efficiency of 19.7 foot-pounds of muzzle energy per grain of propellant.

Efficiency of Hall Rifles

It is clear from the figures that the Hall firearms did not perform anywhere near as well. The Hall rifle with a barrel of 35 inches gave a muzzle velocity of 1490 feet per second and a muzzle energy of 1077 foot-pounds. This resulted in an efficiency of 15.4 foot-pounds of muzzle energy per grain of propellant. This lower efficiency was despite the fact that the ball fitted the barrel very closely in the Hall rifle and yet had .045 of an inch clearance in the Model 1830 musket which had a similar barrel length. This significant drop in efficiency can only be attributed to the severe gas leakage at the breech of the Hall rifle. This gas leakage corresponded to a loss of 15 grains of powder charge.

The performance of the Hall-North percussion carbine Model 1840 was even worse. This carbine had a barrel length very similar to that of the Jenks percussion carbine and both had a similar percussion ignition system which limited gas leakage through the nipple or cone. The resulting muzzle velocity was only 1240 feet per second and a muzzle energy of 746 foot-pounds corresponding to an efficiency of only 10.66 foot-pounds of muzzle energy per grain of propellant. Here again the sad performance must be laid to severe gas leakage at the breech corresponding to a gas loss of over 22 grains of powder charge. The muzzle energy of the Hall carbine was only 54 percent of that of the Jenks carbine firing the same cartridge.

JENKS BREECH-LOADING FIREARMS

William Jenks of Columbia, South Carolina, created the design of a remarkably efficient breech-loading firearm. He did his experimental work in the 1830's and received patent No. 747 on May 25, 1838. The construction details defined in the patent differ substantially from the final model of Jenks carbines and rifles which were used by the Army and Navy. The

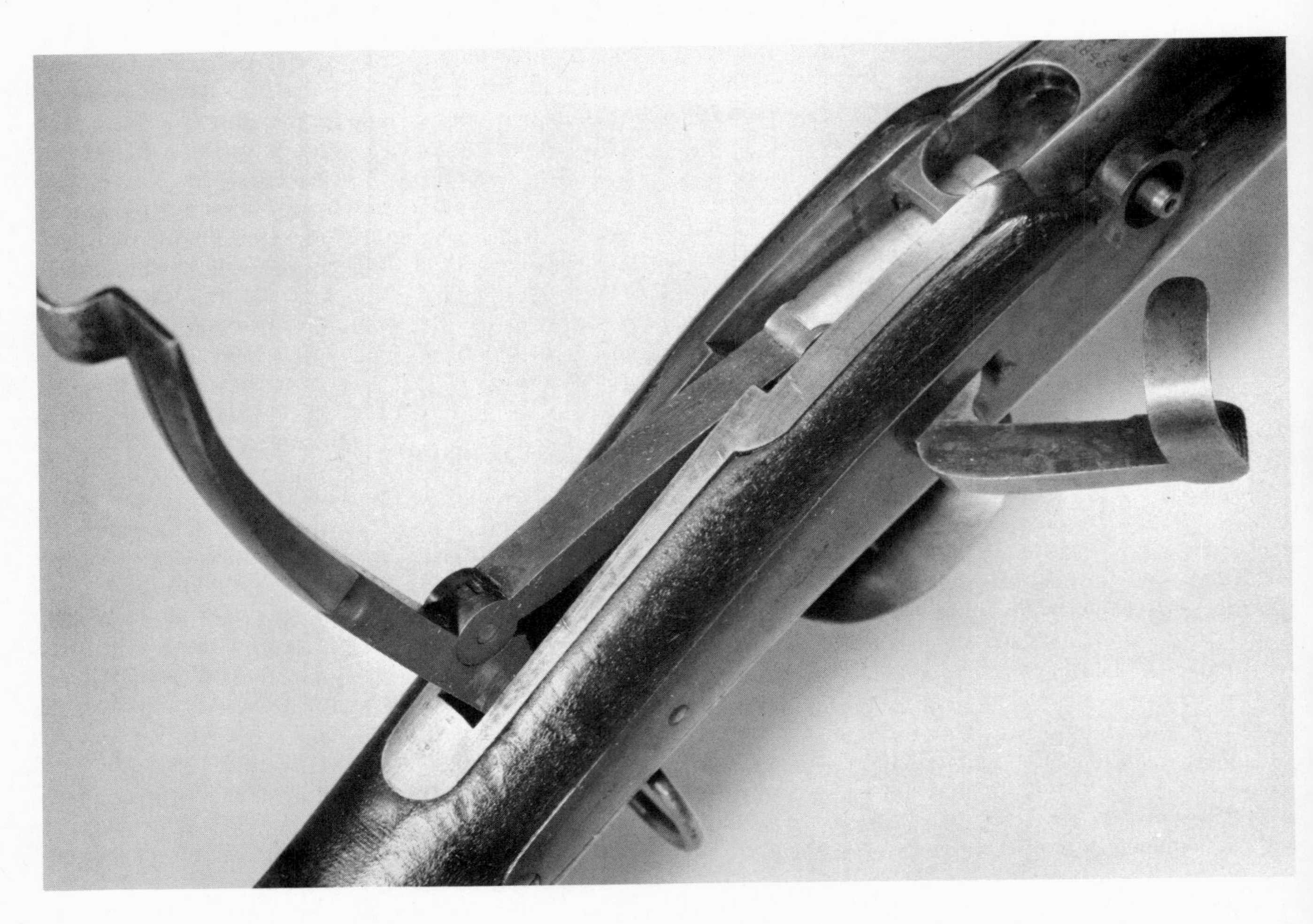

FIGURE 5-8 Closeup of Jenks action.

patent shows a conventional flintlock rifle with a slot cut in the top of the barrel running about 3 inches forward of the breech. The breech end of the barrel was sealed by a short cylindrical breechblock designed to fit the barrel closely. A hook-shaped handle was fastened to the top of the breechblock with two screws. This allowed the user to move the breechblock to the rear about an inch and a half, exposing an open loading port in the top of the barrel. The rifle was loaded by dropping in a ball which rolled forward in the chamber until stopped by the rifled section of the barrel. A loose powder charge was poured in the opening from a powder flask and then the breechblock was shoved forward to seal off the opening. Obviously if the breechblock could be moved easily by hand the gas force would blow it smartly to the rear, allowing the gas to escape out the port. Jenkins solved this by mounting a large spring on the left side of the rifle with a rectangular block which extended inward and filled the space between the breech tang of the rifle and the rear of the bolt when it was in its forward or locked position. To reload the rifle the spring was pulled laterally to the left, removing the prop from in back of the breech bolt and allowing it to be pulled to the rear with the hook-shaped handle.

William Jenks rapidly refined his design into a more effective arrangement. The refined design included a top lever which was swung upward and to the rear, automatically moving the breech bolt to the rear and giving access to the loading port in the barrel top.

By 1839 Jenks received an order for 100 flintlock carbines. Thirty-five of these were issued to troops at the Carlisle Barracks for trial. The remainder were soon converted to percussion ignition so that Jenks flintloading firearms are exceedingly rare. These firearms were officially known as musketoons and had a smoothbore .64 caliber barrel firing a 1 ounce ball. The barrel was a little over 25½ inches long and the over-all length was about 42¼ inches. The weight was about 7 pounds. The barrel was held to the long oil finished walnut stock by two barrel bands retained by cross pins. The barrel bands, trigger guard and butt plate were all brass, polished bright. A polished steel ramrod was fitted beneath the barrel.

The flintlock mechanism had a rounded double necked hammer typical of the standard musket of this period. A brass pan was bolted to the lock plate and it was fitted with a high fence to the rear.

The Jenks flintlock design was quickly modified to take advantage of the new percussion ignition system. Since the top of the barrel was pretty well covered with loading ports and top levers, the hammer mechanism was located on the side. A typical Jenks percussion carbine design is shown in Figure 5-8 with the action open. The locking lever has been pivoted upward to about a three quarters open position so that the front of the breech bolt is still visible through the loading port. When fully open the breech bolt is flush with the rear of the loading port. The side hammer action is clearly shown in this illustration. This was a popular commercial design and was known as a "mule ear" hammer design. It was well designed from a safety standpoint, at least for a right-handed shooter. The percussion ignition system was on the side away from the face, and safety was further enhanced by the design of a metal ring projecting from the barrel which completely surrounded the cone or nipple. The hammer was designed with a deep cavity so that the copper percussion cap was completely surrounded by steel when ignition occurred. There was a tail on the hammer which extended up over the top of the barrel. This hook-shaped extension served two purposes. First it was a surface which was grasped to cock the hammer and, second, it extended over the locking lever retaining the locking lever in a down position when the hammer was fired.

A late model Jenks carbine is shown in Figure 5-9. This is a pretty typical Jenks carbine as issued to the Navy or Cavalry with the exception that it has a box on the side of the lock plate containing a Maynard tape priming mechanism. The Jenks carbine is a very neat and compact design. Everything folds in place and it looks even simpler than the standard muzzle-loading percussion carbine of the 1840's. The Jenks percussion rifles and carbines were generally made in .52 caliber with either smoothbore or rifled barrels. The comparative tests performed at the Washington Arsenal in 1844 demonstrated that the Jenks was a remarkably efficient firearm equivalent in performance to the muzzle-loading rifles and carbines of the same period.

It was also an extremely tough firearm, according to reports of the 24th Congress, which included the results of the 1841 trials of Jenks carbines by the First Regiment Dragoons and later endurance trials at Fort Adams. Four Jenks carbines were tested for accuracy, force, rapidity of fire and endurance. The endurance test of one carbine was extended to 4500 rounds at which point the board reported that it was "well adapted to and capable of performing all the requirements of the service." The test was then extended an additional 10,313 shots, making a total endurance trial of 14,813 shots, when the nipple or percussion cone split, ending the test. This was a very minor malfunction and the Jenks carbine certainly demonstrated remarkable toughness and endurance.

The rate of fire of a Jenks carbine was substantially

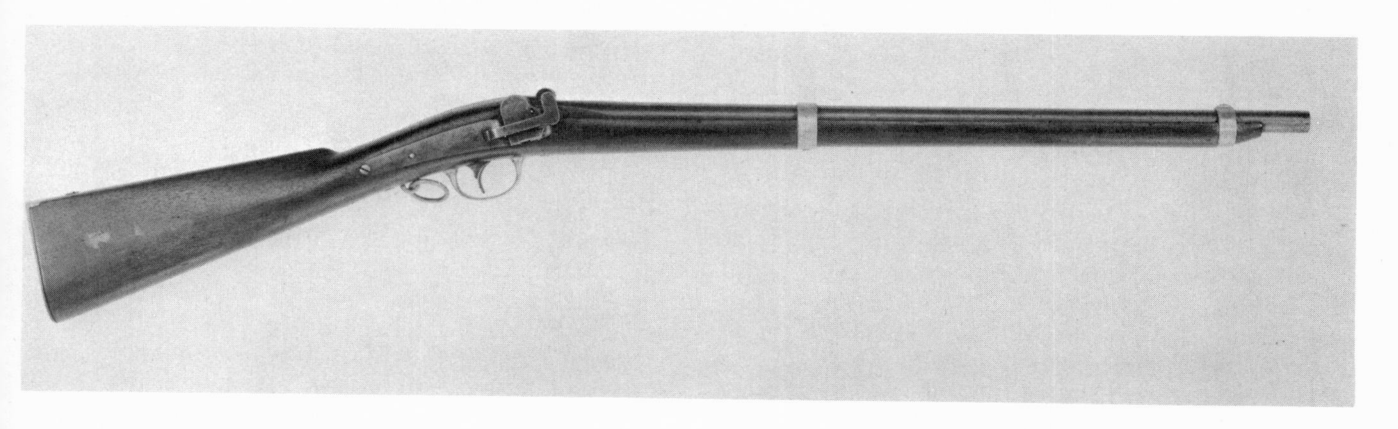

FIGURE 5-9 Late-model Jenks carbine.

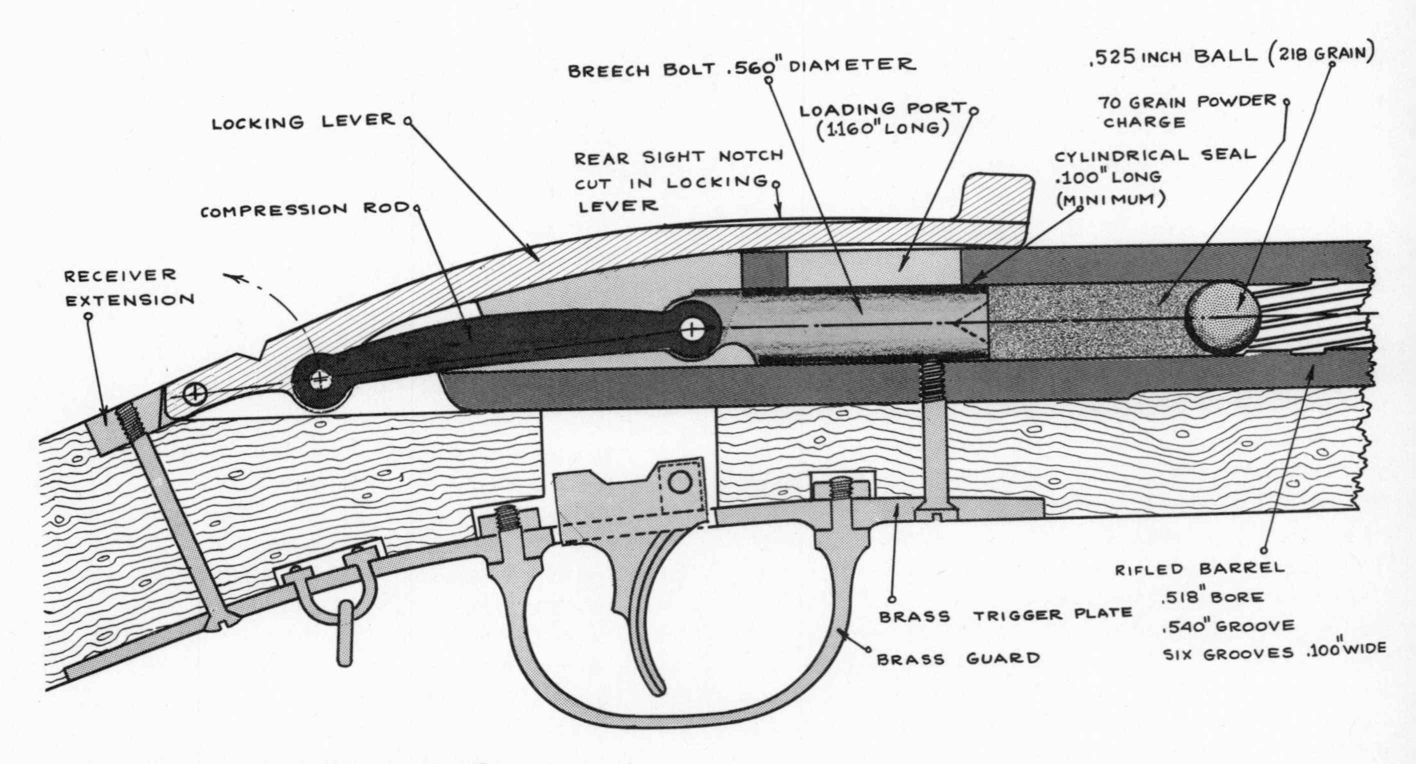

FIGURE 5-10 Cross-section of Jenks rifle action.

higher than that of the muzzle-loading musket. It was probably not quite as high as the Hall percussion rifle, for the Hall could be loaded with the entire paper cartridge while the Jenks had to be loaded with loose powder and ball.

A cross-section drawing of the Jenks percussion action is shown in Figure 5-10. Many different models of Jenks rifles and carbines were manufactured in fairly small quantities during the 1840's and there were many minor variations. This drawing and the photograph in Figure 5-8 are both of a Jenks Navy carbine manufactured in 1845. The top of the barrel is marked with Wm Jenks and USN, RP, P and 1845, in four vertical lines toward the breech. The lock plate is marked Wm Jenks near the tail and then in the center on three lines is N.P. Ames, Springfield, Mass. The carbine has a brass butt plate and trigger guard and two brass barrel bands. The barrel has a land diameter of .518 of an inch, and is rifled with six grooves, each .100 of an inch wide and .011 of an inch deep, resulting in a groove diameter of .540 of an inch. The breech bolt is .560 of an inch in diameter and 1.67 inches long from the bolt face to the center line of the pivot. The loading port is .560 of an inch wide and 1.16 inches long and there is a very solid bridge across the rear of the loading port .135 of an inch long.

Loading the Jenks Carbine

After the Jenks was fired the mule ear hammer extension held the locking lever down. First step in loading was to move the hammer to the half-cocked or safety position and clear the broken pieces of copper from the nipple or cone. The locking lever was then lifted upward through an arc of about 90 degrees. This motion gave a very powerful leverage for the compression rod to move the breech bolt to the rear about 1¼ inches until the face of the breech bolt was just flush with the rear of the loading port. The soldier lowered the muzzle of the rifle into a downward position and dropped in a .525-inch ball which rolled forward in the chamber until stopped by accumulated fouling or by the "ball seat" where the rifling starts.

The soldier then took his powder flask and measured out a charge of 70 grains of black powder and poured that into the loading port. The locking lever was then moved clockwise into a closed position as shown in Figure 5-10, which cammed the breech bolt forward, compressing the powder charge into the chamber. The rifle was ready for firing as soon as the hammer was moved to a full-cocked position and a fresh percussion cap put on the cone.

The Jenks carbine provided excellent sealing as proven by the comparative tests performed at Washington Arsenal in 1844. This excellent seal was accomplished by a close fit between the cylindrical bolt and the carefully reamed chamber in the barrel of the rifle. The minimum sealing length was at the top of the bolt, sealing against the barrel just forward of the loading port which was .100 of an inch long. The sealing length on the sides was substantially greater. The right side of the bolt had a triangular cut shown in dotted lines in Figure 5-10. For some reason the cone was located slightly to the rear of the chamber. This angled cut provided a connecting passage for the flame between the cone and the main powder charge. This angled cut may also have caused the black powder to pack on this side of the chamber during the ramming operation, thus insuring that a fresh charge of powder was immediately adjacent to the flame when the percussion cap ignited.

When the Jenks carbine fired, the breech bolt slammed smartly to the rear. The rear of the breech bolt struck the "compression rod," which transmitted the thrust to the pivot point between the compression rod and locking lever. This placed the rear section of locking lever in compression. The force was transmitted to the receiver through the rearmost pivot of the locking lever. The entire receiver and rear section of the barrel were placed in tension by the firing forces. Since long parts were involved with high forces considerable stretching and compression occurred. This is technically known as having a lot of "dynamic headspace." On the Jenks it did not matter, but on a cartridge rifle it could allow the head of the cartridge case to burst.

On the Hall rifles the locking surfaces or the bolt were very close to the breech face, and only a short section of the receiver was placed into tension. The dynamic headspace of a Hall rifle was much less, but the poor sealing of the Hall breech offset this advantage.

The links on the Jenks rifle were in line when the shot was fired. The linkage on the Jenks rifle was arranged so that gas pressure on the bolt face tended to rotate the links into a more tightly locked position. Since this line of thrust was at a slight angle to the axis of the bolt, it was a slight upward component, tending to lift the rear of the bolt and this force was absorbed by the very important bridge at the rear of the loading port.

Success of the Jenks Action

The Jenks action appeared to have everything going for it. It was simple and compact, sealed the breech very well so that it gave excellent power, and had proven excellent endurance in official government trials. Official Government boards which had tested the firearm found it an excellent firearm. One joint Army-Navy Board, including Alfred Mordecai of the Ordance Department, convened at Washington Arsenal in January 1845 and reported as follows:

> The Board is of the opinion that this carbine combines, in an eminent degree, the two great advantages attending arms loading at the breech, that of propelling the ball with great force, and that of being loaded rapidly easily in situations where the use of a ram is inconvenient; the latter consideration would recommend it for use in both service and "tops" of vessels, as well as in the cavalry service.
>
> The arrangements adopted by Mr. Jenks for effecting the above objects appeared to the board to be ingenious and in many respects well adapted to the purpose; the numerous trials heretofore made with this carbine seem to have shown that the apparatus posseses sufficient strength and security from accident in common practice, but whether it is entirely free from the objections which have been heretofore found to attend contrivances for loading at the breech it is not in the power of the board to determine.

Despite these glowing recommendations, the Jenks carbines and rifles were only procured in small quantities for experimental trail and the arming of a very limited number of troops. The reasons would appear to lie in the climate of the early 1840's. Hall's flintlock and percussion rifles and carbines had been in service more than 20 years. Although these firearms were satisfactory when in new condition, the common soldier could not be relied upon to take extreme care of his firearm, and a little sand or grit in the breech would tend to scratch the sealing surfaces between the breechblock and barrel. The field armorers did not have all the tools and gauges and polishing equipment to restore the tight head space and smooth sealing surfaces required for effective functioning. The result was that as the Hall rifles got older gas leakage at the breech became more severe and complaints from soldiers began to increase.

The Army had also tested the Colt revolving rifle during the 1840's. These were the early models manufactured at the Paterson, New Jersey, factory before the processes were entirely perfected, and many cylinders blew up. There was another serious problem — if the rifles were not carefully loaded flame from one chamber would flash over to the others, firing several chambers on one shot. This was disastrous if the soldier had his left hand on the forearm of the rifle.

The Ordnance Department had been approached by many inventors of patent breech-loading rifles. Many of the inventors had political supporters in Congress who brought pressure to bear on the Ordnance Department to test and accept a wide variety of breech-loading firearms. The over-all result was that by the early 1840's just the words "Patent breech-loading firearms" were sufficient to cause field officers to become apoplectic and for members of the Ordnance Department to resist political requests for the testing of new patent firearms with all the strength they could muster. This was not all based on simple prejudice. Many field officers had the bitter experience of being out on a campaign with semi-developed firearms and finding that they became unserviceable due to breakage of minor parts and could not be repaired far afield. These officers were emphatic in their insistance that arms be fully reliable before being issued to troops. Many experienced field officers simply refused to issue "patent rifles" to their units if a hard campaign was anticipated, leaving the breech-loaders in the barracks racks and issuing reliable muzzle-loaders instead.

THE SHARPS RIFLE

By far the most successful and famous breech-loading rifle to fire caseless ammunition was invented by Christian Sharps and patented on September 12, 1848. Sharps was born in 1811 in Washington, New Jersey, where he received an education in the public schools. During his teens he became apprenticed as a machinist and became skilled in the manufacture of firearms. During the 1830's he worked for John H. Hall at Harpers Ferry Armory in Virginia, learning about the manufacture of the Hall breech-loading rifles. Christian Sharps was in an excellent position to benefit from his early training and his experience with Captain Hall. He had a clever mind and was a fine craftsman, and when the manufacture of the Hall rifles was discontinued at Harpers Ferry about 1844, Sharps was well aware of the principles of interchangeable manufacture of gun components and knew all about the gas leakage problems with the Hall rifles which led to its failure in Army service.

During the late 1840's Sharps lived in Cincinnati, Ohio, where he continued his experimental work to develop the basic principles of his rifle. He proposed to solve the problem of sealing the breech by making a rectangular breechblock which slid vertically on tracks within a short rigid receiver. The Sharps sealed by having carefully machined flat surfaces on the rear of the barrel and on the face of the breechblock. This allowed the machining of more accurate surfaces than the slightly curved sealing surfaces required on the Hall rifles. By 1848 Sharps had received his basic patent covering the design in crude form and by 1850 had secured an official test by the Army Ordnance Board. Captain Alfred Mordecai was a member of the Board which issued an official test report on November 27, 1850. The report of the Board was highly favorable:

> This is an arm loading at the breech which is opened and closed by a vertical slide or shear cutting off the end of the cartridge. This arm has withstood all the trials the Board has considered necessary to make with it. It was fired several hundred times without cleaning, during which the movements of its machinery were not obstructed. The arm is loaded with great ease and rapidity by using a simply prepared cartridge which Mr. Sharps has arranged: and also the ordinary rifle and musket ammunition with its percussion caps, can be used with facility.
>
> The penetration, range and accuracy of fire from the rifle thus arranged, with the cartridge and conical ball prepared for it, were superior to that of any other breech-loading piece offered to the Board. With Maynard's Primer (which, as well as the cap, may be used) this arm was fired 10 times per minute, and when discharged over water, a second charge was fired before the ricochet of the first had ceased.
>
> From the observations of the use of this rifle, the Board are of the opinion that it is superior to any of the other arms loading at the breech, and think it would be well to have further trials made, and to put some of them in the hands of troops to determine whether they are suitable for the military service.
>
> All of which is respectfully submitted.

Despite this glowing report and the strong support of other forward looking Army officers, Christian Sharps did not receive much encouragement or large orders for his rifle.

The Sharps patent No. 5763, which was issued in

September 1848, was a "basic" patent with very broad claims.

> What I claim as my invention and desire to secure by letters patent, is a combination of the sliding breech with the barrel, the breech supporter (receiver), and the stock, in such a manner that when the sliding breech is forced down, the breech bore will be so exposed as to enable it to receive a cartridge on a line with the bore; and when the sliding breech is forced up, it will sheer [SIC] off the end of the cartridge, so as to expose the powder to the fire communication, and will firmly and securely close the breech bore, substantially as herein set forth.
>
> I also claim the combination of the cap nipple with the sliding breech, substantially in the manner and for the purpose herein set forth.

This is a very broad statement covering the principle of a gun sealed at the breech by a vertically sliding breechblock and using a percussion ignition system. Such broad patent coverage put Sharps in an excellent position to control all inventions of this type during the crucial years of the Civil War.

This broad patent statement was followed by five claims covering the broad features listed above plus a description of important specific features of the design. One important element was the finger lever linkage which locked the breechblock so firmly in an up position that no amount of downward force on the breechblock could force the finger lever to swing open. The breech bolt could only be moved by operating the lever. Another combination listed was the addition of a knife on the front upper edge of the breechblock designed to shear off the rear end of the projecting cartridge from the breech, thus exposing fresh powder to the flame of the percussion cap. Another important safety feature of the Sharps rifles was the design of the hammer stop which prevented the hammer from reaching the cone on the breechblock and firing the percussion cap unless the breechblock was in a fully up position and the gun locked.

Sharps Model of 1851

By 1851 the design of the Sharps product had evolved into the carbine shown as the upper illustration in Figure 5-11. The carbine had a .52 caliber round barrel and a walnut forearm retained by one flat barrel band. The breechblock was rectangular and mounted at an angle to the barrel so that it slid downward and forward as the lever was opened.

Early Sharps rifles leaked fire at the breech very badly, as did the Hall rifles. By 1851 Christian Sharps had attempted to solve the problem by inletting a hard ring of platinum into the face of the breech bolt which fitted the machined breech face of the barrel very closely. The detail of the breechblock design is shown on the left-hand side of Figure 5-12. The platinum alloy selected was a very hard material and represented a sophisticated approach to the sealing problem for the 1850's. Despite this approach, the Model 1851 rifles had serious leakage at the breech and powder residue built up rapidly on the large flat surfaces of the breech bolt, making the rifle hard to operate after a few shots were fired. The earliest designs required the removal of a screw to take out the breechblock, but by the early 1850's the design had been modified so that the breechblock was easily removed without tools. This pivot is located at the lower front edge of the receiver and on the Model 1851 an S-shaped tail had been added to the pin so that the soldier could grasp the tail and twist the pin, rotating it and pulling it out of the action after which the entire breechblock and finger lever assembly could be removed for cleaning.

Lock Mechanism

The back action lock design as shown in Figure 3-20 was ideally suited to the needs of the Sharps action. In the Model 1851 Christian Sharps added some ingenious features of his own. The hammer was mounted inside the lock plate and a Maynard tape priming mechanism was built into the forward section of the lock assembly. The hammer was directly in line with the tape priming and a small "hand" similar to that used to rotate a revolver cylinder was mounted in the front side of the hammer with a long slender arm extending upward into the channel which carried the tape primers up to the nipple or cone. As the hammer was cocked this slender arm pushed the paper tape upward one primer length. When the hammer fell the arm snapped rapidly downward and to prevent it from carrying the paper strip back down again a second slender spring-loaded arm was mounted in the lock mechanism so that once the hammer hand had raised the paper tape upward, the second arm locked it in an upward position.

The back lock action in the Model 1851 showed rather early features. For example, the mainspring had a curved extension which rode directly on the rear surface of the hammer similar to the design of the Brown Bess mainspring shown in Figure 1-5. A separate sear spring was fitted rather than using the lower extension of the mainspring.

Sharps Models of 1852 and 1853

A Model 1853 Sharps carbine is the second illustration in Figure 5-11.[5] The Model 1852 was very similar in appearance. This design continued the .52 caliber round barrel to which the walnut forearm was retained by one flat barrel band. A long-range rear sight was fitted to this model with a long leaf which is folded flat down onto the barrel. For lang-range firing this leaf could be flipped up into a vertical position to provide accurate sighting at a distance. Unfortunately these early Sharps could not take advantage of a long-range rear sight for their accuracy was pretty poor. During the 1850's Sharps rifles and carbines were manufactured at several factories and not all the manufacturers used the same barrel dimensions. Christian Sharps was a very ingenious inventor and he came up with the solution shown as the third illustration down in Figure 4-1. This shows a cross-section drawing of a typical paper Sharps cartridge of the 1850's. The bullet is designed with three driving bands. The front band is .52 caliber, the middle band is .54 caliber, and the rear band is .56 caliber. With this solution Sharps felt that the bullet should be reasonably accurate no matter what the barrel diameter! There was a reduced diameter section of the bullet extending to the rear of the third driving band into which a groove was cast. The cylindrical tube of a paper cartridge was fitted over this reduced diameter section and the paper tube was securely tied into the groove with cartridge thread. A 50- or 60-grain powder charge was poured into the open paper tube which was then folded over and the tail folded along the powder cavity.

The design of the Sharps bullets and barrels has led to great confusion among historians. Do you call the cartridge a .52 caliber or a .56 caliber? Sharps rifles and carbines of this period are generally listed as .52 caliber, but occasionally they will be found listed as .54 or .56 caliber.

[5] D. F. Butler, *op. cit.*, P 35

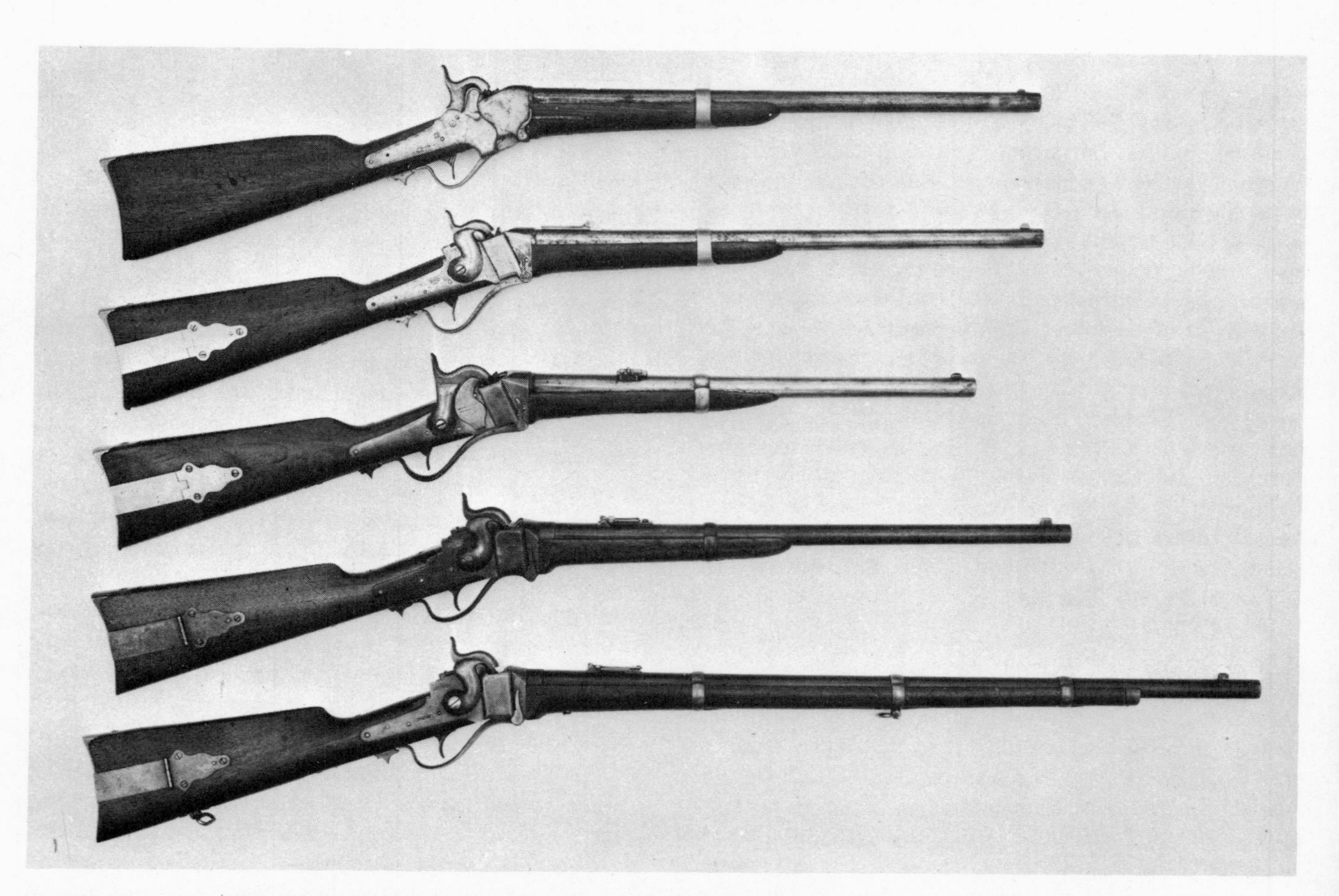

FIGURE 5-11 TOP: Sharps Model 1851 carbine; SECOND: Sharps Model 1853 carbine; THIRD: Sharps Model 1855 carbine with Maynard tape primer mechanism; FOURTH: Sharps Model 1859 carbine with pellet primer mechanism; BOTTOM: Sharps Model 1859 rifle.

The Model 1852 and 1853 rifles and ammunition were still not very satisfactory. Tests performed at Harpers Ferry Armory in 1853 and 1854 had a very sour note:

> The bullets are too large for the diameter of chamber of barrel. After being fired four or five rounds, it is impossible to force the cartridge in without bursting and spilling the powder. This firing was continued by resorting to the expedient of separating the bullet from the cartridge, forcing it into the chamber with a stick, and afterward pouring in the powder. The slide frequently became very difficult to move. When the arm was taken into the shop to be cleaned after the firing was concluded, the slide could not be moved at all until thoroughly soaked in oil to soften the dirt around it. The paper of the cartridge is always left behind in the chamber after each shot, and it is frequently on fire when the succeeding cartridge is inserted.

The Model 1852 and 1853 rifles both looked very similar to the second illustration in Figure 5-11. The major difference between the two models was that the 1852 design continued the use of a platinum ring inserted into the bolt face as a gas seal while the Model 1853 had an expanding ring which will be described later.

The Model 1852 and 1853 Sharps carbines look much more like the familiar Civil War designs. The hammer had been moved to the outside of the lock plate and the Lawrence pellet priming system had been added. The interior of the lock still retained the early design features including a separate sear spring and the tail of the mainspring bearing directly on the tumbler — a source of high friction and wear. The development of the Lawrence pellet priming mechanism was a result of the manufacturing arrangements which Christian Sharps had made with the Robbins and Lawrence Company of Windsor, Vermont. At this time Sharps rifles were also being manufactured by the Maynard Gun Company of Chicopee Falls, Massachusetts, and by the Massachusetts Arms Company, also in Chicopee Falls.

The 1850's were a time of great turmoil in the United States and many could see that the differences between North and South were rapidly moving toward a crisis. The Robbins and Lawrence Company purchased a 25-acre plot of land in Hartford, Connecticut, to build an additional factory for the manufacture of Sharps rifles. Robbins and Lawrence had established a reputation as manufacturers of high precision parts and also as the designers and builders of precision machinery, and they had the skill and knowledge to manufacture Sharps rifles to the very exacting tolerances required for success. Richard S. Lawrence did a great deal of experimental work on the rifle during the 1850's. Apparently Christian Sharps was a prolific inventor and could never "freeze" anything for production. After machinery was purchased and production started he wanted to change the design again. By 1853 disagreements between Sharps and Robbins and Lawrence had become so basic that Sharps ceased his work as technical advisor and set up a separate C. Sharps and Company to manufacture his rifles in Philadelphia.

Samuel E. Robbins, the other partner of Robbins and Lawrence, was not a technical man but was a very active salesmen. This ultimately led the firm into disaster for it became involved in some very unfortunate contracts with the British Government for the manufacture of Enfield rifles and by 1856 the company was bankrupt. The wheel of fortune turned again, and Lawrence became Chief Armorer for the C. Sharps and Company in Philadelphia.

Lawrence contributed a great deal to the design of the Sharps rifles. One of his early contributions was the pellet priming mechanism which was first fitted to the Model 1852 and 1853 carbines. A vertical hole was drilled through the forward edge of the lock plate. A stack of shallow metal cups filled with priming compound was placed into the hole and pushed upward by a spiral spring. A cutoff plate at the top of the hole prevented the pellets from popping out. A horizontal slide was fitted with a small tail which fitted a cut in the hammer. As the hammer was cocked this slide was drawn rearward, allowing a primer to pop up against the top plate. When the trigger was pulled and the hammer fell the slide picked up the top priming disk and propelled it forward so that it arrived over the top of the percussion cone just before the hammer struck the cone. Obviously the timing of this device was pretty tricky. It turned out to be very successful and was widely used on the Civil War percussion Sharps rifles and carbines.

The pellet primers were more rugged and waterproof than the Maynard primer system and gave excellent service during the Civil War. The pellet primers were contained in a small brass tube and could be inserted very quickly into the magazine in the lock plate. If the soldier did not have a special pellet primer, the rifle could easily be loaded with regular percussion caps.

BREECH SEALS A major improvement in the Model 1853 design was the addition of the Conant breech seal. This is shown in the lower illustration of Figure 5-12. It consists of a small flanged steel ring fitted into a shallow cylindrical cut in the breech bolt. The ring was designed with a lip on the forward side. When the rifle was fired gas pressure got behind the lip and

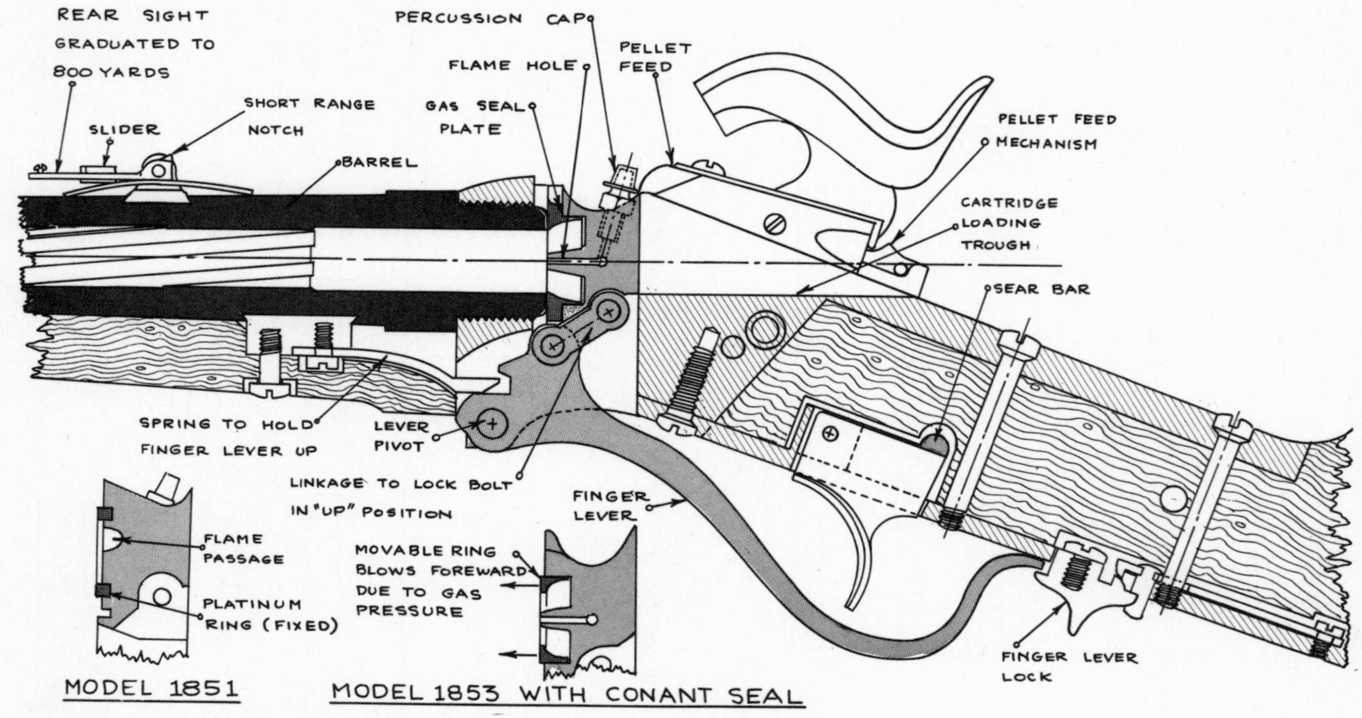

FIGURE 5-12 Cross-section of Model 1859 Sharps percussion action.

drove the ring forward against the face of the barrel. This design represented a major improvement for it meant that the gas pressure would be utilized to automatically take up any tolerance or clearance between the bolt face and the barrel every time a shot was fired. *The gas pressure itself was used to choke off the gas leakage.* There were two models of the Conant design and Figure 5-12 shows the improved version which was developed late in 1853 and became a basic design feature for the Sharps models made in the late 1850's.

Sharps Model 1855

The third illustration down in Figure 5-11 shows a Model 1855 Sharps carbine. The carbine is fitted with a short round barrel and the forearm is retained by one rounded barrel band. A long-range rear sight with three folding leaves has been mounted on the barrel. The breech mechanism was fitted with a Maynard tape primer and a hammer design very similar to that used on the 1855 series of standard U.S. muzzle-loading rifles and rifle-muskets.

Sharps Model 1859

It was in the year 1859 Sharps brought out its final design of percussion action which was widely manufactured during the Civil War. The Model 1859 carbine is shown as the fourth illustration down in Figure 5-11 and a Civil War Sharps rifle such as that used by Berdan's Sharpshooters is shown as the lowest illustration. The rifles and carbines were fitted with post front sights and a folding leaf rear sight. In the position shown in the illustration the rifle was sighted for short ranges. With the leaf flipped into up position, there was a sighting notch for 200 yards at the bottom of the leaf and 800 yards at the top. A sliding sight bar was used to adjust for ranges in between.

During the early 1940's the author purchased an old, broken-down Model 1859 Sharps percussion carbine and a Model 1859 carbine which had been converted to caliber .50/70 center-fire during the 1870's. The rifles both had minor parts missing and it was a labor of many weeks to clean and restore them to first class condition. One carbine had a shattered buttstock and this was eventually replaced with a brand-new buttstock which had been manufactured during the Civil War and had lain in storage for 80 years. During the past year the author was able to locate and purchase a rear sight for the percussion Sharps carbine which had been stored for almost 110 years. The original blued finish is spotted with rust, but it is accurately machined with clear sharp graduations and the slide has just about the right amount of tension to move smoothly from one graduation to another and stay properly in place.

The 1859 models were the first models to have a vertically sliding breechblock. The Lawrence pellet priming system was continued and the lock mechanism showed all the modern back lock design features, such as those shown in Figure 3-20. The mainspring provided its force to the tumbler through a stirrup and swivel, reducing the friction force. The sear spring was an extension of the lower arm of the mainspring so that the entire hammer and sear mechanism required only the one spring. Both of these improvements had been included in the Model of 1855.

An improved gas seal was included in the Model of 1859 and later designs. This was the final development of the Sharps percussion action, and the design is shown in the main illustration of Figure 5-12. The principle of the Conant gas seal had been continued, but instead of a ring a separate face plate was fitted to the breech bolt. This face plate had a flange extending to the rear which fitted into a hollow cylindrical cut in the face of the breechblock. When the rifle was fired the gas pressure got behind this flanged ring and drove it forward to seal against the face of the barrel. Here again the gas pressure was utilized to shut off gas leakage, and as long as the parts were kept reasonably clean and the surfaces were smooth, the result was excellent gas sealing at the breech.

Many other details of the Sharps action are shown in Figure 5-12.[6] While the breechblock looks like a rugged, solid chunk of steel, it was, in fact, cut away internally to fairly thin sections. There was a large counterbore in the face to take the Conant seal and the lower section of the block was cut away in the center to allow room for the connecting link and finger lever motion. The connecting link was an ingenious design. Figure 5-12 shows that the three pivot points between the finger lever and the two link pivot points were out of line with the action fully locked. This geometric arrangement meant that a force downward on the breech block would tend to rotate the connecting link into a jammed position. The more force that was applied the tighter the action would be jammed shut so that the only way to move the breechblock vertically was to drop the finger lever, thus rotating the lower pivot point of the connecting link to the rear and then pulling it downward.

With the finder lever fully open the top of the breechblock lay below the cartridge loading trough. The trough provided a smooth guide to slide a cartridge quickly into the chamber. The upper surface of the gas seal plate was formed with a sharp edge to cut off the rear of a paper cartridge as the breechblock was lifted. This was unnecessary for most of the Civil War cartridges were contained in a combustible cloth case which had been soaked in saltpeter or in a heavy paper tube with a thin paper membrane at the rear, and the blast of flame from the percussion cap passing downward through the passage and then forward through a flame hole in the center of the breechblock would penetrate the rear of either cartridge design and ignite the main powder charge.

The Sharps design included a leaf spring mounted underneath the barrel which held the finger lever either in a fully up or fully down position. In addition a finger lever lock mechanism was placed behind the trigger. This was a somewhat complicated assembly of parts and is shown in Figure 5-12 position to lock the lever upward. The components were arranged so that it could be quickly snapped into an off position allowing fast reloading, but a separate motion, depressing the pin behind the finger lever lock was required to put the lock in the on position. This is a sophisticated design approach in requiring the soldier to make a very deliberate motion to lock the action shut, but a very easy motion to unlock it.

The over-all result was that the Model 1859 design was perfected just when it was needed, at the opening of the Civil War. The many design changes during the 1850's reflected Sharps' own experimentation, the ideas of Richard Lawrence, and many improvements recommended by field experience. Although only 5540 Sharps rifles and carbines had been purchased by the United States Government during the decade of the 1850's, there were 80,512 Sharps carbines and 9141 Sharps rifles purchased during the Civil War. It has been estimated that over 100,000 Sharps rifles and carbines were actually in use, since many were purchased by volunteer regiments which armed themselves. A total of slightly over 16,306,508 Sharps rifles and carbine cartridges were purchased during the Civil War.[7] This averages out to approximately 160 cartridges per Sharps. This appears to be a very low figure compared with our modern ammunition requirements and yet it is much higher than most Civil War breech-loaders, for the Sharps was widely deployed during the entire conflict.

There were two major objections to breech-loaders by the pre-war Ordnance Department: unreliability and excessive ammunition consumption. The Sharps did a great deal to prove these judgments false and pave the way toward the widespread adoption of breech-loading firearms. The Sharps also solved the extremely difficult problem of gas leakage of caseless ammunition more successfully than any other widely used breech-loader. The seal principles evolved in the 1850's and applied to the Sharps design are still being utilized in some of our most advanced modern caseless firearms designs.

[6] D. F. Butler, *op, cit.*, P 36

[7] B. R. Lewis, *op, cit.*, P 157

Single-Shot Cartridge Rifles

CHAPTER 6

At the end of the Civil War it was clear to everyone that the future belonged to breech-loading firearms and metallic cartridges. As the fighting ceased there was a mad scramble to design conversions of muzzle-loading rifles to handle the breech-loading ammunition.

MODEL 1867 SHARPS "BL" RIFLES

The Sharps company worked vigorously to convert its percussion rifles and carbines to handle metallic ammunition. An early conversion was to modify thousands of carbines to use a short, stubby rimfire cartridge virtually identical to the Spencer .56/.50. This was a relatively easy conversion for the bullet fitted the .52 caliber Sharps barrels, and the firing pin was installed on the right side of the breechblock. The converted carbines were introduced about 1867.

Sharps military rifle conversions were introduced about the same time. These were designed for a more powerful .52/70 Sharps cartridge or for a .50/67/487 rimfire cartridge. The ".50 caliber" of this latter cartridge is actually a misnomer for it carried a .52 caliber bullet designed to fit the Sharps barrels and the 67-grain powder charge provided a lot of power for the relatively weak rimfire case. The commercial Sharps Model BL rifle, exhibited at the Paris Exposition of 1867, had a 30-inch barrel and weighed slightly over 11 pounds. The designation of ".50 caliber" was apparently to give customers the impression that this was a new and modern cartridge similar to the .50/70/450 Springfield cartridge rather than a design to convert obsolete percussion barrels to metallic ammunition.

During the Civil War the .56 Spencer was the outstanding metallic cartridge in service. At the end of the war there was intense study to determine if rimfire or center-fire cartridges were the best design for the future. While the Model 1865 Springfield rifle fired a .58 caliber rimfire cartridge, the balance had swung to center-fire as early as 1866 and the Springfield Models of 1866, 1868, and 1870 all fired the .50/70 center-fire cartridge.

Conversion of the Sharps percussion rifles and carbines to center-fire ammunition was very difficult. The Sharps hammer was located high on the right side of the action. The breechblock was very short and the hammer blow had to be transmitted to a firing pin blow at the center of the breechblock. Most conversions of muzzle-loading rifles utilized a long breechblock and diagonal firing pin which took the force high on the right side of the breechblock and carried it diagonally down to the center line of the barrel at the front of the breechblock. The Sharps breech design was simply too short for this solution. A series of experimental designs were tried and the Sharps company finally evolved a design with an S-shaped firing pin. One end of the S was the point of the firing pin. The body of the S was a bar which went from the center line to the right side of the breechblock, and the other end of the S was a bar which extended upward to the rear to receive the hammer blow.

Small quantities of experimental rifles were manufactured by Sharps in the mid 1860's to study the best methods of conversion. During 1867 the Sharps Rifle Manufacturing Company received a contract for the conversion of 31,098 carbines to the caliber .50/70 center-fire cartridge. A new breechblock was installed carrying the S-shaped firing pin. An extractor was mounted on the left side of the action. This was pivoted low in the receiver and as the breechblock reached the lower end of its travel it struck a short arm which cammed the extractor smartly to the rear, ejecting the fired cartridge case. The post-war economy move was in full swing, and the Sharps Rifle Manufacturing Company received only $4.50 apiece for converting carbines to metallic ammunition. The old barrels were even reused by boring out the .52 caliber rifling and inserting a liner rifled for the .50 caliber bullet. The barrel relining was done at Springfield Armory and the remainder of the work by the Sharps Company. The contract was completed in October 1869. A second contract for the modification of 1086 Sharps percussion rifles was completed in 1869.

MODEL 1870 SHARPS RIFLES AND CARBINES

More Sharps rifles and carbines were converted in 1870 in preparation for a series of Government trials to determine the best breech-loader to use in the following decade. The economy move had eased a little and these rifles and carbines were fitted with brand-new barrels manufactured by the Springfield Armory.

ORDNANCE TRIALS OF 1871

On March 10, 1871, the Ordnance Department issued orders to the field forces for comprehensive tests of Remington, Springfield, Sharps, and Ward-Burton single-shot rifles. The field officers were much happier with maneuvers and field exercises than they were with written reports, so very explicit instructions were given as to the type and detail of reports. The following information was required:

1. Number, kind, and caliber of arms in company.
2. Number of each kind rendered as unserviceable.
3. Number and names of parts of each of the above kind which have broken or become unserviceable during the month.
4. What modifications or improvements do you suggest for each arm?
5. Number and kinds of musket-cartridges fired from each kind of arm, and number of failures in each arm.
6. Which of the four systems of breech arrangement would you prefer for uniform use in the rifled muskets and carbines of the military service?

The reports were accumulated monthly and summarized in a comprehensive report which was issued in May 1873. The Army had intended that this field trial provide the basis for a decision as to the best firearm to use during the following decades. The questions clearly indicate that the contribution of the field forces was actively solicited. The recapitulation of the results of the trials are shown in the table below:

		Remington	Springfield	Sharps	Ward-Burton
Number of arms originally issued and reported on		1,502	1,828	2,470	1,089
Number of monthly reports rendered		810	814	584	384
Last expression of preference by officers commanding companies		10	84	1	0
Proportionate number of principal parts broken, as by 1,000 guns in 1,000 months.	Stocks	35.0	21.0	21.0	58.0
	Receivers	0.0	0.0	0.69	0.0
	Blocks or bolts	0.82	0.67	0.69	49.0
	Mainsprings	25.0	6.0	8.0	14.0
	Extractors	6.0	0.67	0.69	6.0
	Levers			13.0	
	Upper guard-screws				35.0
	Total	66.82	28.34	44.07	162.0
Number of cartridges fired		89,828	96,479	76,628	40,070
Number of cartridges failed		2,595	1,882	2,699	970
Percentage of misfires		0.0288	0.0196	0.0352	0.0242

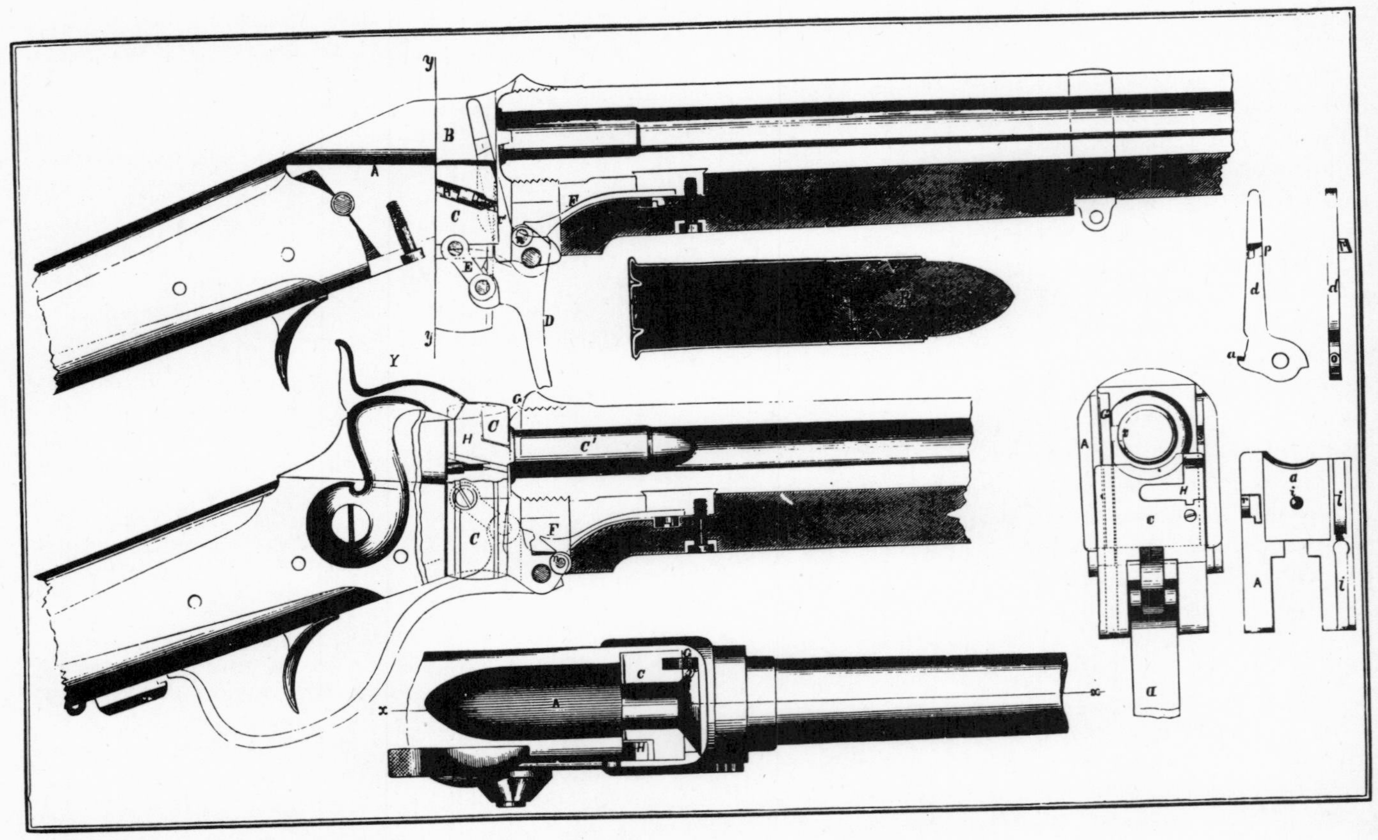

FIGURE 6-1 Sharps Model 1874 breech-loading rifle action.

A careful analysis of the breakages, misfires, and comments from the field officers convinced the Army that the "trap door" Springfield design was the best choice for their future firearms. Unfortunately for the Army, Congress did not agree. Congress felt that the "trap door" Springfield was an automatic choice because it had been developed within the Government system. Many inventors were petitioning Congress claiming that they had not had a fair evaluation of their firearms. When the Ordnance Department approached Congress in 1873 for funds to manufacture an improved Springfield rifle in .45-70 caliber, Congress appropriated the magnificent sum of $150,000 only on condition that a comprehensive test of inventions from all over the world be performed by the Ordnance Department.

The Model 1870 Sharps rifles and carbines had fared quite well in the extensive field trials. For example, the Sharps had the second lowest number of broken parts. The breakage index for the Springfield was 28, 44 for the Sharps, 67 for the Rolling Block Remington, and 162 for the Ward-Burton bolt action rifle.

The Sharps had had the highest percentage of misfires at 3½ percent, which was only slightly higher than the Remington at 2.9 percent. The Springfield was the lowest at just under 2 percent and the Ward-Burton had 2.4 percent. The Sharps had not fared well in the solicitation of comments from the field officers for only 1 had recommended adaptation of the Sharps compared with 84 recommending the Springfield, and 10 recommending the Remington. Nevertheless, it was clear that the Sharps was a rugged, reliable rifle with a long record of successful military performance and the strongest breech-action design available in the early 1870's.

Model 1870 Sharps rifles and carbines were entered into the comprehensive field trials of 1872-1873. The results of these detailed trials are given in Ordnance Memorandum No. 15. It is very significant that the Memorandum contains photographs of the disassembled rifles with numbers on each of the small components. Considering that Matthew Brady had been carrying cumbersome wet glass plates around the battlefield only a decade before, utilization of photographic plates with overlaid printed numbers is a remarkably advanced presentation technique for 1873.

First trials of the Sharps were performed on October

22, 1872. The rifles were first tested for safety and then for gas leakage at the breech by using a piece of paper above and below the action. They were next tested for accuracy and for difficulty of extraction. Early in the trials there were problems with hard extraction and this was commented upon during the preliminary trial of 400 rounds. Five hundred additional rounds were fired the following day and then the rifle was exposed to the elements for a rusting test. The breech opened very hard after these tests although 50 rounds were fired without any failure. After a second exposure to the elements the breech opened quite readily and the gun easily passed an additional 50-round test. The third exposure test was so incredibly rugged that few modern firearms could pass it. The barrel was greased and then plugged at the breech and muzzle. The entire action and barrel were then dipped in a brine solution and left outside to rust for 44 hours. The test report reads:

> The gun, after dipping and exposure for 44 hours, was found to be thoroughly rusted. The breech was opened with difficulty. Twenty shots were fired without failure. The lever required a sharp blow to extract the shells, the solution having slightly leaked into the chamber. After this was cleaned, the mechanism remained rusty as before, one shot was fired and the shell extracted without the slightest difficulty.

Even after this rigorous test the Sharps, upon a careful examination, was found to be uninjured.

Since the Sharps passed the first echelon of tests, it entered a second series in February 1873. It received another series of exposure tests on February 21. It opened and worked easily. By February 26 the situation had changed drastically,

> It worked so hard that it had to be opened by blows with a hammer upon the block. Three shots out of the five missed fire, once owing to the accumulation of rust on the firing pin. The extractor also worked hard. Before firing excessive charges the mechanism was oiled. In firing the high charges everything worked well.

The second Sharps rifle ran into serious trouble in the February 19 tests.

> After first exposure opened very hard and also after the second two defective cartridges had been fired. After second exposure the gun opened very hard; the difficulty was so much increased by firing the first cartridge that on applying force to the lever with the foot it was broken off about 2½ inches from the end. On examination by an expert this was declared due to overheating of the metal in manufacture. The arm was then laid aside. The cartridge-shell was easily removed from the chamber by tapping on the projection of the extractor, showing that the resistance was not due to the sticking of the shell.

The Sharps was dropped at the end of the second series of tests and only six out of almost a hundred rifle designs survived to go into the final series of trials.

SHARPS CARTRIDGE RIFLE DESIGN

By 1874 the Sharps cartridge rifle had evolved into the design shown in Figures 6-1 and 6-2. The design still utilized many parts from the Civil War percussion firearms. The geometry of the finger lever, breechblock linkage, barrel, receiver, buttstock and forearm were virtually identical. The lock plate on the earlier Sharps cartridge rifles utilized all of the percussion components except that a redesigned hammer with a solid

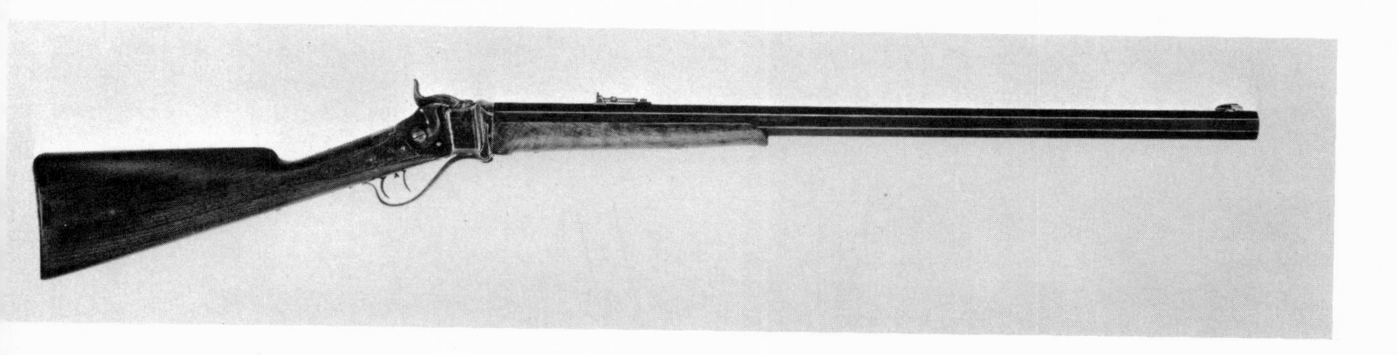

FIGURE 6-2 Sharps Model 1874 "Buffalo Rifle."

head was fitted. The author has a Sharps percussion rifle which was converted into a .50/70 cartridge rifle during the early 1870's. The Lawrence pellet priming mechanism was left in place and the hammer was even machined from a percussion hammer. The only reason the pellet priming mechanism did not work was that the small extension on the slide which rode the cam cut in the hammer had been removed.

A new lock plate was designed for the 1874 models and the pellet priming mechanism was eliminated. The hammer was redesigned with a more stylish filigree near the hammer screw. A new breechblock and barrel were fitted, but most of the rest of the components were either of Civil War vintage or manufactured on the same tooling.

The rifle is shown with the action open in the upper illustration. The forearm was held up to the barrel by a barrel band, and was positioned longitudinally by the single screw which extended upward into a block dovetailed into the barrel. The same dovetailed block carried the finger lever spring which was very similar to that on the percussion Sharps. The barrel screwed into the receiver and extended to the rear beyond the inner receiver face. The left side of the chamber was cut away to accept an extractor which rode in a slot in the left side of the receiver and breechblock. The detail of the extractor is shown on the extreme right-hand side of the illustration. The small projection P engaged the rim of the cartridge and flipped it smartly to the rear. The small surface a was struck by a matching cut in the breechblock as it reached its lowest position, thus rotating the extractor rapidly in a counterclockwise direction and flipping the shell clear of the action. When the rifle was reloaded the act of chambering the shell pushed the extractor forward so that it was flush with the barrel. The extractor cuts are shown as areas i, i on the front view of the breechblock.

A center-fire cartridge for the Sharps action is also shown in Figure 6-1. The design shows very deep lubricant grooves in the bullet and it has the appearance of having a zinc washer plus two wads between the bullet and the powder cavity. This cartridge case was a "Martin folded head" design. It was a center-fire design with the priming cup retained by the formed head material. Such elaborate working of the thin material was only possible with a very ductile metal such as copper.

The Sharps action is shown at the moment of ignition in the center illustration of Figure 6-1. The hammer Y has struck the firing pin H driving it forward into the primer of the cartridge C′. The breechblock CC is locked firmly in an upward position by the rotating link E. The finger lever D is held in an *upward* position by the downward pressure of the spring F, acting forward of the finger lever pivot.

A top view of the action is shown in the lower illustration. The loading trough is shown as A and the firing pin H is shown on the right side of the breechblock C. Small details of the action in an open position and a detail of the breechblock alone are shown on the right side of the illustration.

SHARPS SPORTING RIFLES

During the 1870's Sharps sporting rifles became very famous. The very strong breech action could handle any black powder cartridges up to the most powerful. They continued a reputation established during the Civil War for a powerful, rugged rifle design. During the 1870's their fame was broadened by buffalo hunters who utilized Sharps rifles, often with powder charges over 100 grains, for long-range hunting on the Western Plains. In addition, Sharps target rifles achieved great distinction in United States and international target shooting. The Sharps center-fire rifles and Remington rolling block target rifles were considered the world's most accurate rifles in the late 1870's.

The 1870's proved to be a last burst of glory, for by 1881 the Sharps company was overwhelmed by the trend toward repeating rifles and had gone out of existence. Inexpensive conversions of the Sharps percussion rifles to center-fire provided strong competition to the company's standard line of product. The Sharps catalogue for 1875 listed sporting rifles starting at $30.00 with a 26-inch round barrel. These hunter's rifles were listed in .40, .44, .45, and .50 caliber, all chambered for cartridges with a long, tapered shape or a very slight bottleneck. The rifles had plain oiled stocks, open sights and single triggers.

The Sharps sporting rifles in 1875 were offered with half octagon barrels starting at $33.00, and with 26-inch full octagon barrels starting at $35.00. Additional barrel length cost $.75 per inch. The fact that the commercial markets were glutted with war surplus Sharps percussion rifles and relatively low-cost conversions made it difficult to sell any new firearms at high prices.

SHARPS BUFFALO RIFLES

During the 1870's the Sharps Rifle Company manufactured special long-range hunting rifles chambered for powerful cartridges. An example is shown in Figure 6-2. This powerful .45 caliber rifle is marked

"Sharps Rifle Company, Bridgeport, Connecticut," which places its manufacture after 1876. The design used a blend of Civil War and new tooling. The basic action and lock mechanism utilized Civil War tooling with a modified design of the hammer and a new breechblock. The lock plate was basically the Civil War design with a graceful curve on upper surface where the Lawrence pellet priming mechanism had been eliminated. Double set triggers were fitted to the rifle with a trigger adjusting screw clearly visible to the rifle with a trigger adjusting screw clearly visible between the two triggers. The rear sight was a typical Civil War rifle design with a long leaf which could be pivoted upward for extended range shooting. The rifle sights were generally calibrated to 1000 yards, and carbine sights to 800 yards. The long, heavy octagonal barrel, redesigned forearm made of ornamental walnut, and shotgun style butt plate were characteristics of Sharps rifles dating in the 1870's.

During the late 1870's buffalo hunters demanded more and more power. The Sharps Company responded by developing extremely long straight brass cases. For example, the 1875 catalog listed all cartridges with 70-grain powder charges, in .40, .44, .45 and .50 caliber sizes. The Catalog of 1877 includes .40 caliber cartridges loaded with 50 to 90 grains of powder and 265- to 370-grain bullets. The .44 caliber loads ranged from 75 to 105 grains of powder with bullet weights of 297 to 520 grains. The .45 caliber loads ranged from 70 grains to 100 grains and bullet weights from 400 to 550 grains. The .50 caliber loads ranged from 70 to 100 grains with bullet weights of 425 to 473 grains. By 1879 the .40 caliber cartridges were loaded with 50 to 100 grains of powder and 190- to 370-grain bullets. The .44 caliber cartridges were loaded with 75 to 105 grams of powder and 277- to 520-grain lubricated or paper patched bullets. The .45 caliber loads were offered with 70 to 110 grains of powder and bullet weights of 293 to 550 grains. The .50 caliber size was sold with powder charges of 70 to 110 grains and bullet weights of 335 to 500 grains.

The minimum cartridge case length was the small .40 caliber style at 1 11/16 inches long. The high powered .40 caliber cases ran up to 2⅝ inches long and the giants of all early center-fire cases were the powerful .45 caliber Sharps cases 2⅞ inches long and the .50 caliber cases at 2½ inches. These were magnificent long straight cases, which are very impressive, even a century later.

SHARPS TARGET RIFLES

Two Sharps target rifles are shown in Figure 6-3. The upper rifle was named after the famous Creedmoor target shooting range on Long Island. It is basically a Model 1874 action, containing many Civil War Sharps design features. It is fitted with a half octagon barrel which is octagonal for the length of the forearm and then round for the remainder of its length. Two rear sight bases are fitted. One is screwed into the tang of the rifle and the second is mounted on a wooden block on the comb of the stock. The rear sight shown mounted on the rifle was the most sophisticated metallic sight available in the 1870's. It included a large cup-shaped eyepiece with a small peep hole in the center. The eyepiece was threaded into a steel block which rode in tracks in the long slotted sight leaf. The vertical position was controlled by a screw which was held in bearings at the top and lower end of the leaf and was turned with a small knob at the top. The final touch was carefully engraved scales on the side of the sight leaf and a vernier scale on the block which held the peep sight itself. This vernier scale allowed vertical adjustments to almost .001 of an inch accuracy.

Highly skilled target shooters of the 1870's could also purchase a front sight assembly which included a leveling bubble such as that used on a carpenter's level, plus the provision for offsetting the front sight to the left or right to compensate for wind. The best of these front sights had screw adjustments and very accurate scales for windage adjustment.

The description in the Sharps catalog for 1875 states:

Sharps Creedmoor Rifle No. 1
Designed exclusively for very long ranges. 44/100 caliber, 32-inch barrel, long, straight, hand made, *pistol grip,* polished stock, checkered grip and fore-end regulation weight and trigger pull; peep, rear sight, with Vernier scale, allowing the necessary elevation for 1,300 yards; wind gage, with interchangeable globe and split bar front sight, with morocco sight case. (This is the very best rifle manufactured, and will be found to give splendid results at the longest ranges.) $125.00
Spirit level attached to front sight, extra ...
Globe and Peep Sight, extra .... $ 5.00
Double triggers, extra .... $ 4.00
Telescope sights, extra .... $ 40.00

The cartridges for the target rifles ranged from 4 to 4½ cents apiece in quantities of a thousand.

A great deal had been learned about the accuracy requirements for black powder rifles and ammunition, and this knowledge flowered into superbly accurate firearms in the 1870's. Europeans favored muzzle-loading firearms with tapered barrels, paper patched bullets, and false muzzles. Americans preferred breech-loading Sharps or Remington rolling block rifles with paper patched soft lead bullets and often used cartridge cases which could be reloaded over 100 times.

The merits of muzzle-loading and breech-loading rifles waxed hot and strong on both sides of the Atlantic during the 1870's. This led to a challenge and a famous international rifle match at the Creedmoor Range in 1877. The results were very close, but the American team defeated the Irish world champions and the Sharps long-range target rifles performed superbly.

The Sharps target rifle shown in Figure 6-3 could be fired in a normal prone position with the rear sight mounted on the forward sight base or from an incredibly awkward position when set up as shown in the illustration. With the front sight mounted at the forward end of a 32-inch barrel and the rear sight mounted on the comb of the buttstock, the sighting radius exceeded four feet. In order to use this arrangement the shooter lay on his back with one leg extended and the other leg with the knee slightly drawn up. The rifle barrel lay along the shooter's leg and the elevation was determined by the shooter's foot. The buttstock was tucked under the shooter's armpit and the right arm gripped the small of the stock and the trigger in the normal way. The shooter's left arm was hooked behind his head and held his head bent sharply upward so that his eye could see through the peep hole in the elevated rear sight.

OTHER SHARPS BREECH-LOADING RIFLES

In the decade from 1865 to 1875 the Sharps Company brought out many different model designations and made minor design improvements. All these firearms were built on the same basic action which used much of the Civil War tooling and was very close in appearance to the Civil War design.

In 1875 the Sharps Company brought out a new model which was entirely redesigned but still utilized the outside hammer. Few of these models were manufactured.

In 1877 Sharps brought out their final design, a highly advanced hammerless, single-shot rifle shown in the bottom illustration of Figure 6-3. While this model is beyond the time period of this book, it rounds out the history of the Sharps Rifle Company and has many interesting facets. The rifle was designed by a German, Hugo Borchardt, who was an exceptionally gifted designer and he incorporated many modern features in the mechanism. He later left Sharps and worked for the Winchester Repeating Arms Company where he became familiar with the toggle locked Winchester action. He designed revolvers for Winchester in the 1880's and then returned to Germany where he designed the Borchardt toggle locked semi-automatic pistol. The toggle linkage was ingeniously arranged in his semi-automatic action and it was only slightly modified to become the famous Luger automatic pistol.

The Sharps-Borchardt action was very similar to th earlier Sharps design in the toggle linkage which locke the breechblock upward, the finger lever and sprin geometry, and the extractor. What was very new wa the complete elimination of the external hammer an trigger mechanism and the substitution of a striker located inside the breechblock backed by a powerful coi spring. The striker had a lateral shaft through the cente which rode in a curved cam track. This feature automatically cocked the striker as the breechblock was depressed. Most models were designed so that a safet was automatically put on when the breechblock reache its fully downward position.

The Sharps-Borchardt was a simple rugged actio with great strength and advanced features. Many considered it almost perfect. It did have one flaw. If th firing pin pierced a primer the gun was virtually locke shut. A special tool sometimes had to be inserted fro the muzzle of the firearm to drive the primer assembl and firing pin to the rear so that the breechblock coul be moved vertically. This can be a very annoying problem. I have a Sharps percussion rifle which was converted to .50/70 caliber in the 1870's. Modern prime are much hotter than the primers of a century ago an it was common experience to have the primer blow bac into the firing pin hole in the breechblock, locking th action shut. The Borchardt action had a similar problem by having the firing pin held firmly forward int the primer indent by the powerful coil spring.

The Sharps-Borchardt rifle shown in the lower illustration of Figure 6-3 is a superb target model with very heavy octagonal barrel of .38 caliber manufacture by H. Warner, one of America's most famous maker This rifle has the most accurate vernier sight manufactured by the Sharps Rifle Company, differing sligh ly from that on the upper rifle. Sharps claimed that th vernier on the Borchardt rifle could be adjusted t within .001 of an inch. The rifle has a very moder appearing pistol grip and a gracefully tapered forear with a small schnabble at the tip.

MANUFACTURE OF SHARPS RIFLES

Although Christian Sharps was an exceptionally gifte inventor, he was not able to create a solid business stru ture to manufacture his products. The result was a seri of short lived companies, reorganizations, and law suit In the decade before the Civil War, Sharps rifles we manufactured by Robbins and Lawrence in Massach setts and in Hartford, Connecticut. In 1859 Christia Sharps moved to Philadelphia and reorganized a ne company under the name of C. Sharps and Compan

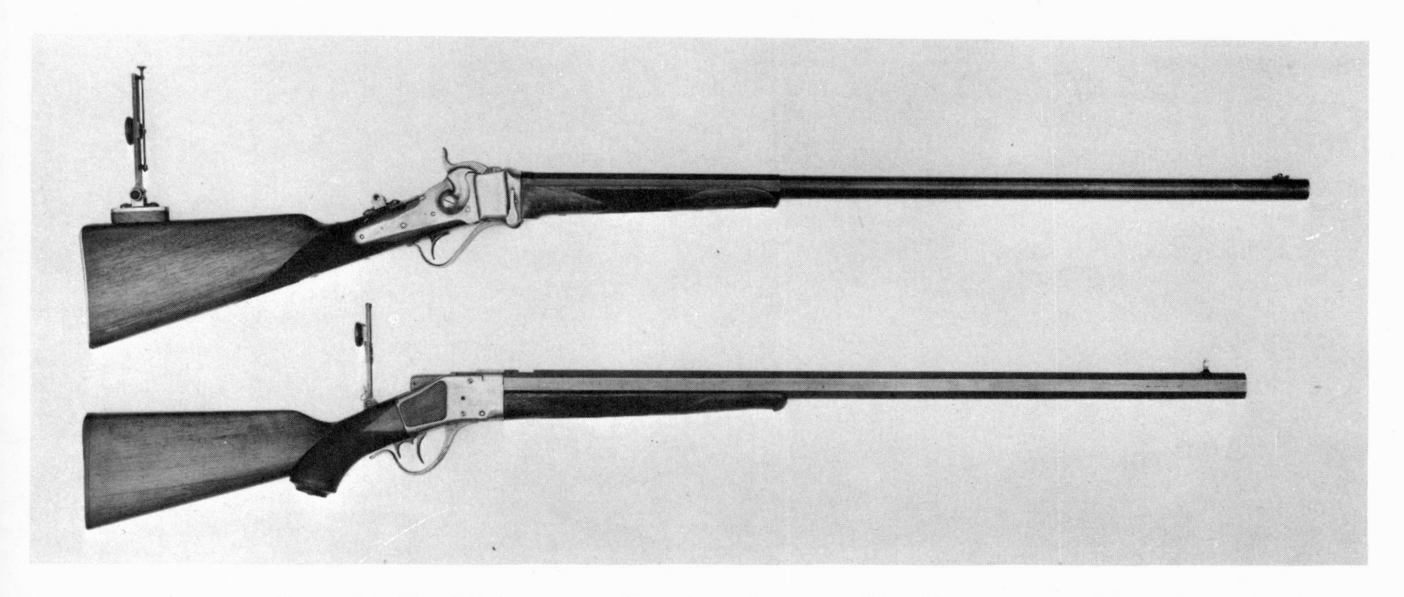

FIGURE 6-3 ABOVE: Sharps Model 1874 long-range "Creedmoor" target rifle, caliber .45 x 2 6/10; BELOW: Sharps-Borchardt Model 1878 hammerless target rifle caliber .38.

This company was reorganized again in 1863 under the name of Sharps and Hankins. Sharps and Hankins failed in 1872 and the manufacture of all Sharps rifles was consolidated into a newly organized Sharps Rifle Company in Hartford, Connecticut, in 1874. In 1876 business was looking good and the company moved to newer and larger quarters in Bridgeport, Connecticut where they remained until final failure in 1881.

PEABODY RIFLES

One of the strongest breech actions of the 19th century was the Peabody falling block design, patented by a New Englander, Henry O. Peabody, in 1862. Peabody actually secured a fairly narrow patent in covering only the particular construction of the finger lever, breechblock and extractor combination utilized in his design. By the late 1860's the Peabody design had evolved into the construction shown in Figure 6-4.

The receiver was a hollow steel box with the barrel screwed into the front end and a breech block pivoted on a cross pin high at the back of the receiver. The pivot point for the breechblock was above the center line of the barrel. The breechblock was moved by a bell crank which was pivoted at J and operated by moving the trigger guard downward. As the lever moved downward the ball joint at the end of the bell crank gave a downward component onto the breechblock, flipping it downward around the rear pivot.

A "back lock action" hammer mechanism was fitted to the rifle. The front end of the lock plate was screwed into the receiver and the remainder of the mechanism was inletted into the grip of the buttstock on the right side.

The action in a position to load is shown in Figure 6-5. This shows the trigger guard plate inletted into the bottom of the buttstock and fastened to the receiver with a screw. The buttstock C is held to the receiver through a long threaded bolt K. The breechblock has pivoted downward around the pivot point (a) and is held in the proper loading position by the detent bar G and a detent spring.

The action could open further. When the finger lever E was snapped downward smartly, the breechblock moved to a lower position contacting the end of the extractor arm F. This caused the extractor to rotate in a counterclockwise direction, flipping the rim of the cartridge case rapidly to the rear. The cartridge case rose up the curved slot in the top of the breechblock and flew clear of the action. When the finger lever was released the detent spring caused it to rebound to the position shown in Figure 6-5, with all the parts positioned for rapid reloading of the action.

A top view of the firing pin is shown as the lower detail in Figure 6-5. The problem was similar to the Sharps in that the hammer blow was taken high on the right rear side of the action and the firing pin blow was

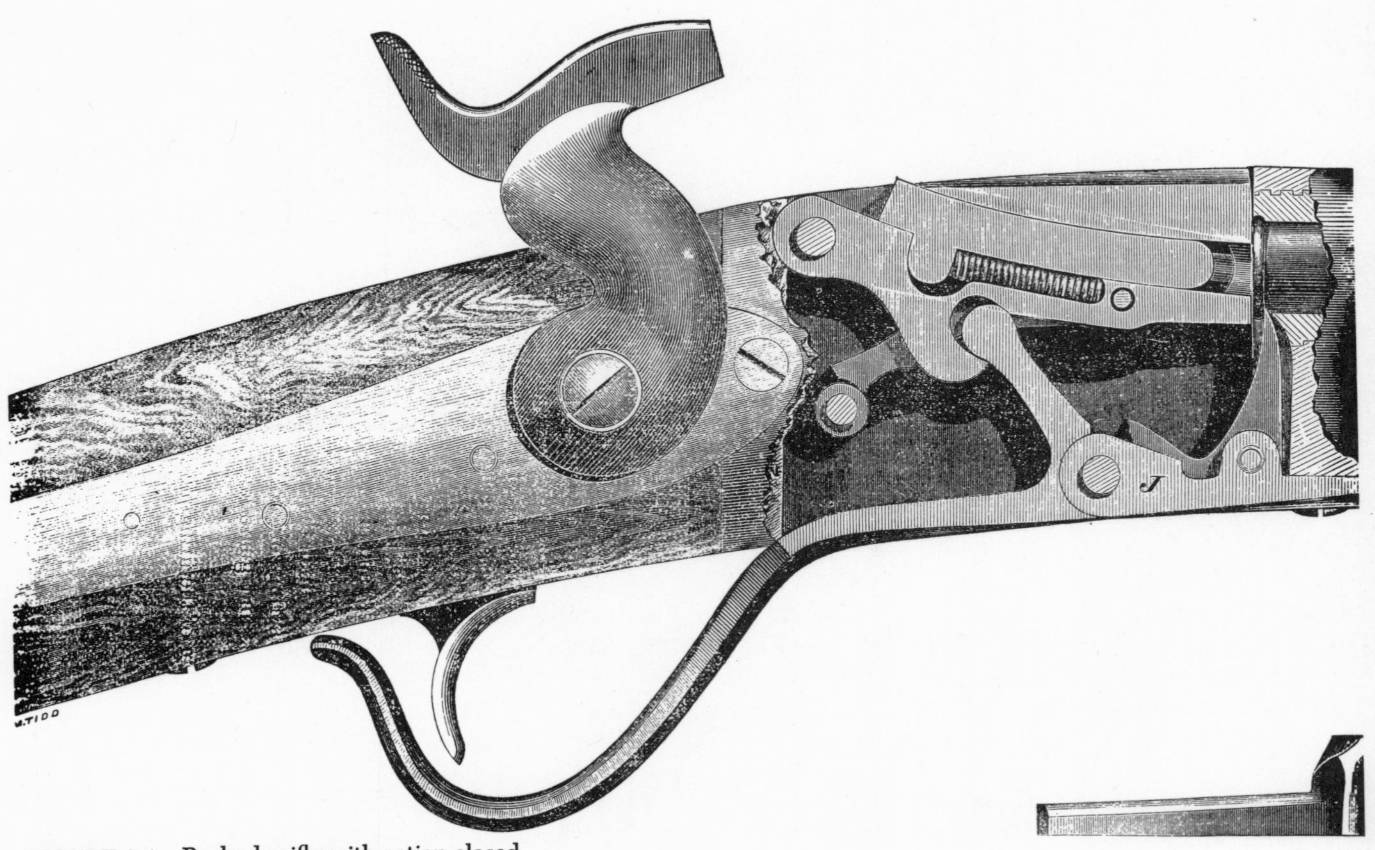

FIGURE 6-4 Peabody rifle with action closed.

needed at the front center of the breechblock. The Peabody breechblock was so much longer than the Sharps that excellent guidance could be given to the pin. Peabody designed a curved firing pin which lay along the right side of the breechblock and is shown more clearly in Figure 6-4. It was held to the rear by a powerful coiled spring inletted into the right side of the breech bolt.

Henry Peabody's objective in designing the rifle and some of the current thinking were printed in the Peabody catalog of 1865.

> Of the two millions of men who at one time were enrolled in the conflicting armies, thousands studied to contrive the most effective fire-arm for field service, while multitudes of mechanics at work in the arms manufacturing establishment of the country — stimulated by patriotic motives, as well as a thorough desire for the fame which would result from success — have competed with patient diligence for the honor or producing the most effective, and at the same time the most simple weapon, which, in the hands of the most clumsy and least intelligent soldier, could be manipulated without danger to the user, and be capable of deadliest effect upon the enemy.
>
> The old fashioned muzzle-loading arms, for infantry and cavalry service, with loose ammunition, must as surely give place to breech-loaders and fixed ammunition, as did the flintlock, smoothbore guns retire before the percussion-rifle-musket of the present day.
>
> The Government of the United States, at an early day, established a uniform caliber for both muskets and carbines and adopted ammunition put up in such form that no change of weather will affect it, and dampness, or even complete immersion in water, will do it no injury. No argument is now necessary to sustain the claim of this ammunition to great superiority. The powder and the explosive fulminate are both deposited in a metallic shell, when a ball (bullet) is entered, and the shell closed tightly around it, a blow being necessary to ignite the fulminate in the rim of the cartridge shell. By this means the powder is preserved from any action of the weather, and the cartridge is at all times ready for use, while it can be transported with entire safety.

The Peabody catalog included outside views and cross-section drawings of the Spencer type of short, squat copper rimfire case such as that shown in Chapter 4. Peabody went on to describe why the Govern-

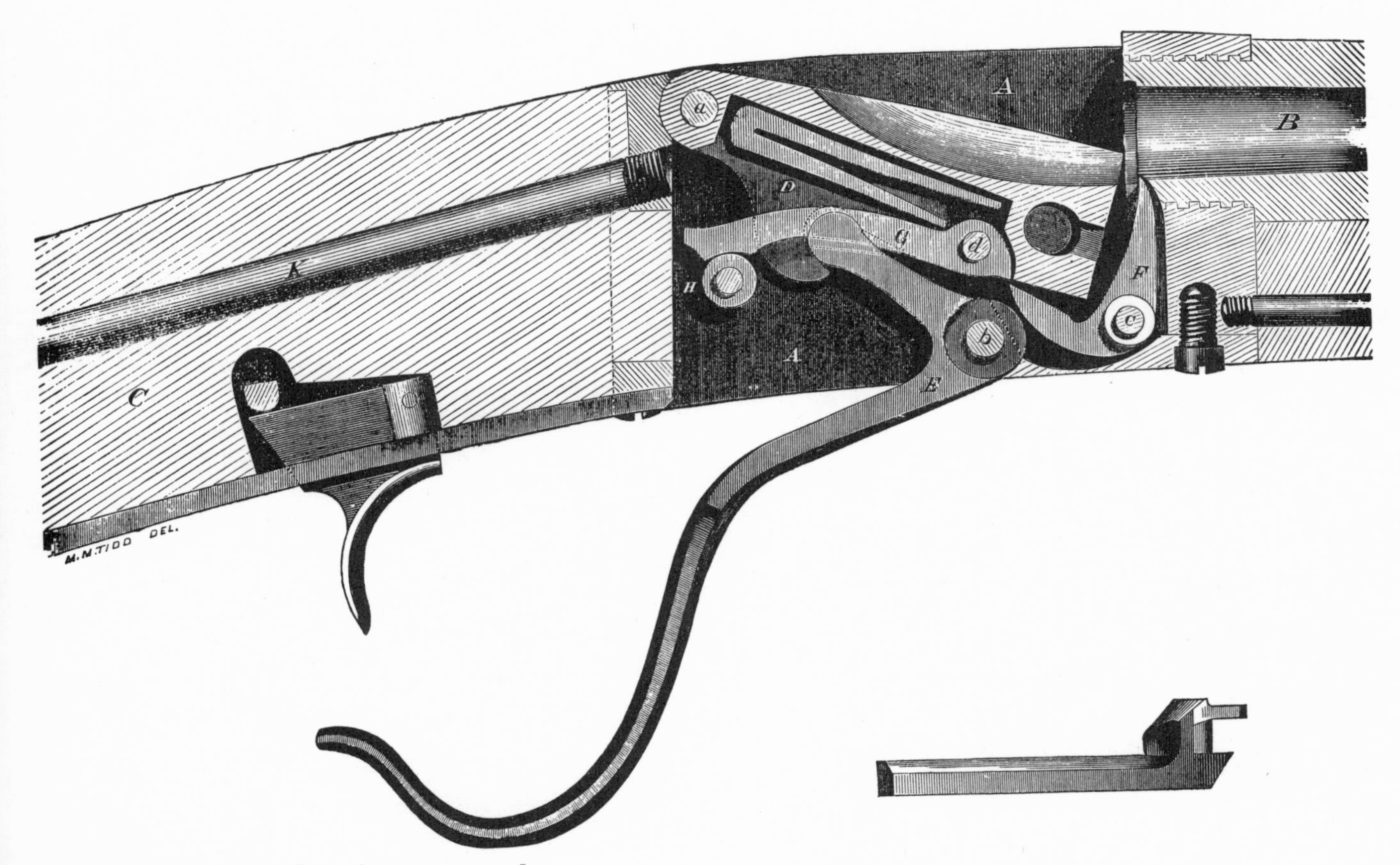

FIGURE 6-5 Peabody rifle with action opened.

ment and private users should choose the single-shot rifle in preference to the repeaters then available:

> Breech loading arms were brought into use, to some extent, during the war, but those were chiefly adapted to a paper cartridge only and most of them were plainly defective even for this.
>
> The Spencer repeating guns were made as early as 1862, and used the metallic cartridge. In the later engagements of the war they did good service. These and all other magazine-guns have, however, proved to be too complicated for general use and should only be put into the hand of veterans.
>
> Magazine-guns for continuous firing cannot be used as effectively, as single shooters which are simple in construction. A magazine-gun is necessarily more complicated and more liable to get out of order, while the time consumed in re-charging the magazine is often of great value, and the loss of it is attended with serious results. Besides, there is far greater danger of premature explosion in a magazine-gun than with a single shooter.
>
> In the opinion of a vast majority of those most familiar with the subject, a single shot breech loader, one that shall possess great strength and simplicity, that shall be absolutely certain of fire possess accuracy, and in the hands of the most inexperienced, or willfully careless man, prove at all times, and under all circumstances, an effective and trusty weapon, is entitled to claim superiority over any variety of gun hitherto known for infantry or cavalry service.

The history of the Peabody rifles is also included in the catalogs from the mid-1860's. The catalog laconically states an early sample of this gun was presented to General Ripley, (then Chief of Ordnance), in 1862, and was by him referred to Captain Rodman, commanding the United States Arsenal at Watertown. His report dated June 5, 1862, detailed the results of the examination, and highly commended the gun. The facts are that General Ripley's dislike of all "new fangled" breech-loaders was so notorious that Lincoln finally found it necessary to remove him in 1863. Ripley blocked the purchase of as many breech-loaders as possible and Peabody was one of those affected.

The Peabody was next tested in the fall of 1864 by a Board of Ordnance officers at Springfield Armory. The objective of the test was to examine all of the breech-loading rifles, and breech-loading conversions of muzzle-loading rifles to determine the best pattern of breech-loader to be used in the United States Service. A total of 65 different guns were submitted and these were given a series of tests such as rapidity of fire, accuracy, exposure and endurance. The weathering test consisted of exposure on the roof of a building with each of the guns being wet down each day. They were withdrawn in the wet condition and fired without cleaning. At the end of ten days they were suddenly dried by exposure to high temperature and fired again for function.

This rugged process reduced the final selection to four guns and these were then tested with overloads. Charges were built up to include three lead bullets driven into the barrel from the breech plus a fourth complete cartridge loaded with a bullet and 80 grains of powder. One of the four guns had blown up with a slightly lighter charge and two more were shattered by this heavy overload. The Peabody was the only one to survive this test. Later someone was curious to find out how much the Peabody could stand, and during 1865 it was fired with six 450-grain bullets and 90 grains of powder and still remained undamaged.

Unfortunately for Peabody sales the timing was very bad. The Peabody could utilize only a small percentage of muzzle-loading rifle and musket components. It utilized a two-piece stock fastened to a central receiver, and a breech mechanism which utilized no parts from the muzzle-loading rifles. The back lock hammer mechanism differed in construction from the normal side lock mechanism used on the Springfield muzzle-loaders. Although the Peabody has shown outstanding performance, the Government was really interested in some inexpensive way to modernize the hundreds of thousands of muzzle-loading rifles in inventory.

Henry Peabody studied this problem and developed a new design on which patent No. 72,076 was issued on December 10, 1867. The patent covered the same basic breech actions shown in Figures 6-4 and 6-5, but instead of an under lever the breechblock was tipped downward by a long extension to the rear which extended over the top of the small of the stock. To open the action this extension was lifted, thus depressing the breechblock, ejecting the old shell and allowing the loading of a new shell. The action utilized a much higher proportion of muzzle-loading components but it still included a back lock hammer mechanism which required all new components, and a brand-new separate receiver which was inletted into the one-piece military muzzle-loading rifle stock. Again the Peabody was an excellent design approach with a rugged simple action, but it was not quite what the Government was looking for.

A second series of Government trials was performed in 1866. There was an interesting comment by Colonel J. G. Benton on the economics and practicality of metallic ammunition:

> Having been charged with issuing and receiving many millions of the metallic cartridges at the Washington Arsenal, I have never known one to explode in handling or transportation. Out of several hundred thousand turned in from the field, very few indeed were found at all injured, while a large portion of the paper cartridges, turned in, had to be broken up, from being either worn or injured by dampness.

Major General E. B. Dyer, Chief of Ordnance, also commented on economics:

> We have not sufficient data from which to determine the relative cost of metallic and paper cartridges; but it is believed, that while the first cost of the metallic cartridge is greater than that of the paper cartridge, the small loss in the field, from accidents of service, of the metallic cartridges as compared with the paper cartridges, would more than counterbalance the difference in first cost.

Both of these comments are 180-degree reversals of opinion compared with the official stand of the Ordnance Department only four years earlier. At the beginning of the Civil War Ordnance had categorized metallic ammunition as a wasteful and unnecessary additional expense which would encourage soldiers to burn off vast quantities of ammunition as well as having an inordinantly high manufacturing cost.

The Peabody did well in the trials of 1866 and was recommended by the Chief of Ordnance for adoption. Instead the Government utilized the Springfield Armory modifications of the muzzle-loading rifles and rifle-muskets which are described in Chapter 7. The Springfield designs were not as strong as the Peabody, but utilized a very high percentage of the old muzzle-loading components, and were much less expensive.

The next official Government trials of the Peabody rifles were the extensive tests of 1872 and 1873. The Peabody design had been refined to the construction shown in Figure 6-4 and 6-5 which really differed very little from the designs of the 1860's. Mr. Peabody attended the tests in October and December 1872 when the rifles did pretty well. The single-shot rifles could be fired remarkably fast. For example, the Peabody was fired at the rate of 19 shots a minute, the Springfield, 19 shots per minute and the Remington rolling block action reached a speed of 21 shots per minute. The Peabody rifle lasted to the final trials in April 1873, but then was dropped in favor of the redesigned trap door Model 1873 Springfield for which most of the tooling was already available at Springfield Armory, and which was a design familiar to the field officers.

COMMERCIAL SALES OF PEABODY RIFLES

Although Peabody had not had much luck selling firearms to the U.S. Government, he had moderate success in the late 1860's and early 1870's on the commercial market. The catalog of 1866 lists a long Army Rifle available with a 36-inch barrel in .45 or .50 caliber at a price of $35.00. A carbine version with a 20-inch barrel in the same calibers was available at $30.00. Commercial models in the same .45 or .50 caliber were available with half-length forearms held to the barrel with screws rather than with barrel bands as on the military models. The Peabody commercial rifles were offered with 20-inch barrels at $38.00 to $42.00 apiece depending on the rear sights and 26-inch or 28-inch barrels at $40.00 to $44.00 depending on the quality of the rear sight.

Peabody actively solicited foreign sales and sales to state militia. Both Massachusetts and Connecticut adopted the rifles as the standard in the very advanced caliber of .433 (11 mm). They were also manufactured in caliber .43 Spanish and other European 11 mm calibers. Some 3000 Peabody rifles were sold to Canada in September 1865 in a .50/60 Peabody rimfire cartridge. Some 15,000 caliber .41 Swiss rimfire were sold to Switzerland in 1867 and 25,000 additional were sold to Roumania chambered for a .45 center-fire cartridge in the late 1860's. The .43 caliber or .433 caliber models were widely sold to state militia including New York, Connecticut, and Massachusetts. Some 39,000 Peabody military rifles were supplied to France during the Franco-Prussian War.

Although the Peabody Rifle Company went out of existence in the 1870's, the design has lived on to the present day. The final modification to the design was provided by a Swiss, Frederick Martini, who eliminated the external hammer and back lock mechanism and substituted a self-cocked internal striker similar to that used on the Sharps-Borchardt rifle. This new rifle became known as the Peabody-Martini and became widely used in Europe. The Peabody-Martini was manufactured in this country for long-range target shooting and was marked "Peabody- and Martini patents." The British adopted the rifle during the 1870's with a special form of rifling developed by an English inventor named Henry. Poor old Peabody got lost in the shuffle, for the rifle became known as the Martini-Henry and was the standard first-line British military rifle until the adaptation of the repeating Lee-Metford rifle in 1888. The Martini-Henry was the primary rifle of British troops in their expansion of the Empire during the late 19th century, and it gave excellent service. It has remained the most popular British single-shot action and is still manufactured as one of the finest .22 caliber rimfire target rifles in the world by the British Small Arms Company in Birmingham, England.

I purchased one of the Peabody rifles in .43 Spanish caliber at Bannerman's in the early 1940's. It was possible to purchase old folded head brass ammunition which had been loaded in the late 19th century for $1.75 for a box of 20.

These old cartridges were none too reliable, but the Peabody action was so strong and rugged that it became one of my favorite rifles to shoot. The long brass slightly bottle-necked center-fire cartridges with their soft lead bullets gave just the right amount of noise, smoke and recoil to be highly satisfying. In shooting at 200 yards there was a very distinct time delay between the noise of discharge and the solid *thunk* as the bullet struck the wooden target.

REMINGTON ROLLING BLOCK RIFLES

At the end of the Civil War in 1865 there were two giant companies in the American firearms industry. The Colt's Patent Firearms Company had been founded in 1836, and by the Civil War had grown to a large manufacturing establishment in Hartford, Connecticut, which turned out hundreds of thousands of muzzle-loading rifle-muskets and more than 125,000 .44 caliber Army percussion revolvers during the war. Colt's also manufactured large quantities of its Navy revolvers in .36 caliber and thousands of "pocket" revolvers of .31 caliber. During the Civil War, Colt's also manufactured 4612 revolving rifles in calibers from .44 to .64. Some of the latter had smoothbore barrels so that they could fire standard cartridges for the .69 caliber muskets in ball, buck and ball, and buckshot configurations.

In 1863 the large Colt's Armory burned to the ground. Although it had walls of stone, the oil-soaked wood floors burned fiercely, destroying virtually the entire main building. By the end of the war Colt's manufacturing capacity had been largely restored in new buildings with new or rebuilt machinery. In the decade following the war the company turned its design and manufacturing capability to the modification of percussion revolvers to handle rimfire and center-fire cartridges. By 1873 they had created the design of the single action Army revolver, a simple and rugged design which became standard on the

Western Frontier and has been found so useful that it is still manufactured today.

The other giant of the American firearms industry was E. Remington and Sons of Ilion, New York. Remington celebrated its 50th Anniversary in 1866 and had established a reputation as the largest manufacturer of high quality percussion rifles in the United States. In 1857 Remington began to manufacture percussion revolvers based on designs by Fordyce Beals and by the time the Civil War opened in 1861 the Remington-Beals revolvers in .44 Army and .36 Navy calibers were ready for large-scale production. The rugged solid frame design and long sighting radius made these very popular in the Federal service and over 100,000 of the .44 Army models alone were produced during the Civil War years. Remington also had extensive war contracts for its famous Model 1862 Zouave rifle. Remington also produced Model 1863 rifle — muskets with 40-inch slender barrels and three barrel bands. In the middle '40's I purchased one of these Model 1863 rifles which was manufactured by Remington in 1865 and had been stored in grease for 80 years. I purchased it as a good quality and safe muzzle-loader and promptly mounted a peep sight on the breech tang and fired it extensively, using patched round balls, or .577 Minié bullets cast in a British Enfield mold. The rifle was great fun to shoot but a nuisance to clean.

A shooter must really get out in the field with these old muzzle-loaders and attempt to fire 50 shots in an afternoon to understand what the Civil War soldiers endured. After the first 20 shots fouling built up in the breech to the point where loading became difficult and it was necessary to either pound the bullets home with the ramrod or clean the barrel with a damp patch. This was the reason for inclusion of a special cartridge with a "Williams" self-cleaning bullet in each package of .58 ammunition issued to the troops. The zinc washer on the base of the bullet scoured the barrel, removing fouling. It was a valuable idea, for the soldier in a hot engagement had no time to go through an elaborate cleaning and drying procedure before getting back into action. It was also common for the percussion cone or nipple to become plugged with burned priming residue causing misfires. On occasion this required removal of the percussion cone, cleaning the vent with a small wire and digging out packed powder residue from the passage between the percussion cone and the main charge in the barrel.

The percussion revolvers were similarly plagued with the necessity to be very careful in loading procedures to achieve good reliability. It is common in firing the old Colt and Remington percussion revolvers to have bits of percussion cap fall between the cylinder and frame, jamming the cylinder and preventing rotation. Skilled shooters developed techniques, one of the more flamboyant being to raise the arm vertically swinging the revolver entirely over the shooter's shoulder to an upside down position, aiming to the rear to recock the gun for the next shot. This motion had the tendency to throw broken bits of percussion cap clear of the mechanism and prevent jams. It was also hazardous to those behind the shooter.

At the end of the Civil War E. Remington and Sons could manufacture percussion rifles and revolvers of the highest quality in large quantity, but they were abundantly aware that the stampede was on and that future business lay in breech-loading cartridge firearms. Fortunately ground work had been laid during the late 1850's and early 1860's. In addition to skilled designers, Fordyce Beals and William Elliot, two other very important men were brought into the team. One was Leonard Geiger and the other Joseph Rider. Geiger had invented a new type of breech action in which the most of the mechanism was located below the center line of the barrel. Philo Remington became aware of Geiger's breech mechanism which was patented in 1863. He brought Geiger into the design team and intensive work started to perfect the design. Joseph Rider added some innovations of his own and received patent No. 45,123 in November 1864. Rider's patent shows a rimfire design with a breechblock which rotated about a pivot. The breechblock was slotted in its upper surface to allow a heavy hammer to rotate into the slot striking the exposed upper edge of the rimfire cartridge. Although the breechblock could be easily rotated when the hammer was cocked, the falling hammer locked it firmly shut. Geiger's design, and Rider's patent for improvements defined what came to be known as the "split breech Remington rolling block." The split breech action was offered to the Ordnance Department and a contract for some 20,000 rifles was executed. The time to prepare production delayed delivery of any rifles until after the Civil War.

Further design improvements were incorporated and patents issued in April 1866, August 1867 and in 1871. The action was adapted to a single-shot pistol design and a contract for 5000 single-shot pistols in .50 caliber was issued in November 1866. These were found so satisfactory that a total of 6500 were delivered under the contract. A contract for 5000 carbines was secured in 1867. Formal Navy tests were performed in 1869 and the Remington rolling block rifle shown in Figure 6-6 was formally adopted for Navy service in 1870. These rifles were manufactured at Springfield Armory

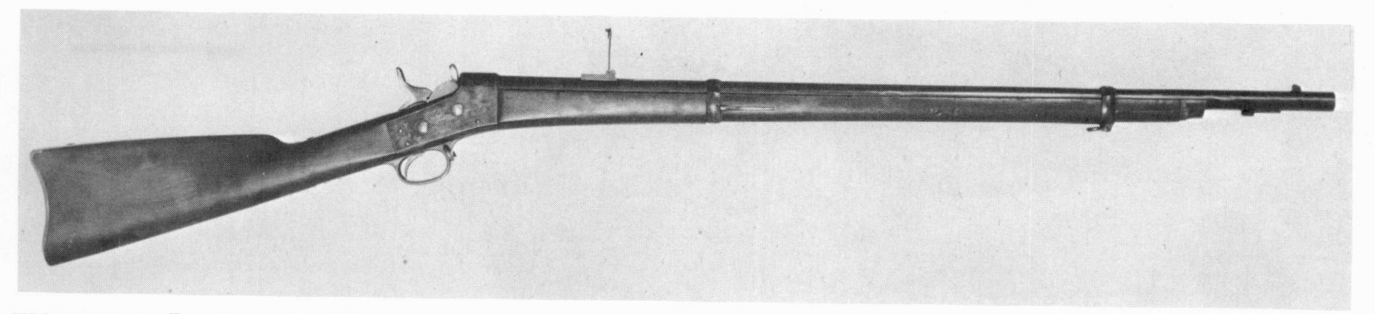

FIGURE 6-6 Remington Model 1870 Navy rifle.

and utilized the 32⅝-inch round barrel which was manufactured for the Model 1868 Springfield rifle. The rifle is shown with two barrel bands held by spring retainers. A steel forearm cap was fitted. A blade front sight was welded to the top of the barrel and a socket for the heavy bayonet welded to the underside of the barrel. At this time the armies of the United States and Europe were changing over from the triangular bayonet to one which looked like a miniature saber with a heavy cast brass handle. The Remington Navy model had a particularly heavy bayonet 20 inches long. The construction was similar to modern bayonets in having a loop on the upper portion of the guard which fitted over the barrel, and slots machined on top of the brass handle which mated with the retaining lug on the underside of the rifle barrel.

Remington rifles were fitted with a leaf type rear sight shown in its long-range position in Figure 6-6. There was a sighting notch for 1000 yards at the extreme top of the blade and graduations on the slider for ranges of 300 to 900 yards. The 200-yard notch was cut into the vertical leaf and the point-blank range of 100 yards was sighted by flipping the leaf down into a horizontal position. The rifles were chambered for the standard .50/70 center-fire cartridge and some 22,000 were manufactured of which 12,000 were issued to the Navy and 10,000 sold to private purchasers.

Two cross-section views of the Remington Navy rifle are shown in Figure 6-7. The position of components after firing is given in the upper illustration. The breechblock E pivots on an extremely strong cross pin (b). As the cartridge is fired the force tends to drive the breechblock to the rear rotating it clockwise about the pivot pin. This motion is resisted by a large curved surface on the hammer C and this force is in turn transmitted to the frame of the receiver through a second large cross pin (b) through the hammer. A weakness in these cross pins could cause a serious failure so they were made of solid steel .455 of an inch in diameter. The hammer was driven by a powerful leaf spring (a) which had a small roller on the working end to reduce friction between the hammer and spring. There was a safety interlock D which rode in a slot in the breechblock and prevented the trigger from being pulled unless the breechblock was in a closed position. This was an excellent safety device. It can be seen in the lower illustration cammed in a counterclockwise direction and the rear tail of the safety lever has been driven upward holding the trigger firmly in the sear notch until the rolling block is in a fully locked position.

I owned a .43 caliber Remington rolling block carbine for 25 years. This carbine had the basic rolling block action which was sturdy and rugged but did not have all the extra interlocks. I fired this carbine hundreds of times with 19th century Spanish ammunition which had been loaded with brass jacketed bullets. It was a short handy carbine and gave a tremendous blast both to the target and to the shooter. The 20-inch barrel did not provide quite enough expansion ratio for the heavy cartridges and the muzzle blast was sensational. I never had any trouble with the action except due to poor ammunition and enjoyed shooting the carbine a great deal. If a dented cartridge or a dirty chamber prevented the breechblock from fully closing the action would misfire. The safety lever D on the Navy model shown in Figure 6-7 was designed to prevent this malfunction.

The action is shown in an open position in the lower view of Figure 6-7. The hammer has been cocked and

REMINGTON NAVY RIFLE.

BREECH SYSTEM.—Sectional View with Breech Closed.

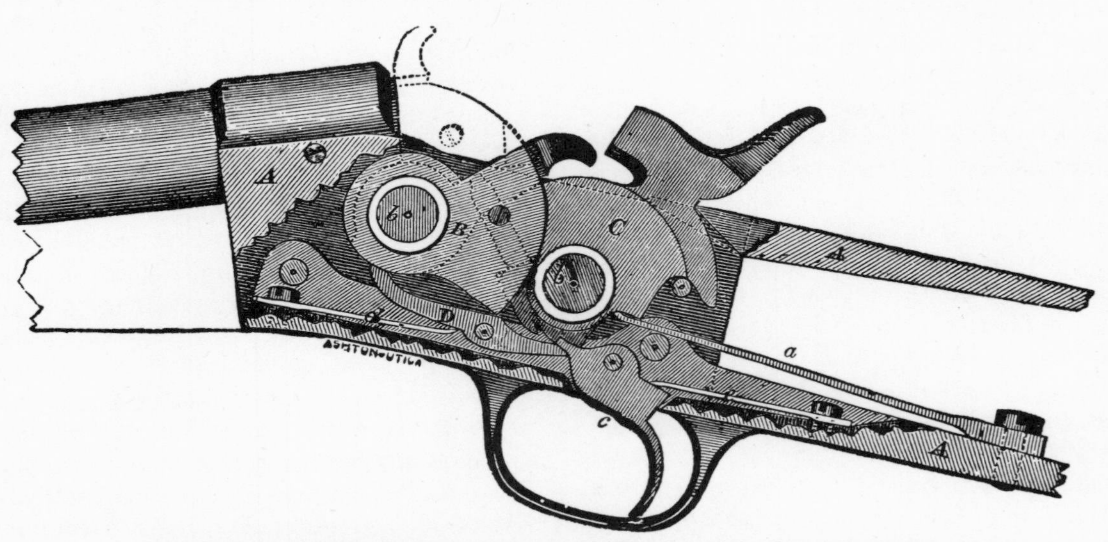

BREECH SYSTEM.—Sectional View with Breech Open.

FIGURE 6-7 Remington Model 1870 Navy action.

is locked in the rear position by the sear. Movement of the hammer fully to the rear removed the prop C from underneath the breechblock B which could then be rotated by the thumb to a fully opened position. In this position a fresh cartridge could be slammed into the chamber with the thumb and the breechblock flipped shut. The breechblock was held in a closed position by a detent spring which is not shown in the illustration. The extractor was a long leaf which lay along the left side of the barrel and was cammed to the rear as the breechblock was opened.

REMINGTON ROLLING BLOCK ARMY RIFLE MODEL 1871

In 1871 the Army adopted a rolling block rifle extremely similar in exterior appearance to the Navy model. About the only external difference was the fitting of a 36-inch barrel and an increase in the over-all length of the rifle to 51¾ inches. "Model 1871" is stamped on the left side of the receiver and the United States eagle with

U.S.
SPRINGFIELD
1872

was stamped on the right side of the receiver. Careful examination of the "Rules for the Management of the Remington Navy Rifle, Model 1870" published at Springfield Armory in 1871 and an actual Model 1871 Army rifle in the author's collection indicate that there were substantial differences in internal construction. The firing pin on the Navy model was retained by a cross screw. In the Army model a rather complex second cross shaft was fitted which had three diameters and two cam cuts. A rotary extractor encircled the main breechblock pivot shaft and was installed in a recess on the left side of the breechblock. This extractor had a camming surface which engaged the second shaft in the breechblock. As the breech was snapped open the extractor plate rotated causing a motion of the cross shaft to retract the firing pin. The cross shaft in turn limited the angular motion of the extractor plate.

If the lower tang of the Army model is removed you will notice that there are a series of springs and rotating arms pivoted on two shafts. These linkages have a very interesting purpose. When the action is snapped fully open the cartridge can be loaded easily into the chamber. When the breechblock is snapped shut the linkages caused the hammer to move up slightly into a deep safety notch. This slight motion places the curved surface of the hammer underneath the rear surface of the breechblock, firmly locking it in a forward position. With this arrangement the rifle can be carried all day with perfect safety and with no danger that an accidental blow on the breechblock would open the action, spilling the cartridge out of the chamber. To fire the rifle requires only a slight motion of the hammer to a fully cocked position, then the trigger can be pulled in a normal manner.

The Model 1871 Army rifle is marked on the tang Remington's Patent, May 3, November 15, 1864, April 17, 1868. It is chambered for the .50/70 cartridge and has the same type of sighting arrangement as the Navy model. Over-all weight of the rifle is 9¾ pounds.

ORDNANCE DEPARTMENT BREECH-LOADING TRIALS OF 1871-1873

The Remington rolling block was one of the designs selected for field trial by the Ordnance Department in 1872. A thousand rifles were specially made up for these trials with 32½-inch barrels. The rifles were issued for field trial with a circular letter from the Ordnance Department dated March 10, 1871. The summary of the field trial was given earlier in this chapter under the discussion of the Sharps rifles. A total of some 89,828 shots were fired in the Remington rolling block tests of which 2595 misfired for a malfunction rate of 2.9 misfires per hundred rounds. By expression of preference by field officers, Remington was No. 2 with 10 recommendations compared with 84 for the Springfield, 1 for the Sharps and 0 for the Ward-Burton.

When more extensive trials were required by Congress, many different versions of the rolling block action were tested. No. 20 was listed as Regular System with Rotary Extractor. This has the rotary extractor of the Army model but apparently did not have the automatic locking feature. Firing pin retraction was by means of a pivoted bar inside the breechblock rather than by the rotary cam. Another model was placed in the trials with a "Ryder Extractor." A third variation, Number 86, had a "wedge extractor." Several of the Navy models were altered to .45/70 caliber and submitted to the trials as No. 85 and No. 86. Remington rolling blocks, which included the automatic locking feature as on the Army models, were listed as "Remington Locking-Rifles." The milita style rifle (Number 21) and Number 82 were variations of the automatic locking system.

Remington rifles made a very strong showing in the trials and two designs reached the finals. In the tests for rapidity of fire, the Remington set the record of 21 shots in a minute, exceeding the record of 19 shots for the Springfield and 19 for the Peabody. In a second more extended trial the Remington achieved a rate of 19.78 shots per minute compared with 18.6 for the Peabody and 15.6 and 16.8 for the Springfield models. The final summary of the trials brought out the facts that the Remington rifle was an extremely fast and rugged breech-loader. It had been successfully utilized in both Army and Navy service and had been widely sold in Europe. The Ward-Burton repeating bolt action rifle had also lasted into the final trials and done remarkably well. The final decision settled down to a matter of economics and the preference of the field officers. With four satisfactory rifles to choose from the recommendation of the Board was to accept the Springfield design for which most of the tooling was already available at Springfield Armory and which had received the highest indication of preference from the field officers.

The Remington rolling block action became probably the most popular military rifle in the world. Models were sold to Denmark in 1867 and about 30,000 were manufactured for Sweden in 1868 chambered for a .45 caliber rimfire cartridge. In 1869 a large number of rifles were sold to Switzerland chambered for the bottle-necked .41 Swiss rimfire cartridge. Spain purchased some 10,000 rifles in .43 Spanish rimfire in 1869 and some of these were manufactured for a .43 Spanish center-fire cartridge. The Egyptians gave large orders to Remington for a rolling block rifle chambered for the .43 Egyptian cartridge. Egypt ran short of money and many of the Egyptian rifles were in the large shipment of 155,000 Remington rolling blocks shipped to France during the Franco-Prussian War of 1870-1871.

The Remington rolling block became one of the most popular rifles for the state militia and New York particularly ordered large quantities. More than a million military style Remington rolling block rifles were manufactured and sold in the United States, Europe and the Middle East.

TARGET RIFLES OF A CENTURY AGO

During the Civil War hundreds of thousands of young men became skilled in the use of the .58 caliber muzzle-loading rifles and the many breech-loading rifles in service. At first the veterans were anxious to forget the war and establish themselves in civilian lives — back in the familiar surroundings of the Eastern United States or pushing westward using their hard won skills of survival to open up the western lands.

By 1870 many of the veterans had mellowed and became interested in using their shooting skills at target shooting. Target shooting was a major sport in Europe, particularly with the Swiss and German Scheutzenfest which combined offhand target shooting with beer drinking and socializing. Long-range target shooting became a major sport in the British Empire and the first meeting of the British National Rifle Association was held at Wimbledon in 1860. The opening shot was fired from a Whitworth muzzle-loading rifle at a range of 400 yards. The superb accuracy of these heavy muzzle-loading target rifles was fully tested in regular matches held at ranges of 300 to 1000 yards. A decade later regular matches were held to establish the shooting champions of the British Empire with teams entered from as far away as Australia. The heavy muzzle-loading match rifle was considered the most accurate rifle that could be built.

Long-range target shooting in the United States grew more slowly, but by 1871 there was sufficient interest to support the founding of the National Rifle Association, which has fostered marksmanship for almost a century. While many American target shooters used the traditional muzzle-loading firearms, experiences of the Civil War showed that breech-loading rifles could be equally accurate. Many small companies manufactured single-shot breech-loading target rifles, but Remington and Sharps were the dominant manufacturers. The Sharps target rifles of the early 1870's were very similar in appearance to the Civil War percussion rifles, and much of the Civil War tooling was still used for manufacturing. A Sharps long-range target rifle is shown in Figure 6-8. These rifles were listed with a wide variety of options, and the sighting equipment on this particular model would identify it as a Sharps Creedmoor rifle No. 3 or No. 4. Sharps rifles of this design had done very well in the matches at Creedmoor, Long Island, in 1873 with competition at 500, 800, 900 and 1000 yards.

Similar long-range matches, but on a much larger scale, were held at Wimbledon, England, in 1873 to determine the champions of the British Empire. The Irish came out victorious, and felt that their exeremely accurate muzzle-loading rifles manufactured by John Rigby of Dublin, Ireland, and the extensive training of the team could beat any rifle team in the world. They issued a challenge to the riflemen of the United States. Formal rifle shooting had not yet been organized on a large scale in the United States, and a special Amateur Rifle Association was formed to accept the challenge. They had no team and no equipment. The Association approached Remington and Sharps as the two leading manufacturers of highly accurate single-shot rifles. Both companies accepted the challenge and provided the prize money for the matches and immediately began to develop powerful, long-range, single-shot rifles to compete at ranges up to 1000 yards. The Sharps version is shown in Figures 6-3 and 6-8, and the Remington rolling block Creedmoor target rifle is shown in the lower illustration of Figure 6-8.

The match was finally held in September, 1874 at the Creedmoor Range on Long Island. It was to be fired at 800, 900 and 1000 yards. The Americans won at 800 yards with a score of 326 to 317. The Irish won at 900 yards with a score of 312 to 310, and they won at 1000 yards with a score of 302 to 298. The aggregate score was 934 for the Americans and 931 for the Irish. There were few restrictions on either the equipment or the shooting positions. Most shooters fired in a prone position but some lay on their backs with the muzzle of the

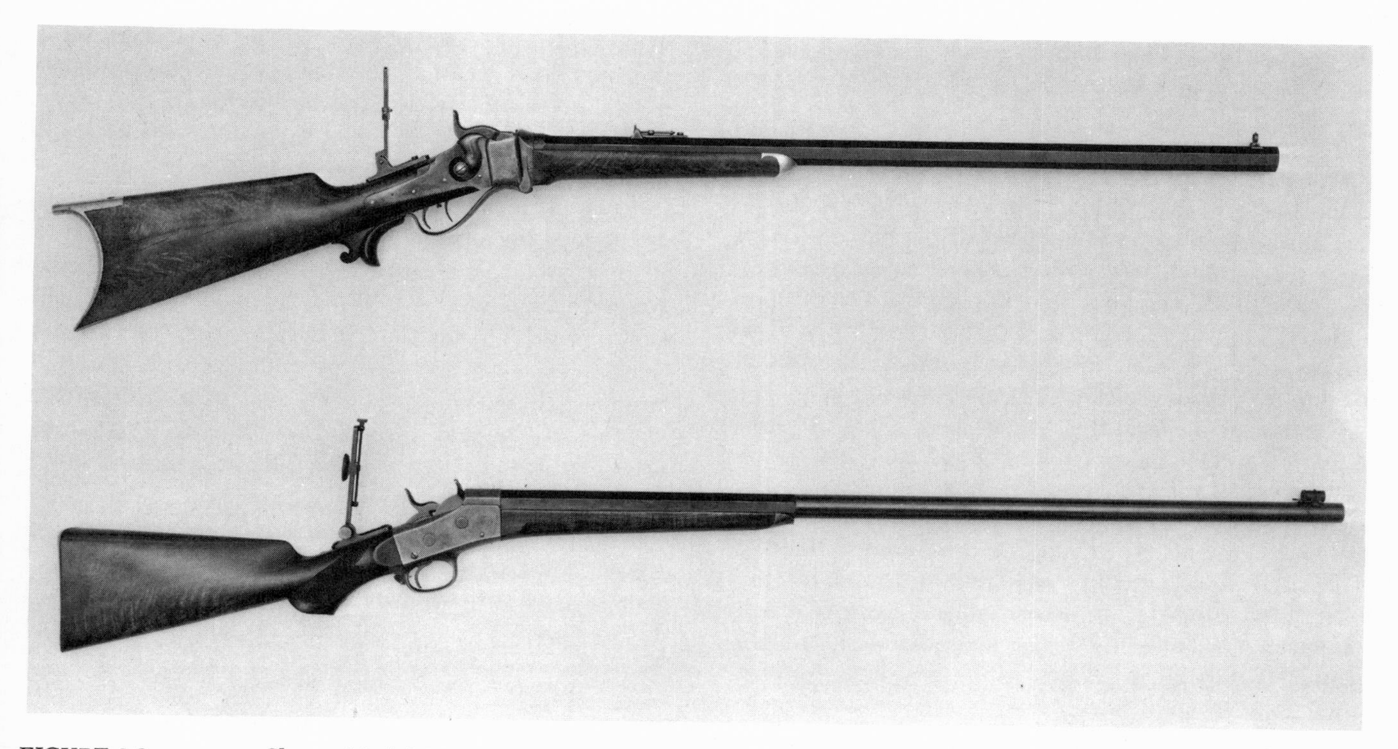

FIGURE 6-8 ABOVE: Sharps Model 1874 Creedmoor target rifle; BELOW: Remington Creedmoor rolling block target rifle.

rifle held between their toes and others lay on one side with the rifle barrel lying along one leg. These unusual positions led to a serious mistake by one of the best Irish shooters, J. K. Milner. Milner normally fired lying on his back and this limited his vision of the targets. One of his 900-yard shots was fired at the wrong target and so counted as a complete miss.

The Americans were jubilant at their win over the Irish champions and there was extensive press coverage throughout the United States. The international event encouraged the construction of ranges with firing points up to 1000 yards and the development of more formalized target shooting in the United States. This sport has been fostered and encouraged by The National Rifle Association for more than a century. Annual 1000-yard matches are fired at Camp Perry, Ohio. Four-position shooting which includes standing, kneeling, sitting and prone positions, and long-range rifle shooting are regular events in Olympic competition.

Remington has manufactured high quality breech-loading target rifles since the early 1870's. The models designed for the International Rifle Match were offered to the public as the Remington Creedmoor model. These were available in various grades with optional special sighting equipment, and double set triggers. The Remington rolling block target rifles were offered with such a wide range of options that the target shooter could literally define his own rifle in terms of barrel style, barrel length, caliber, stock shape, sighting shape, sighting equipment, and trigger mechanism. Some of the fussiest shooters even went so far as to use a blank cartridge case loaded from the breech, and a paper patched bullet loaded from the muzzle. This system was supposed to combine all of the advantages of breech- and muzzle-loading and to minimize deformation of the bullet during firing. By the 1880's most target shooters were convinced that breech-loading rifles and fixed ammunition were fully as accurate as any laborious combinations of breech- and muzzle-loading.

Later in the 1870's annual matches were sponsored by the National Rifle Association at the Creedmoor, range which regularly included events at 500, 600, 800, 900 and 1000 yards. The finest target shooters chose a .44 caliber cartridge packed with 90 grains of black powder, and a paper patched smooth bullet weighing approximately 500 grains. This cartridge had been developed to provide superb accuracy and minimum deflection due to a crosswind over a 1000-yard range, within the limits of bearable recoil. Even so, the time of flight was approximately 3 seconds and a 10 mile per hour crosswind caused a lateral drift of 12 feet.

These problems were overcome by the development of special features in the highest quality target rifles. A cross section of a Sharps target rifle of 1875 is shown in Figure 6-9. A heavy octagonal barrel 30 or 32 inches long was fitted to the action. This was an elaborate barrel with 1¼-inch round section at the breech, and tapered, milled octagonal flats varying from 1.05 inches at the breech to one inch across the flats at the muzzle. A special target front sight was held in a dovetail cut near the muzzle. This sight allowed micrometer adjustments for windage and the details are shown in the right-hand side of Figure 6-10. The sight consisted of two dovetail slides. The lower dovetail was permanently driven into the barrel of the rifle. The upper sight assembly was fitted to this base with a micrometer adjustment screw, thus allowing a calibrated movement of the upper sight assembly to compensate for windage. Very accurate scales were engraved on the front side of the sight assembly so that a precise measurement of the windage could be made. The sight tube was slotted so that interchangeable sighting discs could be used to provide an optimum sight pattern for various target conditions.[1]

The Sharps action shown in Figure 6-9 was basically the Civil War receiver, finger lever assembly, and lock mechanism. The remainder of the rifle had been redesigned to improve the mechanism and adopt it to long-range target shooting. For example, a double set trigger mechanism was fitted to many of the long-range target and hunting rifles. The double set trigger mechanism was operated by pulling back the rear trigger. This compressed the powerful leaf spring shown just behind the trigger. A trigger adjusting screw is shown between the two triggers, allowing fine adjustment of the sear engagement. A very light motion of the front trigger released the rear trigger which flew in a clockwise direction, striking the sear. The Sharps lock mechanism was fitted with powerful springs and the tumbler had a deep safety notch. Experience showed that the quick motion of the set

[1] D. F. Butler, "Match Rifles Then and Now" *The American Rifleman* January 1971, P 74.

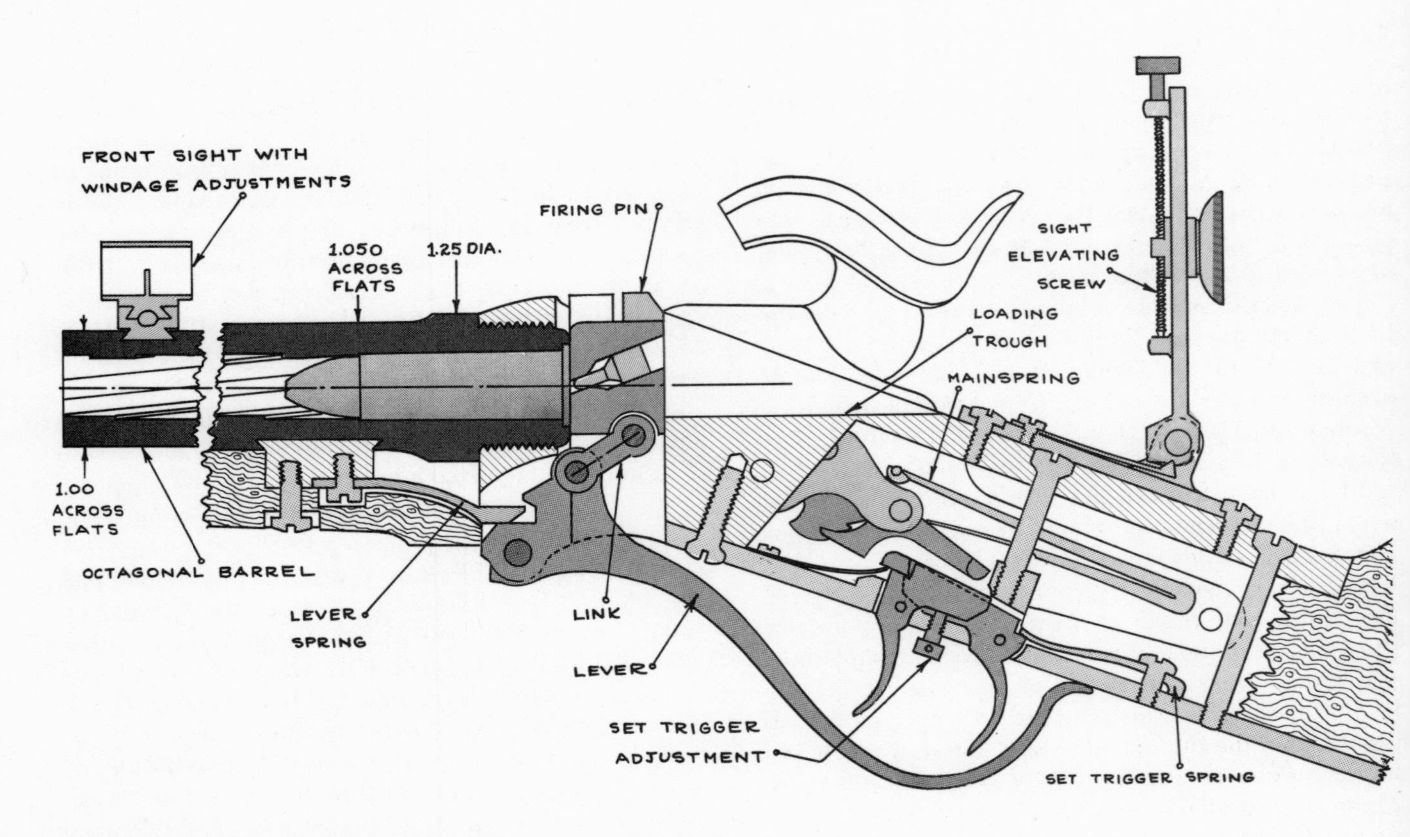

FIGURE 6-9 Sharps Model 1874 target rifle—cross-section of action.

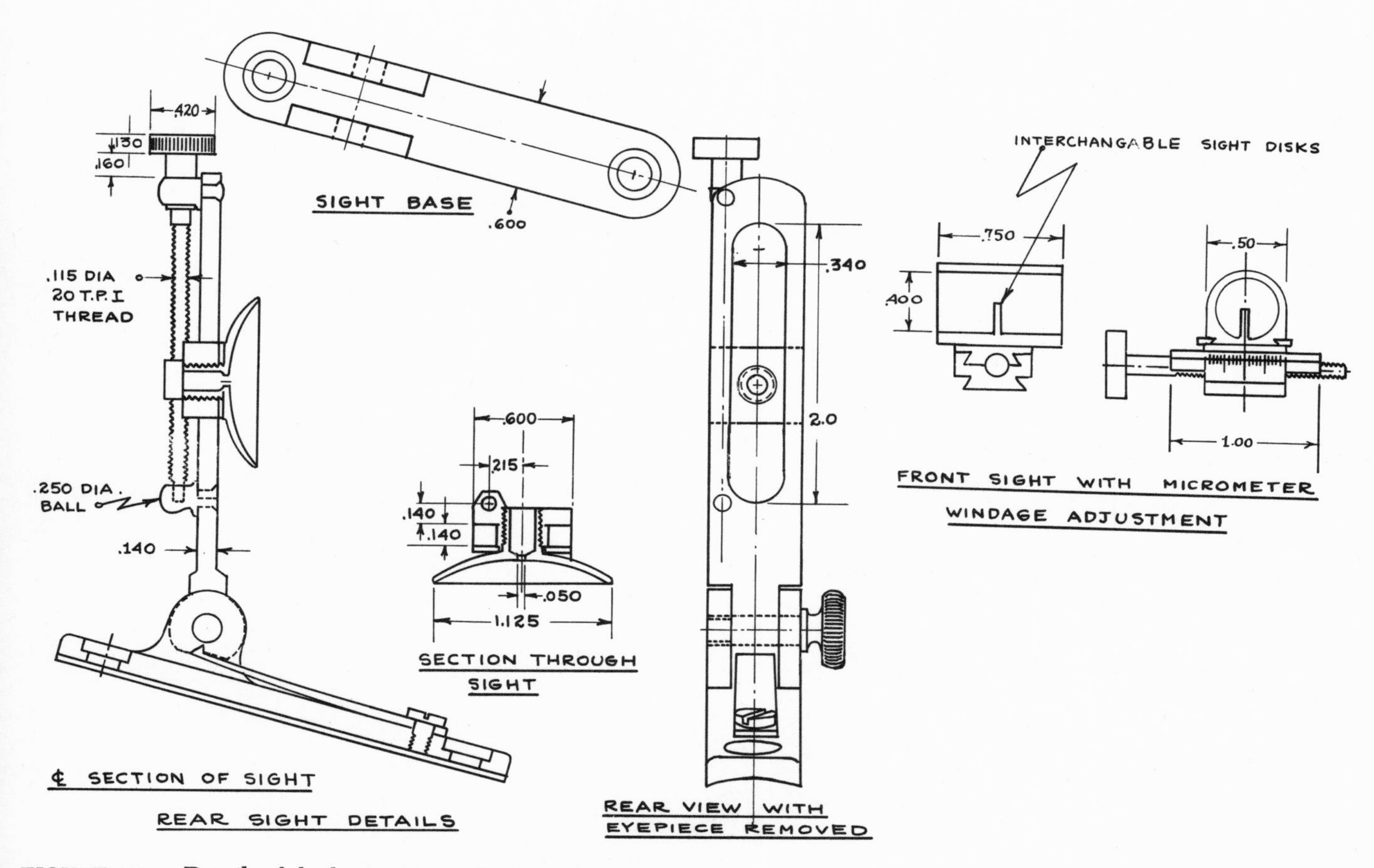

FIGURE 6-10 Details of the best target sights of 1875.

trigger striking the sear would disengage the sear from the tumbler notch, but the sear was not held disengaged and the powerful mainspring would snap the sear up into the safety notch before the tumbler and hammer could rotate to a fully fired position.

Careful examination of a Civil War Sharps and a Sharps Model 1874 target rifle show many small refinements to make the double set trigger mechanism work properly. For example, the main and sear springs were reduced in strength and an ingenious little "fly" was added to the tumbler. The fly was designed so that once the sear was disengaged from the sear notch the fly prevented it from engaging the safety notch as the hammer was falling.

The Sharps and Remington target rifles of the early 1870's were fitted with elaborate rear sights. The sights were generally mounted on the tang of the rifle very close to the shooter's eye. Details of the sight are shown on the left side of Figure 6-10. A sturdy base was fastened to the tang of the rifle. A long leaf was pivoted to the base and held with a close fitting cross screw. The shooter aimed through the hemispherical dish slightly over one inch in diameter with a very tiny peep hole through the center. The vertical position of the sight was determined by a long slender screw only ⅛ of an inch in diameter with a 20-pitch thread which allowed very accurate vertical adjustment for elevation. The Sharps catalog of 1875 lists the adjustment required for the .44/90/500 long-range target cartridge. With the rifle zeroed at 100 yards adjustments of ¼ inch were required at 300 yards, .57 of an inch at 500 yards, 1.1 inches at 800 yards, 1.51 inches at 1000 yards and 1.73 inches at 1100 yards.

A close up view of the long-range target sights is shown in Figure 6-11. The wind gauge front sight, which allowed micrometer adjustments for windage, is shown mounted on the muzzle of a Winchester "high wall" target rifle. This sight even included a bubble leveling device so the shooter could check that his rifle was exactly vertical before firing. A long-range peep sight is shown on the Sharps Model 1875 Creedmoor No. 3 rifle. The most elaborate rear sight with a vernier adjustment for elevation is shown on the Remington Creedmoor rolling block rifle. These tall sights were precision instruments and the most careful shooters would remove them entirely from the rifle and carry them in a small Morocco case. Others would fold the tall leaf down flat along the tang of the rifle during transportation.[2]

When the standard model Sharps or Remington hunting rifles with round barrels sold for about $30, the best quality Remington and Sharps target rifles with all of the equipment shown in these illustrations ran about $125 — a truly colossal sum for a century ago. By the 1880's Remington brought out a new single-shot target action known as the Improved Creedmoor Hepburn. This was a dropping block single-shot action operated by a side lever and was slightly simpler and quicker to operate than the rolling block action. Both the Remington rolling block and Sharps actions required that the hammer be cocked, and the action open to reload. The later Remington Hepburn and the Winchester single-shot both automatically cocked the hammer as the lever was thrown down.

The Sharps rifle company went out of business in 1881. In the mid-1880's Winchester brought out a new dropping block action designed by John Browning, and by the late 1880's Winchester and Remington were competing intensely to provide American shooters with the very finest long-range target rifles that American ingenuity could devise. This situation has continued for almost ninety years. While the Winchester single-shot is beyond the scope of this book, the Winchester rifle shown in Figure 6-12 is very similar in appearance and equipment to the early breech-loading Schuetzen rifles widely used for offhand shooting at moderate ranges during the post-Civil War period. It is fitted with an adjustable palm rest below the forearm. The Winchester Schuetzen target rifle is fitted with a heavy octagonal

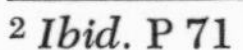

[2] *Ibid.* P 71

FIGURE 6-11 LEFT: Target front sight with windage adjustment; CENTER: Sharps Model 1874 target rifle with windage adjustment on tang sight; RIGHT: Remington Creedmoor target rifle with Vernier Tang rear sight.

FIGURE 6-12 Winchester "Scheutzen" style target rifle.

barrel and a wind gauge front sight. The palm rest was swung to a vertical position for firing and the ball was held in the shooter's hand. The shooter's elbow was then braced against his hip to provide increased steadiness in the offhand position. The action is fitted with double set triggers and an elaborate finger lever typical of the ornamental designs of the late 19th century. The rifle has a high comb buttstock to properly locate the shooter's face in the offhand position. An elaborate hooked butt plate was installed on most Schuetzen rifles and this served a very useful purpose. The Schuetzen rifles were muzzle heavy and there was a tendency for them to ride up on the shoulder in the offhand position. The long hook passing over and under the shooter's shoulder accurately positioned the butt of the rifle during firing.

There were many small manufacturers of accurate muzzle and breech loading target rifles during the post Civil War period. Some such as Ballard, Marlin-Ballard, Peabody-Martini, and Wesson manufactured rifles in quantity, but most of the makers were custom gunsmiths whose expensive products were manufactured in very limited quantity to the customer's specifications. The investment in time and skill required to create the most accurate target rifles has always been a major problem to manufacturers. In 1875 the standard Sharps rifle cost $30. The best Sharps target rifle was over four times as expensive at $125. Most shooters look at these target rifles as high priced arms, and yet the required investment in manufacturing time and equipment has seldom provided a profit.

Springfield Single-Shot Breech-Loading Rifles

CHAPTER

7

At the end of the Civil War in 1865, it was obvious to everyone that the breech-loading cartridge rifle had come to stay. There were hundreds of companies manufacturing firearms to meet the demands of the war, and three quarters of them were out of business a decade later.

The firearms industry was in a period of transition and retrenchment after the war. The market was so glutted with war surplus firearms that Bannerman's, Inc., of New York City, still had substantial stocks of Civil War rifles when World War II broke out 75 years later.

The actions of the United States Government had a tremendous influence on the postwar firearms developments. The urgent need for reliable firearms on the frontier was another powerful factor. During the last years of the war, the Ordnance Department carried out a survey of the troops using breech-loading rifles. The survey was to establish the advantages and limitations of the many breech-loading designs in the field and provide guidance for the direction the Army should go in the future.

Springfield Armory and Frankford Arsenal both experimented with a wide variety of cartridge designs all through the 1860's, and the Commandant of Frankford Arsenal published in 1873 a very valuable description of many of the experiments in a volume entitled *Metallic Ammunition — Ordnance Memoranda No. 14.* Some of the highlights of that report are included in Chapter 4.

In his introduction to the report, the Commandant highlighted the developments of the 1860's, and it is a valuable comment on the complete change of official attitude which had occurred in this decade. He wrote:

> For a long time the idea of the general adoption of breech-loading arms for troops of all services met with almost no encouragement among military men, and it was not until as late as after the battle of Gettysburg that it became popular and prevailed in the service. This prejudice once overcome, by what may be fairly termed an entire revolution of the character of the arms and ammunition, the new breech-loaders became rapidly popular, and gained many advocates throughout the Army, where their great superiority to the old muzzle-loaders is now universally recognized and assured. The use of some effective breech-loaders and magazine-arms had, for some time, popularized them for cavalry, but many of the best infantry and artillery officers were adverse to their employment by foot-soldiers. A marked contrast of the two systems was furnished the department by the recovery of upwards of 25,000 stands of muzzle-loading arms from the battle-field of Gettysburg. These were sent to the Washington Arsenal, and there, overhauled and examined, and were found to be nearly all loaded; some with one, two, three, four, six and even as many as twenty rounds of cartridges in the barrel. This fact gave an active impulse to the necessity for an arm which, by its construction and cartridge, could never produce such a result as the above, and which, by materially reducing the motions for loading and firing, was capable of greatly enhancing the power of the individual soldier.

As an advancing step in the right direction, various systems of breech-loading arms had been devised, using, instead of paper or linen, metal cases holding the powder and bullet, but not as yet self primed. Ingenious samples of these may be named the Burnside, Maynard, etc. Still further progress developed more perfect systems using self-primed ammunition, including magazine-arms, as Spencer, Henry, etc. and the speedy adaptation of all then known systems of any pretensions to the use of such ammunition.

No branch of invention has been more rapidly or beautifully developed and improved in the past ten years, especially in the United States, than that under consideration; it is believed that it may be fearlessly asserted that the use of expanding metallic self-primed ammunition, acting as a perfect gas check to breech mechanism, has been the chief cause of rendering effective the very many existing breech-loading systems now claiming attention in this country and abroad, which would otherwise be useless and worthless.

In the earlier stages of the solution of the problem of the production of an efficient breech-loading rifle, paper and linen ammunition was used, but the perfect *fermeture* of the joint between the breech mechanism and barrel was never successfully accomplished until the adoption of the expanding cartridges, although some of the earlier arms were very ingenious, and found to give good results in practice. Among them may be named the justly celebrated, and perhaps most prominent and popular, Sharp's Rifle and Carbine, which, as is well known, has given an excellent record of its performance in the field and on the experimental ground. These arms were most excellently well-made weapons, and believed by many military authorities to be the very best breech loader produced for the use of paper or linen cartridges. The gas check in this arm was an expanding metallic ring in the breech-block, which did its work well. Other meritorious systems, with ingenious means of closing the breech-joint, were in use, with fair results, but by far the most numerous varieties were not effective systems, and, in fact, were only tolerated and used in consequence of the dire emergency of immediate warfare, and the necessities of the Army.

Rimfire cartridges are much simpler to manufacture than the center-fire designs. During the first half of the 1860's the large copper rimfire cartridges firing heavy bullets at velocities between 900 and 1150 feet per second seemed to be the way to go. The most popular of these was the .56/.56 caliber Spencer cartridge. Over 58,000,000[1] of these cartridges were purchased during the Civil War. Data on 50,000 of these cartridges loaded at Frankford Arsenal in 1864 and 1865 shows a cartridge with a 40-grain powder charge and 450-grain bullet. This was an extremely low powder charge in relation to the bullet weight and resulted in a relatively low velocity of approximately 900 feet per second with a muzzle energy of only 800 foot-pounds. Other .56/.56 Spencer cartridges were loaded with 45 grains of powder and a lighter bullet at 350 grains which provided a muzzle velocity of approximately 1075 feet per second and 900 foot-pounds of muzzle energy. Such low powder charges and low bullet velocities were necessary so that the relatively weak copper cartridge cases did not blow up when the rifle was fired. Even the .44 caliber Henry lever action repeater, firing a much lighter 200-grain bullet with a 28-grain powder charge, could achieve a muzzle velocity of only 1125 feet per second.

Springfield Armory carried out experiments to increase the velocity of the Spencer ammunition by developing a slightly tapered cartridge known as the .56/.50 which fired a 350-grain lead bullet with a 45-grain powder charge. This increased the muzzle velocity from the 900 feet per second of the arsenal loaded .56/.56 ammunition to approximately 1075 feet per second for the .56/.50 with a lighter bullet and heavier powder charge.

SPRINGFIELD MODEL 1865 RIFLE

Springfield Armory was directed to study the problem of developing a simple and effective conversion of the hundreds of thousands of muzzle-loading .58 caliber rifles into single-shot breech-loading rifles. E. S. Allin, Master Armorer of Springfield Armory, developed experimental designs in the mid-1860's. A design was finally selected which utilized almost all the existing components of the muzzle-loading rifles and fired a .58 caliber *rimfire* cartridge. The upper illustration in Figure 7-1 shows a sideview of the Model 1865 rifle, and a comparison with the standard Model 1861 and 1863 Springfields shows that all the changes were limited to the hammer and breech area. A patent, No. 49,959, was issued to Allin on September 19, 1865, describing the design.

The Model 1865 action in an open position is shown in the upper illustration of Figure 7-2. The breech mechanism was simply placed into an opening milled in the top of the existing .58 caliber muzzle-loading barrel. The breech assembly was attached to the barrel with two screws at the forward end of the mechanism. The breech assembly consists of a pivoted breechblock which was hinged at the top in line with the breech face and was locked into a recess in the breech tang, thus holding the back of the breech bolt down against the firing forces. A complicated ratchet arrangement was designed which moved an extractor to the rear as the breechblock was pivoted upward. A new hammer was fitted to the lock. The firing pin was located in the upper part of the bolt, and struck the rim of the cartridge case at the top.

[1] B. R. Lewis, *Small Arms and Ammunition in the U.S. Service,* Smithsonian, 1968, P 170.

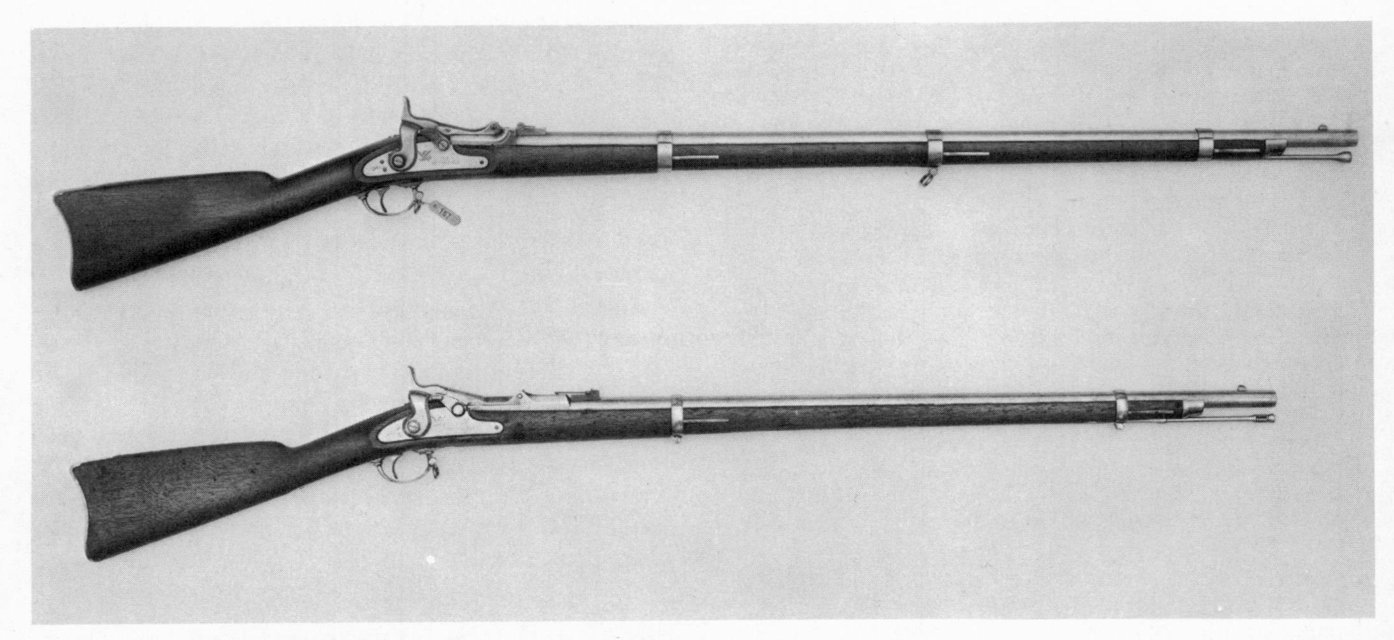

FIGURE 7-1 UPPER: Springfield Model 1865 conversion to .58 caliber rimfire breech-loading rifle; LOWER: Springfield Model 1868 Rifle in .50-70-450 Center-Fire Caliber.

Economy in the conversion was carried to an extreme degree. Even so, the model included 38 new pieces and modifications of five old parts of the muzzle-loader. The Commanding Officer of Springfield Armory wrote to the Chief of Ordnance in January 1866 commenting that 95 new milling fixtures were required and that he was employing 66 tool makers to perform the work as rapidly as possible.

A careful examination of Figure 7-2 will show one of the major weaknesses of the Model 1865 action. The breech bolt was an extremely complicated component and the ratchet extractor mechanism incorporated many delicate small parts. The second limitation in the Model 1865 design was the utilization of a low velocity .58 caliber rimfire cartridge shown as the upper illustration in Figure 7-3. The large copper cartridge case held a soft lead 500-grain bullet with no external grooves. The bullet was seated .330 of an inch into the copper case which was then crimped into a shallow groove in the bullet. By 1864 Frankford Arsenal had developed a centrifugal priming machine and these cartridges were probably primed in the same manner as that used for the Spencer cartridges with what was known as Sharps Mixture consisting of 6 parts by weight mealed powder, 3 parts of fulminate and 3 parts of ground glass. The powder charge consisted of 60[2] grains of black powder. The ballistics of these Springfield cartridges are shown in Figure 7-4.

Another .58 caliber cartridge was designed for commercial conversions of the muzzle-loading Springfield rifles. This was the .58 musket cartridge, shown as the upper part of Figure 7-5.

The .58 center-fire cartridges were quite popular, and were used in commercial conversions. They were not officially adopted. The .58 rimfire cartridge and .58 musket centerfire cartridge both had low powder charges compared to the bullet weights, and muzzle velocities were quite low.

The .56/56 Spencer, and .58 Springfield Rimfire represented early cartridge designs with weak cases. In addition, the breech mechanism on the 1865 Springfield conversion was rather weak. For both reasons it was important to keep breech pressure low, and this limited the muzzle velocity of the bullet.

Ballistic tests of some early cartridges are available, and analysis of the known data allows quite close predictions of other similar cartridges. The technique is to calculate the "efficiency," or the foot-pounds of muzzle energy of the bullet, divided by the powder charge in grains. Most of the rimfire cartridges of the 1860's averaged between 19- and 21-foot pounds of muzzle energy per grain of propellant. Using a value of 20 foot-pounds per grain of propellent, we arrive at a muzzle energy of 1000 foot-pounds and a muzzle velocity of only 950 feet per second for the .58 rimfire cartridge. This was about the same velocity as the Frankford Arsenal .56/.56 Spencer cartridge, and gave a poor trajectory.

SPRINGFIELD MODEL 1866 RIFLE

During 1865 and 1866 a comprehensive series of Ordnance tests were performed to evaluate all the breech-loading rifles available at that time and select a future standard rifle for Army use. The tests were complicated by the fact that an economy wave had swept the country and there was great pressure to use the large stocks of surplus muzzle-loading rifles. Springfield Armory had been studying the deficiencies of its Model 1865 rifle and its relatively weak ammunition and had submitted a redesigned model which fired a .50 caliber cartridge with 70 grains of propellant. The .50/70 cartridges were developed in both the *rimfire* and *center-fire* designs and the center-fire version is shown as the third cartridge in Figure 7-5. Display boards of the Union Metallic Cartridge Company from 1875 and 1881 at the Smithsonian in Washington show both rimfire and center-fire versions of the .50/70 ammunition.

The conclusion of the comprehensive tests was that

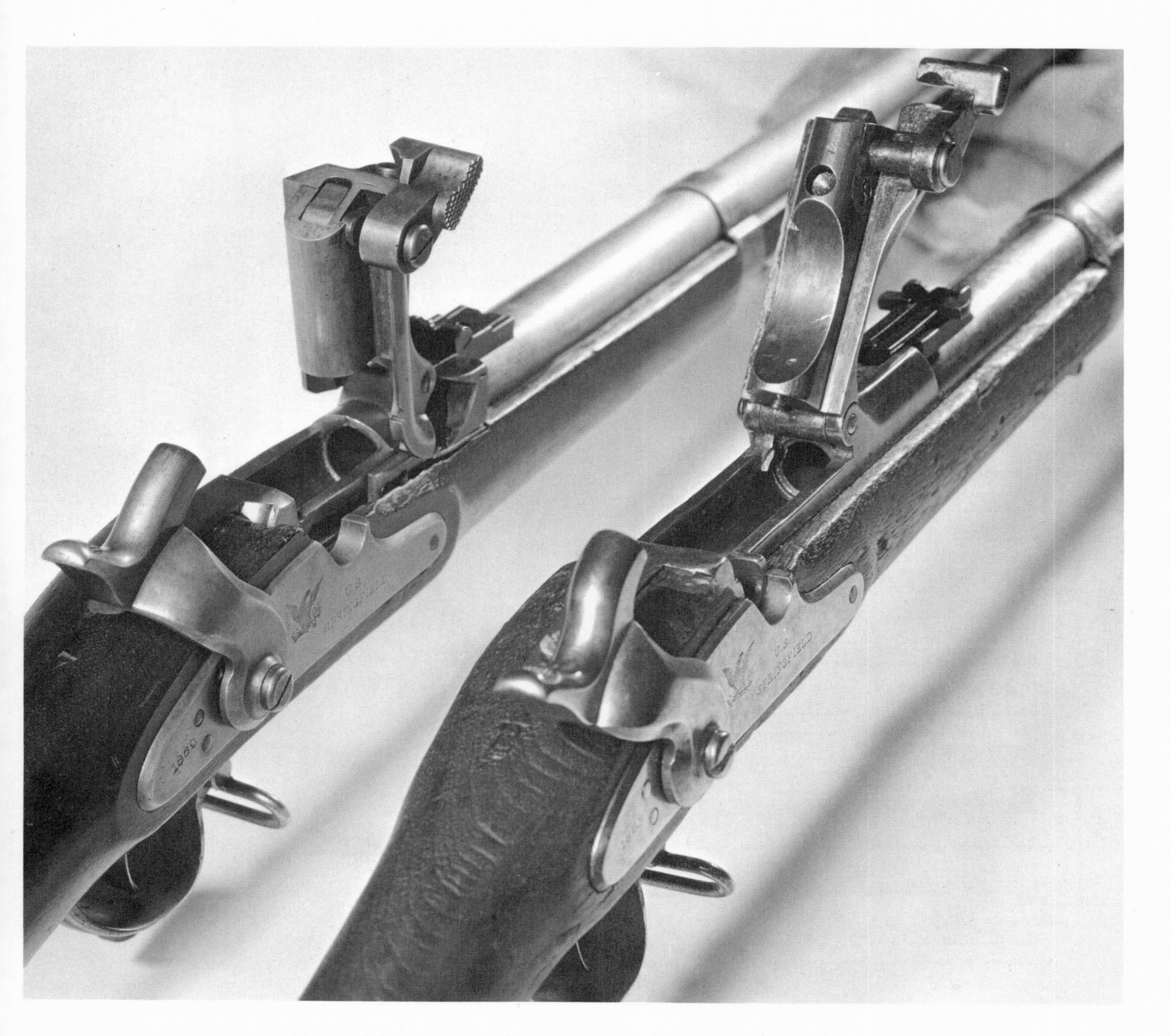

FIGURE 7-2 Breech details of Springfield rifles. Model 1865 at left, and Model 1868 at right.

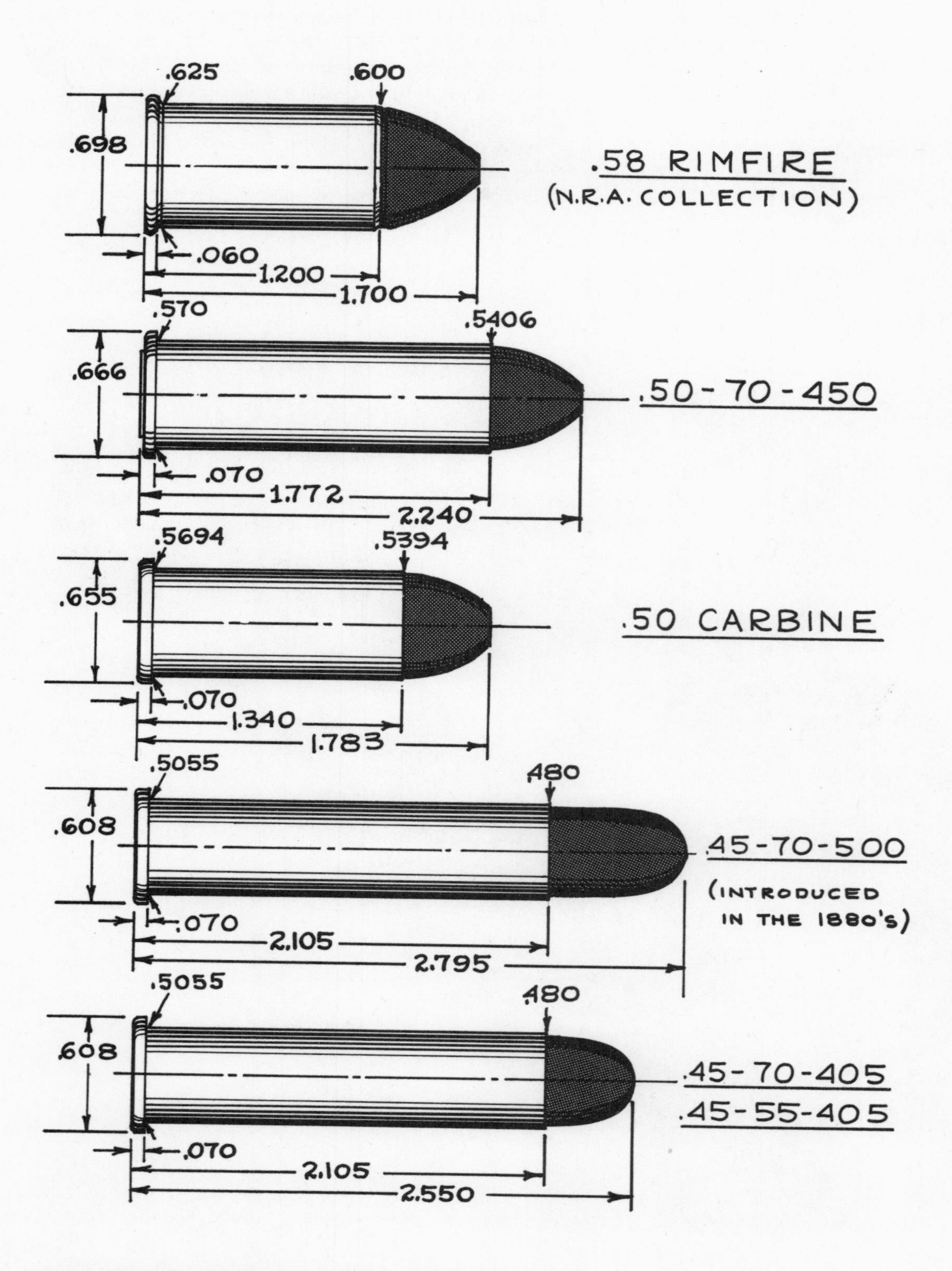

FIGURE 7-3 Cartridges for Springfield Single-Shot Rifles.

no repeating rifle was "fully satisfactory" for acceptance as the standard military arm. The Spencer rifle was judged the best of all breech-loading repeaters at that time. The board recommended acceptance of the Springfield Armory conversion of the .58 caliber muzzle-loading rifle to a .50 caliber single-shot breech-loader which is shown in Figure 7-6. In July 1866 the Armory was directed to take immediate measures for the conversion of 25,000 Springfield muskets into breech-loaders of their "best pattern." Springfield was to study the problems of rimfire and center-fire ammunition and establish the proper powder charge and design of the cartridge case and bullet. They were also to establish the process of manufacture for the cartridges and transmit this information so that ammunition manufacture could be tooled up at Frankford Arsenal in Philadelphia. E. B. Dyer, Chief of Ordnance, stated:

> A center primed cartridge is preferred to the rim primed, if one suitable for the military service and equally sure of fire can be devised.
>
> You will direct your attention particularly to getting up a proper cartridge, but the conversion of the arms will not be delayed in order that you may determine whether center primed cartridges may be adopted.

In the Model 1866 Springfield rifles economy was carried out to an extreme degree. The old muzzle-loading barrels were even reused by boring out the rifling and soldering in a liner to reduce the caliber from .58 to .50. The 40-inch barrel of the standard Civil War musket was retained and an opening cut into the upper breech area of the barrel into which the pivoted breechblock assembly was inserted. The breech pivot was held to the barrel with two screws. The design of the breechblock was considerably simplified. The rifle was very similar to the Model 1865 Springfield shown in Figure 7-1. The main difference was that the breechblock was slightly longer and of a simplified design. The complex ratchet ejector mechanism had been eliminated and a simpler design had been incorporated using a U-shaped spring to kick the shell to the rear. The over-all length of the rifle was 56 inches, and the weight was about 9¾ pounds. A smaller version of the rifle was made up for cadets, and the weight-saving was about ¾ of a pound.

The cartridges for the 1866 Springfield rifles and carbines are shown as the third and fourth illustrations in Figure 7-5. These are catalog illustrations from a Winchester catalog of the 1880's. An illustration of the center-fire .58 Carbine cartridge is shown, as these were widely used in commercially converted .58 caliber Springfield muskets. The .58 center-fire cartridges were never officially adopted by the Army. Although Winchester loaded a large number of rimfire cartridges including the .56 caliber Spencer series, they never tooled up for the .58 caliber rimfire cartridge for the Model 1865 Springfield, which apparently was not very popular. The .58 rimfire was quite similar in appearance to the top illustration of Figure 7-5 (the .58 carbine cartridge) except that the head was perfectly plain with no markings.

SPRINGFIELD MODEL 1868 RIFLE

In January 1868 a board of officers met to review the performance of the Model 1866 Springfield rifle in the field. The Ordnance Department had kept careful note of the monthly reports of company commanders who generally considered the rifle powerful,

Cartridge	Powder Charge	Bullet Weight	Muzzle Velocity	Muzzle Energy	Ratio: Bullet Powder	Energy per Grain
.58 Rimfire	60	500	1,040*	1200*	8.33	20*
.50-70	70	450	1,240	1535	6.4	21.9
.50 Carbine	55	430	1,130*	1210*	7.8	22*
.45-70	70	405	1,330	1580	5.8	22.5
.45-70 Carbine	55	405	1,125	1138	7.35	20.7

*Calculated Figures

FIGURE 7-4 Ballistics of cartridges for Springfield Single-Shot Rifles.

accurate and serviceable. There were some minor defects such as the strength of the ejector and the tendency of some components in the breech latching mechanism to work loose.

Surprisingly there were no reports of the soldered barrel liners coming loose. Since this is a long slender liner with a wall only ⅛ of an inch thick, this reflects considerable care in the manufacture at Springfield Armory.

The Board made a number of recommendations which had far-reaching effect in establishing the basic design features of the "trap door" Springfield for the next 24 years. These recommendations were incorporated in the Springfield Model 1868 which is shown in the lower illustration of Figure 7-1. The breech detail may be seen in the right illustration of Figure 7-2. For the first time the action was contained in a separate receiver. The breechblock was simplified and lightened and the latching system was modified so that unless the action was fully locked the hammer struck an extension on the cam latch rather than striking the firing pin. Another feature of the action was that after the hammer had fallen and struck the firing pin the forward part of the hammer rested on top of the cam latch retaining it in a fully locked position until the hammer had been retracted.

There was a long cylindrical section at the front of the receiver into which a new 32½-inch solid barrel was screwed. Rifling was very deep at .010 of an inch at the breech, tapering to .005 inches at the muzzle, (this compares with .004 of an inch in a modern .30 caliber rifle). The rifling was machined with 3 lands and 3 grooves and a twist of 1 turn in 42 inches.

A new sight was designed and was placed immediately forward of the receiver. The standard Civil War musket sight consisted of an L-shaped assembly with a V notch in the short leg of the L for short range firing and a peep sight in the middle of the long leg of the L for middle range. The longest range was provided by a V notch at the end of the long leg of the L. This V notch was a full 1⅜ inches above the top of the barrel to compensate for the tremendous bullet drop at extended ranges. On the Model 1868 Springfield rifle this three-position sight was replaced with a graduated sighting system. The sight leaf remained L-shaped with a notch in the short leg for short-range firing. The notch in the top of the long leg was raised to 1⅞ inches above the top of the barrel. A sliding cross bar with a V notch in it was provided which could be moved up and down the long leg of the sight leaf and matched up with engraved graduations for 200, 300, 500, 700 and 900 yards.

It took very skilled and experienced shooters to hit anything beyond 300 yards with these old-time rifles with the rapidly falling trajectory of the heavy, low speed, blunt-nosed lead bullets.

Another significant change in the Springfield Model 1868 were the use of a shorter wooden stock with two barrel bands — which again set the pattern for all the remaining "trap door" Springfield rifles. There are references in the literature of Arsenal modifications of the longer three-band stocks to shorten them to the two-band length. This may have been done, but there were thousands of two-banded Civil War muzzle-loading rifles in the Government inventory and these seem to have been selected for most of the Model 1868 rifles.

The over-all length of the rifle was reduced from 56 inches on the earlier models to 52 inches on the Model 1868. The weight was reduced to about 9¼ pounds. A new ramrod was designed and a special steel shoulder was set into the stock to lock the ramrod in a rearward position. On the Civil War muzzle-loading rifles the ramrod was, of course, removed at each shot, and a spring arm was provided to retain the ramrod during carrying but yet not hinder the speed with which the ramrod could be removed and replaced during the loading sequence. On the breech-loading rifles, the ramrod was redesigned with a smaller head and a corrugated exterior surface and a cross slot into which a cleaning patch was placed. The function of the ramrod was limited to cleaning the rifle and the removal of a stuck cartridge case in emergency conditions (providing the head had not torn off). One of the improvements in the 1868 model was the incorporation of a ramrod with a solid shoulder and a metallic stop set into the stock to prevent the ramrod moving forward due to recoil. This locked the ramrod in a rearward position until the trooper sprung it slightly downward, past the abutment and removed it from the rifle.

DESIGN CHANGE IN THE SPRINGFIELD ACTIONS

Cutaway views of three of the trap door Springfield actions are shown in Figure 7-7. The upper illustration shows the design of the Model 1866 action. The middle illustration shows the Model 1868 action and the lowest illustration a Model 1873 action. The strong similarity between all three actions is apparent in the illustrations. Careful examination shows many minor differences. For example, the Model 1866 action has a breech assembly held to the barrel with two screws into the top of the barrel immediately forward of the hinge pin. The Model 1868 has the separate receiver with a long barrel shank. The Model 1873 action has a sepa-

CENTER FIRE CARTRIDGES.

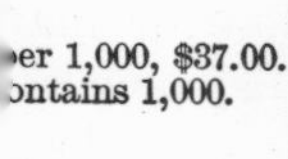
per 1,000, $37.00.
contains 1,000.

Powder, 40 grains.
Bullet, 530 grains.
Composed of pure lead.

Primed Shells, per 1,000, $18.00. Bullets per 1,000, $15.00.
Adapted to various transformed Carbines.

per 1,000, $44.00. contains 1,000.

Powder, 85 grains.
Bullet, 530 grains.
Composed of pure lead.

Primed Shells, per 1,000, $24.00. Bullets, per 1,000, $15.00.
Adapted to various transformed Muskets.

per 1,000, $37.00. contains 1,000.

Powder, 70 grains.
Bullet, 450 grains.
Composed of 1 part tin and 16 parts lead.

Grooved Bullet.

Primed Shells, per 1,000, $22.50. Bullets, per 1,000, $12.00.
Adapted to United States Rifled Muskets, and Sharp and Remington Rifles and Carbines.

per 1,000, $30.00. contains 1,000.

Powder, 50 grains.
Bullet, 400 grains.
Composed of pure lead.

Primed Shells, per 1,000, $15.50. Bullets, per 1,000, $10.50.
Adapted to United States, Sharp, and Remington Carbines.

per 1,000, $38.00.
contains 1,000.

Powder, 70 grains.
Bullet, 500 grains.
Composed of 1 part tin and 16 parts lead.

Primed Shells, per 1,000, $22.00. Bullets, per 1,000, $15.00.
Adapted to New Model Springfield, Hotchkiss Repeating Rifles, Model 1883, and Winchester Single Shot and Repeating Rifle, Model 1886.

per 1,000, $35.00.
contains 1,000.

Powder, 70 grains.
Bullet, 405 grains.
Composed of 1 part tin and 16 parts lead.

Primed Shells, per 1,000, $22.00. Bullets, per 1,000, $12.00.
Adapted to New Model Springfield, Hotchkiss Repeating Rifle, and Winchester Single Shot and Repeating Rifles, Model 1886.

FIGURE 7-5 Cartridges for single-shot converted muskets and Springfield rifles.

rate receiver with a much shorter joint between the receiver and barrel.

Other small differences can be noted in the design of elements such as the firing pin. In the 1866 design the firing pin is held in by a threaded plug at the rear of the breechblock. In the 1868 and 1873 designs the firing pin was retained by a screw riding in a recess in the firing pin and this detail is shown by dotted lines with the breechblock in the open position.

The design of the extractor differs with a U-shaped spring shown in the 1866 design, and a pivoted extractor shown in the later designs. The Model 1868 action has features common to all the later actions. The receiver was a cylindrical section with the top half cut away for the rear two thirds of the length. The breechblock was pivoted on the cross shaft located immediately above the breech face.

The 3¼-inch bolt fitted into the cylindrical recess and formed the upper half of the receiver. A .225-inch diameter pivot pin passed through the upper section of the breech bolt and through matching bosses in the receiver. The center line of the pin was exactly in line with the breech face and the axis of the pin was .55 of an inch above the center line of the bore.

The firing thrust of the powerful .50/70 cartridge was taken in three places:

1. The .225-inch diameter breech pin was placed in double shear by the backward motion of the breech bolt.
2. The angled surface on the back of the breech bolt abutted the interior surface of the receiver at the back end and absorbed the majority of the firing forces.
3. The pivoted lock hooked in a semicircular cut in the back of the receiver and absorbed the forces tending to cause the rear of the breech bolt to rotate upward out of the receiver.

If no locking system were provided the firing thrust of the cartridge would cause the breechblock to pivot around the cross pin and it would ride up out of the beveled surface in the rear of the receiver and fly open. The lock consisted of a small pivoted cam which fitted into a semicircular recess cut into the breech tang in the rear of the receiver. The small breech lock was controlled by a cross shaft which extended through the breechblock and out the right side of the rifle. A cam latch lever was attached to the end of this shaft and was used to open the action. The cam latch lever in turn was so constructed as to block the hammer from striking the firing pin unless the action was fully locked. With the action fully locked, the falling hammer rode over the top of the cam latch lever locking it in a fully engaged position during the remainder of the firing cycle.

The operating sequence was as follows:

1. Recock the hammer to the safety notch.
2. Lift the pivoted cam latch lever.
3. Flip the breechblock open.
4. As the breechblock pivoted upward its cam surface struck an extractor which bore on the rim of the cartridge case and flipped it rearward out of the chamber.
5. The cartridge case, moving to the rear, struck an angled ramp located in the bottom of the receiver which deflected it upward out of the action of the rifle.
6. A fresh cartridge was inserted in the chamber.
7. The breechblock was flipped shut and automatically locked.
8. The hammer was moved to full-cock position.
9. The rifle was aimed and fired.

The trap door Springfield was not a particularly strong action, but it was amply strong for the pressures of that day. The early breech bolts were made of a low alloy steel and left completely soft. Heat treatments were experimented with all through the late 1870s and 1880's.

The Model 1868 Springfield proved to be a satisfactory rifle and established a pattern for the following 24 years. Many surplus Civil War components were used in the construction, including the lock assembly, trigger assembly, stock and all the stock furniture such as barrel bands, end cap, and butt plate. The new components were limited to the hammer, breech assembly, barrel and sights.

The major problems with the Springfield action were its weak extraction system, which caused the rifle to fail to extract under hot conditions, and its slow rate of fire which put the U. S. Army troopers at considerable disadvantage when fighting Indians or outlaws armed with lever action repeating rifles.

The author has a Springfield Model 1868 rifle, Serial No. 39,602. While the receiver and action date from 1870, the remainder of the rifle was manufactured in 1863. Modern shooters would consider the rifle somewhat muzzle heavy, but it is a very pleasant old cannon to shoot. The noise is more of a soft *boom* than a sharp *crack*, and a long column of smoke pours out fifteen feet toward the target. The sound of the heavy, slow moving bullet striking a hard target 100 or 200 yards away is distinctively separate from the sound of the cartridge firing.

CADET RIFLES AND CARBINES

Shorter and lighter versions of the single-shot Springfield rifle were made up for use by the cadets at West Point. The difference consisted of slightly shorter barrel and stock and lighter weight. These were known as the U. S. Cadet Rifles and, since they were made up in limited quantities, the documentation is not very complete and published data varies widely. Data gathered at the Smithsonian Institution in Washington, the National Rifle Association Collection and the Winchester Gun Museum, as well as private collections has been summarized in Figure 7-8.

MODEL 1865 CADET RIFLE Short versions of the Model 1865 rifle-muskets were made up in .58 rimfire caliber. An excellent example of this model is on display in the Winchester Museum in New Haven, Connecticut. The weight of the rifle has been reduced by 6/10 of a pound. The length of the barrel, measured from the head of the cartridge to the muzzle, is 33½ inches or 4 inches shorter than the standard 1865 rifle-musket. The over-all length of the rifle is 51.75 inches or about 4 inches shorter than the standard rifle-musket.

MODEL 1866 CADET RIFLE The Model 1866 Springfield rifles were extremely heavy. The rifle-muskets,

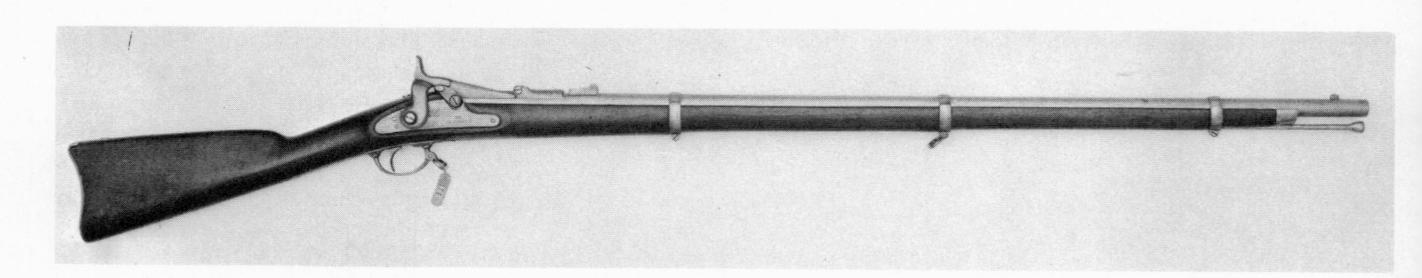

FIGURE 7-6 Springfield Model 1866 rifle in .50-70-450 Center-Fire Caliber.

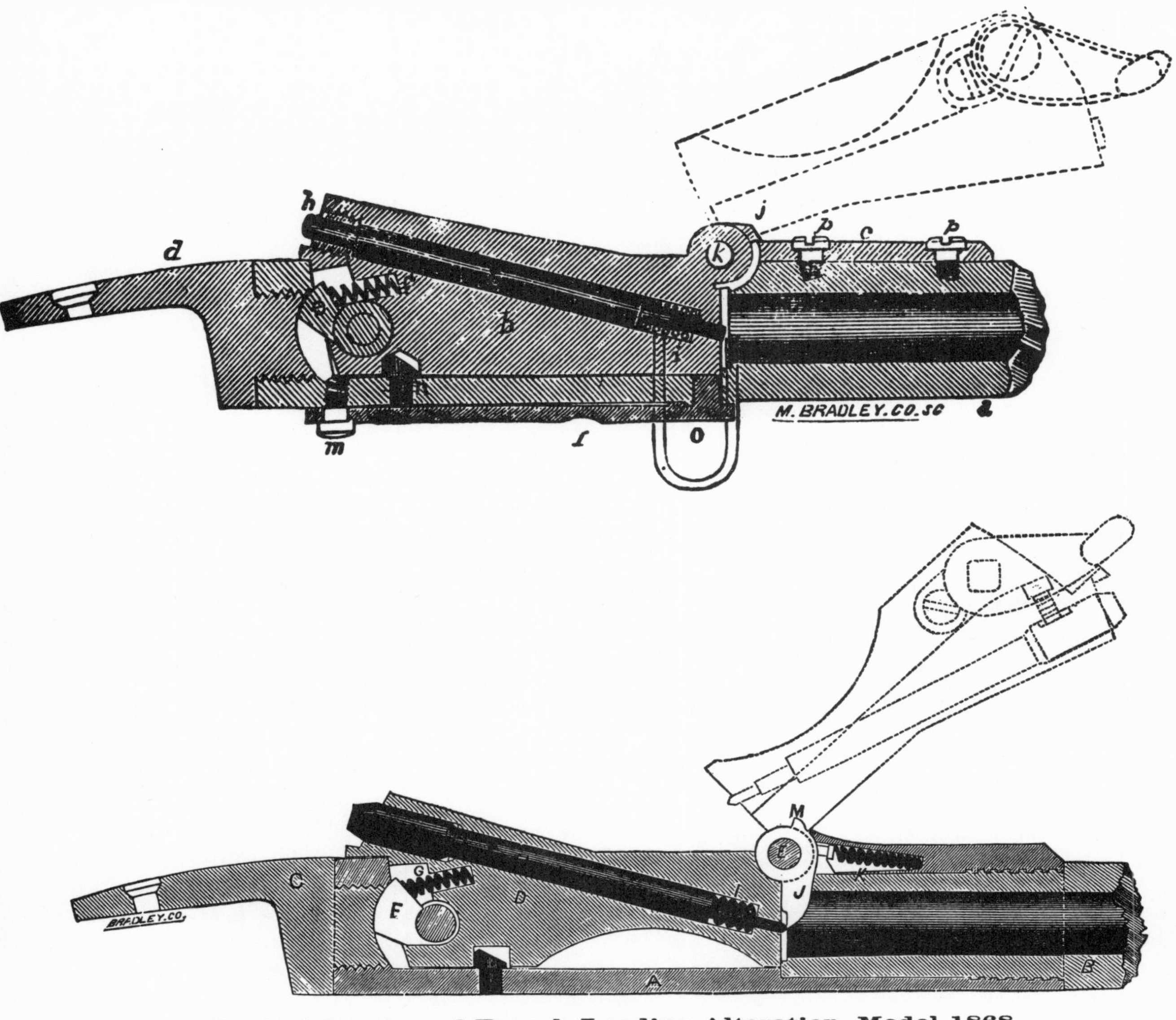

Vertical Section of Breech-Loading Alteration, Model 1868.

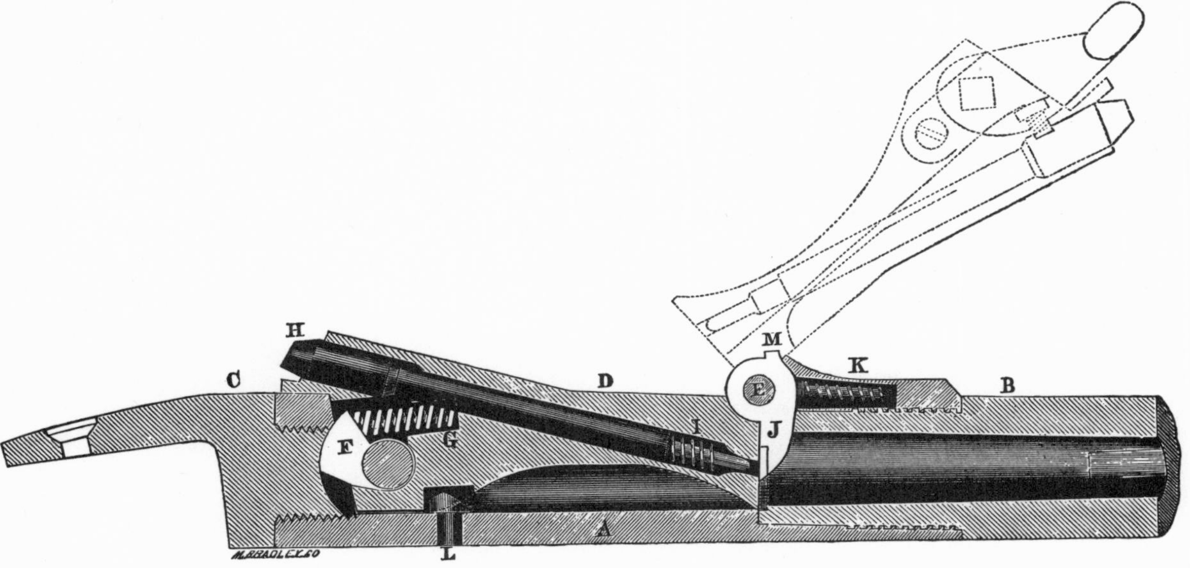

Vertical Section of Breech-Loading System.

FIGURE 7-7 Cross-section illustrations of Springfield Model 1866, 1868 and 1873 actions.

made by converting the Models 1861 and 1863 muzzle-loading rifles had the additional weight of the breech mechanism plus the barrel liner which reduced the caliber from .58 to .50. The result was a full 10 pounds measured on a gun in the Winchester Museum. There is an excellent example of a Model 1866 Cadet Rifle in the Museum and, surprisingly, this weighs exactly the same — 10 pounds. The barrel has been shortened by about 2 inches and the over-all length by slightly over an inch. It is to be expected that the weight of the Cadet Rifle would be slightly less, but apparently the density of the wood offsets the reduction of the weight of the metal parts.

MODEL 1869 CADET RIFLE In 1868 a major change was made in the design of the rifle-musket with the addition of a separate receiver, a brand-new barrel of smaller outside diameter and shorter length, and a shorter over-all length of the rifle. The result was a reduction of ¾ of a pound in the weight of the rifle-musket to 9¼ pounds.

The improved design features were carried over into the Cadet Rifle the following year. the Model 1869 Cadet Rifle had an even shorter barrel at 29.6 inches and an over-all length reduced to only 49 inches. This rifle was very light at 8.3 pounds. The Model 1869 Cadet Rifles were manufactured in 1869 and 1870. Two examples in a private collection are dated 1870 on the receiver. Both have been converted from rifles manufactured in 1864 and the serial numbers are between 1360 and 1975.

SPRINGFIELD MODEL 1870 RIFLES

The new Army rifle standardized in 1870 for the infantry and cavalry was virtually identical in appearance to the Model 1868 shown in Figures 7-1 and 7-2. The most visible change was that the receiver had been shortened about ¾ of an inch at the barrel joint. Minor mechanical changes had been made in the breech mechanism to allow the breech bolt to be thrown further forward, providing a more stable position with the action open. The breech mechanism was almost identical in appearance to the Model 1873 action, but the lock plate was raised and had a beveled edge similar to that on the 1868 and earlier designs. The sights were modified by silver plating the front sight, and providing finer notches in the rear sight. The ramrod was redesigned with a double shoulder so that it still had the stop to prevent it from riding forward due to recoil, but with the design modified so that the shoulder did not strike the edge of the barrel during cleaning.

During 1870 production of the Cadet Rifles was switched over to incorporate the new receiver and the other improvements of the 1870 rifle. In other respects the Model 1870 Cadet Rifle was virtually identical to the Model 1869. These were in fact, extremely handsome rifles and their slightly shorter length and lighter weight make them very easy to handle and provide an excellent weight distribution.

MODEL 1870 CAVALRY CARBINE

The United States Cavalry found that the features of the Spencer Lever Action Rifle were excellently suited to their needs during the Civil War. The bulk of the carbines used during the war had a 20-inch barrel, a 37¼-inch over-all length and a weight of 8.8 pounds. During the late 1860's the Cavalry struggled valiantly to retain their Spencer carbines while the Ordnance Department put on considerable pressure to standardize on one rifle and cartridge design for all troops. By 1870 the tide was running against the Spencer and a special cavalry model of the 1870 Springfield Rifle was designed. This was a shorter lighter version with a 22-inch barrel, a 41.4-inch over-all length and a weight of only 7.1 pounds. It was slightly longer than the Spencer but weighed 1½ pounds less. The recoil of the carbine firing the standard musket cartridge was too heavy, and so a special cartridge was loaded. The same case with 450-grain bullet was used, but the powder charge was reduced to 55 grains. The cartridges for the Springfield rifles are illustrated in Figure 7-5. The fourth cartridge down from the top shows a commercial carbine cartridge loaded in the late 19th century. The printing on the illustration states 45 grains of powder and a 400-grain bullet while the printing to the right shows 50 grains of powder with a 400-grain bullet. The cartridge case is obviously shorter than the standard .50/70 case. The original cartridge designed for use in the Model 1870 carbine was identical in appearance to the .50/70/450 rifle load and the empty space above the 55-grain powder charge was filled with wads.

ARMY TESTS OF VARIOUS MAKES OF RIFLES

FIELD TRIALS OF .50/70 CALIBER SINGLE-SHOT RIFLES AND CARBINES

In March 1871, the Ordnance Department started field trials of three designs of single-shot rifles and carbines, and a fourth was added in May 1872. The first three were the most popular single-shot rifles of the period:

1. Springfield Model 1870 "trap door" in rifle and carbine models.

Model	Caliber	Barrel Length	Overall Length	Weight
1861 and 1861 Special Rifle-Muskets	.58 Minié	40	56	8.8
1863, 1863 First and 1863 Second Rifle-Muskets	.58 Minié	40	56	8.8
1865 Breechloading Rifle-Musket	.58 Rimfire	37.5	56	9.6
1865 "Cadet" Rifle	.58 Rimfire	33.5	51.75	9.0
1866 Rifle-Musket	.50-70-450	36.6	56	10.0
1866 Cadet Rifle	.50-70-450	34.6	54.8	10.0
1868 Rifle-Musket	.50-70-450	32.75	52	9.25
1869 Cadet Rifle	.50-70-450	29.6	49	8.3
1870 Rifle	.50-70-450	32.5	52	9.25
1870 Cadet Rifle	.50-70-450	29.5	49	
1870 Carbine	.50-55-450	22.0	41.4	7.1
1873 Rifle	.45-70-405	32.6	51.9	8.4
1873 Cadet Rifle	.45-55-405	29.6	48.9	8.2
1873 Carbine	.45-55-405	22.0	41.3	6.9

FIGURE 7-8 Comparison of Civil War muzzleloading rifles and early Springfield breechloading rifles.

2. Remington Model 1870 "rolling block" in rifle and carbine models.
3. Sharps Model 1870 rifles and carbines, with vertically sliding breechblock.
4. In May 1872 the Ward-Burton single-shot bolt action firearms in rifle and carbine styles were issued for trial.

These were very significant selections, since an outstanding model was selected from upward swinging breechblock (Springfield), downward rotating breechblock (Remington), vertical sliding breechblock (Sharps) and a bolt action (Ward-Burton). There were a number of important omissions, such as the extremely strong Peabody single-shot action, and all repeaters, such as the rimfire Spencer and Winchester lever action rifles.

A "circular letter" from the Ordnance Office dated March 10, 1871, stated that each company commander was to render a detailed monthly report on the performance of the arms. In addition to the number, kind and caliber of the rifles and carbines in test, a thorough analysis of the number of shots fired, the number of mis-fires, the type of broken parts, and the number of guns becoming unserviceable. In addition the Company Commanders were asked:

"What modifications or improvements do you suggest for each arm? Which of the four systems of breech arrangement would you prefer for uniform use in the muskets and carbines of the military service?"

The image of the overworked and underpaid Company Commanders coping with this added paperwork demand, writing late at night with a quill pen by the light of a sputtering candle, leads one to suspect that much colorful language accompanied the reports on their way to the Ordnance Department. Page after detailed page summarizes these extensive field tests, in the Ordnance Memorandum No. 14. The rifles and carbines were all 1870 models, and a typical specification was:

MODEL 1870 SPRINGFIELD RIFLE:
Caliber: .50-70-450
Weight: 9 pounds 3 ounces
Weight of Barrel: 4 pounds
Rifling: Three lands, and three grooves .010 inches deep at breech tapering to .005 inches at the muzzle.
Twist: One turn in 42 inches.
Barrel Length: 32½ inches
Overall Length of Rifle: 52 inches

The final summary of the tests and the note of preference of the company commanders is found in the table on page 187.

1872 Trials of Breech Loading Rifles and Carbines

A board consisting of experienced officers from Ordnance Cavalry and Infantry was convened in New York City in September 1872. The Ordnance Department had requested $150,000 from Congress to tool up for the manufacture of a new model Springfield rifle at the National Armory. Congress, however, was very clear in its demand that comparative trials be performed on inventions submitted from all over the world stating:

> For manufacture of arms at the National Armory, $150,000: *provided,* that no part of this appropriation shall be expended until a breech loading system for muskets and carbines shall have been adopted for the military service, upon the recommendation of the board to be appointed by the Secretary of War, which board shall consist of not less than 5 officers as follows: one general officer, one ordnance officer and three officers of the line, one to be taken from the cavalry, one from the infantry, and one from the artillery: *and provided further,* that the system, when so adopted shall be the only one to be used by the Ordnance Department in the manufacture of muskets and carbines for the military service; and no royalties shall be paid by the Government of the United States for the use of said patent to any of its officers or employees, or for any patent in which said officers or employees may be directly or indirectly interested.

When the word got out that there was a competition open to manufacturers and vendors from all over the world the response was overwhelming. A total of 89 rifles and carbines were submitted for trial. The Ordnance Department was in a somewhat sticky situation. Both the Congress and the inventors were likely to consider the tests biased since the Ordnance Department had already stated its choice in advance. The result was that the tests were very carefully structured and exhaustively performed. Procedures were established so that the inventors could demonstrate the potential of their particular firearm, but the actual tests for record were to be fired by teams of soldiers who would provide a common level of ability for all the firearms tested. The final report of the board has many nuggets of information which must be read very carefully. For example:

> *Value of Magazine-Arms*
> It was further
> *resolved,* that, in the opinion of the board, the adoption of magazine-guns for the military service, by all nations, is only a question of time; that whenever an arm shall be devised which shall be as effective, as a single breech-loader, as the best of the existing single breech loading arms, and at the same time shall possess a safe and easily manipulated magazine, every consideration of public policy will require its adoption.

Despite this statement tests were structured which provided little credit for the benefit of a magazine on the firearm and in fact demanded that these firearms be equally as rugged in every way as the single shot rifles.

The two leading contenders in the repeating rifle category were the Winchester lever action rifle firing a .45 caliber cartridge, and the Ward-Burton .45 caliber bolt action rifles and carbines. The tests are so voluminous that it is very difficult to abstract the essence, but a description of several of the tests may be illuminating.

> Ward-Burton magazine-carbine, carrying 8 shots in a magazine and one in the chamber, firing a special recessed copper-cap cartridge, holding 55 grains of powder and 360 grains lead. The safety test was complied with (10 shots fired remotely with the lanyard). The following modifications of the required tests were agreed to and carried out, with the specification that throughout, when practicable, the magazine should be held in reserve:
>
> 1. Firing 10 rounds as a single-loader, holding the magazine in reserve. Everything worked well.
> 2. Number of shots in one minute, with aim at the usual target and distance, using the arm as a single-loader and holding the magazine in reserve, 23 shots, 13 hits.
> 3. Time required to fire nine shots, starting with a full magazine and chamber, 10½ seconds.
> 4. Time required to fire nine shots as a single loader, starting with a full chamber, 17½ seconds.
> 5. Endurance — everything worked well firing the 500 shots, the last 8 of which had been in the magazine throughout the test. During the eighth 50 rounds, one cartridge missed fire from having no cap or fulminate. (No priming compound.)
> 6. Dust — the gun was started, working with some difficulty, but afterwards fired 20 shots with ease. Everything worked well. (This is after the second dusting test.)

	Model 1870 Remington	Model 1870 Springfield	Model 1870 Sharps	Model 1870 Ward Burton
No. of Arms Originally Issued and Reported On	1,502	1,828	2,470	1,039
No. of Monthly Reports Rendered	810	814	584	334
Last Expression of Preference by Officers Commanding Companies	10	84	1	0
Proportionate Number of Principal Parts Broken, as by 1,000 Guns in 1,000 Months	66.82	28.34	44.07	162.0
Number of Cartridges Fired	89,828	96,479	76,629	40,070
Number of Cartridges Failed	2,595	1,882	2,699	970
Percentage of Misfires	2.9%	1.96%	3.5%	2.4%

The test of the Winchester Magazine-Musket No. 78 is similarly illuminating:

"Magazine-musket, carrying 10 shots in the magazine, besides one in the carrier, if necessary, the charge being 70 grains of powder and 360 grains lead.

The safety test was complied with. II. As a single loader, with aim, holding magazine in reserve. Eleven shots besides one in chamber not fired. One cartridge failed from having no powder; 7 hits.

III. Rapidity at will, first emptying the magazine and then contining as a single loader. 22 shots in one minute.

IV. Rapidity at will, as a single loader, holding the magazine in reserve. 18 shots, beside one in chamber not fired. One cartridge missed, but went under the prick-punch. [Cartridges which misfired were later tested by whacking them with a hammer and center punch — this is hardly a procedure we recommend in the present day.]

V. The time required to fire three magazinefuls (30 shots) starting with a full magazine. 28 *fires in one minute, 9 seconds.* In the haste of loading, one cartridge was omitted from each of the last two magazinefuls.

VI. The time required to fire 11 shots in the magazine, one cartridge being in the carrier, 10 shots in 18½ seconds. On a second trial of this test 11 shots were fired in 7½ seconds.

VII. Eleven shots as a single loader, holding full magazine in reserve, fired in 31½ seconds.

VIII. Endurance — 200 rounds were fired, everything working well.

IX. Dust — The arm worked well throughout.

At the conclusion of this test the cartridges which had been retained in the magazine from the beginning were fired. Although the balls were much flattened and upset by the repeated concussion of firing, everything worked well.

To stand back and look at these tests in light of the clear statement of the Ordnance officers of the magazine rifle as "the arm of the future" or to try and understand these tests in light of the proven usage of the Spencer carbines during the Civil War [when cavalry troopers were sometimes equipped with preloaded tubes of 7 cartridges each so that a fresh magazine could be slammed into place without the necessity for fumbling with individual cartridges under the stress of combat] frankly make these tests appear to be extremely biased. It is very clear that these tests were structured with the viewpoint that a magazine firearm was in essence *a single shot rifle which could on rare occasions be used as a magazine arm.* This curious idea of retaining a fully loaded magazine with a cutoff preventing the magazine from being used except in a last-ditch emergency was an amazingly conservative idea — yet it appeared as an "improvement" on the Spencer carbine of 1865 and was, in fact, retained on our Springfield .30/06 rifles manufactured during World War II.

The best test of the Winchester rifle under repetitive fire was 11 shots in 7½ seconds. Using the rifle as a single loader holding the magazine in reserve, the same number of shots required 31½ seconds or *over*

4 times as long. It was obvious that a repeater was used as a repeater, and should have been evaluated as a repeater.

By January 1873 there were still enough guns in the running to require a supplementary series of tests. The survivors included:

1. Peabody — No. 63
2. Whitney Carbine — No. 77
3. Springfield-Stillman — No. 66
4. Elliot Carbine — No. 80
5. Ward-Burton Magazine-Carbine — No. 58
6. UPdegraff — No. 42
7. Sharps — No. 5
8. Springfield — No. 69
9. Remington-Ryder — No. 67
10. Russian-Verdan — No. 57
11. Freeman — No. 76
12. Dexter — No. 38
13. Lee — No. 61
14. Roberts — No. 2
15. Remington Locking Rifle — No. 82
16. Winchester — No. 78
17. Broughton — No. 79
18. Sharps — No. 81
19. Remington Navy Rifle — No. 85
20. Martini Werndl

About three-quarters of the rifles were eliminated in the supplementary series of tests including the Winchester which was removed by the rusting test "after the first exposure the utmost exertion in working the lever and other parts failed to clear the piece of dust sufficiently for movement of the carrier." (It is believed that this should read rust rather than dust since the rifle had already passed the dusting test in the earlier series.) The arm was then dropped.

> The Sharps rifle similarly failed after more rusting: after first exposure opened very hard, and also after the second two defective cartridges had been fired. After second exposure the gun opened very hard; the difficulty was so much increased by firing the first cartridge that on applying force to the lever with the foot it was broken off about 2½ inches from the end. On examination by an expert this was declared to over heating of the metal in manufacture. The arm was then laid aside. The cartridge-shell was easily removed from the chamber by tapping on the projection of the extractor, showing that the resistance was not due to the sticking of the shell.

FINAL SERIES OF TESTS

The tests for rapidity of firing were fired in the spring of 1873 on the surviving six rifles. These averaged as follows:

Elliott — No. 80 . . . 17.7 shots per minute
Springfield — No. 88 . . . 15.65 shots per minute
Springfield — No. 88 with new mainspring . . . 16.8 shots per minute
Remington — No. 86 . . . 19.78 shots per minute
Freeman — No. 76 . . . 16.03 shots per minute
Peabody — No. 63 . . . 18.6 shots per minute
Ward-Burton Magazine Musket — No. 97 . . . 22.92 shots per minute

(The firing tests with the Ward-Burton were run by firing three magazinefuls, starting with seven cartridges in the magazine and one in the chamber, including the time to charge the magazine twice, the cartridges being placed in rows of seven each in a block on a table. Twenty-two shots were fired in 63 seconds. At the end of these tests firing rates of 50 shots per minute were achieved per magazine with two test series in which 1 cartridge in the chamber and 7 in the magazine were fired in 9½ second intervals.)

FINAL REPORT OF THE ORDNANCE BOARD

In the final report of the board the following recommendation was made:

> *Merits of Ward-Burton magazine arm and cartridge-recommendation of the Ward-Burton magazine arm.*
>
> Resolved further, that the experiments before the board with the magazine-carbine, made upon the Ward-Burton system at the Springfield Armory and using the Metcalfe cartridge, has so impressed the board with the merits of this gun that they consider it more nearly fulfilling the conditions above specified than any other magazine-gun tried by them or of which they have any knowledge. Therefore while unwilling to recommend the immediate adoption of this system in face of the unanimous reports from the Army against the Ward-Burton single loader [These were adverse results of the field trials of the 1870 model Ward-Burton single shot rifle] it does recommend that a small number of magazine-muskets be made on this plan for further trial in the field. The overall recommendation of the board was: Resolved that the board recommended that the Springfield breech loading system be adopted for the military service of the United States, in accordance with the provisions of the Act of Congress entitled "An Act Making Appropriations for the Support of the Army for the year Ending June 30, 1873, and for other purposes," approved June 6, 1872. The board also recommended "whereas the Elliott system has exhibited remarkable facility of manipulation in requiring one hand to work it, and therefore rendering it especially adapted to the man in service; therefore be it
>
> *Resolved*, that it be recommended that a limited number of carbines be made after this system for issue to the mounted service for trial in the field.

The recommendation of the board was forwarded to the Ordnance Department, and the Chief of Ordnance replied quite succinctly:

> Respectively returned to the Secretary of War, with the recommendation of the board that the Springfield breech loading system be adopted for the military service be approved, and that 45 inch caliber be adopted for small arms.
>
> The law of June 6, 1872 expressly provides that the system adopted "shall be the only one to be used by the Ordnance Department in the manufacture of muskets and carbines for the military service," should therefore, the Springfield system be adopted as recommended, the law prohibits the manufacture of the Ward-Burton magazine and the Elliott gun for trial, as recommended by the board. Were it not for this provision the trial of these guns in the field would be recommended.

Signed E. B. Dyer, Chief of Ordnance, U. S. Army. This was further approved by William Belknap, Secretary of War, on May 20, 1873.

ANALYSIS OF THE 1872 TESTS FROM THE VIEWPOINT OF A CENTURY LATER

The recommendation of the Ordnance Board for the adoption of the single-shot .45 caliber Springfield rifle Model 1873 was accepted and this became the standard rifle to be used by the Armed Services. The appearance of the carbine version is shown in Figure 7-9. It was very similar in appearance and features to the earlier Springfield Model 1868 and 1870 rifles and was a rugged model which remained in Government inventory until after the World War I. Some volunteers in the Spanish-American War actually carried these single-shot black powder rifles blowing clouds of dense smoke to attack entrenched Spanish infantry armed with the latest Mauser repeating bolt action rifles during the invasion of Puerto Rico.

The decision to select a powerful single-shot rifle in preference to a repeater apparently hinged on four critical factors:

1. MANUFACTURING ECONOMY — the Ordnance Department had requested the sum of $150,000 to tool up for the new breech-loading rifle at Springfield Armory. The funding request was based on the conversion of a great deal of existing tooling which was in use at the Armory for the manufacture of the Model 1870 Springfields and the fabrication of some new tooling. If the Board chose any other rifle besides the Springfield, they would have to go back to Congress for substantial additional appropriations to tool up for an all-new design. The year 1873 was one of severe financial recession and panic. There was little chance of the Ordnance Department receiving large sums of money for tooling up an entirely new rifle.

2. PREFERENCE OF THE FIELD OFFICERS The Army had already carried out its own tests to select a new breech-loading rifle in the field tests of 1871-1872. The field officers had voted overwhelmingly for the Springfield single-shot rifle, and none had voted for the single-shot bolt action Ward-Burton rifle on which the later Ward-Burton magazine rifle of the 1872 trials was based.

3. RUGGEDNESS AND RELIABILITY The Ordnance Board placed great stress on the ability to withstand extreme abuse. For example, rugged tests with defective ammunition, dusting tests, and rusting tests were included. An extreme example was the strong brine rusting test. *It is extremely doubtful if any modern infantry rifle in use by the major powers today could pass so severe a test.* It was a matter of record that the Spencer rifles had performed very well under extremely difficult conditions such as the winter campaigns of the Civil War. No rifles were perfect and, for example, the Springfield rifles had a notoriously weak extraction system that caused the rifles to jam occasionally when fired rapidly in hot weather.

4. EUROPEAN COMPETITION A subtle factor in the conclusions was the fact that all the major European powers were selecting powerful single-shot rifles at the time. French, British, German and Austrian rifles were submitted for trials as well as the rifle manufactured in the United States for Russia.

In the face of all these factors it would have taken a bold and imaginative board willing to risk a great deal of adverse comment both from Congress and from the field officers to recommend the advanced capabilities offered by the Ward-Burton bolt action repeating rifle. There was no clear superiority of the Springfield rifle in these tests. It was in fact, one of six rifles which survived the test and there was nothing to mark it as the best except for its economy of manufacture and the clear preference of the field officers for this rifle.

It is interesting to follow the developmental threads of the following decade. What in fact happened was that some Winchester repeating lever action rifles were sold to the Turkish Government in the 1870's and were used with outstanding success in the Russo-Turkish War of 1878. This caused the major European powers to reevaluate their position and in the early 1880's France and Germany converted their single-shot bolt action rifles to firearms very similar in construction to the Ward-Burton repeating rifle of 1872. The Swiss were sufficiently impressed with the Winchester rifle to design a very interesting bolt action repeater which utilized the Winchester bolt, carrier, carrier lifter and feeding system and blended this with a rear locking bolt type action.

The structure of the 1872 tests made it clear that a magazine repeating rifle, despite the philosophical statements of the Board was considered primarily as a single-shot rifle which would occasionally be used with a magazine in dire emergencies. In retrospect a magazine rifle would have been of tremendous advantage in the short nasty battles of the Plains wars of the 1870's and 1880's. Hunters, trappers and Army scouts armed with the commercial breech-loading repeating rifles were much better equipped for the relatively short-range, nasty ambush battles of the Plains than were the Army and Cavalry with more powerful, slow-firing single-shot rifles.

POST-TRIAL SPRINGFIELDS

Model 1873 Rifle

The Springfield Model 1873 was finally standardized in three different designs. The standard was the infantry rifle which fired a .45/70 cartridge loaded with 70 grains of black powder and a 405-grain hardened lead bullet. Dimensions of the rifle were very similar to the 1870 model with a 32.6-inch barrel, a very similar design of receiver, and a 51.9-inch over-all length. The reduction in caliber reduced the weight to 8.4 pounds. Some old parts were very similar in size and appearance. Minor design changes had been made in almost all components so that very few were interchangeable. For example, the lock plate had been simplified by eliminating the bevel all around the edge and mounting the lock plate flush with the wood in the stock. A few parts were still the same as that used in the Model 1855 and these included the butt plate assembly, sight, sear, trigger and trigger guard. The Springfield was a good, solid design and it could be tooled up at much less expense than an all new design.

Model 1873 Carbine

The Springfield Model 1873 Carbine is shown in Figure 7-9. The barrel length, at 22 inches, and the over-all length at 41.3 inches were the same as on the 1870 carbine. The weight of most carbines was slightly over 7 pounds. Recoil was again a serious problem and a special cartridge was loaded for the carbine with only 55 grains of powder compared with 70 grains in the standard load. The half-stock design was the same as on the Model 1870 carbine and continued to be a design characteristic of the Springfield carbines up into the 1890's.

The Ordnance Manual for the 1873 rifles lists a muzzle velocity of the .45/70/405 cartridge fired from the rifle at 1350 feet per second, compared with 1100 feet per second velocity from the .45/55/405 cartridge fired in the carbine. The Army paid careful attention to the recoil levels and measured these using a spring scale attached to the butt of the rifle. The tabular data given in the Ordnance Manual shows that with a rifle weighing 9.13 pounds the recoil was 174 pounds. The recoil of a 6.87-pound carbine with this cartridge was measured at 182 pounds which was judged too heavy for a mounted man on horseback. With the .45/55/405 cartridge fired in the carbine the recoil was only 155 pounds.

Model 1873 Cadet Rifle

Limited production of the Cadet models was continued. The Model 1873 Cadet Rifle was very similar in appearance to the standard infantry rifle. The barrel had been shortened by 3 inches to 29.6 inches and the over-all length had been reduced to 48.9 inches. The weight was reduced about .2 of a pound to 8.2 pounds. Sights on the Cadet rifle were adjusted for the .45/55/405 carbine cartridge. These are very handy and lightweight rifles and their limited production quantities makes them a valuable addition to a collection.

1. Accuracy in all winds.
2. Cleanliness, or sustained accuracy.
3. Flatness of trajectory.
4. Penetration at long range.
5. Moderate recoil.
6. Lightness of arm.
7. Lightness of ammunition.

The detailed recommendations included: .45 caliber barrel, 32½ inches long with three lands and three grooves .005 of an inch deep, and 1 turn in 22 inches. The cartridge was to have: 70 grains "musket" powder.

A bullet 1.11 inches long made by the "compression process" of an alloy of 12 parts lead to 1 part tin. Five grooves to be swaged in and filled with a mixture of bayberry wax (8 parts) and graphite (1 part). Over-all bullet weight 405 grains.

This cartridge is shown as the bottom illustration in Figures 7-3 and 7-5 and the ballistics fired in a standard Winchester test barrel in the 1880's are shown in Figure 7-4. There are wide discrepancies in the ammunition velocities from various sources, making a positive statement "This was *it*" very difficult. For example: The test conditions used in the Winchester laboratories are a good standard, for the data can be correlated down through the years, and checks with the SAAMI (Sporting Arms and Ammunition Manufacturers' Institute) lists of the 1930's. Here is the range of data on the 45/70:

1872 AMMUNITION TESTS

A separate Board was convened in May 1872 to determine the "Proper Caliber for Small-Arms," and this is is included as a second section of the 1872 Ordnance Memorandum No. 14. The Board established the design of ammunition to be used in the future infantry rifle and in pursuit of this objective they performed a wide range of ammunition tests. One of the criteria was penetration at 500 yards, to be measured as average penetrations of a series of shots through pine boards.

The results were as follows:

Caliber	Powder Charge	Bullet Weight	Inches of Pine Boards
50	70	450 (soft)	7.2
45	70	405 (hardened)	8.8
45	70	400 (soft)	6.8
42	65	365 (soft)	8.6
40	65	350 (soft)	8.1
45*	85	484 (hardened)	11.2

*British Martini-Henry Ammunition

While the British ammunition was superior in these tests, it was rejected on the grounds of excessive recoil. The following recoil levels were measured on a spring scale:

.50-70-450 . . . . 129.6 pounds
.45-70-405 . . . . 123.6 pounds
.45-85-484 Martini Henry 139.3 pounds

There is also some interesting data on pressure and velocity, although well buried in table after table of very dull (!!) test data showing bullet styles, accuracy results and sighting elevations for the endless tests which were performed:

1872 TEST RESULTS

	PRESSURE AND VELOCITY (Averages of 10 shots)				VALUES CALCULATED BY THE AUTHOR IN 1969		
CALIBER	Powder Charge	Bullet Weight	Velocity (Feet/ Second)	Pressure (Pounds/ Inch^2)	Muzzle Energy Foot-Pounds	Efficiency of Ammunition (Foot-pounds of Muzzle Energy per Grain of Propellant)	Muzzle Impulse (Pound-Seconds)
.40 straight	65	340	1388	19,900	1455	22.5	2.50
.42 straight	65	370	1312	16,250	1415	21.8	2.53
.45 straight	70	400	1300	16,300	1501	21.4	2.71

Tests of bottlenecked cartridges gave no velocity increase and slightly higher pressures, and these designs were, therefore, eliminated:

CALIBER	Powder Charge	Bullet Weight	Velocity (Feet/ Second)	Pressure (Pounds/ Inch^2)	Muzzle Energy Foot-Pounds	Efficiency of Ammunition	Muzzle Impulse (Pound-Seconds)
.42 bottleneck	65	370	1293	17,150	1374	21.1	2.50
.45 bottleneck	70	400	1320	18,500	1548	22.1	2.76

The weight of the cartridges was also taken into account. The weight of 40 cartridges given as:

.50-70-450 . . . . 3 pounds 13 oz.
.45-70-405 . . . . 3 pounds 7 oz.
.45-85-484 Martini Henry . 4 pounds 6 oz.

Various forms of rifling were evaluated, as well as cleanliness, flatness of trajectory, and wind bucking ability.

The conclusions of the ammunition board were that the .45-70 cartridge provided the best combination of factors based on:

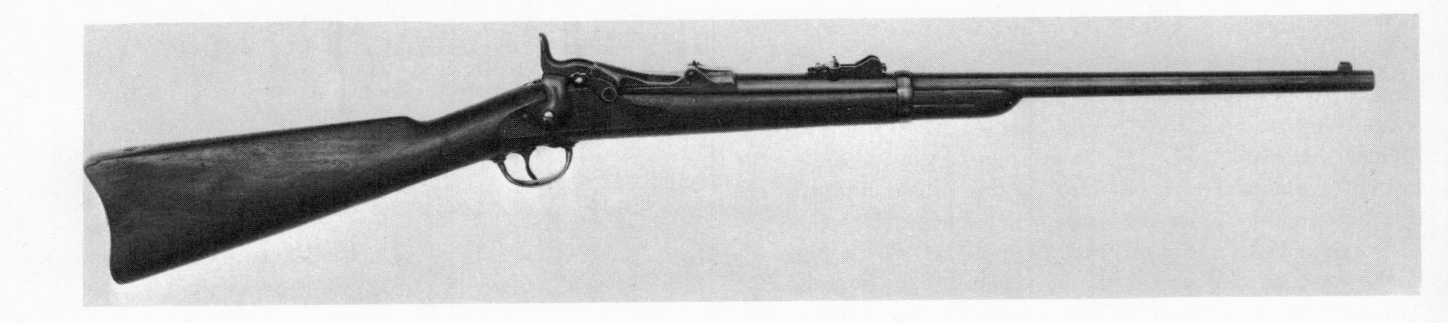

FIGURE 7-9 Springfield Model 1873 carbine.

Cartridge	Bullet Weight (Grains)	Test Firearm	Muzzle Velocity (Feet/ Second)	Muzzle Energy (Foot-Pounds)	Efficiency (Foot-Pounds Per Grain)	Source
.45-70	405	26″ Barrel	1318	1562	22.2	1916, Winchester[1]
.45-70	405	Rifle	1271	1452	20.7	1897, Winchester[6]
.45-70	405	Rifle	1364	1672	23.8	Whelen[2]
.45-70	405	Rifle	1350	1639	23.3	1874 Ordnance Manual
		Average Value	1330	1580	22.5	

The data on the carbine loads show more modest performance:

Cartridge	Bullet Weight (Grains)	Test Firearm	Muzzle Velocity (Feet/ Second)	Muzzle Energy (Foot-Pounds)	Efficiency (Foot-Pounds Per Grain)	Source
.45-55	405	Carbine	1150	1189	21.6	Whelen[2]
.45-55	405	Carbine	1100	1085	19.8	1874 Ordnance Manual
		Average Value	1125	1138	20.7	

The data on the later 500 grain bullet loads gives even wider spreads of velocity and efficiency.

Cartridge	Bullet Weight (Grains)	Test Firearm	Muzzle Velocity (Feet/ Second)	Muzzle Energy (Foot-Pounds)	Efficiency (Foot-Pounds Per Grain)	Source
.45-70	500	Rifle	1201	1602	21.9	1916, Winchester[1]
.45-70	500	—	1320	1930	27.5	Sharpe[4]
.45-70	500	32½″ Barrel	1301	1875	26.8	Bu Ord[5]
.45-70	500	Rifle	1315	1919	27.4	Whelen[2]
.45-70	500	26″ Barrel	1179	1540	22.0	1897, Winchester[6]
		Average Value	1263	1772	25.3	

[1]Winchester Catalog, 1916.
[2]Colonel Townsend Whelen, "Our Rifles at the Birth of the N.R.A." American Rifleman, 1931.
[3]Ordnance Manual, 1874, [Note: Peak Pressure given as 19,000 pounds/inch²]
[4]Philip Sharpe, *The Complete Guide to Handloading,* 1941 Edition.
[5]Bureau of Ordnance, 1884.
[6]Winchester Catalog, 1897

There is no question that the series of tests on the ammunition were exceedingly thorough, and the many experiments were designed to objectively test many variables on a side-by-side basis. The result was the standardization of the .45/70/405 cartridge for both rifle and carbine. Originally the ammunition was loaded by Frankford Arsenal in copper cartridge cases, and this practice was followed up through the middle 1880's. The cases were made of brass by Winchester and Union Metallic Cartridge Company in the late 1870's, and Frankford Arsenal changed over about ten years later.

In the early 1880's, a 500-grain bullet was designed for the .45/70 and this gradually became the standard rifle load in the Service. It was found that the carbine did not burn all the powder in the short 22-inch barrel, and so the powder charge was cut to 55 grains for cartridges specifically intended for Army carbine use. The commercial customers preferred higher velocity and a little less kick than the .45/70/500 provided, and the most popular commercial load was the .45/70/405 load, shown as the bottom illustration of Figure 7-5, and it is still loaded today. During the late 1880's many additional bullet weights were added, including 200-, 300-, 330- and 350-grain sizes. The SAAMI list of 1938 four .45/70 loads, including a smokeless load boosting a light 300-grain bullet at 1880 feet per second and the heaviest launching a 435-grain bullet at 1280 feet per second.

The .45/70 was a carefully designed cartridge, with each dimension established on the basis of the 1872 tests, and it was one of the most efficient black powder cartridges, particularly with the 500-grain bullet.

Repeating Firearms

CHAPTER 8

When muzzle-loading firearms were first developed in Europe, probably during the early 14th century, they represented as much danger to the owner as to the enemy. The ingredients of the black powder were impure and were often mixed on the battlefield before being poured into the cannon or matchlock. The metals available to forge barrels were impure and of low strength. Explosions became so frequent that it was difficult to find men willing to risk their lives handling this new "black magic." Knights in armor recognized that these sorcerers might cause the end of chivalry and their domination of the battlefield and were often prejudiced against cannoneers. The common soldier, armed with pike and bow and arrow, did not want to be too near the cannoneer for fear that he would be injured if some slight miscalculation caused the cannon to blow up. The round stone projectiles, or roughly cast iron projectiles did not represent too great a danger to the enemy for they were inaccurate, and their low velocity made them clearly visible in flight.

There was one major advantage to the early firearms and it was in the area of psychological warfare. The ignorant and superstitious soldiers of the Renaissance were likely to believe that the enemy had overwhelming power when a cannon fired at them with a heavy roar, flame and smoke, irrespective of where the projectile landed. From these early beginnings firearms developed rapidly into three distinct classes: artillery, shoulder arms, and small compact firearms designed for one hand operation. There was a very serious disadvantage to all these firearms. The loading procedures were slow and cumbersome. Once the soldier, hunter, or civilian defending himself from attack had fired his shot, his equipment was useless until he had gone through a laborious reloading procedure. At a time when he may have been in very great danger his attention had to be split between the danger in front of him and the manipulation of powder, ball, and ramrod to recharge his weapon. Under such stress, mistakes often occurred — with sometimes disastrous consequences for the owner of the firearm.

The need for a firearm which could be loaded with several shots in advance or which could be reloaded rapidly and simply was obvious to every shooter. Many attempts were made to solve the problem but few were successful. Repeating flintlock firearms were described in Chapter 3. These were often designed with a powder magazine in the buttstock, and a magazine for spherical lead balls either in the buttstock, or in a tube under the barrel. None achieved wide acceptance for they required the highest skill in manufacture and were both expensive and complex. The internal mechanism fouled rapidly due to the powder residue making the action difficult to operate and there was the ever-present danger of a flashback through the breech mechanism into the powder magazine in the buttstock. As a result few shooters were enthusiastic over this approach to firearms design.

The most successful approach to provide additional firepower was simply to build a multi-barreled firearm. The design of over-under flintlock firearms was described in Chapter 3. These were often constructed with one rifled and one smoothbored barrel. To fire the second shot the shooter recocked the hammer, released the lever in front of the trigger guard and rotated the barrels 180 degrees. The combination of one rifled and one smoothbore barrel gave great flexibility for use on birds or animals. The smoothbore barrel could be loaded with a single round ball and provide a very effective second shot at close range. The over-under flintlock rifle remained a rare and expensive firearm for the additional cost of the second barrel, plus the complexity of the joint in the middle of the gun which would hold the pair of barrels in proper alignment and permit rotation, taxed the skills of American 18th century gunsmiths.

The idea of using a rotating cluster of barrels for increased firepower resulted in some pretty massive designs. A six-barreled .34 caliber percussion rifle is shown in Figure 8-1. The rifle has been designed with hexagonal barrels with front and rear sights fastened to each barrel. In between each of the percussion nipples a hole was drilled into the solid portion of the barrel. A spring loaded catch was fitted to the front of the trigger guard with a prong which fitted into the hole at the rear of the barrel. After the shooter laboriously loaded each barrel and placed a percussion cap on each nipple, the firing procedure was relatively simple. The hammer was cocked and the catch at the front of the trigger guard released. The barrel cluster was rotated one barrel and the catch released. The conical hole at the rear of the barrel would automatically line up the barrel cluster as the catch moved into a locked position. The rifle was then fired and the process repeated for the next shot.

Even though the barrels were relatively small in diameter and were much shorter than the standard percussion barrels of the period, such multi-shot firearms were extremely heavy. This rifle weighed slightly over 10 pounds and weights of 13 to 20 pounds were not unusual. The expense of fabricating and assembling many barrels into a cluster and designing the receiver and pivot joint to provide adequate strength made these firearms expensive. The high quality of construction has been carried through to the buttstock details with an elaborate engraved patch box and ornate brass furniture such as the trigger guard, butt plate, comb and grip inlays.

While multi-shot rifles such as that shown in Figure 8-1 remained rare and expensive, the design became quite popular in the "pepper box" pistol designs. These pistols were built on much the same principle, but normally used a "mule ear" type of hammer and automatically rotated the barrel cluster as the trigger was pulled. The pepper box pistols were excellent for personal protection at relatively close range. The heavy double action trigger pull and rotating barrel assembly made accurate shooting rather difficult.

DOUBLE-BARRELED SHOTGUNS

The first multiple-shot firearms which flowered into a highly successful system were the double-barreled flintlock shotguns developed in England and on the Continent in the late 18th century. European gun-

FIGURE 8-1 Six-barreled .34 caliber percussion rifle.

makers were highly dependent upon the aristocracy for their business, and the competition was intense. Wildfowl shooting was a popular aristocratic sport and many owners demanded the highest perfection technology could provide. By the late 18th century the best British gunmakers were creating works of art in wood and metal. Four top quality British double-barreled shotguns are shown in Figure 8-2. These guns, selected by Thomas Hall, from the Winchester Gun Collection, represent four examples of the "state of the art" of the late 18th century. The upper shotgun is marked Manton, London on the barrels and was manufactured between 1780 and 1800. The barrels have a fine Damascus pattern and gold bands have been inlaid at the breech end. Over-all length of the shotgun is 47½ inches with the 34-inch barrels. The bore size is about 28 gauge. The locks are marked Manton, and have rollers on the frizzens to reduce friction as the frizzen snapped open under the blow of the flint. The hammers are a graceful gooseneck design with much artistic detail and engraving even on the heads of the hammer screws. Reliability of flintlock firearms was often affected by rust in the tiny touchhole. On this shotgun the problem was solved by inserting a platinum bushing in the right-hand touchhole and a gold bushing in the left-hand touchhole.

The walnut stocks have a high gloss finish and the grip is checkered with a curious, relatively coarse square pattern. The wooden ramrod is brass tipped, and retained under the barrel by two brass thimbles.

The second shotgun in Figure 8-2 dates from a slightly later period. This is marked Joseph Manton and was constructed between 1806 and 1820. The 16-gauge barrels are 30⅜ inches long and the over-all length of the shotgun is 47½ inches. This shotgun is fitted with Joseph Manton's patented elevated rib to provide a straight, accurate sighting pattern. The design of the feature was covered in a British patent issued in 1806. Other features of the shotgun were also locked up in patents, including a special design of breech plug to provide improved ignition, were covered in a British patent issued in 1792. The flintlocks on this shotgun show about the highest form of development of this mechanism. The frizzens are artistically formed with all the contours rounded with flowing lines. The frizzen spring is fitted with a roller to reduce friction. The pans are quite different from those fitted to the ordinary flintlock musket. The pans are rather small, holding only a tiny quantity of powder. There is a flat sealing surface surrounding the pan. Immediately outside the sealing surface a deep V-shaped trough was machined. These were known as "rain proof" locks and the purpose of the outer gully was to carry water away from the priming charge. The pan construction was designed to provide an excellent seal between the frizzen and pan. Ignition in damp weather was always a crucial problem with flintlock firearms and this construction, with carefully fitted parts, provided improved reliability.

Both touchholes on this shotgun are bushed with gold. The ornate brass trigger guard has an extension which is inletted into the front section of the one piece stock. It is engraved in a pineapple pattern typical of the era. The fine grained walnut stock is checkered at the pistol grip and carefully fitted with brass furniture. The wooden ramrod is brass tipped and held in two guides beneath the Damascus twist barrels.

The third shotgun down in Figure 8-2 is a Joseph Manton shotgun manufactured between 1806 and 1812. It is marked "Manton, London," and is very similar to the example above. The Damascus twist barrels are 31⅛ inches long and the over-all length of the shotgun is 48 inches. The shape of the engraved lock plates is slightly different with an extension to the rear and the brass trigger guard has a curled extension which forms something of a pistol grip. It was constructed in the same time period as the shotgun above it and is very similar in most details.

The bottom shotgun in Figure 8-2 was constructed between 1832 and 1834, well after most top shooters had shifted over to the more reliable percussion ignition system. The shotgun is marked John Manton and Son. Careful research by Tom Hall has established its manufacture within this two-year time frame since John Manton died in 1834, and his son joined the firm in 1832. John Manton is generally considered to have taken over the position as the manufacturer of the finest quality shotguns from Joseph Manton about 1815. This superb example is 45 inches long over-all with 29 3/16-inch Damascus twist barrels of about 24 gauge. The shotgun is fitted with an elevated rib marked John Manton and Son, Dover Street and has a silver bead front sight.

Flintlock shotguns began to go out of style about 1820. By 1825 most of the top shooters had changed over to percussion ignition so that this example represents a very rare design. The lock work and ignition system have been further refined. The pan is a deep narrow V with an open end. The rain trough is deep around the pan and the sealing surfaces between the frizzen and pan are quite narrow. The frizzens are a very ornate design with long sweeping curves and a large roller has been fitted to the end of the frizzen spring to reduce friction. The hammers are very elaborate with an extra sweeping curve and ornate

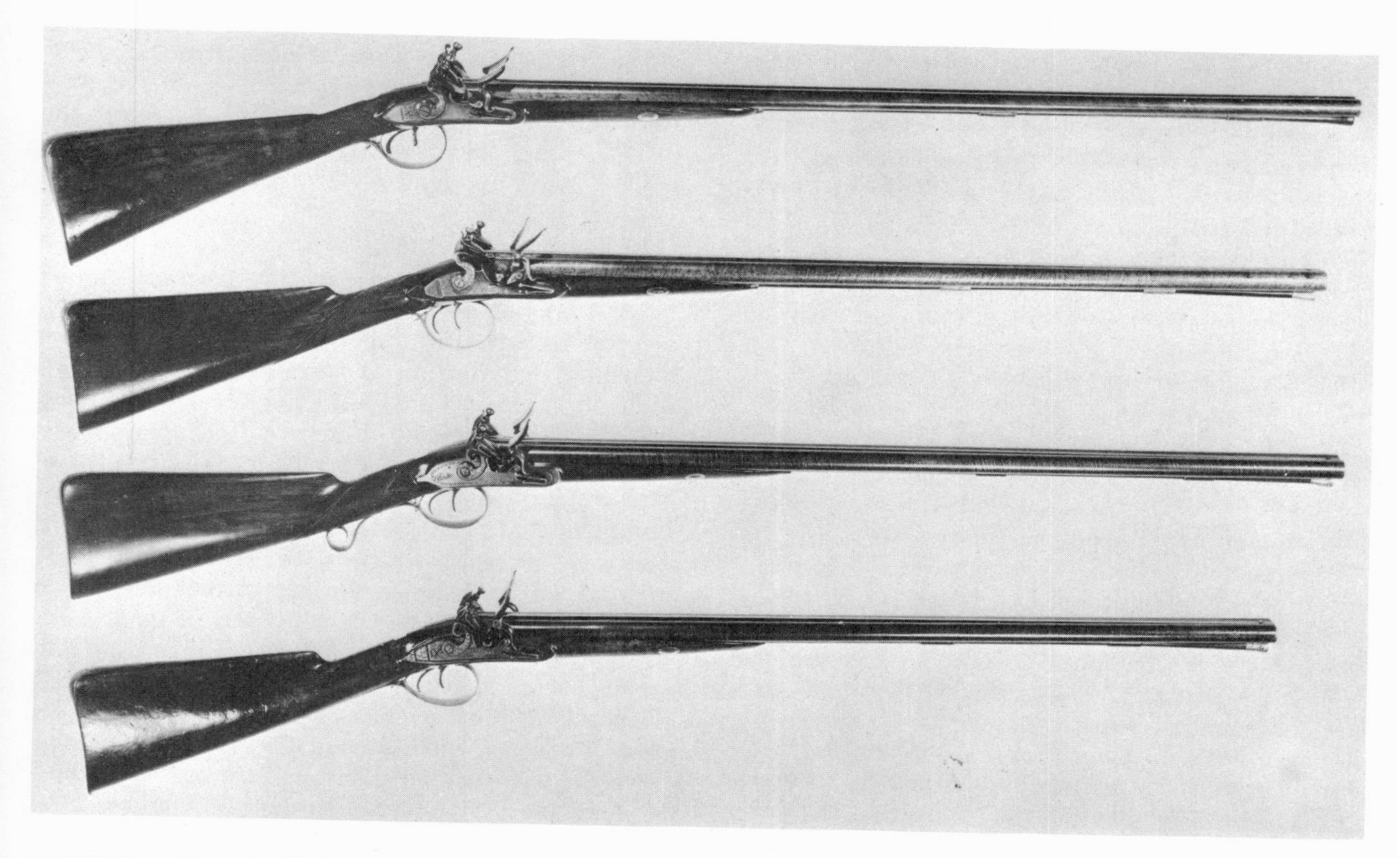

FIGURE 8-2 Four double-barreled flintlock shotguns.

carving on the hammer and lock plate. The furniture is similar to that of other shotguns. The brass trigger guard has a pineapple design extension inletted into the forward part of the one-piece stock. A brass butt plate and forearm cap are fitted, and a wooden ramrod is brass tipped and held in two guides beneath the barrel.

The shotguns shown in Figure 8-2 were completely out of reach of the average sportsmen. Since the aristocracy and the country-folk of England and the Continent lived on such entirely different economic levels, it is hard to put an equivalent price on such firearms. It is fair to say that these firearms would represent several years' wages for the average worker.

PERCUSSION SHOTGUNS

After 1825 percussion shotguns came into wide use. Placing the fulminate priming material inside a metallic cap provided an ignition system that was much better sealed from the weather than that of earlier shotguns. The hot flame from the fulminate passed through the small tube in the percussion cap and impinged directly on the powder charge in the barrel so that the reliability of ignition was very much improved. The second advantage to percussion firearms was the much faster ignition. This was particularly important in wing shooting where the hunter had to track the bird throughout the ignition period. Even the best flintlocks had a very perceptible delay from the sparking of the flint to ignition of the main charge in the barrel. There was nothing to force the pan flash into the barrel. The flash literally went in all directions and a small percentage of it passed through the touchhole into the main charge in the barrel. At best this was a weak ignition system and the ignition lag was many times longer than with percussion ignition.

British and continental gunmakers developed beautifully engraved percussion shotguns which were very similar to the designs shown in Figure 8-2 with the substitution of percussion locks. The loading procedure was still quite complex and it was easy to make a mistake. The shotgunner carried a powder flask, a shot flask, percussion caps, and wads. First a black powder charge (measured in drams) was measured and dropped into each barrel. Wads were placed in the muzzle of each barrel and ramrodded down onto the powder charge. The shot charge was measured from a second flask and dropped into each barrel. An over-shot wad was then placed in each muzzle and driven down onto the charge, to hold the shot firmly in place. The ramrod was withdrawn and replaced below the barrel. The hammers were cocked to the safety notch and percussion caps loaded onto each nipple.

There was great competition to develop light shotguns with good aiming qualities and even on high quality guns the barrels were much thinner at the breech than on a typical military musket. With such a complex loading procedure it was easy to make mistakes. In the excitement of the hunt both powder charges could be placed in one barrel or the wads forgotten. A double charge in a single barrel usually blew out the thin side of the chamber with disastrous consequences to the shotgun and sometimes to the shooter. Percussion caps were often of mediocre quality and eye injuries occurred from flying bits of copper.

The percussion shotgun represented a great improvement over the flintlock system both in speed of ignition and reliability in damp weather. The high quality double-barreled percussion shotgun was considered the best possible design from about 1830 until replaced by the breech-loader during the decade of the 1860's.

BREECH-LOADING SHOTGUNS

Most experiments with breech-loading firearms were directed toward military applications. As the ideas were reduced to practice, inventors considered them for other types of firearms. The French were particularly active in applying these ideas to shotguns. By 1836 the French gunsmith Lefaucheux developed a pinfire double-barreled shotgun which had many advanced features. The barrels had the traditional tip up design and were locked down by a swinging lever pivoted in front of the trigger guard. The chambers were similar to those on a modern double-barreled shotgun except that there was a cut-out at the top of the rear of the chamber for a vertical pin which projected up above the barrels. Each Lefaucheux cartridge was constructed with its own firing pin. The appearance of the shells was similar to a modern low-based shotshell with the exception of a vertical pin projecting out at right angles to the shotshell. The shells were loaded into the shotgun barrels so that the vertical pins fitted into the slots in the chambers. The gun was fired by the hammer falling and driving the projecting pin downward which exploded a percussion cap within the shotshell. This in turn ignited the main charge, driving the shot package out the muzzle. The Lefaucheux pin fire breech-loading system became very popular for both shotguns and low-powered revolvers.

Inventors on both sides of the Atlantic got into the act and almost every possible pattern of breech-loading was tried for shotguns. Designs were developed with rotating barrels, barrels that swung to one side on a vertical pivot, barrels that slid longitudinally to open, and barrels that remained fixed with breech bolts which slid to the rear to allow access to the chamber.

Shot cartridges were developed for the Sharps breech-loading action during the 1850's. The Sharps used a paper shot cartridge with two chambers. First a paper tube was rolled up and pasted shut at one end and loaded with one ounce of shot. This package in turn was placed within a longer paper tube into which wads were assembled followed by a 60-grain black powder charge. The shot cartridge could be used interchangeably with the bullet load in the Sharps rifles and carbines, but the spin of the rifling and lack of choke must have provided fairly poor patterns.

By the late 1850's shotshells containing many modern elements were being developed. These shotshells included a paper tube with a built up paper head covered by a brass reinforcement. Battery cup primers of fairly modern appearance were included in the Daw center-fire shotshell introduced into England in 1861. During the 1860's inventors even came up with ideas of the hammerless shotgun and successful models were demonstrated.

The double-barreled shotgun with outside hammers became the dominant European type of shotgun until near the end of the 19th century. Americans imported these firearms and gradually began to manufacture the designs in the United States. There has been a great deal of manufacturing engineering study during the past century, but good quality double barreled shotguns have always required a high input of skilled labor and are relatively expensive to manufacture.

EARLY COLT REVOLVERS

The first truly successful repeating firearms using a single barrel were the revolving pistols developed in the first half of the 19th century. Flintlock revolvers had been developed in Europe during the 18th century and crude percussion revolver designs were created early in the 19th century. The revolving pistols developed by Samuel Colt of Hartford, Connecticut, during the 1830's were the final breakthrough to wide use. Sam Colt had a tireless drive toward success and pursued many lines to get there. He experimented with underwater mines for the defense of American harbors, utilizing electric ignition through waterproof underwater cables. He developed crude ideas for a percussion revolver mechanism in the summer 1830 while serving as a crew member on the sailing ship *Cotlo* on a voyage from Boston to Calcutta. Although Colt was only 16 years old at the time, he gradually worked his ideas into specific designs by whittling out small parts from wood. On his return in the summer of 1831 Colt hired Anson Chase of Hartford to construct an experimental model revolver based on drawings and the whittled-out wooden components. The first design included automatic rotation of the cylinder by the cocking of the hammer, but locking and unlocking the cylinder was accomplished by a separate motion. Unfortunately this first model blew up during the first test for there were no partitions between the nipples on the rear of the chambers, and the flame from the first shot spread to the others.

Colt found that the experiments were expensive and he had chronic financial troubles. In March of 1832 he set off on a scientific lecture tour demonstrating the amazing properties of nitrous oxide (laughing gas) to the American public. Sam Colt was a born showman and had cards printed up as "Dr. Coult" claiming an impressive scientific background and listing all the points of his sailing voyage as locations around the world where his scientific background was well known. The lecture tours were quite successful in providing funds to continue his revolver experiments and the preparation of patent applications during the mid-1830's. By 1836 the "Patent Arms Manufacturing Company of Paterson, New Jersey, Colt's Patent," was formed and chartered by the legislature of New Jersey. Manufacture of a complete line of revolvers in .31 and .40 caliber was started with many options of barrel length and ornamentation.

A basic asset of the new company was Colt's patent for a revolving gun which was issued on February 25, 1836. Several of the illustrations are shown in Figure 8-3. The illustrations include designs of both pistols and rifles showing six-shot percussion cylinders. The claims were extraordinarily broad and it is remarkable that the patent office allowed all of them. The patent states:

I claim as new —

1. The application of the caps at the end of the cylinder.
2. The application of a partition between the caps.
3. The application of a shield over the caps as a security against moisture and the action of the smoke upon the works of the lock (this feature was shortly dropped from all of the production pistols.)
4. The principle connecting-rod between the hammer and trigger.
5. The application of the shackle to connect the cylinder with the ratchet.
6. The principle of locking and turning the cylinder.
7. The principle of uniting the barrel with the cylinder by means of the arbor running through the plate and the projection under the barrel.
8. The principle of the adopter and the application of the lever, neither of which is used in pistols.

Many of these claims are specific to the Colt design but claims numbers 1 and 6 were very basic claims and provided the Colt's Company with a strong position to control the marketing of revolving percussion firearms. The construction defined in the patent differed in many respect from the Colt's percussion firearms which achieved such wide manufacture during the Civil War. For example, a basic design feature of all of the Colt's percussion revolvers was a heavy shaft, upon which the cylinder rotated, securely fastened to the rear frame of the revolver. The shaft had a cross slot in it and the barrel was aligned with the cylinder by being fitted over this longitudinal shaft (or arbor) and being retained by a key. In the original patent (Figure 8-3) the center shaft is shown as "Fig. 1" in the second illustration down from the top. The "shackle" referred to in Claim 5 is a small splined sleeve "Fig 2" which fitted over the "arbor". The splined "shackle" fitted inside the cylinder at the front and inside the ratchet shown as "Fig 5" in the exploded illustration, at the rear. The cylinder was actually rotated by a "hand", fitted to the hammer which rotated the ratchet. The turning force from the ratchet in turn was transmitted through the splined "shackle" and into the cylinder causing the cylinder to rotate.

Such complicated construction resulted in very difficult manufacturing problems due to the extreme tolerance build ups within the mechanism. In addition the large number of small parts were easily corroded by powder residue and were complex to disassemble for cleaning. In the 20 years following the patent Sam Colt, with the assistance of some very ingenious mechanics such as Elisha K. Root, simplified the mechanism, and made the components more rugged and reliable.

The early Colt's Paterson revolvers are extremely valuable firearms, although the mechanism was com-

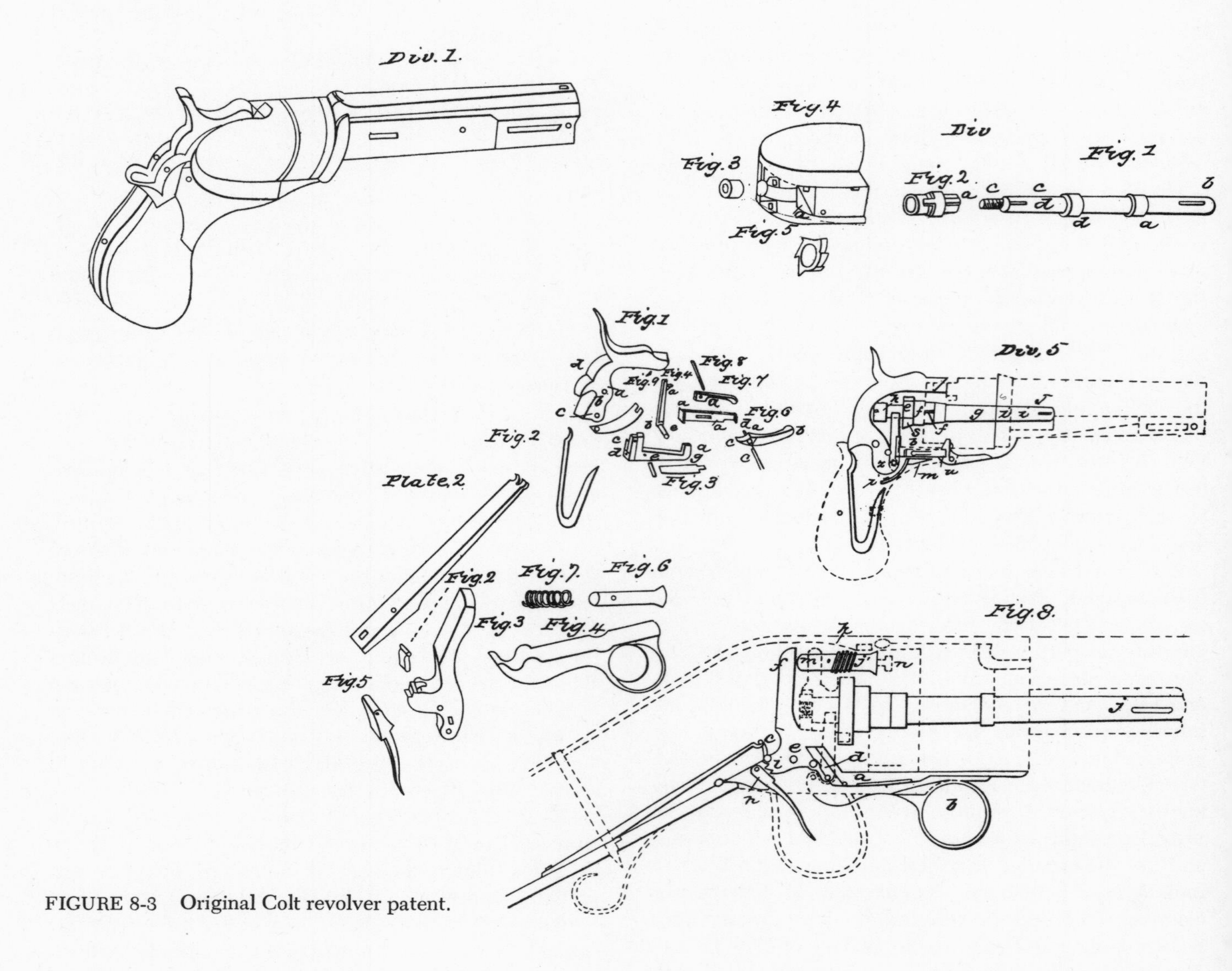

FIGURE 8-3 Original Colt revolver patent.

plex and delicate. The pistols were generally disassembled for reloading and a five- or six-chambered powder flask was furnished which would throw all charges at the same time. A separate ramming tool fitted into a slot in the barrel and could be used to ram the bullets down tight onto the powder charges. Most of the pistols were furnished with a complete kit including powder flask, percussion capper, bullet mold, cleaning rod, and a combined tool which served as screwdriver, rammer, nipple wrench, and nipple picker. The loading procedure was so laborious that purchasers often secured a spare cylinder which could be kept loaded and quickly assembled to the pistol to provide an additional five shots. The Paterson pistols are easily recognized by their lack of a trigger guard and the fact that the trigger is invisible unless the hammer is cocked. By 1839 the loading lever had been permanently attached to the pistol so that disassembly was not required for reloading.

Sam Colt had a great many difficult problems to overcome in the manufacture of percussion pistols. He was very clear in his own mind how to surmount these problems and his ideas were correct, but few in the company shared his vision, so he had to perform as sales manager, manufacturing superintendent, and inventor of machinery and to constantly urge the other shareholders to invest additional sums for the modification of tooling to incorporate design improvements. Despite his heroic efforts the plant went bankrupt in 1842.

Colt's Paterson pistols were used in the Seminole War in Florida during the early 1840's and veterans of that fracas were very favorably impressed. When clouds began to gather for the Mexican War, General Zachary Taylor sent an urgent request for the purchase of Colt's pistols and carbines to equip some of the troops. One hundred and fifty firearms were purchased from an arms dealer in New York who had been connected with the Paterson Company in August, 1845. Insufficient new firearms were available to fulfill the order so some used firearms were purchased to complete the Government order.

When war broke out the effectiveness of the Colt revolvers was fully proven and urgent requests were sent from the field forces in Mexico to the Ordnance Department. Ordnance in turn contacted Sam Colt who tried to locate a single model of a Paterson pistol. As it turned out it was fortunate no Patersons were available, for in 1846 Sam Colt got together with the very gifted Captain Samuel H. Walker representing the United States Mounted Rifles. Captain Walker brought back detailed knowledge of field experience and made many valuable recommendations for a greatly improved revolver model. During the fall of 1846 an order was finalized for 1000 heavy .44 caliber revolvers. Since the Colt's factory had gone out of existence most of the components were manufactured at Eli Whitney's Armory in Whitneyville, Connecticut, just north of New Haven. These were monster revolvers with an over-all length of 15½ inches and an average weight of 4½ pounds. The original contract with the government specified that separate iron ramrods were to be used in loading, but the final design included a hinged lever which provided a powerful camming force to ram the bullets into the cylinder. The ramrod was retained in a upward position under the barrel by a very small spring lever fitted just forward of the pivot. This was not a very satisfactory design and was modified during 1848.

The contract specified 1000 pistols which became known as the Model of 1847 Army Pistol, the Whitneyville-Walker or Walker-Colt. The contract specified a price of $27, which was in include accessories such as bullet mold, powder flask an disassembly tool. The 1000 arms were finished in the summer of 1847, but there was protracted discussions with the Government inspector over a number of small design changes which had been made in the design of the pistols. Some of the changes were to facilitate production and others were improvements based on detailed discussions with Captain Walker and as a result of production experience. The Government finally accepted the pistols late in the summer, and they started their long trip to the Mexican operations.

Captain Walker was killed on October 9, 1847, in a skirmish in the town of Huamantla. The main shipment of revolvers had not arrived at the time of his death and the Mexican War was pretty well over by November of 1847 so the actual participation of these firearms in the conflict was very minor. Sam Colt claimed to have lost about $5000 on this first contract, since he had to buy expensive tooling and machinery for manufacture. But the contract was a turning point in his fortunes, for, although the contract was performed at the Whitneyville Armory, Sam Colt retained title to the patents and tooling and moved right ahead to set up his own factory.

MODEL 1848 HOLSTER PISTOL (No. 1 Dragoon)

Sam Colt was negotiating a second contract with the Ordnance Department during the manufacture of the Whitneyville-Walker pistols. In the fall of 1847 he removed his machinery and tooling from the Whitney Armory and started his own factory on Pearl Street in Hartford, Connecticut. He received the second contract from the Ordnance Department in November 1847, and Colt pistols have been manufactured in Hartford ever since that date. The improved model became known by many different names is shown in Figure 8-4. The size of the pistol was reduced in two areas. First the barrel length was reduced to 7½ inches and the length of cylinder was shortened slightly to limit the powder charge. Over-all length of the pistols was reduced from 15½ to 14 inches. Despite these reductions, the .44 caliber Dragoon pistols are enormous firearms which could be held at arm's length by the average soldier for only short periods of time.

The basic features of the Colt revolver design is shown in Figure 8-4. Colt did not use a large forged frame into which all the components were assembled, but instead built up his revolver from many small pieces. Thus the frame of the revolver was only the L-shaped section beneath and behind the cylinder. The trigger guard was a brass casting screwed to the frame. A second brass casting formed the back strap of the revolver and the wooden grip was clamped between these two brass straps. The cylinder rotated upon a shaft (or arbor) which was permanently screwed into the revolver frame. The shaft had a cross slot cut in the front. The barrel assembly had a large block at the rear which held two small locating pins at the bottom, which mated with recesses in the revolver frame. A hole in the center of the block fitted the "arbor". The entire barrel assembly was held to the revolver by a key which fitted through the hole in the arbor and which may be seen on the flat panel of the barrel block. The ramrod assembly was pivoted on a pin at the front of the barrel block. It was held in position by a catch dovetailed to the lower side of the barrel and a spring loaded latching arrangement in the ramrod. The barrel block was designed with a clearance cut on the right side so that conical bullets could be partially seated by hand in the open mouth of the cylinder chambers and then rammed home by the powerful action of the ramrod assembly.

Sam Colt used advanced manufacturing techniques in many components for the pistol. The revolvers were sophisticated pieces of machinery for the 1840's and great care was required in production to insure reliable functioning. Colt also used advanced techniques for ornamentation, including the roll engraving of a Cowboy and Indian battle on the exterior of the cylinder.

Colt continued to obtain small Government orders of about 1000 pistols at a time during the late 40's and received his first larger order in May 1851 for 2000 pistols. Minor design improvements continued to enhance the utility and functioning of these pistols.

MODEL 1849 SECOND DRAGOON (Old Model Army Pistol)

The .44 caliber percussion revolvers built to the basic design established by Captain Walker and Sam Colt in 1847 remained in production until 1860. During 1849 more design changes were made. The square-backed brass trigger guard was modified into a more conventional round design. The oval cylinder-locking slots were replaced with rectangular notches with lead-in grooves. The Model of 1849 became known as the No. 2 Dragoon Pistol and a minor variation of this model, which was cut and fitted with shoulder stocks and long-range sights, is often called No. 3 Dragoon Pistol by collectors. These were usually issued with one shoulder stock for each two pistols.

Sam Colt was an inveterate experimenter and willingly accepted ideas from many sources to improve his pistols. The No. 2 and No. 3 Dragoons at 66 ounces, or slightly over 4 pounds were slightly lighter than the earlier pistols. The lock mechanism had been improved so that it contained only five moving parts compared with seventeen in the Paterson revolvers. Experiments with rifling had led Colt finally to specify seven lands and grooves with a gain twist—a relatively sophisticated manufacturing problem for the 1850's.

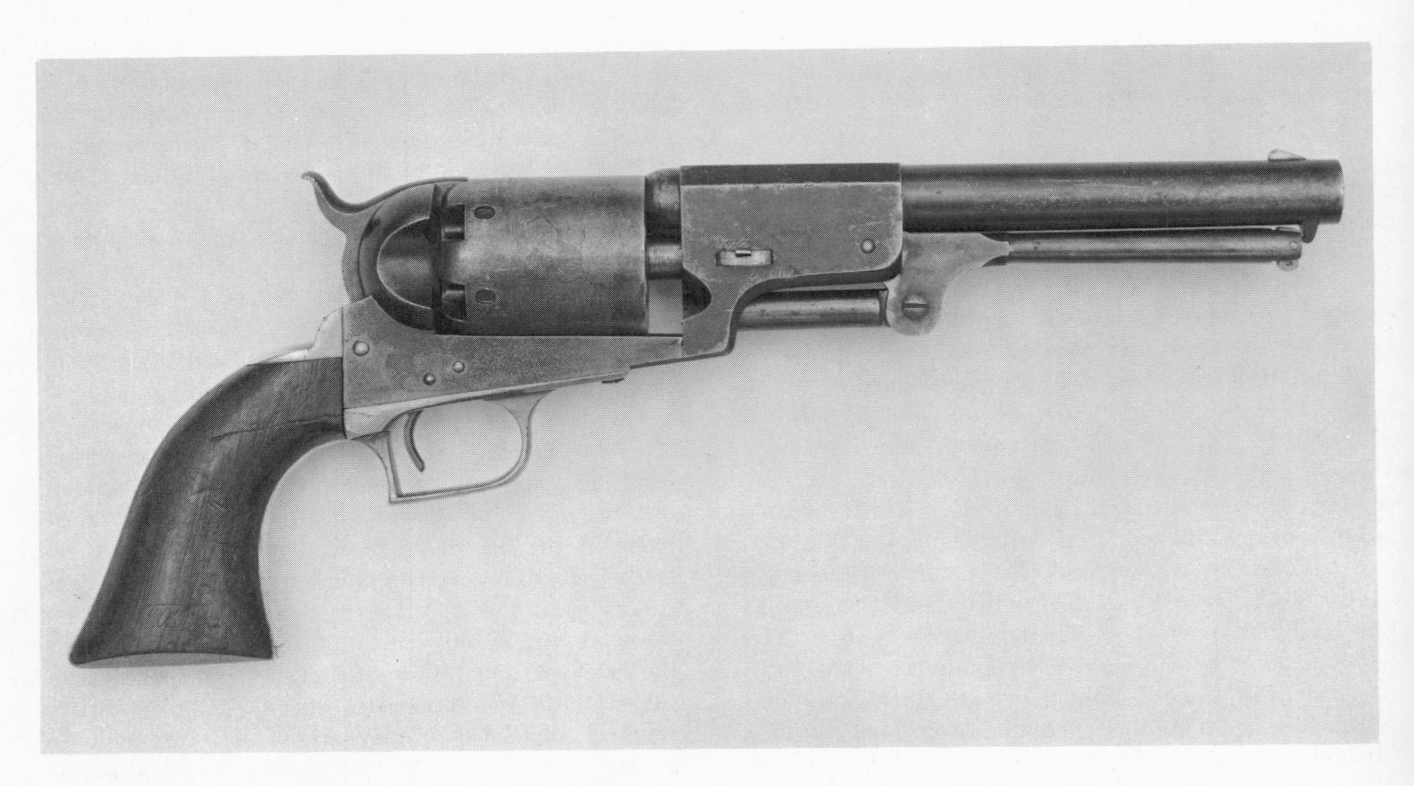

FIGURE 8-4 Colt Model 1848 .44 caliber "First Dragoon" revolver.

The later Dragoon pistols were also fitted with a rudimentary safety by fitting short pins in the solid material in between each pair of nipples at the rear of the cylinder. A small slot was milled in the face of the hammer. After the pistol was fully loaded the hammer could be lowered carefully so that the slot in the face of the hammer locked into one of the pins in the solid section of the cylinder. Conventional practice with percussion revolvers was to load only five chambers and to lower the hammer on the empty sixth chamber for safety purposes.

AMMUNITION FOR THE COLT REVOLVERS

The original Colt revolvers were designed for use with loose powder and spherical lead balls. The Paterson pistols were disassembled for reloading. Powder flasks were manufactured which would measure five or six powder charges simultaneously. The flask generally had five charge tubes projecting from the powder reservoir and these could be inserted into the mouth of the chambers and the five charges thrown simultaneously. A soft lead ball .001 or .002 of an inch larger in diameter than the chamber was placed over each cavity. The lead ball was then force fitted into place, slightly compressing the powder charge. It was very important that the lead ball be slightly oversize and fit tightly in the chamber. Any loose ball would move forward under the recoil as the pistol was fired. If the motion were sufficient for the ball to project beyond the cylinder mouth the revolver would jam.

During the late 1840's experiments were performed in the United States and Europe with pointed lead bullets. These are technically known as ogive-shaped bullets, but the common jargon of the mid-19th century was to refer to these as conical bullets. Scientific tests quickly established the greatly improved exterior ballistic performance of the pointed bullets and they became the military standard for many countries during the 1850's.

Sam Colt designed his heavy .44 caliber percussion revolvers to handle either lead balls or pointed lead bullets. The loading procedure with the pointed bullets was more complex for it was important that the axis of the bullet be parallel to the barrel center line. If the lead bullet was rammed in place at an angle to the bore, the point would describe a circle upon firing and the bullet would wobble off on a very inaccurate flight path. Colt's solution to this problem may be seen in Figure 8-4. The right side of the barrel block just to the rear of the loading rammer has been cut away. The revolver was placed on halfcock position where the cylinder could be freely rotated. The conical lead bullets were designed with a reduced diameter heel which allowed the shooter to start them in the cylinder with his fingers. After the bullet was partially placed in the chamber it was rotated underneath the loading rammer and the lever activated to ram the bullet home in a straight line. In effect, Sam Colt had designed a miniature loading machine to go with his revolvers.

The probable performance of the powerful .44 caliber ammunition for the Walker-Colt revolvers is shown on the upper lines of Figure 8-5. It has not been possible to locate accurately documented ballistic tests of these early revolvers. To give a picture of the performance of the standard ammunition specified in the late 1840's in a Walker-Colt revolver in good mechanical condition, some complicated analytical techniques have been utilized. Modern tests of replica .44 and .36 caliber revolvers have been performed by Lyman Gun Sight Products and are included in the latest edition of the *Lyman Handbook*. These test results were fed into a small ballistic computer program which predicts the maximum theoretical muzzle velocity attainable under ideal conditions. The actual test results were then compared with the theoretical maximum.

The probable performance of the .44 caliber Walker-Colt revolver was then calculated by the same computer program. The predicted muzzle velocity shown in Figure 8-5 have been calculated on the same percentage of theoretical maximum as that found for the actual test conditions with the replica revolvers.

A second analytical technique was used as a cross check. This was to gather all ballistic data of early tests of revolvers reported in Colonel Berkely Lewis' *Small Arms and Ammunition in the United States Service*. The performance of the muzzle-loading pistols as well as the percussion revolvers reported in the Lyman Handbook are calculated on an efficiency basis. These calculations involve computing the foot-pounds of muzzle energy per grain of black powder. This method of analysis also provided consistent measurements of percussion revolver performance.

The results of this analysis are shown in Figure 8-5. The Walker-Colt .44 caliber revolvers were loaded with both 136-grain ball, and a 212-grain pointed lead bullets. The 212-grain pointed bullet backed up by a 50-grain powder charge had a muzzle velocity of about 950 feet per second, and 425 foot-pounds of muzzle energy. With a 136-grain round lead ball the powder charge could be increased to 58 grains of powder which launched the bullet at close to 1,200 feet per second. Generally the efficiency of either antique or modern firearms is higher with a heavy lead bullet and moderate powder charge, and this rule calculates out for the Walker-Colt revolvers. The efficiency with a conical lead bullet is about 8.5 foot-pounds of muzzle energy per grain of propellant and drops down to 7.4 for the spherical ball.

AMMUNITION FOR THE .44 DRAGOON REVOLVERS

The length of the cylinder was reduced in the Model 1848 Colt Dragoon revolvers and in all later models. This reduction limited the powder charge to 40 grains with 212-grain pointed bullet. Calculations indicate that the muzzle velocity would drop to about 820 feet per second, delivering slightly over 300 foot-pounds of muzzle energy. The efficiency was approximately 7.9 foot-pounds of muzzle energy per grain of propellant.

SMALL CALIBER COLT REVOLVERS

During the development of the Model 1847 Walker-Colt Revolvers, and the Model 1848 First Dragoon models, Colt was considering designs of smaller calibered revolvers specifically for the commercial market. In 1848 he started production of pocket revolvers in .31 caliber. These were designed to be as light and compact as possible with the intention of providing personal protection for travelers. The Model 1848 Pocket Pistols had five shot cylinders, and were made with barrels as short as 3 inches. They were fitted with octagonal barrels, but the entire loading lever assembly was eliminated. The result was an extremely compact, lightweight pistol, with an over-all length of only 8 inches and a weight as low as 24 ounces. The pistols were reloaded by removing the barrel and cylinder. Fresh powder charges were thrown into the cylinders and .31 caliber spherical lead balls were then seated in the chambers using the arbor to force the bullet down upon the powder charge. These pistols were very effective as personal defense weapons. The businessman or traveler had five rapid shots available if confronted with thugs or a highwayman — all within a package weighing 1½ pounds and of such size that it could easily be fitted into a pocket.

The Model 1848 pocket pistols were also known as the Old Model Pocket Pistols or Baby Dragoon. They had many features from the First Dragoon models, including round locking slots in the cylinders and square-backed trigger guards. New models of the pocket pistol were brought out in 1849 reflecting the improvements developed in the Second Dragoon models. The design is shown in Figure 8-6. The changes included the use of a round trigger guard and rectangular locking slots in the cylinder, and the addition of a hinged loading lever assembly. These models were produced all during the 1850's and early 1860's.

In 1850 an additional model was brought out in .36

Revolver	Grains Powder Charge	Bullet Shape	Grains Bullet Weight	Ft/Sec Muzzle Velocity	Ft-Lbs Muzzle Energy	Pistol Efficiency Ft/Lb Per Grain
.44 Army	50	Ogive	212	950[1]	425	8.5
Walker-Colt	58	Ball	136	1200[2]	435	7.5
.44 Army						
Cold Dragoons	40	Ogive	212	820[1]	320	7.9
.44 Army	39	Ball	136	995[2]	300	7.6
M1860 Colt	26	Ogive	155	815[2]	230	8.8
1861 Ord. Manual	30	Ogive	216	740[1]	263	8.7
36 Navy	25	Ball	78	1005[2]	175	7.0
M 1851 Molt	15	Ogive	145	690[2]	153	10.2
1861 Ord. Manual	17	Ogive	145	745[1]	175	10.2

[1]Calculated on ballistics computer program
[2]Lyman handbook

FIGURE 8-5 Ballistics of percussion revolvers.

FIGURE 8-6 Colt Model 1850 .31 caliber pocket revolver.

caliber. This became known as the Model 1851 Navy Pistol. This model combined excellent weight and balance and became very popular in the Colt line. The .36 caliber was standardized for the Navy and these models are generally referred to as the Old Model Navy Pistol. They were also known as the Old Model Belt Pistol. Normally fitted with 7½-inch barrels they had an over-all length of 13 inches and a weight of only 2 pounds 10 ounces. The six-shot cylinder was engraved with a naval battle and the large boss on the barrel was cut away to allow the use of either spherical or pointed lead bullets. Typical ballistics for this pistol are shown in Figure 8-5. The round lead ball weighed slightly under 80 grains and was launched at a muzzle velocity very close to 1000 feet per second. The muzzle energy was 175 foot-pounds and the efficiency 7 foot-pounds of muzzle energy per grain of propellant. Pointed lead bullets of 125 to 145 grains were also used in the Colt Navy pistol. Tests with modern replica revolvers using 145-grain pointed bullets are described in the latest edition of the *Lyman Handbook*. A muzzle velocity of 690 feet per second was achieved with a 15-grain powder charge for an efficiency of 10.2 foot-pounds of muzzle energy per grain of propellant. The standard Civil War load for this revolver is listed in the 1861 *Ordnance Manual* as 17 grains of black powder with the same 145-grain pointed bullet. Calculations indicate that the muzzle velocity would be approximately 745 fet per second and the muzzle energy about 175 foot-pounds.

The Colt Navy model was exceptionally successful and remained in production from 1850 through the end of the percussion era in 1872. Even the development of an improved and more streamlined model in 1861 did not cut off demand for the Model 1851 Navy, for it had achieved a tremendous reputation due to its good balance of power, light weight, and pointing ability. A great many variations were manufactured during the 1850's. Very few Navy models were made with barrels as short as 4¾ inches. Some were cut for shoulder stocks and a few models were made on special order with round barrels, and elaborately checkered and carved oak and cherry stocks.

In the late 1850's Colt began experimenting with designs which would reduce the weight and bulk of the percussion revolvers. The designs were finalized in 1860 and represented the highest development of Colt's percussion revolvers. The new Colt Navy model which became known as the Model of 1861 is shown in Figure 8-7. The rear half of the pistol remained much the same, but the barrel assembly was entirely redesigned to include a very streamlined rounded contour and what became known as the "creeping lever" ramrod. Instead of being pivoted on a cross shaft, the ramrod had a series of teeth cut into an arc. Holes were drilled in the underside of the barrel in the enlarged boss and as the long arm of the ramrod was swung downwards the teeth "crept" along the holes drilled into the barrel, providing a very powerful camming action.

The Model 1861 Navy became known as the New Model Navy Pistol, or the New Model Belt Pistol. Specifications were similar to those for the Model 1851, with a barrel of 7½ inches and an over-all length of 13 inches. The weight had been reduced slightly to 2 pounds 9 ounces, but the basic features of an oval brass trigger guard and brass backstrap had been continued. The frames were case-hardened and the cylinders were engraved with scenes of a naval battle.

MODEL 1860 ARMY REVOLVER

The greatest improvement in the redesigns of the late 1850's was in the creation of a new Colt Army revolver design which retained the .44 caliber but allowed this large cylinder to be installed on the small frame of the Navy revolver shown in Figure 8-7. This was accomplished by using a two-diameter cylinder. The front half of the cylinder was large enough to carry .45-inch diameter lead balls or .45 caliber pointed lead bullets, but the rear half of the cylinder was turned down to the diameter of the .36 caliber Navy cylinder. The front portion of the frame was cut away to provide clearance for the increased cylinder diameter at the front. A new barrel assembly very similar to that shown in Figure 8-7 was designed and fitted to the revolvers.

Official government tests were performed in 1860 comparing the power and accuracy of the New Model Army pistol with the .44 caliber Second Dragoon pistol with which the Army was then equipped. Surprisingly, tests with the same cartridge in both revolvers showed greater accuracy and penetration with the Model 1860 revolvers than with the Dragoon design. The Ordnance Board was enthusiastic in approving the new model since it provided increased accuracy and power with a great reduction in both weight and bulk.

The Model 1860 Colt Army was very widely used during the Civil War and a total of 129,730 were purchased by the Ordnance Department between 1861 and 1866. The average price for these revolvers was slightly over $17.50. Colt could have manufactured a great many more except that the Colt Company maintained this price level during the Civil War while both Remington and Starr reduced their prices later in the war and were favored with additional contracts in 1864 and 1865.

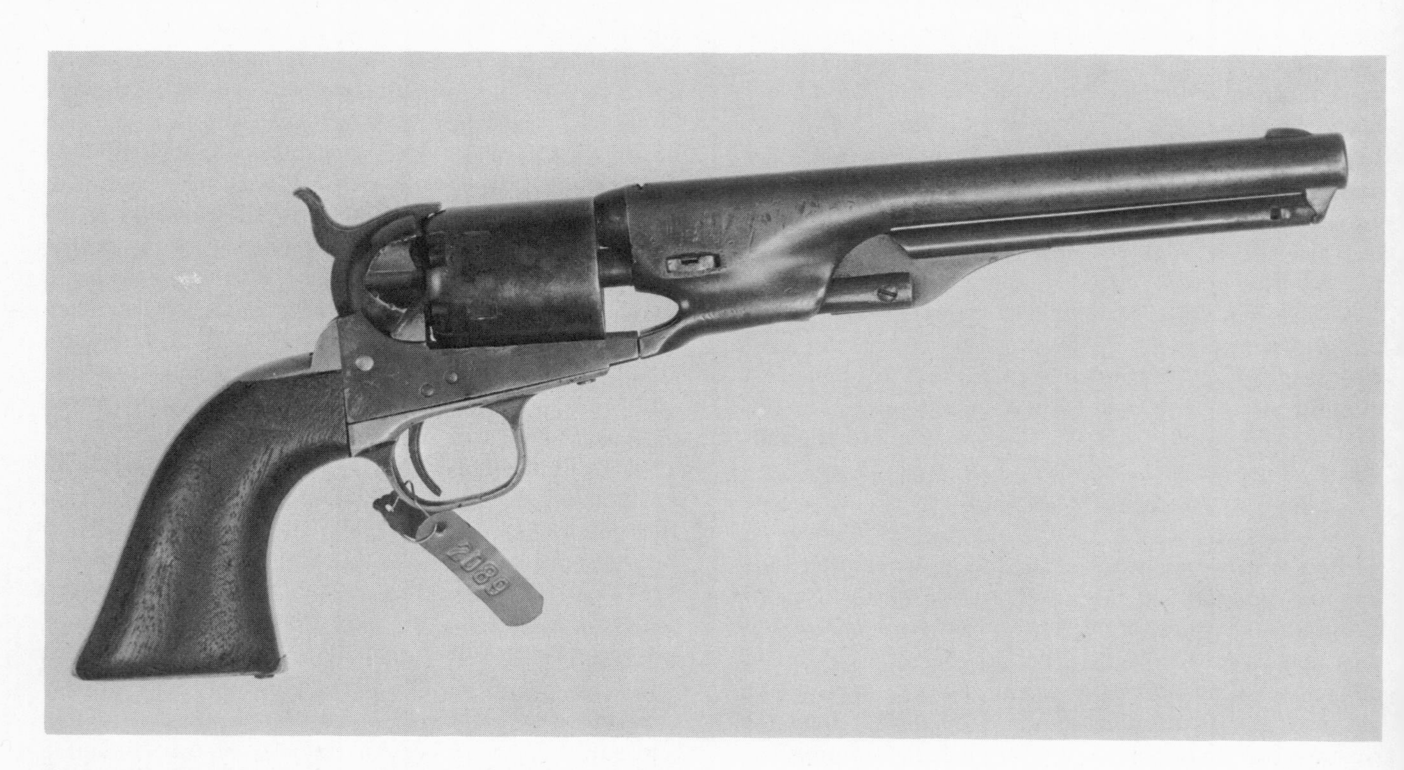

FIGURE 8-7 Colt Model 1861 .36 caliber Navy revolver.

By 1864 the Northern cavalryman was very heavily armed with two .44 caliber percussion revolvers, a seven-shot Spencer repeating carbine, and a cavalry saber. Such fire power had a significant effect on Northern success during the latter years of the war. The cavalry could deploy rapidly into a position flanking a Southern force and then dismount and fight as infantry with the tremendous firepower of their Spencer carbines. During mounted attacks they had the use of both cavalry sabers and percussion revolvers.

The ballistics of the Model 1860 Colt army are shown in Figure 8-5. Tests with modern replica revolvers reported in the *Lyman Handbook* show a velocity of slightly under 1000 feet per second for a .45 caliber ball driven by 39 grains of black powder. This calculates out to a muzzle energy of 300 foot-pounds and an efficiency of 7.6 foot-pounds per grain of propellant. The 155-grain pointed bullet driven by 26 grains of powder has a muzzle velocity of 815 feet per second and a muzzle energy of 230 foot-pounds.

The standard cartridge specified in the 1861 Ordnance Manual included a 216-grain pointed lead bullet driven by 30 grains of black powder. Calculations indicate that the bullet would be launched at a muzzle velocity close to 740 feet per second with a muzzle energy of slightly over 260 foot-pounds. The performance of this ammunition was well balanced for the .44 Army revolver. The powder charge and muzzle energy were reduced to keep the recoil of the lighter revolver within reasonable limits. The large diameter bullet was very effective at any reasonable pistol range. Some of the revolvers were fitted with shoulder stocks to permit firing at extended ranges, but there was considerable trouble with this approach since the point of aim of the pistol was significantly shifted by the addition of a shoulder stock. Furthermore the Northern cavalry would seldom need to use a pistol at extended range, shifting to their Spencer or Sharps carbines when firing beyond pistol limits.

REMINGTON PERCUSSION REVOLVERS

The second major supplier of percussion revolvers to the Union forces during the Civil War was E. Remington and Sons of Ilion, New York. Remington had been in business for over 40 years and had a reputation for production of high quality firearms. As the Civil War approached, Eliphalet Remington, son of the founder, did everything possible to create a modern manufacturing plant which could make maximum contribution to the Union cause. Remington was a major producer of .58 caliber muzzle-loading rifles, including their famous Model 1862 Zouave.

Remington also produced heavy caliber percussion revolvers for the Union forces. Patents supplied by S. M. Alvis, manager of the Remington Ilion Research Division, trace the evolution of the heavy percussion revolvers through the late 1850's and early 1860's. In 1858 patent No. 21,478 was issued to Fordyce Beals of New Haven, Connecticut, for an improvement in revolving firearms. The Beals patent shows a solid revolver frame into which all the components are assembled — a very different system of construction from that used on Colt revolvers. The frame had a cut-out opening for the cylinder and the barrel was screwed into the front. The cylinder rotated upon a removable pin which was locked in place by the rammer lever. When the loading lever was dropped into a downward position the center pin could be removed and the cylinder removed from the frame.

Revolvers based on this patent approach were placed into production by Remington in 1858. An Army model was manufactured in .44 caliber with an 8-inch barrel, and a Navy model in .36 caliber with a 7½-inch barrel. Both were marked Beals Patent Sept. 14, 1858 manufactured by Remington's Ilion, New York.

Studies of improved revolver designs continued at Ilion under the leadership of W. H. Elliot of the Remington design staff. Patent No. 33,932 was issued to Elliot on December 17, 1861, for design improvements which allowed the cylinder rotating shaft to be removed without dropping the loading lever. These models became known as the Remington Model 1861 percussion revolvers and were produced in the same calibers and barrel lengths. These are marked on the barrels Patented Dec. 17, 1861. Manufactured by Remington's Ilion, N.Y. Field experience with the Elliot design showed that the cylinder pin would occasionally move forward due to recoil forces jamming the revolver. The design was modified again into the New Model of 1863 which was an extremely successful design. The general appearance of this revolver is shown in the Samuel Remington patent of 1863 shown as Figure 8-8. The specific design features of this patent were not included in production, but it shows the general arrangement of the elements of the Remington percussion revolvers. These revolvers were produced in .44 Army caliber with 8-inch barrels, and .36 Navy caliber with 7½-inch barrels. They were generally marked Patented Sept. 14, 1858. E. Remington and Sons, Ilion, New York, USA New Model. Over 125,000 of the Remington .44 caliber Army revolvers were produced during the Civil War, making it the second most popular percussion revolver. Replicas of Remington and Colt revolvers are made today and shooters enjoy target practice with them.

SHOOTING THE PERCUSSION REVOLVER

If you are interested in shooting a percussion revolver, the use of a replica model is recommended. I did quite a bit of shooting with my genuine 1860 Colt .44 percussion revolver, but experience has shown that it is not a good idea. Revolvers have much more delicate components than long arms such as the Sharps and Remington breech-loading rifles or the percussion muzzle-loaders. Clearances had opened up on the old revolver and eventually internal components such as the hand and locking mechanism wore down or broke. Genuine Colt and Remington revolvers are now so valuable that the use of replicas made with new modern steel for the internal components is a much better approach.

Ballistic tests with the old Colt revolver also showed a significant drop in performance due to gas leakage. For example a 133-grain round ball was driven at only 690 feet per second by 23.3 grains of black powder. This corresponds to an efficiency of only 6 foot-pounds of muzzle energy per grain of propellant. The same powder charge drove a 233-grain conical bullet at an average velocity of 545 feet per second and a muzzle energy of 154 foot-pounds. This was slightly better performance but still provided only 6.6 foot-pounds of muzzle energy per grain of propellant. These efficiencies can be considerably improved by using a modern replica revolver which has the original factory fit and clearances, thus minimizing gas leakage. The ballistics of the replica revolvers are given in Figure 8-5.

CARTRIDGE REVOLVERS

During the late 1860's there was a rapid shift toward cartridge firearms. An inventor named Rollin White obtained a patent for a revolver with cylinders bored straight through. This was a crucial patent for the obvious way to load a cartridge into the chamber was from the rear, using the cartridge case itself to seal the back of the chamber.

The young Smith and Wesson Company purchased

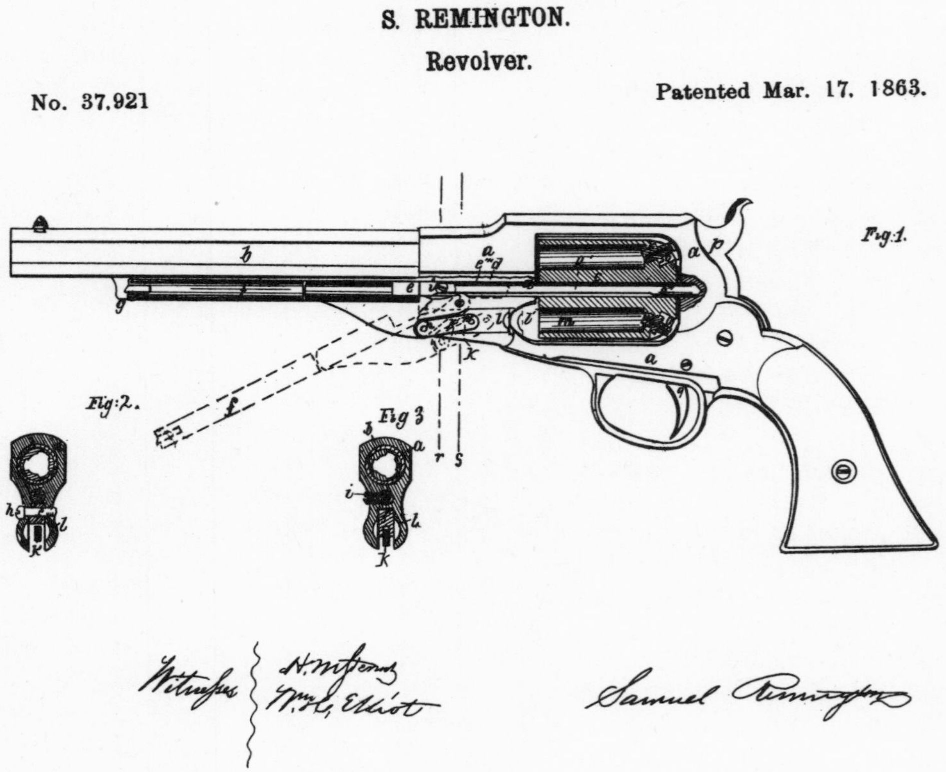

S. REMINGTON.
Revolver.
No. 37,921 Patented Mar. 17, 1863.

FIGURE 8-8 Remington revolver patent of 1863.

FIGURE 8-9 Colt Model 1873 .45 caliber Army revolver.

control of the Rollin White patent and effectively blocked Colt's from the use of this invention until patent expiration in the early 1870's. Colt's responded by developing a number of ingenious modifications to their percussion revolvers to allow their use with cartridges.

By 1871 Colt's could anticipate the expiration of the Rollin White patent and they started work on the design of an all new revolver reflecting all the design knowledge which had been gained in the past 40 years. The result was the Model 1873 single action Army revolver shown in Figure 8-9. This was the most famous revolver ever designed and remained in the Colt commercial line for almost 80 years. The cross section of this revolver taken from the 1874 Army Field Manual is shown in Figure 8-10. It combined in remarkable degree an excellent balance of features and in addition to its widespread use in the expansion of the West during the latter half of the 19th century, it has appeared in innumerable 20th century Western movies.

The revolver was built on a solid frame — a box-shaped forging with a square hole cut for the cylinder. The barrel screwed solidly into the front of the frame and the cylinder rotated upon a pin which had two sturdy bearing surfaces within the frame. This construction was similar to that used on the Remington and Whitney percussion revolvers during the Civil War, and had also been used on the Root side hammer Colt revolvers of 1855. The Colt practice of using separate brass castings to form the backstrap and trigger guard were continued. The cross section shown in Figure 8-10 shows the details. The screw T bolts the upper end of the trigger guard to the frame. Two screws just to the rear of the trigger guard on each side also fastened this brass casting E solidly to the frame of the revolver. The backstrap of the revolver F was another brass casting and it was also fastened to the frame with two screws on each side of the hammer. The two brass castings were fastened together by the screw V. The hammer rotated upon the pivot J and was fitted with a roller I to reduce friction with the mainspring. As the hammer was cocked the "hand" L was raised, rotating the ratchet cut into the rear of the cylinder and rotating the cylinder. The cylinder locking bolt M was disengaged from the cylinder by the initial motion of the hammer. As the hammer continued rotating, the thin arms extending to the rear of the locking bolt M slipped off the camming pin and the locking bolt snapped upward, riding against the outside of the cylinder. As the hand L rotated the cylinder into the proper alignment for the next shot, the locking bolt M snapped into the locking slot cut into the exterior of the cylinder, providing an exact alignment between the chamber C and the barrel.

Colt Army revolvers were fairly slow to load. A loading gate on the right side of the frame was snapped open and the hammer placed on half-cock. In this position the cylinder could be freely rotated and six cartridges could be dropped into the cylinders one after the other. Ejection of the fired shells was accomplished by swinging the loading gate open again and placing the hammer on half-cock. An ejection rod Q could be moved back and forth by a thumb piece R. As the chambers were rotated past the loading gate the ejection rod R moved smartly to the rear, kicking the fired shell out of the chamber. There were, therefore, twelve separate operations to reload the revolver.

The Model 1873 Colt revolver was made in three models. The basic Army model had a 7½-inch barrel and an over-all length of 12½ inches. The weight was 2.31 pounds. The shorter model with 5½-inch barrel and 11-inch over-all length was designed for the artillery. Commercial models were made with barrels as short as 3 inches but these gave a tremendous muzzle blast. Normally short-barreled models were fitted with 4¾-inch barrels which came just to the end of the ejector.

The commercial .45 Colt cartridge was originally brought out with a 230-grain bullet and 40 grains of black powder. The 1874 Army Field Manual lists the cartridges with the same bullet weight but a powder charge of 28 grains. It states: "The cartridge case is metallic centre fire, and resembles in its construction the rifle cartridge, . . . its charge has been lightened . . . to adopt it to the Schofield-Smith and Wesson pistol."

The single action Colt revolver was also chambered for the 44/40 Winchester cartridge during the mid-1870's and this provided the frontiersman with great flexibility. Both his rifle and revolver could be chambered for the same cartridge, greatly simplifying ammunition problems in the wilderness. The 200-grain soft lead bullet backed by 40 grains of black powder was an excellent short- to medium-range cartridge with great knockdown power.

In later years the single action Colt became known as the "Peacemaker" and was adapted to a wide range of cartridges from .32/20 up to the powerful .357 magnum cartridge. Modern high intensity cartridges tend to shake the screws loose, but the old Model 1873 Colt is still an excellent revolver with moderate power cartridges.

SMITH AND WESSON REVOLVERS

The famous team of Horace Smith and Daniel Wesson did a great deal to assist in the founding of the Winchester Repeating Arms Company before going on to found their own pistol manufacturing firm. Their experiments with rimfire cartridges during the 1850's led to the production of their first revolvers chambered for .22 rim fire. With control of the Rollin White patent, they moved rapidly during the 1860's to secure a strong position in the manufacture of cartridge revolvers.

In the late 1860's Smith and Wesson began experi-

FIGURE 8-10 Colt Model 1873 revolver cross-section.

FIGURE 8-11 Smith and Wesson–Schofield Model 1873 .45 caliber revolver.

menting with more powerful cartridges including the .41 rimfire, and the .44 Henry rimfire cartridge. By 1870 they had developed the first of their powerful large revolvers which became known as the Smith and Wesson American. It was offered in .44 Henry rimfire, and in .44 Smith and Wesson American — a center-fire cartridge.

In May 1870 one of these revolvers was submitted to the Army Small Arms Board, and tests resulted in an order for 1000 pistols later that year. In 1871 the Russians ordered 20,000 revolvers with minor design changes, and chambered for a .44 center-fire cartridge which became known as the .44 Russian.

Smith and Wesson were constantly alert to design changes which would improve the functioning of their revolvers. In 1873 models were prepared reflecting design improvements patented by Colonel George W. Schofield on April 22, 1873. These revolvers were successful in the Government trials of 1873 and both Colt and Smith and Wesson revolvers became standardized for the Army. The design of the Schofield-Smith and Wesson Army revolver is shown in Figure 8-11. The construction was very different from the Colt's design. There were three major assemblies, the barrel, frame, and cylinder. The barrel assembly was pivoted to the frame by a cross shaft just forward of the cylinder. In the locked position, the top strap for the barrel assembly was firmly held to the frame by a sturdy latch just forward of the hammer. When the hammer was placed in a half-cocked position the latch could be swung rearward and the revolver opened as shown in Figure 8-12. The design was very ingenious. As the action was opened the cam JK drove the ejector rod H to the rear. The star-shaped plate GG hooked under the rim of all six cartridges and carried them to the rear, ejecting them from the cylinder. As the revolver reached a fully open position the cam JK overrode the lever L which allowed the ejector return spring to snap the ejector assembly forward flush with the cylinder face. In this position it was easy to place six fresh cartridges in the cylinders and snap the revolver shut.

As the hammer N was drawn to the rear to a fully cocked position the hand W rotated the ratchet on the ejector plate G-G′, rotating the cylinder. When the cylinder reached the point of proper alignment with the barrel, the cylinder latch V snapped up into a locking recess cut into the outside of the chamber preventing further rotation. When the trigger T was pulled, the hammer fell driven by the mainspring O. The strength of the mainspring could be controlled by the adjustment screw Q. As the hammer fell the nose of the hammer passed through the recoil plate U igniting the cartridge. An upper surface on the hammer interlocked with the barrel latch D which firmly locked the barrel assembly downward as long as the hammer was in a forward position.

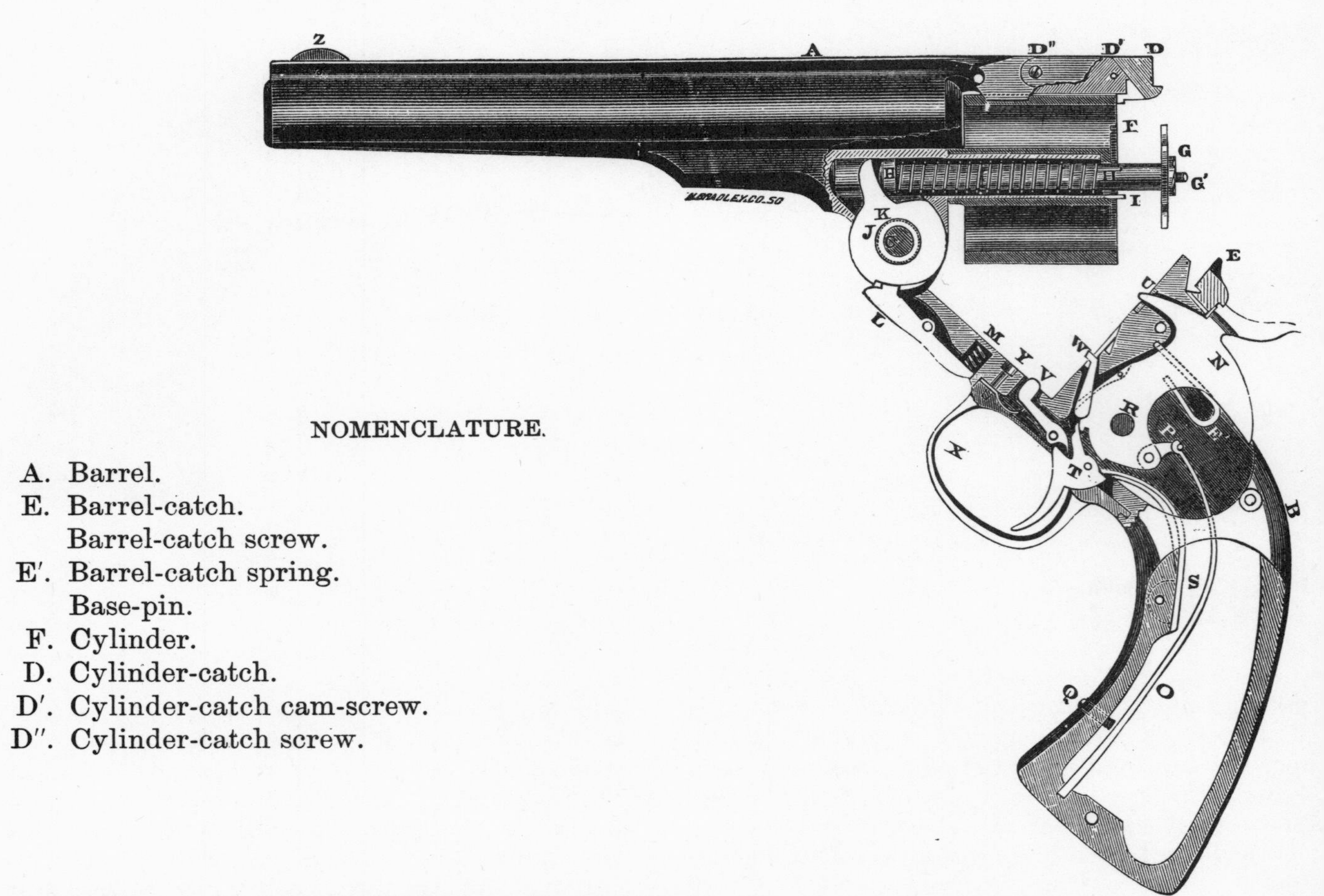

FIGURE 8-12 Smith and Wesson—Schofield revolver cross-section.

The total length of the Schofield-Smith and Wesson revolvers was 12½ inches with a 7-inch barrel. Bore diameter was .436 of an inch and groove .448 of an inch. The revolver weighed 2.5 pounds and was chambered for the .45 Smith and Wesson center-fire cartridge with a 230-grain soft lead bullet driven by 28 grains of black powder.

BALLISTICS OF 45 REVOLVER AMMUNITION

The ballistics of the .45 Smith and Wesson center-fire cartridge are given in the 1874 Ordnance Manual. The actual ballistics quoted are for the Colt revolver with a 7½-inch barrel, but the values would be very similar for the Smith and Wesson. The 230-grain soft lead bullet was launched at a "mean initial velocity" of 730 feet per second. This corresponds to a muzzle energy of 272 foot-pounds and an efficiency of 9.7 foot-pounds per grain of propellant. The Ordnance Manual states that the Colt revolver could be fired 18 times in one minute and 54 seconds, beginning and ending with the chambers empty. This probably represents performance of a skilled shooter under good test conditions, and not a realistic field performance. The Smith and Wesson would be much faster to fire due to the automatic ejection and ease of reloading. Accuracy for the Colt is given as 8.3 inches mean absolute deviation for 12-shot targets at 100 yards. Penetration in white pine is listed at 3½ inches at 100 yards and 2¼ inches at 300 yards with a note that one inch penetration corresponds to a dangerous wound.

Both the Colt's and Smith and Wesson revolvers saw extensive service on the western frontier, and during the Plains Wars of the 1880's. They were so different in operation that great rivalry developed between those favoring one design over the other.

American revolvers were sold all around the world. The Smith and Wesson design became a particular favorite of the Russians and over 60,000 were manufactured under Russian contracts during the 1870's. The Russian Crown Prince used a Smith and Wesson revolver similar to that shown in Figure 8-11 during a buffalo hunt in the late 1870's in which Buffalo Bill served as guide. Both the Colt's and Smith and Wesson revolvers provided a great deal of power to the limits of pistol range. They were working tools of men in dangerous country who depended upon their reliability and performance out on the frontier far from the conveniences and protection offered by civilization.

REPEATING RIFLES

In the early 19th century inventors on both sides of the Atlantic began serious work to develop a true repeating firearm — one with a single barrel which could be loaded repetitively. There were serveral new factors to encourage this spurt of activity. One was the greatly improved manufacturing techniques in the early 19th century, and the second was the availability of the new percussion ignition system.

One of the highly creative American inventors in the field was Walter Hunt of New York City. The design of his rocket ball ammunition was described in Chapter 4. He held patent No. 5701 which was issued in 1848 and reissued as No. 164 in 1850. Hunt shows a spherical lead ball with a long cylindrical skirt extending to the rear and forming a hollow cavity in the base. This cavity was packed with compressed black powder and the cylindrical opening covered by a metallic cup such as a modern copper gas check, or by a washer. As quoted from patent No. 5701:

> . . . which in form resembles the Chinese gong, with a central perforation F, in its discus head, which is the point of ignition from the priming. Over this perforation upon the inside face of said cap (washer) is placed a thin waterproof tissue or seal. . . . This seal may be made of any thin material through which the fire from the priming may penetrate, and which will at the same time secure the powder in the cartridge from escape or accidental injury. This ball and thimble should be formed in molds by pressure. The powder being well packed in the cavity . . . [the assembly] . . . should then be subjected to a second pressure, in order to fix the cap firmly and produce a uniformity in the size of the cartridges.

This was a very significant attempt to develop a complete cartridge assembly, and similar designs were being developed in Europe at about the same time.

Hunt developed a rather comple rifle to handle this new ammunition and filed for a patent on September 17, 1847. Patent No. 6663 was issued on August 21, 1849. The rifle is shown in Figure 8-13. This is one of the earliest patents in which the magazine is located beneath the barrel of the rifle. The magazine held 12 rocket ball cartridges. Operating the rifle required swinging both levers shown in the illustration. This moved a single cartridge from the magazine into the breech, cocked the action and locked the breech bolt in back of the cartridge. The Hunt cartridges did not contain any priming material. A separate ignition system using percussion priming material was required to provide the flame which ignited the rocket ball cartridges. The action of the Hunt rifle included many delicate components and it was not a practical system. The rifle shown in Figure 8-13 may be the only model ever built.[1]

THE JENNINGS RIFLES

Walter Hunt was an inventor with great talent and wide ranging interests, but he did not take an idea

[1] T. E. Hall, "Forerunner of The First Winchester" *The Gun Digest*, 1958.

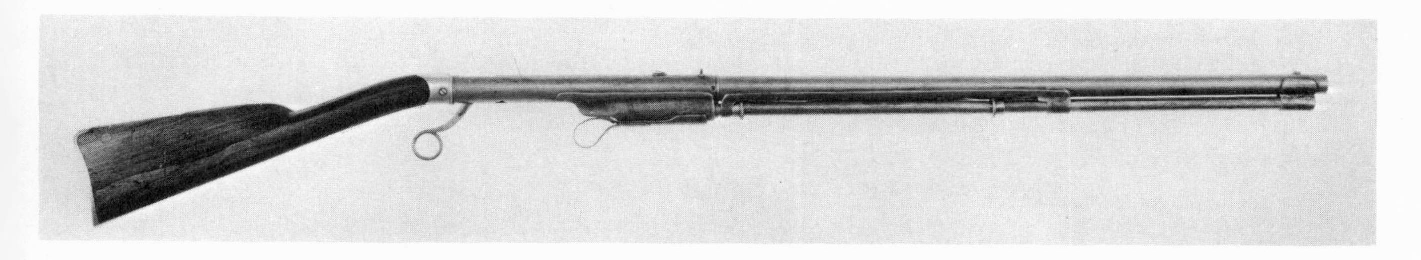

FIGURE 8-13 Walter Hunt's repeating rifle.

and nurture it to a final successful conclusion. He worked with Lewis Jennings on repeating rifle ideas, and it remained for Jennings to carry the idea the next step toward a successful solution. Jennings picked up the ideas developed by Walter Hunt and developed an improved mechanism to handle Hunt's rocket ball ammunition. He filed for a patent in August 1848 and the patent, No. 6973, was issued on Christmas Day 1849. Jennings and Hunt were both employed by a New York machine shop owner, George Arrowsmith, and the patents for rifles and ammunition were assigned to Arrowsmith.

The design of Jennings' first rifle is shown in Figure 8-14. Jennings developed an improved breech mechanism to handle the ammunition, and he also developed a very complex magazine feeding system which had little value. The feeding system included a fixed ratchet running the length of the tubular magazine and an assembly of spring-driven magazine followers with latches which "crept" along the ratchet, allowing the cartridges to move only to the rear. The magazine follower components and the ratchet may be seen in the third illustration from the top in Figure 8-14.

Lewis Jennings' major contribution was in his breech mechanism which moved another step toward a successful repeater. Jennings had the cartridges feed out of the magazine into a carrier which slid vertically on tracks. He arranged a sliding stop which prevented a cartridge from feeding out of the magazine when the carrier was in the up position. The action was

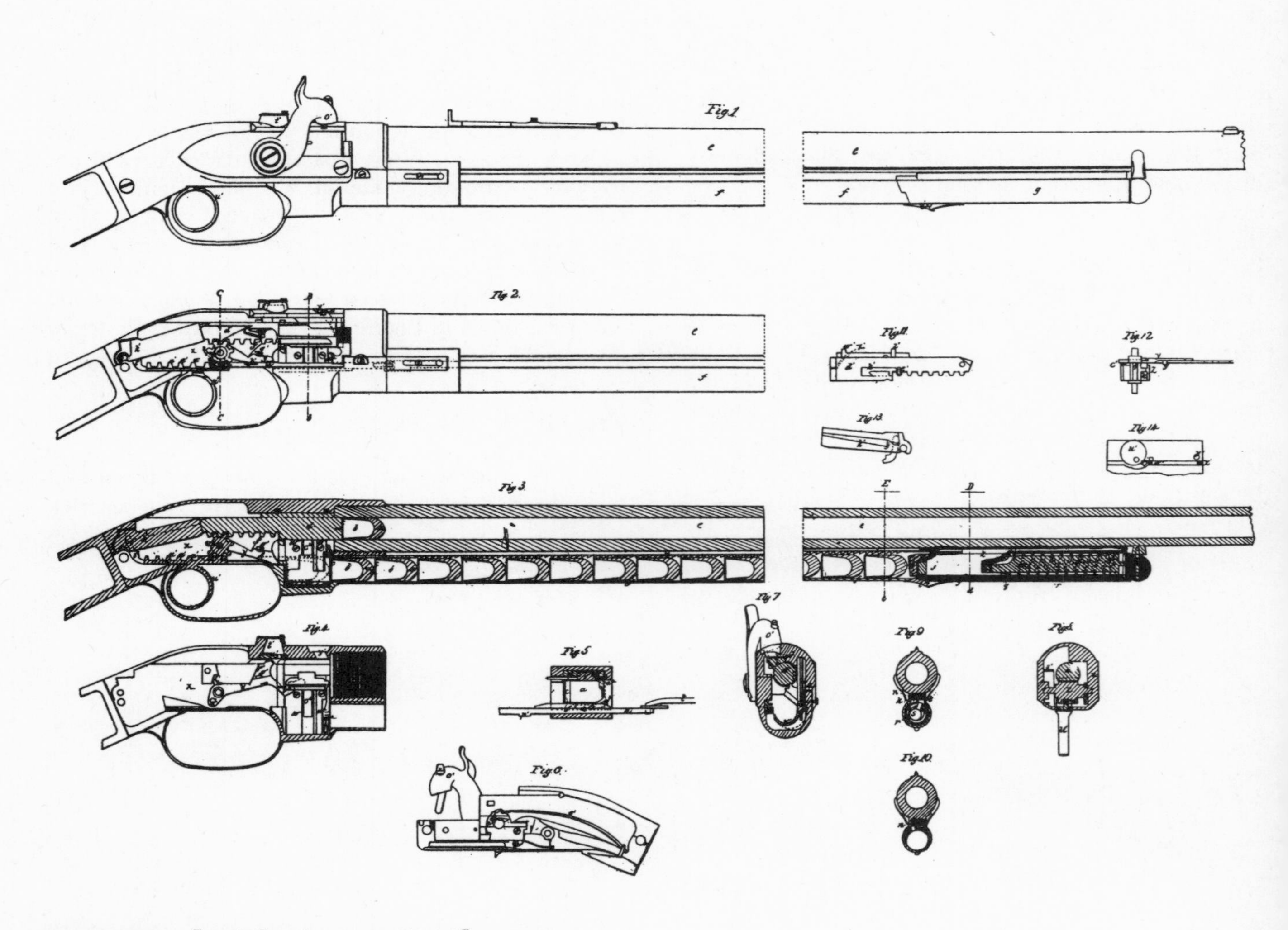

FIGURE 8-14 Lewis Jennings repeating rifle patent.

operated by the ring located within the trigger guard. As the ring was pulled forward a breech lock was removed from in back of the breech bolt and a rack and pinion arrangement drove the breechblock to the rear. With the breechblock in a fully rearward position the carrier rose, bringing a fresh cartridge in line with the chamber.

When the motion of the ring was reversed the breech bolt moved forward, driving the cartridge into the chamber and sealing off the back of the chamber with a close fitting cylindrical sealing surface. When the breech bolt was fully forward the design allowed a little extra motion of the ring and this motion caused an extension arm to lift the breech lock from a horizontal plane to an upward tilted position as shown in the third illustration from the left in Figure 8-14.

The Hunt ammunition used in the Jennings rifle had no priming so that a separate ignition system was required. The Jennings design was ingenious, but complex. There was a reservoir T′ on the top of the receiver. This was a dome-shaped affair which is shown in the two left-hand illustrations and it is also shown on the extreme right-hand cross section of the action. The dome may also be seen on the top of the receiver in the second style Jenning rifle in Figure 8-15. The reservoir was filled with small priming pellets which were made of compressed primary explosive such as fulminate of mercury. The bottom of the reservoir was closed off with a circular plate which had a cavity which could hold one pellet. As the action was operated this disc rotated and received a pill of percussion powder from the magazine.

As the breech bolt reached a fully rearward position it cammed an arm on the rotary plate, bringing the hole containing the priming pellet in line with a second cavity on top of the breech bolt. The pellet then dropped from the plate into the breech bolt. When the breech bolt moved forward into a fully locked position, the priming pellet arrived under a hole in the top of the receiver which may be seen in the extreme right-hand cross section illustration in Figure 8-14.

As the rifle was fired and the hammer fell, the long nose extension on the hammer passed through the top of the receiver and penetrated the cavity in the breechblock, crushing the powder pellet and causing ignition. The flame passed forward through a diagonal hole in the breechblock emerging at the center in position to penetrate the thin membrane at the rear of the rocket ball cartridge, thus igniting the main powder charge.

The rocket ball cartridges had several serious deficiencies. There were no lubrication grooves and the thin lead skirt was likely to tear off due to frictional drag in the bore. Thomas Hall in his series of articles on *Forerunners Of The First Winchester*[2] quotes a newspaper interview with R. S. Lawrence of Sharps rifle fame describing his experiences with the manufacture of the Jennings rifles. Courtland Palmer of New York contracted with the Robbins and Lawrence Company of Windsor, Vermont, to manufacture 5000 of the Jennings rifles:

> A portion of the lot was then called single loaders, and a portion repeating rifles, carrying 20 charges. The charge of powder was contained in the ball, consisting of 22 grains of powder only. With the repeating rifle I have often fired 20 shots within one minute, but not with any accuracy, for the reason that all breech-loading guns up to this time used what is called the naked ball without any patch or lubricating material. The result in firing the gun was that the ball leaded the barrel by building on, to such an extent that in firing 20 shots from a 50/100 caliber bore there would be a hole in the barrel less than 25/100.
>
> In the winter of 1850, while the guns were being manufactured at Windsor, [Lajas] Kossuth [Hungarian revolutionary leader] arrived in this country, as was supposed by many for the purpose of purchasing rifles. Mr. Palmer was anxious to sell his rifles and telegraphed on to Windsor that Kossuth would purchase largely, if he could be shown that the Jennings rifle could be fired with sufficient accuracy to hit the size of a man 10 times out of 25 at a distance 500 yards. I answered by saying that it was impossible to do any such thing with the Jennings rifle. Another message was sent to Windsor to come to New York by the first train and bring the best gun and ammunition. I complied with the request. Mr. C. P. Dickson, Mr. Palmer's agent, had all things arranged for the trial at Astoria, Long Island. I did my best in trying to accomplish the desired effect asked for, but not one of the 25 shots hit the target. Mr. Dickson said that we must make another trial the next day. I went to his hotel, more than ever disgusted with breech-loading rifles, as all efforts had failed to make any accurate shooting with any naked ball. All gun men will understand this. My business is manufacturing rifles for the Government and for the Sharps Rifle Manufacturing Company. Most of the night at the hotel was spent in trying to devise some remedy for the trouble then existing with breech loading guns. At last a simple remedy came, which has proven the salvation of all breech loading guns.
>
> Early the next morning we started for the target field. I did not tell Mr. Dickson at first of my discovery. I simply told him that the trouble was all over with. If he would stop at the Fulton Market and purchase a small piece of tallow the rifle would do all that was required of it, but he had so little confidence in the gun that he would not be prevailed upon to purchase the tallow. I then thought that I would keep the new discovery to myself for

[2]*Ibid*, 1958.

awhile, but changed my mind on arriving on the target field and tramped a mile on the ice to a farm house, and purchased a small piece of tallow. With the aid of a lathe in the cartridge shop on the ground, I turned out a number of grooves on the balls and filled them with tallow. I then went on to the stand and hit the target 10 times in 20 shots. By this time I had the sights regulated and could hit the target about every shot and finished after many shots with a clean gun barrel. This was the first instance of lubricating material being used in breech loading guns or any other gun. I challenge any dispute on the subject. This was the salvation of breech loading guns.

It is very doubtful that Mr. Lawrence was the first to apply lubricant to lead bullets, but he did make a major improvement in the functioning of the Jennings rifle and rocket ball ammunition. Christian Sharps was a rather stuffy individual and called Lawrence's improvement a "humbug." He grudgingly tested it, however, and a week later, ordered that all Sharps rifles and ammunition be modified to handle the lubricant improvement.

The Jennings rifles, such as that shown in Figure 8-15, were carried through other minor modifications but all were too complex for practical manufacture. In order to secure some income, Mr. Palmer had Robbins and Lawrence alter some of the guns to be single-shot breech-loading firearms. With this modification the shooter opened the action utilizing the ring trigger mechanism and dropped a single rocket ball cartridge into the carrier, at the right side of the action. As the ring trigger was returned to its rearward position the carrier rose and the breechblock carried the rocket ball cartridge forward into the chamber and was locked into a forward position.

Other Jennings rifles were converted into high quality muzzle-loading rifles. The magazine tube was modified to house a ramrod. The priming magazine on the top of the receiver was smaller in size and designed so that a single pill of the priming material could be dropped through the hole in the top and serve the function of a percussion cap. On some of these muzzle-loading Jennings rifles a long trigger guard such as that shown in the patent in Figure 8-14 was bent upward in the center to prevent the ring trigger from being slid forward.

Neither the Jennings nor Hunt rifles were successful, either in a financial or technical sense, but they were extremely important links in the development of satisfactory breech-loading rifles. It required inventors of great creative ability and drive to push the technology forward in the face of extremely difficult obstacles, and it required financiers such as George Arrowsmith who were willing to risk large sums of money to make the equipment available for experiments and finance the conversion of inventors' dreams into realistic and practical products. George Arrowsmith lost heavily on these experiments and in 1850 sold his interest in the Hunt and Jennings patents to Courtlandt C. Palmer, a New York financier. Palmer's attempt to manufacture profitable products by contracting with Robbins and Lawrence for the 5000 Jennings rifles involved further financial loss, for the design was not yet perfected. The Jennings rifle did not function satisfactorily enough to achieve a satisfactory sales volume.

THE VOLCANIC RIFLE

The next step in the development of a successful repeater was the work of a very gifted pair of New Englanders. Courtlandt Palmer hired Horace Smith, a very experienced Connecticut gunsmith, to work on developing improvements in the Jennings rifle. Smith had established a small manufacturing plant in Norwich,

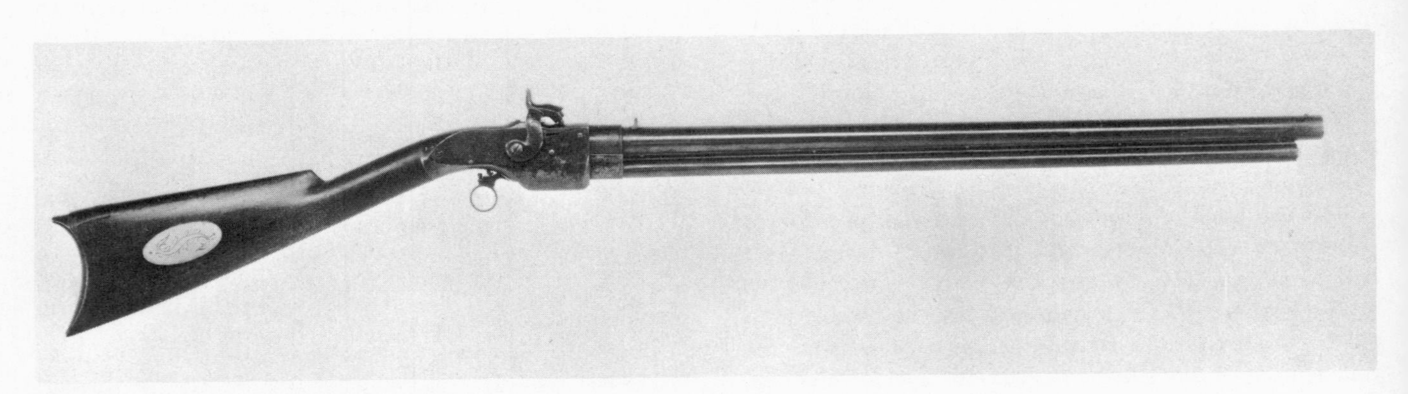

FIGURE 8-15 Outside view of Jennings rifle.

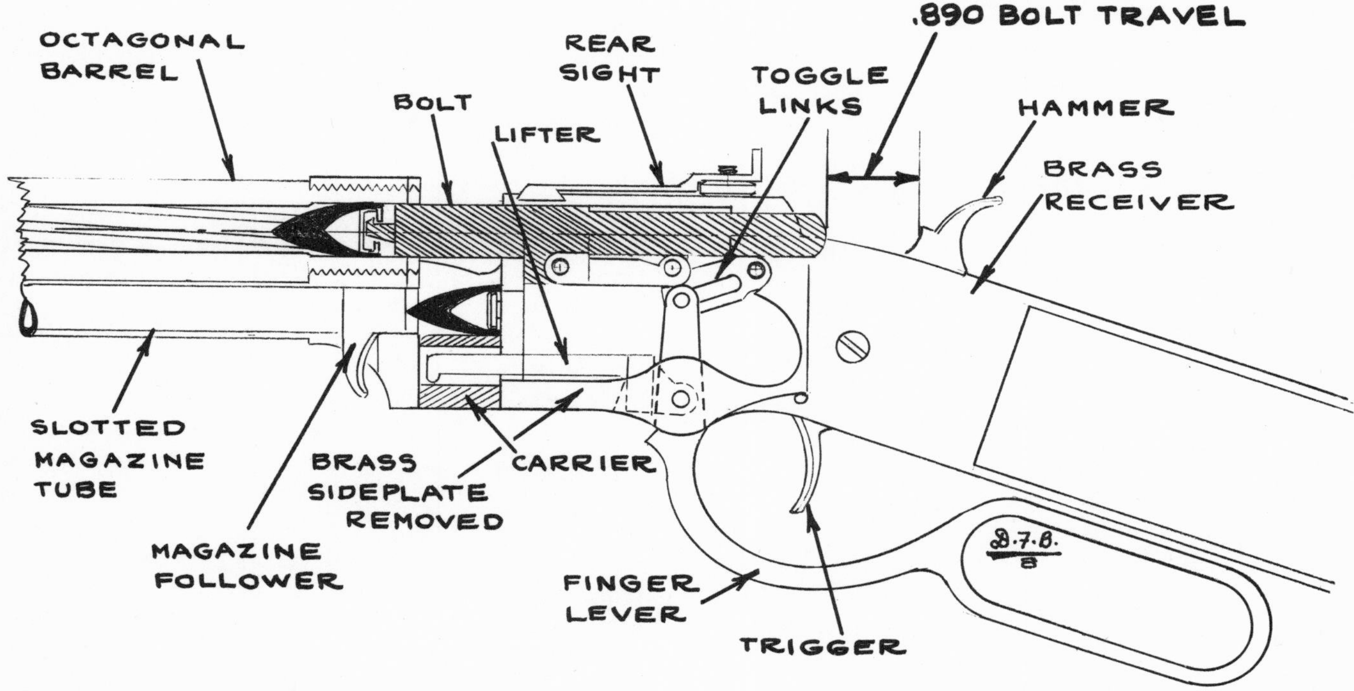

FIGURE 8-16 Volcanic rifle cross-section drawing.

Connecticut, around 1846. A young man named Daniel Baird Wesson, working for the Robbins and Lawrence Company, also became interested in the Jennings rifle designs in 1850. Although Wesson was some 14 years younger than Horace Smith, they got along very well and established the famous partnership of Smith and Wesson. Funds for experiments were supplied by Courtlandt Palmer, and the team set to work to create the design of a successful repeating mechanism. Smith and Wesson were aware of developments in the United States and in Europe.

One of the designs patented by Walter Hunt enclosed the base of his rocket ball cartridge in a shallow copper cup. The Hunt design required a hole through the center of the cup to permit flame from the separate percussion system. Horace Smith was aware of the French developments of an extremely low-powered pistol cartridge which used a hollow copper cup which contained a charge of fulminate priming compound and a lead ball pressed into the mouth of the cup. This cartridge was so low in power level that it was only suitable for use as an indoor target game, but it was self-contained ammunition. Italian designers had been experimenting with lever action repeating pistol mechanisms and Smith and Wesson may also have drawn ideas from these experiments.

The first in a series of very significant Smith and Wesson patents was issued on February 14, 1854. The design of a Volcanic lever action pistol was specified in patent No. 10,535. While the patent shows a pistol, both pistol and rifle models were manufactured in small quantities. It was an exceptionally important patent for it provided the design foundation for the Model 1860 Henry rifle and the Winchester models of 1866, 1873 and 1876.

By 1856 Smith and Wesson had added further improvements to the ammunition and had secured patent No. 14,147 on January 22, 1856, defining a completely self-contained Volcanic cartridge. The design of this ammunition is illustrated and described in Chapter 3 and is also shown in Figure 8-19. It basically consisted of a hollow lead bullet with four lubricant grooves rolled on the outside and a deep hollow cavity filled with a compressed charge of black powder. A priming assembly was contained in two nested copper cups which held a charge of fulminate of mercury priming compound and a sealer disc of cork to provide weather protection. In the Volcanic firearms the ammunition supply was contained in a long tube beneath the barrel of the rifle or pistol. The magazine assembly was much simplified from the Jennings design. It was used on all of the Volcanic firearms, and the Model 1860 Henry rifle.

Figure 8-16 shows a Volcanic rifle with one cartridge in the chamber, and with the last cartridge in the magazine being pushed by the follower on the carrier. The action is shown in a position ready to fire. When the trigger was pulled the hammer was driven forward by a powerful spring and it slammed into the breechblock. There was clearance designed into the linkage which held the breechblock forward so that the breechblock could jump forward slightly when struck by the hammer. The projection at the front of the bolt then crushed the pellet of priming against the innermost copper cup causing ignition. The flame propagated through holes in the forward copper cup and ignited the main charge in the cavity of the bullet. Flame also passed through the opening in the rear copper cup and tended to leak out at the rear. This leakage was blocked by a cylindrical seal between the breech bolt and the rear of the chamber. From the design of the Volcanic ammunition it appears probable that the two copper cups separated from the bullet during ignition since the main propellant charge was forward of the cup. The powder charge was so small that the bullet velocity was rather low and performance was really not very satisfactory.

After the shot was fired the lever was operated to reload. The extension on the finger lever moved the center pivot of the link downward thus drawing the breach bolt to the rear. As the finger lever was rotated to a fully open position, a camming surface (shown just above the R in carrier of Figure 8-16) struck the carrier lifter which was pivoted on the same shaft as the finger lever. A small additional motion of the finger lever caused the lifter to snap the carrier into the fully up position.

The carrier was a U-shaped brass trough and it held the Volcanic projectile in line with the chamber when it was in an up position. As the motion of the finger lever was reversed the breech bolt moved forward, passing through the opening of the carrier and pushing the projectile into the chamber. When the breech bolt reached a fully forward position the finger lever struck a second camming surface on the lifter which returned the carrier to the down position. The magazine follower then pushed another cartridge into the carrier ready for the following shot.

The entire motion of the breech bolt was slightly under .9 of an inch on the .40 caliber Volcanic rifles. This short motion was sufficient to cock the hammer, raise the carrier, chamber the round on the return stroke, and lock the action shut.

Details of some of the important elements in the Volcanic system are shown in Figure 8-17. The construction of the magazine system is shown in some detail in the upper illustration. Volcanic rifles were fitted with octagonal barrels with a section at the forward end of the barrels cut down to a small diameter, round shape. A movable figure 8-shaped magazine section was machined up and slid on to this forward section of the barrel. The upper section of the magazine assembly was machined octagonal to match the barrel contour. The movable section of the magazine was held on to the barrel with an octagonal muzzle attachment. This attachment held the front sight, and had cam cuts which controlled the angular motion of the magazine section. It was held in its longitudinal position by a screw. When the movable section of the magazine was swung over as shown in the upper illustration of the figure, the slotted magazine tube could be filled with fresh cartridges.

The lower illustration in Figure 8-17 shows the details of the breech bolt. On the .40 caliber Volcanic rifles the front section of the breech bolt was .420 of an inch in diameter. There was a solid block at the center of the breech bolt and a long cylindrical extension .335 of an inch in diameter extending to the rear. The extension to the rear provided guidance for the breech bolt, recocked the hammer, and served to transfer the hammer energy from the rear of the action up to the ignition area. The block in the center of the breech bolt was drilled with a transverse hole only .100 of an inch in diameter. Two links were fitted, one on each side and held with a .100-inch diameter cross pin. A major problem in the Volcanic design was the removal of an unfired or misfired cartridge. William C. Hicks, the superintendent in the mid-1850's, proposed to solve this by the design of a combined firing pin and extractor which is shown on the nose of the breech bolt. This was installed as an insert in the bolt face and had a basic diameter of .220 of an inch and a chisel-shaped firing pin plus a hook on the top. As the breech bolt chambered a fresh round of ammunition this insert passed through the hole in the rear copper cup pushing on the cork insert which rested on the fulminate priming compound. The hammer blow was supposed to be sufficiently sharp so that the cork disc would be split and the firing pin would crush the fulminate compound against the forward primer disc. In the event that the shooter changed his mind or that there was a misfire, the hook on the top of the insert was designed to grasp the upper edge of the rear copper cup and withdraw the entire Volcanic cartridge from the chamber. It is doubtful if this worked very reliably.

A major weakness in the Volcanic design was the lack of adequate breech seal. All the components were so miniaturized that the sealing surface was less than 1/10-inch long on typical Volcanic rifles measured in

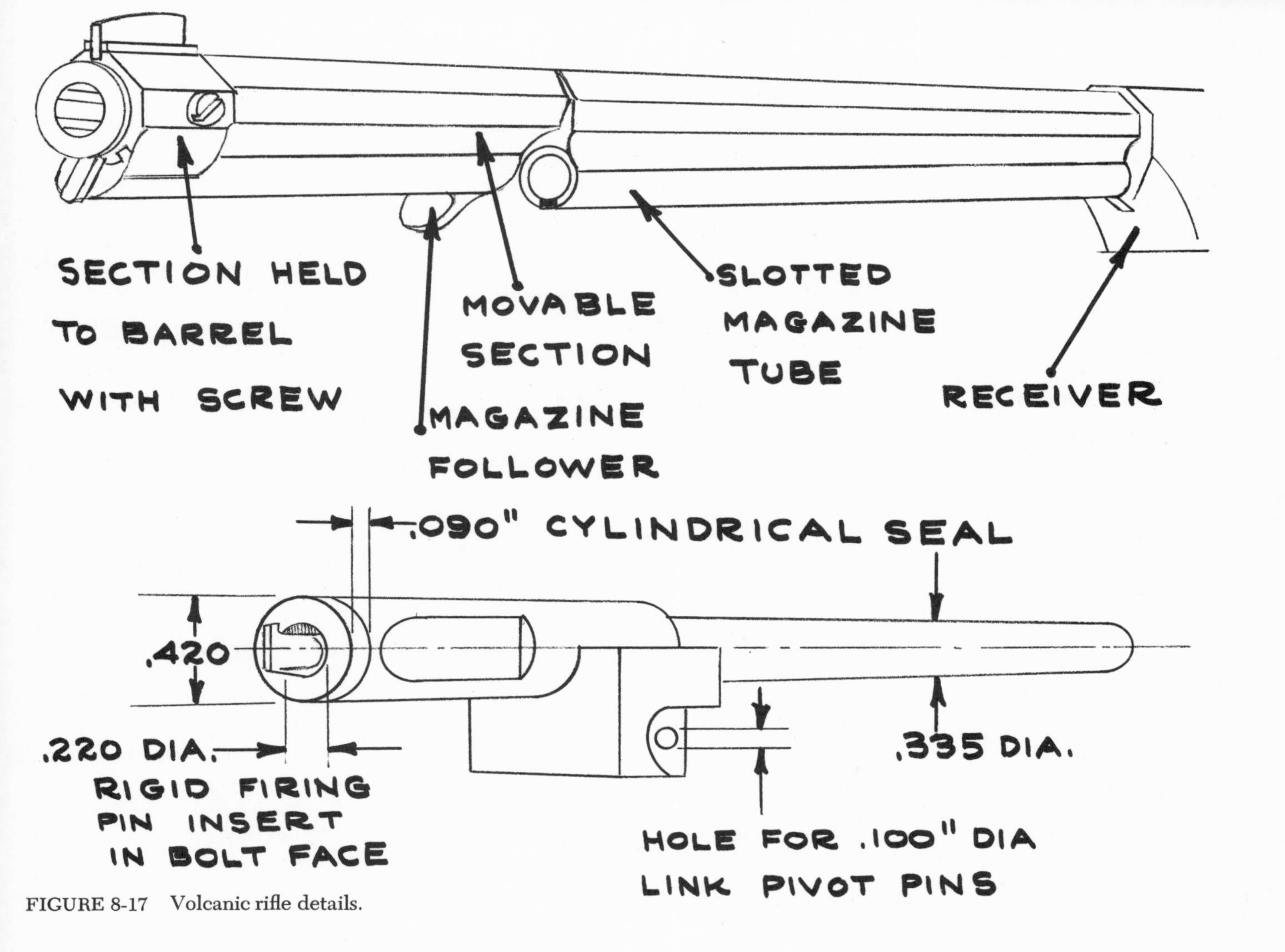

FIGURE 8-17 Volcanic rifle details.

the Winchester Museum. As the Volcanic cartridge was fired, the gas pressure generated by the powder drove the entire breech bolt to the rear about .050 of an inch. This allowed the breech bolt to get a "running start" and then impact the locking surfaces in the toggle linkage. Examination of Volcanic rifles in the Winchester Gun Museum shows heavy impact between the bolt and hammer due to this blow-back motion.

MANUFACTURE OF VOLCANIC PISTOLS AND RIFLES
Thomas Hall, Curator of the Winchester Gun Museum, has researched the history of the Volcanic firearms and provided the following data:

On June 20, 1854, Courtlandt Palmer, and Smith and Wesson formed a limited partnership to manufacture Volcanic firearms at Horace Smith's plant in Norwich, Connecticut. After about a year of operation, in June 1855, the company was reorganized and 6000 shares of capital stock was offered at $25.00 a share. Oliver F. Winchester, a successful manufacturer of shirts in New Haven, purchased 80 shares of stock and became involved in firearms manufacture for the first time. Some of the early struggles were described by Mr. Winchester during a court case in 1871:

> After the organization of the Volcanic Repeating Arms Company they purchased from Smith and Wesson, in the month of August 1855, all their machinery, tools and fixtures and arms, finished and unfinished, and removed them from Norwich to New Haven the same month. Among these assets purchased were about 300 pistols of both sizes, finished and unfinished and the parts of some 280 to 300 more pistols, not assembled. The company was occupied in part for nearly quite a year in overhauling and repairing and assembling these 600 pistols, more or less, and manufacturing a new model and the tools and fixtures for that model. The company continued for the remaining 6 months of its existence in finishing and selling pistols of this new model until the third of February 1856, when they passed a vote to go into insolvency and made an assignment accordingly.

At another time Winchester stated:

> The first superintendent of the company (Volcanic Repeating Arms Company) was Daniel B. Wesson, appointed soon after the organization of the com-

pany. He continued on that capacity until on or about the 11th of February 1856. On his retiring, William C. Hicks was appointed as, I think, assistant superintendent.

Hicks put great effort into solving the problems of improving the reliability of ignition, and developing a satisfactory means for extraction. Sales remained unsatisfactory and the company went bankrupt in late 1856.

It was reorganized again as the New Haven Arms Company with Oliver Winchester as President. During the late 1850's Winchester invested much of his personal fortune in funding experiments to develop a satisfactory breech-loading rifle which would fire metallic ammunition and in manufacturing and selling Volcanic rifles and pistols.

Examples of Volcanic pistols and rifles researched by Tom Hall indicate that the pistols were offered in .30, .38 and .40 caliber with barrel lengths of 4, 6 and 8 inches. An intermediate model was made in the shape of a pistol with a 16½-inch barrel and an optional shoulder stock. The rifle models were offered in .32, .38 and .40 caliber with barrel lengths generally ranging from 16 to 24 inches. A .38 caliber model with a 16-inch barrel is shown in Figure 8-18. This model Volcanic was manufactured between 1858 and 1860 and is the design used in Figure 8-16. The receiver was made of cast brass with large side plates which slid into dovetailed tracks machined into the receiver casting. An elaborate rear sight was fitted with a screw adjustment for elevation. The rifles had a butt stock, but no forearm since the magazine tube was slotted on the underside for its entire length. A small hook extending from the magazine follower may be seen at the forward end of the receiver.

Volcanic Ammunition

A cartridge box containing Volcanic ammunition is shown immediately below the carbine in Figure 8-18. The printed description sheds considerable insight on the technical problems that existed with the Volcanic ammunition all through the 1850's. It states:

> 200 No. 2
>
> PISTOL CARTRIDGES
> Manufactured by
> THE VOLCANIC REPEATING ARMS CO.
> NEW HAVEN, Connecticut
>
> The balls should be kept in a box, and well greased. If, by accident, a ball should misfire, it must be carefully pushed back with the rod, leaving the carrier down. The too frequent snapping of the hammer when the arm is not charged, may injure it.
> Patented August 8, 1854

Typical .40 caliber Volcanic ammunition of the late 1850's is shown in Figure 8-19. It was a very ingenious design and merits careful attention. The bullet is .675 of an inch long and has a maximum diameter of .425 of an inch. Four grooves have been rolled into the outside and the diameter to the bottom of the grooves is .385 of an inch. The diameter immediately forward of the foremost groove is only .410 of an inch.

The over-all design of the bullet with its rounded nose profile and deep cavity are quite similar to a modern rifled slug. The center cavity was filled with a compressed charge of black powder. An assembly consisting of two copper cups was fabricated. It is a little difficult to see in the illustration, but the forward cup is nested inside the rearmost cup. The forward cup is of fairly heavy material and has several flash holes punched through the flat surface. The fulminate of mercury priming compound was placed into this heavy cup and a large disc of cork was placed over the priming compound. The rear copper cup was made of thinner material and had a .160-inch diameter hole punched through the center. The rear cup encircled the heavier forward cup and the copper material was formed over at the front to retain it as a permanent assembly. The entire primer assembly was then pressed into the base of the lead bullet and the lead skirt was rolled over to retain the primer assembly in the cartridge. The grooves in the bullet were filled with lubricant and the cartridges packed for shipment in the paste board boxes. Careful examination of .40 caliber Volcanic bullets show no casting marks which would confirm the use of the "compression forming" process for swaging lead bullets which had been developed in the 1840's. There is a circumferential groove near the nose of the Volcanic bullet which suggests that the nose section was formed by a separate punch which may have served to eject the bullet from the die after the outer shape and circumferential grooves were formed.

Thomas Hall made available a .40 caliber Volcanic projectile which was typical of production in the late 1850's. The cartridge weighed 110.6 grains on an electronic powder scale. It was then carefully sawn in half with a jeweler's saw behind a steel barricade. The sectioned cartridge is shown with an untouched .40 caliber Volcanic cartridge in Figure 8-19. When the two halves of the sectioned bullets were put back on the electronic scale, they weighed 107.56 grains. The cartridge was then disassembled. The primer assembly, after correction for the weight loss due to sectioning, weighed 8.15 grains. The hollow lead bullet with no powder or primer assembly weighed 95.6

grains. Since some of the powder was lost during sectioning and disassembly, the powder weight had to be calculated by the difference between the weight of the bare lead bullet and primer assembly and the weight of the entire cartridge. The calculated powder charge works out to 6.8 grains.

As a cross-check the powder charge was calculated by a different method. The internal cavity of the bullet was carefully measured by a micrometer. These measurements were correlated with a highly magnified photograph of a cross section of the bullet. The interior cavity on the photograph was broken down into five truncated conical segments. The measurements were cross-checked with the actual specimen and a total internal volume of .0222 of a cubic inch was determined.

Early black powder center-fire cartridge cases were designed for full charges of black powder (100 percent loading density). The internal volume for a .32/20 center-fire cartridge was calculated and works out to a density of 300 grains of black powder per cubic inch of cartridge case volume. This same density would give a charge weight in the Volcanic cartridge of 6⅔ grains of powder. Examination of the sectional Volcanic cartridge shows that it was a highly compressed load. (The area in the forward portion of the cavity has been filled with loose powder to replace that which was lost during sectioning.)

Consideration of all these factors leads to a probable powder charge of 6.8 grains, with a maximum charge limit of 7.0 grains. Literature of the 1850's indicates that the average Volcanic leaked fire at the breech and did not have very satisfactory ballistic performance. No instrumented velocity tests have been located, so it has been necessary to reconstruct probable ballistics by analytical techniques. Percussion black powder revolvers had very similar ballistic systems. The two standard calibers were the .36 caliber Navy size with a .375 lead bullet, and the .44 Army models with .451 lead bullets. These calibers span the size of the .40 caliber Volcanic. The percussion revolvers had minor gas leakage through the ignition cone at the rear of the chamber, and major gas leakage between the cylinder and the barrel. Available data on percussion revolvers in first class condition are described in detail earlier in this chapter. The bullet weights ranged from 79 to 155 grains and the efficiency of five different percussion revolver systems averaged 9 foot-pounds of muzzle energy per grain of propellant.

The muzzle velocity of the Volcanic can be calculated at this same efficiency as 540 feet per second muzzle velocity for the 96-grain hollow lead bullet. The weight of the primer assembly is disregarded in these calculations for the powder charge was all ahead of the primer and, it would come out of the muzzle at an extremely low velocity. It is possible that on some shots primer assemblies were found in the barrel after the action was opened.

A muzzle velocity of 540 feet per second for the Volcanic cartridges would provide a muzzle energy of only 62 foot-pounds — far less than the 158 foot-pounds of a modern .22 long rifle high speed cartridge. This low muzzle velocity would result in a very arched trajectory and poor penetration. These factors plus the undesirable gas leakage at the breech led to a poor reputation in the field.

The unfinished Volcanic firearms purchased from Smith and Wesson were assembled and every attempt was made to sell them. The unsold stocks built up rapidly and the financial situation headed again for bankruptcy. There were three courses of action to be weighed carefully before a decision could be made. One was to accept failure and terminate the business venture, selling off the machinery and gun components to manufacturers of more conventional muzzle-loading firearms. The second was to develop a more powerful Volcanic

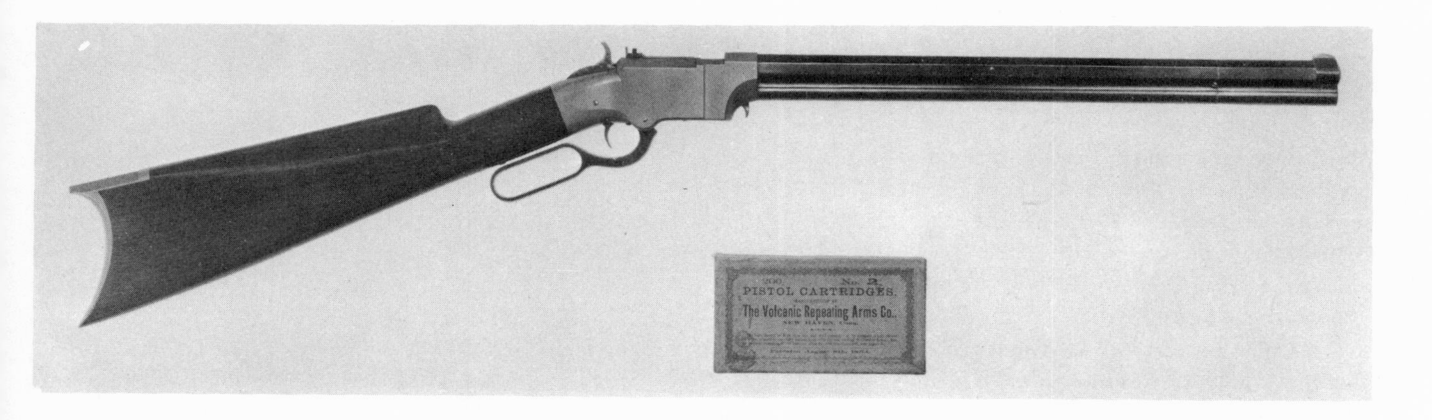

FIGURE 8-18 .38 caliber Volcanic rifle.

type cartridge which would give commercially acceptable ballistic performance. The third course was to continue limited production and redouble efforts on the Volcanic firearms and push Research and Development toward the conversion of the system to handle some form of metallic ammunition.

The second course of action was not practical. The ammunition shown in Figure 8-19 had reached the limit of technology for the 1850's. The hollow lead bullet was very heavy in relation to the powder charge. The only way this ratio could be improved and higher velocities achieved was to thin the bullet walls and increase the size of the powder cavity. These changes would result in higher internal pressure which would drive the thin lead skirt harder against the barrel surface, increasing friction. This in turn would increase the stress in the thin lead bullet wall, causing separation of the forward nose of the bullet from the skirt. These problems had already been encountered before the lubrication grooves were added with very serious lead build-up in the barrel and poor accuracy.

The final decision was to adopt the third course of action. The agreement with Smith & Wesson had included a clause which allowed the Volcanic company to utilize any further ammunition techniques developed by Smith & Wesson. This clause was activated and parallel work went forward at the restructured Volcanic Arms Company and by Smith & Wesson from 1858 through 1860.

SPENCER REPEATING RIFLES

The Spencer lever action was the outstanding repeating rifle used in the Civil War. The only other breechloader to come near it in popularity was the single-shot Sharps rifle which used combustible cartridges. Seldom has a firearm been so far ahead of competition in features and performance — and yet the Spencer Firearms Company was in business for less than a decade — from 1860 to 1869. Facts about the Spencer Company are hard to pin down, for there is widespread confusion over the cartridge designations and the factory records were destroyed after the company ceased business.

Christopher M. Spencer was born in Manchester, Connecticut, on June 20, 1833. He learned a great deal about firearms manufacture at the Colt's Armory in Hartford during the 1850's. At this time Colt's was experimenting with advanced production techniques.

The Colt's Armory utilized the most modern and complex machinery to manufacture high quality percussion pistols to the close tolerances and smooth finishes required for long lasting, reliable performance. In many ways Samuel Colt in the 1850's was innovating and experimenting with manufacturing techniques much as Henry Ford developed advanced production techniques for automobile manufacture in the early 20th century.

Christopher Spencer learned a great deal at Colt's and realized that his interest in experimenting with improved rifle mechanism designs was likely to end up in "conflict of interest" problems with the Colt management. He therefore left Colt and went to work at the Cheney Silk Mills in Manchester, Connecticut. His great natural ability and mechanical skill came to the attention of the owner of the silk mills, Charles Cheney, who made the machine shop of the silk mills available for Spencer's spare time experiments.

By the late 1850's Christopher Spencer had created the design of a radically advanced breech-loading firearm. At the same time that Christian Sharps was completing the design of his Model 1859 single-shot breech-loading carbine firing caseless ammunition with percussion cap ignition, Christopher Spencer was creating wooden mockups of a 7-shot lever action repeating rifle designed to fire .36 caliber rimfire ammunition. Spencer was awarded patent No. 27,393 on March 6, 1860, for the design of his lever action mechanism. The patent drawing shows an experimental design probably dating from early 1859. In 1860 and 1861 Spencer manufactured very limited quantities of the .36 caliber rifles.

At the outbreak of the Civil War he went to Washington to try and secure a Government contract for manufacture. Ordnance officers at that time were pulling their hair out trying to organize the procurement and manufacture of sufficient quantities of muzzle-loading rifles and rifle-muskets which was a staggering job in itself. They were not in much of a mood to encourage the swarms of inventors, most of whom had half-developed models of weapons requiring specialized ammunition. Spencer had no luck until Charles Cheney,

FIGURE 8-19 Ammunition for Volcanic rifles.

owner of the silk mill presented information on Spencer's gun to Gideon Wells, who was Secretary of the Navy. Through this connection, the Spencer rifle was tested at Washington Navy Yard in June 1861. This trial was successful and Spencer received the first of many Government orders. Government tests in 1861 identified the extraction system as a major weakness of the Spencer design. Spencer experimented with improved designs and received patent No. 36,062 for a leaf extractor to replace the earlier sawtooth design on July 29, 1862.

Spencer had been working all through 1861 to secure additional orders. The task was very difficult for the Chief of Ordnance, General Ripley, was strongly opposed to all breech-loading firearms and was particularly opposed to repeaters. When finally pressed by President Lincoln to put down his reasons in writing, Ripley stated that he objected to the breech-loading repeaters as being too heavy with fully loaded magazines, and also found them objectionable since they would not fire standard paper cartridges or loose powder and ball. His real objections seemed to lie in the field of economics and supply. The breech-loading rifles cost at least twice as much as the standard single-shot muzzle-loaders, and the ammunition was several times as expensive. For example, the average price paid for .56 Spencer cartridges during the Civil War was 2.44 cents apiece,[2] and the average price for the .44 Henry cartridges was 2.33 cents. Not only was the ammunition expensive but the Ordnance Department was extremely worried that the high rate of fire of these rifles would result in wastage of large quantities of ammunition and make a difficult supply situation almost impossible.

Finally in late 1861 Cheney was able to intercede with Gideon Wells, who placed an order for some 10,000 Spencer rifles and carbines. Even this order was blocked by General Ripley who knew perfectly well that most of the rifles would be used by the Army, not the Navy. Finally Lincoln personally had to intercede and order Ripley to sign the contract. Despite approval of the contract, most of 1862 was spent in tooling up for the manufacture of the improved Spencer rifle, shown in Figure 8-20. These rifles were generally manufactured with 30-inch barrels and were chambered for the .56/.56 Spencer cartridge. The Government purchased 12,471 Spencer rifles during the war in Army and Navy models. An Army model is shown in the figure. The Navy model differed in having a slightly shorter forearm and a bayonet lug welded to the underside of the barrel to hold a long, heavy brass-handled saber bayonet. The Army model shown in Figure 8-20 was designed for the standard Army triangular bayonet.

The Model 1861 Spencer was also manufactured in carbine versions. When large deliveries started in 1863 these carbines were found so successful for cavalry use that Spencer production ran at full capacity for the remainder of the war. A total of 94,196 carbines were delivered at an average price of $25.40 each. The carbines had a barrel length of 22 inches and an over-all length of 39 inches. They weighed 8¼ pounds empty compared with 10 pounds for the rifle model. The carbines were also chambered for the .56/.56 ammunition. The Spencer carbines were the most popular and technically advanced breech-loader used during the Civil War.

Early in the Civil War the Southern Cavalry could out maneuver and out fight the Northern Cavalry in almost every engagement. By 1864 the situation had changed, leading Southern cavalrymen to say, "It ain't fair — them Yankees is learning to both ride and shoot."

The firepower of Northern Cavalry units armed with Spencers was truly impressive. By 1864 some Northern Cavalry were armed with the standard cavalry saber, two .44 caliber percussion revolvers with ammunition,

[2] B. R. Lewis, *Small Arms and Ammunition in the U.S. Service*, Smithsonian, 1968, P 280.

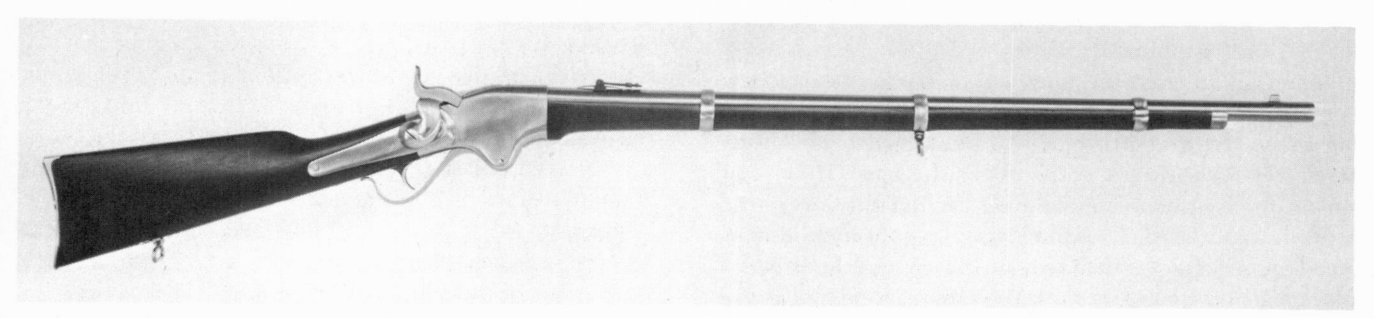

FIGURE 8-20 Spencer lever-action repeating rifle.

Price per 1,000, $40.00.
Case contains 1,000.

Powder, 45 grains.
Lead, 330 grains.

Adapted to Spencer Sporting Rifle.

Price per 1,000, $40.00.
Case contains 1,000.

Powder, 45 grains.
Lead, 350 grains.

Adapted to Spencer, Remington, Sharp, and other Rifles and Carbines.

Price per 1,000, $40.00.
Case contains 1,000.

Powder, 45 grains.
Lead, 386 grains.

Adapted to Spencer Military and other Rifles.

Price per 1,000, $40.00.
Case contains 1,000.

Powder, 45 grains.
Lead, 350 grains.

Adapted to Spencer, Ballard, and Joslyn Carbines.

FIGURE 8-21 Cartridges for Spencer lever-action rifles.

and a 7-shot Spencer carbine with spare magazines. Early Spencer models had to be reloaded with individual cartridges after the magazine was exhausted. An improvement known as Blakeslee's cartridge box was patented on December 20, 1864. This consisted of a leather covered hexagonal wooden block which was drilled with ten holes. Lightweight tinned sheet metal tubes were preloaded with seven Spencer cartridges. These were placed into the Blakeslee cartridge box for carrying in the field. This improvement allowed the trooper to reload his Spencer very rapidly, by sliding all seven cartridges into the magazine in one motion.

Seldom in the history of warfare have two competing forces been armed with such a wide discrepancy in equipment, for late in the Civil War many Southern cavalry were still armed with a single-shot muzzle-loading carbine plus a saber.

A simplified cross-section view of the Spencer action is shown in Figure 8-22. A tubular magazine, containing seven rimfire cartridges was contained in the butt-stock. The cartridges were urged forward by a coil spring in the magazine follower. When the lever was moved downward it pulled the breechblock downward against the vertical coil spring. When the breech-block had bottomed in the cut in the carrier block, the entire assembly could rotate clockwise. The ejector was urged downward as the breechblock went down so that it formed a ramp over which the ejected shell rode upward and flew clear of the action. When the breech-block was in a fully open position the magazine spring pushed the fresh cartridge up ahead of the breech-block. As the lever was returned toward a closed position the fresh cartridge rode upward under the ejector which guided it into the chamber of the carbine. As the carrier block reached the position shown in Figure 8-22, it stopped rotating and the final closing motion of the lever lifted the breechblock into the position shown in the illustration. In this position the rear face of the breechblock solidly abutted a matching cut in the receiver wall. The locking surface shown in the illustration transferred the firing force from the breech-block to the receiver.

The Spencer mechanism required only three motions to reload. One was to cock the hammer, the second was to swing the breechblock downward, and the third was to return it to the shut position.

More details of the Spencer action are shown in Figure 8-23. This is a cross-section drawing from the Spencer catalog of 1866. It shows the action in considerably more detail. The spiral magazine spring (18) is shown urging the round-nosed magazine follower (21) toward the breech of the rifle. The complicated looking assembly in the butt plate was merely an L-shaped lever (13) which could be rotated 90 degrees and withdrawn to allow reloading of the magazine. All other parts in the butt plate were merely retainers and catches for the magazine tube.

As the trigger was pulled the hammer (7) struck the firing pin (6) which was a flat steel plate recessed into the right side of the breech bolt. The hammer was powered by a back lock type of hammer mechanism similar to that fitted to European muzzle-loading rifles or the Peabody breech-loading rifle. The hammer spring had a great deal of energy and the firing pin blow of the Spencer crushed the rim of the cartridge case over a broad area. This was necessary because of the imperfect priming available in the early rimfire cartridges.

The receiver is shown as (2) in the illustration. The Spencer receiver was a heavy steel forging with a large semicircular cut on the underside and a rectangular window broached through vertically into which the breechblock fitted. The ejector (22) is shown in proper position with the ejector spring (25) putting a counterclockwise force onto the ejector. This was important so that the ejector rode down with the breechblock and formed a ramp which guided the fired case up and out of the action.

Christopher Spencer's improved extractor of 1862 is

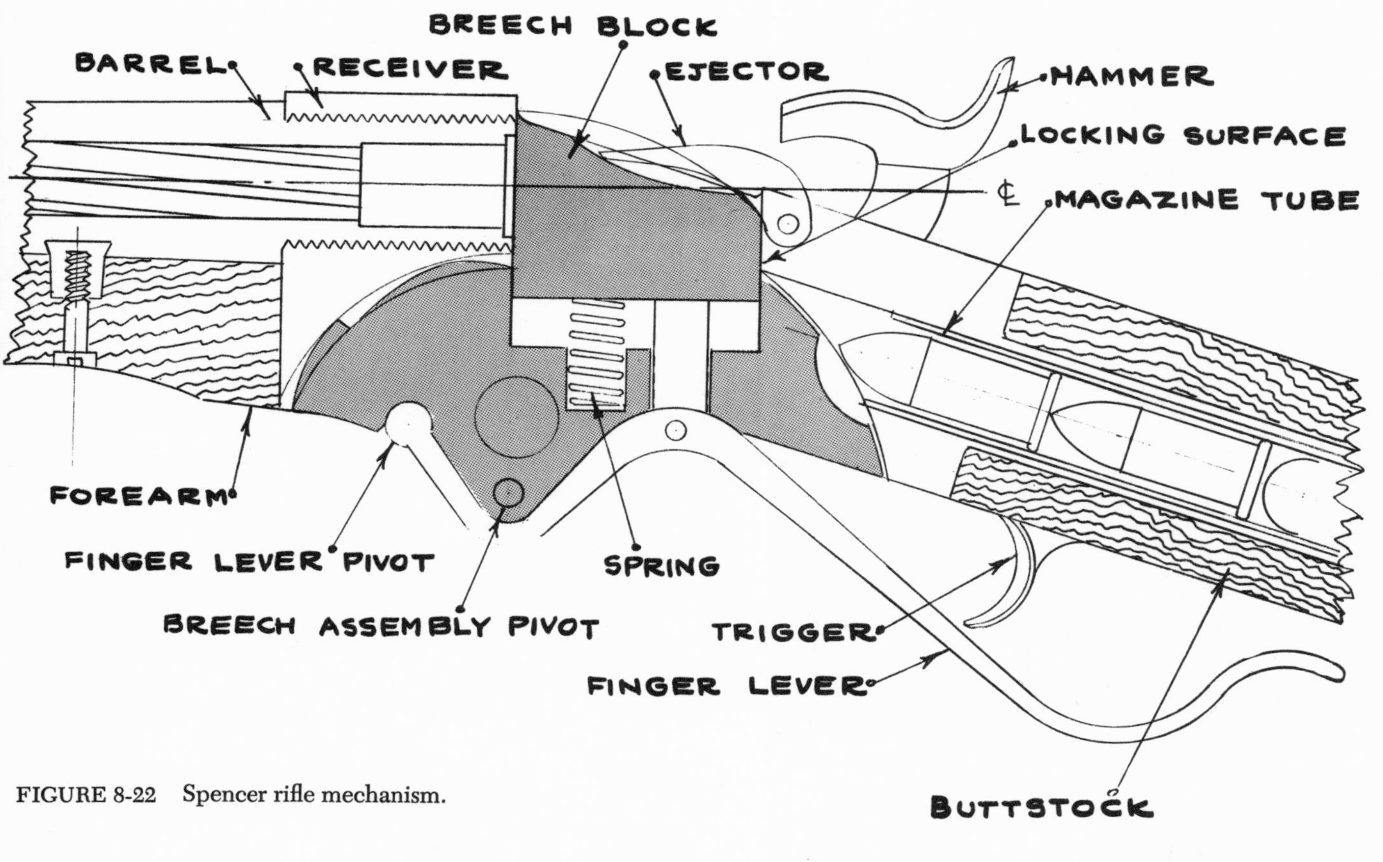

FIGURE 8-22 Spencer rifle mechanism.

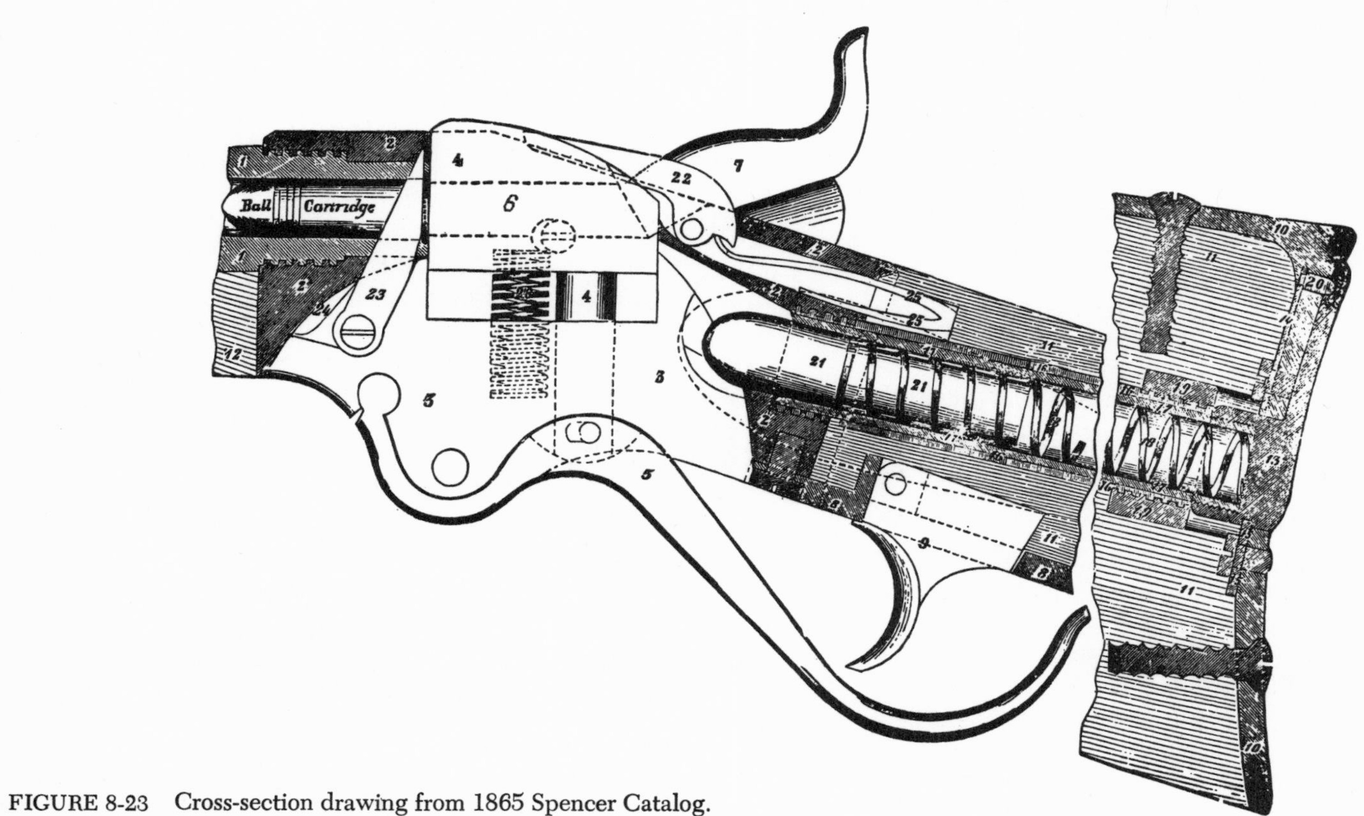

FIGURE 8-23 Cross-section drawing from 1865 Spencer Catalog.

shown in this illustration. The extractor (23) was a thin loose lever which was inset into the left side of the carrier block and rotated upon a small screw. As the carrier block rotated the extractor pivot moved to the rear while the tip was restrained by a cut in the barrel. This geometry gave a powerful "primary extraction" to force the fired case out of the chamber. At this point the breechblock was down and the ejector was in a fully downward position. The fired cartridge case was given a kick to the rear and as it slid out of the chamber it rode up on the ejector or "cartridge guide" and flew clear of the action.

When the action was fully open the breechblock was down below the level of the tubular magazine. A fresh cartridge was pushed out of the magazine in front of the breechblock with its upward position controlled by the spring loaded cartridge guide. The return motion of the lever saw the cartridge forced toward the chamber with its upward position controlled by the spring loaded ejector or cartridge guide (22). After the cartridge was chambered, the breech bolt (4) was urged upward by the cylindrical shaft (4) and the coiled spring (26) into the fully locked position shown in Figure 8-22 and 8-23.

PURCHASES OF REPEATING RIFLES DURING THE CIVIL WAR

The three most import repeating rifles used in the Civil War were the Spencer, the Colt, and the Henry. The Spencer was by far the most important of the three. The Civil War purchases by the United States Government from 1861 to 1866 were as follows:[4]

The figures must be studied carefully, for they include arms and ammunition contracted for and delivered, but some arms were delivered too late to be used in the conflict. On the other hand, the figures do not include rifles purchased by the troops privately. It is estimated that most of the 8,000 Henry rifles produced through the end of 1864 saw service in the conflict.

Many bodies of troops became so frustrated at the refusal of the Ordnance Department to buy modern breech-loading arms that they scraped up money by one means or another and purchased rifles on the commercial market. An informal agreement existed that the Government would purchase ammunition to supply the rifles. An analysis shows that many more Henrys were purchased privately than by the Government. The total number of Spencers purchased was 106,667. The average number of cartridges purchased *per Spencer rifle or carbine* was 545 rounds. At the same number of rounds per rifle in service the calculations indicate that there were about 8,500 Henry rifles used in the conflict. There were slightly under 10,000 Henry rifles manufactured in the Civil War period and it appears probable that most saw service in the conflict. The Henry was a much more fragile rifle than the Spencer so that the path to Government acceptance was very difficult, and most were purchased privately by volunteer troops who were willing to accept the responsibility for careful maintenance of the Henry rifles in the field in return for the tremendously increased firepower over the conventional muzzle-loading military rifle.

Ammunition for the Spencer Rifles and Carbines

Ammunition for the Spencer rifles and carbines is shown in Figure 8-21. The standard Spencer cartridges used during the Civil War are shown in the lower illustration, the caliber .56/.56. This curious cartridge designation refers to the fact that the diameter of the cartridge case just forward of the rim was .56 and the diameter of the cartridge at the mouth was .56. The construction of the cartridge is shown in more detail in the illustration of the Spencer carbine cartridge in Chapter 4. Actual .56/.56 cartridges in the author's collection have a diameter of .565 of an inch just forward of the rim and .560 of an inch at the mouth of the case just to the rear of the conical crimping. The bullets measure .550 of an inch in diameter just forward of the cartridge case mouth. The bullet diameter just forward of the single lubrication groove averages .545 of an inch.

The Spencer .56/.56 cartridges were manufactured from 1861 until 1920. There were two well known loadings. Commercial cartridges were generally assembled with 45 grains of black powder and a 350-grain soft lead bullet. The Frankford Arsenal cartridge shown in Chapter 4 carried a 450-grain soft lead bullet with three lubrication grooves and a 40-grain powder charge. Most of the Spencer cartridges I have examined have a single outside lubrication groove which has been knurled into the bullet. The rimfire heads are .640 to .645 of an inch in diameter and the rim thickness is about .075 of an inch. Four typical loaded cartridges from different sources and one blank cartridge were analyzed on the precision electronic scale. Calculations indicate that all four loaded cartridges had 350-grain bullets.

Almost all the rimfire cartridges used during the Civil War were based on technology specified in the Smith and Wesson patent for rimfire cartridges of March 1860. There were great difficulties in manufacturing these early cartridges. Copper was the most malleable material available but not enough was known about annealing of copper, proper lubricant for dies and punches, and the design of dies for deep drawing techniques. These limitations resulted in the development of short squat cartridge cases. As improved techniques were developed the cartridge cases got longer and thinner. Surprisingly there were few tests to establish the pressure and velocity of the Sharps, Spencer or Henry cartridges. Colonel Berkeley Lewis in his *Small Arms and Ammunition in the United States Services* states:

> One of the first service records of firing of rimfire weapons is contained in Navy test reports of 1862. The Henry cartridges as recorded at that date . . . contained the following components: ball — 216 grains, powder — 25 grains, tallow — 2 grains, case — 50 grains, fulminate (priming) — 2 grains, Total — 295 grains. The cartridge most used during the War had a pointed bullet. In 1862 the charge of the Spencer cartridge was 34 grains.
>
> An Ordnance Board, convening on September 24, 1863, recommended changes to reduce the number of types of ammunition required for carbines. There has been a great variation in the relationship of powder charges to bullets, some loads being comparatively weak. The Board suggested that a minimum charge be established at 1/10 the weight of the ball. They also recommended that Sharps, Gibbs, Starr, Spencer, Joslyn, Sharps and Hankens, and Ballard Carbines all be made with bores of 0.52 of an inch. The first three were to use the Sharps paper or linen cartridge, the last four to use the copper Spencer cartridge. No changes were recommended in the cases of several carbines, "using peculiar cartridges not adopted to interchangeability."

The Spencer cartridges of 1862 with a 34-grain powder charge, or the Spencer cartridges of 1864-1865 with a 40-grain powder charge, both had powder charges well under 10 percent of the bullet weight. The Spencer Repeating Rifle Company catalog of 1866 contains many glowing references to the performance of these low velocity cartridges in combat. The large diameter bullets with their heavy weight had tremendous momentum and although they had a very curved trajectory they retained their velocity well at long range. Colonel John T. Wilder, Commander of the First Brigade of mounted infantry of the 17th Indiana Regiment, Army of the Cumberland, wrote to the Spencer Company in November 1863 stating,

> Your favor, requesting my opinion concerning your repeating rifle came to hand, and in reply I am happy to state, as the result of about eight months' constant practice with them, that I believe them to be the best arm for Army use that I have ever seen. My Brigade of mounted infantry have repeatedly routed and driven largely superior forces of rebels, in some instances five or six times our number and this result is mainly due to our being armed with the Spencer repeating rifle. Since using this gun we have never been driven a single rod by any kind of force or number of the enemy. At Hoover's Gap in Tennessee, on June 24, 1863, one of my regiments fairly defeated a rebel brigade of five regiments, they admitting a loss of over 500, while our loss was forty-seven.
>
> My experience is that no line of men, who come within fifty yards of another force armed with the Spencer repeating rifles, can either get away alive, or reach them with a charge, as in either case they are certain to be destroyed by the terrible fire poured into their ranks by cool men thus armed.
>
> My men feel as if it is impossible to be whipped and the confidence inspired by these arms added to their terribly destructive capacity, fully quadruples the effectiveness of my command.
>
> . . . The gun has been put to the severest test this past summer, and fully sustains all the claims made for it.
>
> I believe that the ammunition used is the cheapest kind for the service as it does not wear out in the cartridge boxes and has the quality of being waterproof — the men of my command carry 100 rounds of ammunition in their saddle bags, and in two instances went into a fight immediately after swimming their horses across streams twelve feet deep and it is very rare that a single cartridge fails to fire.
>
> As a sample of their value the contrast in numbers of prisoners lost and taken by my command is a good criterion — our captures since last April number over 2,800 officers and men, our losses in prisoners for the same period number only six men.

Another letter from a Captain Barber, commanding the First Battalion of Ohio Volunteer Sharpshooters from Chattanooga, Tennessee, November 8, 1863, describes really incredible long-range performance for this low velocity ammunition.

> I have just returned with my command from an expedition in which we have had a good opportunity to test our rifles with the rebel Sharpshooters. About six miles below Chattanooga the main road, over which supplies for the whole Army must be drawn, lays along the banks of the Tennessee River, the south bank of which was held by the enemy, and their Sharpshooters played havoc with our teams and drivers. The river is 500 yards wide, and I was ordered to protect the road. The 18th Kentucky, armed with the Enfield rifle [the British .577 caliber Enfield muzzle-loading rifle], had been skirmishing with them for two days, and lost three men, and had no effect on the enemy. The first day we opened on them we killed two, wounded several, and drove them from every position along the river. We found by actual trial that our guns had longer range and greater accuracy. We seldom missed at 700 yards. I had 125 men with me, and for two weeks kept 600 Rebels at bay, and, as I afterwards learned, killed

and wounded over thirty, with a loss of one man wounded.

It was a genuine trial of arms, and resulted in proving the superiority of the Spencer Repeating Rifle over every other arm in service.

General Reynolds, Chief of Staff, said to me "It is the best rifle on the face of the earth," and I am fully convinced that his remark is literally true.

High Velocity Spencer Ammunition

Despite good performance by Spencer rifles and carbines in 1863 and 1864, a great deal of experimentation went forward to provide higher velocities and flatter trajectories. The rimfire copper cases were relatively weak and this severely limited the pressure which could be generated in the cartridge case. Some of the problems with the experiments to develop increased velocity are described in the *Ordnance Memorandum No. 14* which was published in 1872. The development of the rimfire concept is described as follows:

> For some time the idea of combining the primer and cartridge did not assert itself, but some inventions were pushed in this direction, and the rim-primed cartridge was produced. In this the fulminate composition was placed in the folded head of the case. This mode of priming requires a large charge of the priming composition, which being thrown into the fold by swiveling, the entire circumference of the head was not always primed thoroughly, and as the cartridge is exploded by striking the rim at a part of the head under the hammer, it not infrequently happened that it failed from the point struck not having any priming. [This priming procedure is described in more detail in the illustration of the Spencer carbine cartridge in Chapter 4. At the bottom of the figure it states: "About 50,000 were fabricated in 1864 and 1865. Primed by a centrifugal machine. Priming in a fluid state, Sharps mixture consisting of six parts by weight of mealed powder, three of fulminate, and three of glass."] The large charge required — about 5 grains against ½ grain for the center fire — was a further objection to rim-priming; the exploding of so large a quantity of quick-powder in the folded-head, the weak part of the cartridge, tending to strain and open the fold to bursting, as it frequently did. Another objection to the rim-primed cartridges is that they are more liable to accident in handling, and in shocks of transportation, and those incident to service; in fact, a number of instances of the explosion in the magazine of repeating-arms and in patent cartridge-boxes for service of such, have been reported by which serious injury resulted to the soldier.
>
> Hence, efforts to produce a still more reliable and satisfactory cartridge, and the development, production and general adoption for service of what is now so well-known as center-primed metallic ammunition, its advantages being sure explosion when struck by the point of the firing pin; less of fulminate and less strain on the head of the cartridge; greater security in handling and using under all exigencies of service.

There were valid reasons for going to center-fire ammunition in the early 1870's but the comments about many accidents in the field with rimfire ammunition seem greatly exaggerated. Field experience during the Civil War, as reported by experienced officers such as Colonel Wilder and other cavalry leaders, reflected great confidence in the safety and reliability of this ammunition. Field experience with the Winchester (Henry) .44 rimfire ammunition throughout the Far West in the second half of the 19th century was excellent, and the Swiss utilized a .41 caliber bottlenecked rimfire cartridge in extensive military service with good results.

The major objection to rimfire ammunition seems to be in the severe limitation on muzzle velocity which could be achieved within rimfire cartridge technology. The head of the case had to be made of relatively thin material so that the firing pin could deform it, and there was a large charge of priming in the hollow rim. In order not to exceed the strength of the thin copper it was necessary to use rather moderate powder charges resulting in low muzzle velocities. The highest muzzle velocity for a rimfire cartridge of the Civil War period was the .44 Henry which achieved a muzzle velocity of about 1125 feet per second.

In 1970 Winchester Group Research developed an analytical formula to predict the muzzle velocity of modern ballistic systems. This is a fairly complex formula requiring the input of seven variables, and it has been programmed into a small computer. While the formula was designed as an analytical tool for the most modern ballistic systems, I have done a minor transformation allowing its application to early black powder ballistic systems. The physical laws remain the same, but most of the seven input variables are greatly different for black powder rifles. Application of this formula to the .44 Henry cartridge gives very close correlation with actual measured velocities taken in the 1880's. The .56/.56 Spencer cartridge loaded with 40 grains of black powder and a 450-grain bullet gives a calculated muzzle velocity of 930 feet per second in the Spencer carbine with 22-inch barrel. In the rifle with a 30-inch barrel the predicted velocity rises to 950 feet per second.

The commercial loading of the .56/.56 Spencer with a 350-grain bullet and a 45-grain powder charge gives a calculated muzzle velocity of 1100 feet per second for the carbine, and 1130 feet per second for the rifle. None of these values was considered satisfactory, for the Sharps rifle and the muzzle-loading Springfield rifle-musket would both provide substantially higher muzzle velocities with their standard 60-grain powder charges. Many experiments were performed by Frankford Arsenal and by the Spencer Rifle Company to provide higher velocities. The trials led to a series of slightly tapered and bottlenecked cartridges and a great deal of confusion among historians. There were two interchangeable cartridges designated .56/.52. All the Spencer cartridges had the same rim dimensions, and the same .56-inch diameter forward of the rim. The .52 refers to the diameter of the copper cartridge case at the mouth. The bullet was actually about .51 caliber to fit a barrel with a bore diameter of .495 and a groove diameter of .512. These cartridges were designed for the "new model" Spencer of 1865 which came into field service during the last year of the war and are shown in Figure 8-21.

The Government settled on .50 caliber cartridges for the Springfield single-shot rifles in a rimfire configuration in 1865 and then in the .50/70 center fire in 1866. The Spencer Company developed .50 caliber rimfire cartridges and listed these as their "standard caliber" in the 1866 Spencer catalog. The Army and Navy rifles were supplied with 30-inch barrels — "caliber 50-100 of an inch." The weight was 10 pounds and the price $38.00 without bayonet. A cavalry model was also offered with a 20-inch barrel, a weight of 8¼ pounds and a price of $35.00.

The Spencer Company also offered a bottlenecked .56/.46 cartridge shown in the upper illustration of Figure 8-21. Calculations indicate that the .56/.50 and the .56/.46 would both provide velocities of slightly under 1100 feet per second in a carbine barrel. The velocity in the rifle barrels calculates out to a shade over 1100 feet per second. The sporting rifles are listed in the 1866 Spencer catalog with a 26-inch barrel, weighing 9 pounds. The price with open sights was listed at $45.00 and the caliber for some strange reason is listed as "44-100 of an inch." The guns were actually chambered for the .56/.46 cartridge.

THE HENRY REPEATING RIFLE

Benjamin Tyler Henry was an inventive craftsman who had a great deal to do with the development of the successful repeating rifle. As an expert mechanic he was employed by Robbins and Lawrence of Windsor, Vermont, to assist in the production of the Jennings magazine rifle in the early 1850's. About 1857 Henry joined the struggling Volcanic Arms Company which was reorganized as the New Haven Arms Company that same year. Henry, working with a skilled staff of mechanics labored from 1857 through 1860 in developing a lever action repeating rifle and a copper .44 caliber rimfire cartridge. The experiments were long and difficult, and the New Haven Arms Company lost money during most of this period. Much of Oliver Winchester's personal fortune was required to keep the venture going and eventual success was primarily due to dogged determination and a faith that success could be achieved.

The long and patient research finally paid off with a greatly improved system. The key element was the .44 caliber rimfire cartridge shown in the upper illustration of Figure 8-24. The cartridge construction was built on technology developed by Smith and Wesson in the late 1850's. The assembly consisted of a deep drawn copper cup with a hollow flanged rim containing the priming material. Since copper is very malleable in the annealed state it was a logical material to use for the deep drawing operations required to make a cartridge case. Special machinery and manufacturing techniques were developed to draw a shallow cup from a disc of copper and then form the cup into a long closed cylinder in successive operations. The copper work hard-

	Quantity	Price Total	Average Price	No. Purchased by Troops at End of War
Spencer Rifles	12,471	$467,309	$37.50	
Spencer Carbines	94,196	$2,393,634	$25.40	8,289 (rifles & carbines)
Spencer Cartridges	58,238,924	$1,419,277	2.44¢	
Henry Rifles	1,731	$63,953	$37.00	808
.44 Henry Cartridges	4,610,400	$107,353	2.33¢	
Colt Revolving Rifles	4,612	$203,000	$44.00	305

ened during these operations and at key points in the manufacturing process the copper cups had to be annealed or softened by heating and quenching in water. The final trick operations consisted of forming a rim with a cavity on the inside. It was important that the copper be soft enough so that the rim could be formed without cracking — and yet not be fully annealed so that it would be too weak to withstand the gas pressure developed by the powder. The trick was to perform the manufacturing processes so that the copper case ended up tough and strong without cracking in either the final manufacturing process or during the firing cycle. The copper cases were then trimmed to a length of about ⅞ of an inch.

Priming techniques required a great deal of research before success was achieved. Early experimenters poured an even layer of priming into the base of the cartridge case. Priming is a "primary explosive" and burns very rapidly, causing an intense shock wave. This violence is technically termed "brisance" and is defined as the shattering effect of a sudden release of energy. Cartridges primed with an even layer sufficient to cause ignition when the rim was struck had too much priming material. The heads tended to bulge in the center, driving the breech bolt backward and rupturing the cartridge cases.

Priming is rather dangerous material, but through patient experimentation techniques were finally developed to place wet priming in the rim of the case and not in the center. This may be done by putting the wet priming mixture in the base of the case, and then spinning the cartridge rapidly. It may also be accomplished by inserting a spinner in the mouth of the cartridge, shaped to move the priming out toward the rim as the spinner is rotated. Both techniques were probably used, but the lack of a reliable way to get a uniform priming charge around the rim was always a serious problem with large rimfire cartridges. The priming charge was then dried out in an oven or warm room and, as the water content decreased, the priming became more and more sensitive. The final steps in the loading procedure were to place a 25 to 28-grain charge of black powder in the case and seat a 216-grain soft lead bullet in the mouth of the case. There was a slight interference fit between the mouth of the cartridge case and the lead bullet. The final manufacturing operation was to crimp the mouth of the case inward to grip the bullet more tightly.

The research and development of the .44 caliber rimfire cartridge was of tremendous importance to the struggling New Haven Arms Company. In honor of this achievement Winchester rimfire cartridges for the past century have been stamped with a capital H for Benjamin Tyler Henry, the inventor. The .44 Henry cartridge achieved a muzzle velocity of about 1125 feet per second and provided over *ten times* the muzzle energy of the .40 caliber Volcanic cartridge. The cartridge assembly was much more rugged than the Volcanic, and the 50-grain copper cartridge case not only contained a much larger powder charge of 25 to 28 grains but sealed off the gas leakage at the breech, thus making a much more effective ballistic system.

Two styles of .44 caliber cartridge were developed, one with a flat, and the other a pointed lead bullet. These are shown in the illustrations in Figure 8-24, and were interchangeable. The primary difference was in style.

The Henry Repeating Rifle catalog of 1866 shows the .44 pointed cartridge. It appears probable that development of the .44 Flat was carried out in the 1860's with a gradual introduction to the market as an alternate and interchangeable cartridge for the Henry and Winchester Model 1866 rifles.

The Model 1860 Henry Rifle

The rifle for the new .44 rimfire ammo was larger and sturdier in all its dimensions than the Volcanic rifles. The intensive work of the late 1850's culminated in the issuance of Henry's patent No. 30,446 on October 16, 1860. The patent drawing is shown in Figure 8-25. This was a very significant design for the basic ideas of the Volcanic action was restructured into an action layout that was the foundation for the Henry and Winchester Model 1866 rimfires, and the Winchester Model 1873 and 1876 center-fire rifles. The central element was the complex receiver which provided alignment for all the action elements. The barrel was screwed into the front of the receiver. The magazine tube assembly was hung below the barrel. The loading

RIM FIRE CARTRIDGES.

Price per 1,000, $24.00.
Case contains 2,000.

Powder, 28 gr
Lead, 200 gra

Adapted to Henry and Winchester Model 1866 Rifles.

Price per 1,000, $25.00.
Case contains 2,000.

Powder, 26 gr
Lead, 200 gra

Adapted to Henry and Winchester Model 1866 Rifles, and Colt's Revolver.

FIGURE 8-24 Ammunition for Henry and Winchester Model 1866 rifles.

procedure was the same as that used on the Volcanic rifle. The magazine follower (plunger P on the patent) was pushed forward compressing the magazine spring M up past the point E at the forward end of the barrel. The front end of the magazine assembly could then be rotated to one side and fifteen .44 rimfire cartridges dropped into the slotted magazine tube. The magazine assembly was then rotated back and the plunger moved down the slot, pressing the cartridges to the rear. The rifle is shown at the instant of firing in "Fig. 1" of the patent illustration (Figure 8-25). The cartridge in the chamber has just been struck by the firing pin. A second cartridge has been pushed into the carrier ready for reloading on the next shot and a third cartridge is shown in the magazine being pressed to the rear by a magazine follower or "plunger."

After firing the finger lever was rotated clockwise into the position shown in "Fig. 2." This caused the toggle links shown in the locked position in "Fig. 8" to be "jacknifed" into the open position shown in "Fig. 9." This motion pulled the breech bolt to the rear, removing the fired cartridge case from the chamber. As the firing pin I moved to the rear it recocked the hammer H which was then locked in the rearward position by the sear in the trigger S. When the finger lever reached the fully open position shown in "Fig. 2" carrier lever G moved upward, lifting the brass carrier block which is shown in "Fig. 6" in the patent illustration. The fresh cartridge was contained in cavity (3) in the carrier block and the lower cavity (2) was a space for

B. T. HENRY.
Magazine Fire Arm.
No. 30,446. Patented Oct. 16, 1860.

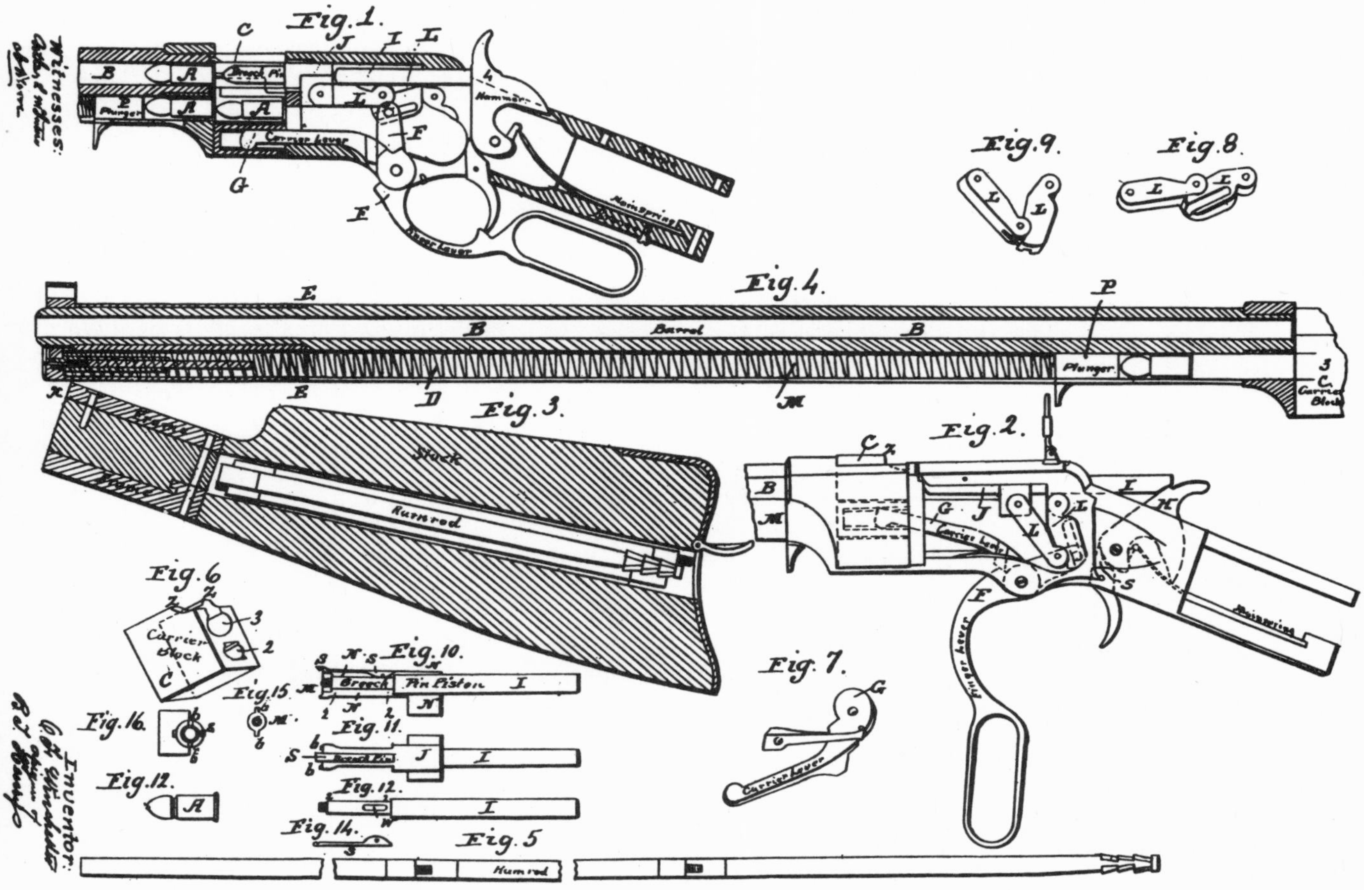

FIGURE 8-25 Henry rifle patent.

the carrier lifter. As the carrier block rose it struck the fired cartridge which was held against the breech face by the extractor. This motion kicked the cartridge case upward, ejecting it from the rifle.

The closing motion of the finger lever moved the breechblock forward. The carrier block was designed so that the fresh cartridge was aligned with the chamber. The breechblock stripped it out of the carrier pushing it into the chamber. The construction of the breech bolt is shown in "Fig. 10" of the illustration. The carrier and breechblock were designed so that the breech bolt could pass through the carrier to chamber the cartridge and yet when the breech bolt was fully locked the slotted carrier could be moved downward into a position to pick up a fresh cartridge as shown in "Fig. 1". This geometry was rather tricky for it prevented a fresh cartridge from falling out of the carrier if the rifle was turned upside down and yet allowed the carrier to move downward around the breechblock when the action was fully closed.

The fully locked position is shown in "Fig. 1" of the patent illustration. The toggle locking links were exactly in line in this position and the firing force generated by the cartridge was transmitted through the three link pivots into the frame of the receiver. The firing force was then transmitted through the tang of the receiver into the wooden buttstock and then to the shooter's shoulder.

The standard Henry rifle is shown in Figure 8-26. It was fitted with a 24-inch octagonal barrel with a magazine capacity of fifteen .44 rimfire cartridges. The front sight was held on an octagonal collar which was locked to the front of the barrel and served to retain the swinging magazine assembly. The rear sight was shown in the short-range position, but the long leaf could be flipped upward and a slider moved along the graduated slot for extended range firing.

The most serious weakness in the Henry rifle was the loading system. The long magazine tube below the barrel was unprotected and was weakened by the slot running the full length. A hook-shaped extension on the magazine follower (or plunger P on the patent) can barely be seen at the forward end of the receiver. This was slid foreward to a position about 4 inches from the muzzle and the entire section of the barrel forward of the small screw between the barrel and magazine tube could be rotated to one side for loading.

There were complaints from the field that the open slot could easily collect dirt and that the magazine tube was subject to denting. There were also some complaints of rusting of the loading sleeve making the loading operation difficult. These objections to the loading system on the Henry rifle led to a long series of experiments to eliminate the delicate construction of the magazine tube and follower.

Although the patent was issued in October 1860, production was limited to a very small scale in 1861 and 1862. It is difficult to get an accurate picture of early production since incomplete records were kept and many of these have been destroyed. The second factor which makes for a great deal of confusion is the difference between actual production figures and orders received by the company. In October 1862 Oliver Winchester answered an inquiry for the purchase of 1000 guns with the statement that the factory could produce about 10 rifles per day had manufactured a total of 900 Henry rifles. By January 1863 a figure of 1500 Henrys was mentioned as the total pro-

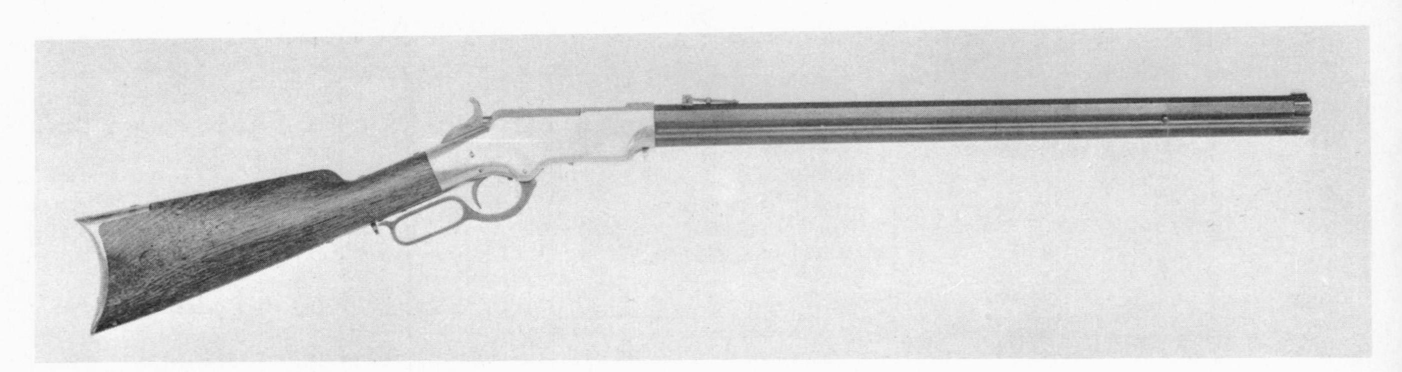

FIGURE 8-26 Henry Model 1860 rifle.

duction to date. The United States government purchased 240 Henry rifles in 1863 and an additional 800 during 1864. Total purchases during the Civil War by the Government amounted to 1731 rifles. In 1867 Mr. Winchester stated that about 10,000 rifles had been sold during the last two years of the Civil War while orders for at least 100,000 more had been received but could not be filled because of lack of production capacity.

The general military judgment of the Henry rifle was that it was too delicate for heavy field service. There were problems of unreliable ignition of the early rimfire ammunition, and this was partially overcome by designing the Henry with two projections on the firing pin which struck both sides of the rim when the hammer fell. There were also some problems with breakage of the firing pin assemblies in the field.

The Henry rifle had two great advantages — an enormous magazine capacity of 15 rounds and the ability to fire faster than any other Civil War rifle. Even the Spencer required two separate motions to reload — one to cock the hammer and the other to operate the lever. The Henry provided twice the magazine capacity and required only the motion of the lever to reload. These advantages led to the private purchase of thousands of Henry rifles by regiments of volunteer troops willing to spend their meagre pay to secure the advantages of the greatly increased firepower. It is another interesting comment that over half the Henry rifles purchased by the Government during the Civil War were purchased by the "veteran volunteers" at the end of the war and taken to the four corners of the United States in the westward expansion of the post-Civil War period.

The value of the Henry rifle to skilled troops is reflected in many of the testimonial letters included in the catalog published by the New Haven Arms Company in 1865. The private purchase of these firearms is also reflected in the following letter:

Chattanooga, November 2, 1863

President
New Haven Arms Company:

Sir:

I take the liberty to enquire about your Rifle, as I have been an owner of one of them a long time, and through my agency twelve of them have been bought in the regiment and many more would have been bought had I been able to get them in any place, and if I do get any the price is very much increased. In the 51st Illinois it is many that will buy them, and the brigade and division both requested me to write to you for information and a price list and the different kinds made, and how many we can get, or when, and express charges from the factory to Stevenson, Alabama, and if we cannot get some good globe sights or if any telescope sights are made, and their cost. I have took pains to go to the General and get permission to sell them in his command, and also to bring them through. We have now four months' pay due us and the boys will have the money ready to send by express to you when we can know how many we can get.

We used your Rifle in the Battle of Chicamauga with good effect, and it is undoubtedly the best gun in the service, far superior to the Spencer rifle or any other Rifle, both here and in Europe, as I have served a long time in both armies; but better sights ought to be made for so good a Rifle. I received ten rifles from Bowen in Chicago, but could not get any more just now. Cannot any heavier guns be made to order, or different caliber? Excuse my many enquiries. Your rifle is my "hobby," so the boys say, and I like to be able to give them all the information possible, and get as many of Henry's Rifles in the Army of the Cumberland, so we could drive the Rebs from Chattanooga, so we could get something to eat.

Yours respectfully,
John H. Ekstrand
Regt. Ordnance Sergt.,
51st ILL. Vols.

Another letter reflecting extensive field service, and a comparison of the Henry and Spencer rifles was also printed in the catalog.

Stetson, Maine
March 15, 1865

Mr. O. F. Winchester
Pres't. N. H. Arms Co.:

Sir:

Permit me to bear testimony in favor of the "Henry Repeating Rifle". It is in my judgment the most effective arm in the service. I have been connected with the first D. C. Cavalry from its first organization, and that arm having been in constant use by my regiment, I feel prepared to pass upon its merits. Its first excellence is the rapidity of its use. We have found no difficulty in firing fifteen shots a minute. Such rapidity of fire is perfectly irresistable by a charging force.

On the 25th day of August, 1864, near Ream's Station we had an opportunity of testing the Rifle. Our Regiment of Cavalry was dismounted at 4 o'clock P.M., marched and stationed on the extreme left of the infantry line, there to build light breastworks for the moment. There we received a most desperate charge from the enemy. We used your Rifle and easily repulsed the foe, while the infantry were broken and swept from their well constructed breastworks.

Our Regiment with your Rifles stood like veterans, and never left the line until the battle ceased. Our men often said, and I concur in the opinion, that with this Rifle and aplenty of ammunition they could safely meet four to one with any other arm.

The Spencer Rifle is a good arm, preferable to Springfield, Sharps or Star's Rifles, and next, in my judgment to the Henry. We used the Spencer in the First Maine Cavalry during the past winter, as well as the Henry and so have tried both.

The Henry excels all others in *accuracy* and *force*. It is also the most *durable* arm. With anything like fair usage a man can use one for his whole term of service without its getting out of repair.

Its *simplicity* of construction, also, is such that almost any soldier can repair one if needed. Another advantage is that the dullest soldier who can use the commonest arm in the service, can quickly and safely learn to use this Rifle.

It is a very safe arm, as there is no half cock to it. The hammer is either down or clear back. Great danger attends the use of common arms from the fact of their going off so often at half cock.

Another great advantage is that it is so *easily* and *quickly loaded*. Two motions loads and cocks the piece. Great advantage is gained by this over the enemy, who may be easily picked off while cocking his piece.

But the best evidence in favor of the Henry rifle, however, does not come from its friends or from our own people who use it. *It comes from the enemy.* I was captured last season and was for a time in the Libby Prison. Several of these rifles were taken when I was, and I often heard the enemy discuss its merits. They all feared it more than any arm in our service and I have heard them say, "Give us anything but your d_____ d Yankee rifle that can be loaded Sunday and fired all the week."

Respectfully your ob't. Servant,

Joel W. Cloudman,
Late Major First D.C. Cavalry

THE END OF THE CIVIL WAR

At the end of the War many troops were allowed to purchase the rifles which they were using. It is an interesting commentary that almost half the Henry rifles in service were purchased by the troops under this plan. The Colt rifles were so unpopular that only 305 were purchased, less than 10 percent of the total in service. Some 8289 Spencer rifles were purchased, accounting for about 9 percent of those in the service.

The prices of the rifles to the U.S. Government varied widely. The Spencer carbines were produced in tremendous quantities and sold for an average price of $25 apiece. The Henry rifles cost about $37 apiece, while the Colt revolving rifles were the most expensive at $44 per rifle. On the used markets, the Henry rifles averaged the highest price at about $10 per rifle compared with $7 for a used Spencer.

The Colt rifle was a very large revolver firing powerful charges. Occasionally, flame from one chamber would flash over and discharge the other chambers in the rifle. When this happened, the bullets would strike the soldier's left hand holding the forearm of the rifle. This dangerous situation led to a reluctance to accept the Colt rifles in service. They were well made, accurate and powerful rifles; but this fault made them quite unpopular.

The Henry rifles were considered expensive and too delicate for rough field service. These judgments were probably true for the average soldier. It was not the kind of rifle that could be used with a bayonet because of the pivoting loading arrangement on the muzzle end of the barrel. The long slotted magazine tube meant that the troops would have to take a reasonable amount of care to keep the gun in good working order. The Henry was fragile in comparison with the standard muzzle-loading rifle which could be used as a club in close combat. In the hands of intelligent troops willing to accept the responsibility of maintaining adequate care of their firearms, the Henrys were very effective. It is obvious that the troops themselves did not consider these guns fragile and unreliable since such a high percentage was purchased by the "veteran volunteers" at the end of the war. It is also apparent that the wide use of these guns on the frontier was another vote of confidence to the reliability of the rifles if given adequate care.

The general consensus of military opinion was that the Spencer rifle was the cheapest, most durable, and efficient of all the Civil War repeating rifles. The Spencer Arms Company suffered from its own success. At the end of the Civil War, the Army sold Spencer rifles and carbines to any "veteran volunteers" who wished to purchase them. Most of the remainder were dumped on the surplus market at prices as low as $6 per rifle. The result was that there was no market for the new Spencer firearms marketed by the company in the late 1860's. The Spencer .56/.46 sporting cartridge was added to the series of .56/.50, .56/.52 and .56/.56 rifles and ammunition to try and build additional markets. No effort by the Spencer Company could overcome a market glutted with surplus Spencer rifles and the company was forced out of business in 1869. By that time, the Winchester Repeating Arms Company was in an excellent financial position and purchased the entire assets, which included 2,000 muskets, 30,000 carbines and 500 sporting rifles. Although Winchester tried hard to sell these rifles, they were unable to dispose of the stock in the United States, and finally sold most of the inventory in Europe during the Franco-Prussian War.

THE WINCHESTER MODEL 1866 RIFLE

The Winchester Model 1866 rifle was announced at a very crucial time in the firearms business. A large number of manufacturing plants had been established during the war and were selling a wide variety of breech-loading rifles. The firearms market was overloaded with war surplus firearms dumped by the Government at low prices. All of these businesses were fighting desperately to secure sales on the commercial market and stay in business.

The Civil War had established conclusively the practicality of the repeating lever action rifle of which the Spencer and the 1860 model Henry were the two best known examples. The Spencer was far better known since over 100,000 had been manufactured and were in use in the field compared with less than 10,000 Henrys.

The Civil War soldiers who streamed westward after the war were knowledgeable in the field of firearms. Most of them selected their arms carefully and were willing to pay a relatively high price for a reliable, rapid firing rifle which might well be the key to survival in a hostile land. The 1860 Henry and the Spencer lever action rifles were just about equal in utility to the frontiersmen. The Henry had a large magazine capacity and a slim profile which was easily carried in the hand or on horseback. It had the deficiencies of a weak loading system and a magazine tube which was easily dented and damaged. There were also weaknesses in the firing pin and extractor system which caused occasional breakages of these key components.

The Spencer rifle, on the other hand, was a much more rugged design but the swelling in the lower part of the receiver made it an awkward gun to carry either on foot or on horseback. It was also slower to fire than the Henry, and the ammunition weighed considerably more.

The improvements in the Model 1866 Winchester rifle eliminated all the serious faults of the Henry design and gave Winchester clearly the best repeating rifle at that point in history. This was obviously a sophisticated gun-buying market, for thousands of purchasers turned down the opportunity to buy a war surplus Spencer for $6 or $7 and instead paid $40 to $50 of hard earned cash for a Winchester Model 1866.

The three leading competitors in this post-Civil War competition are shown in Figure 8-27. A Spencer rifle is

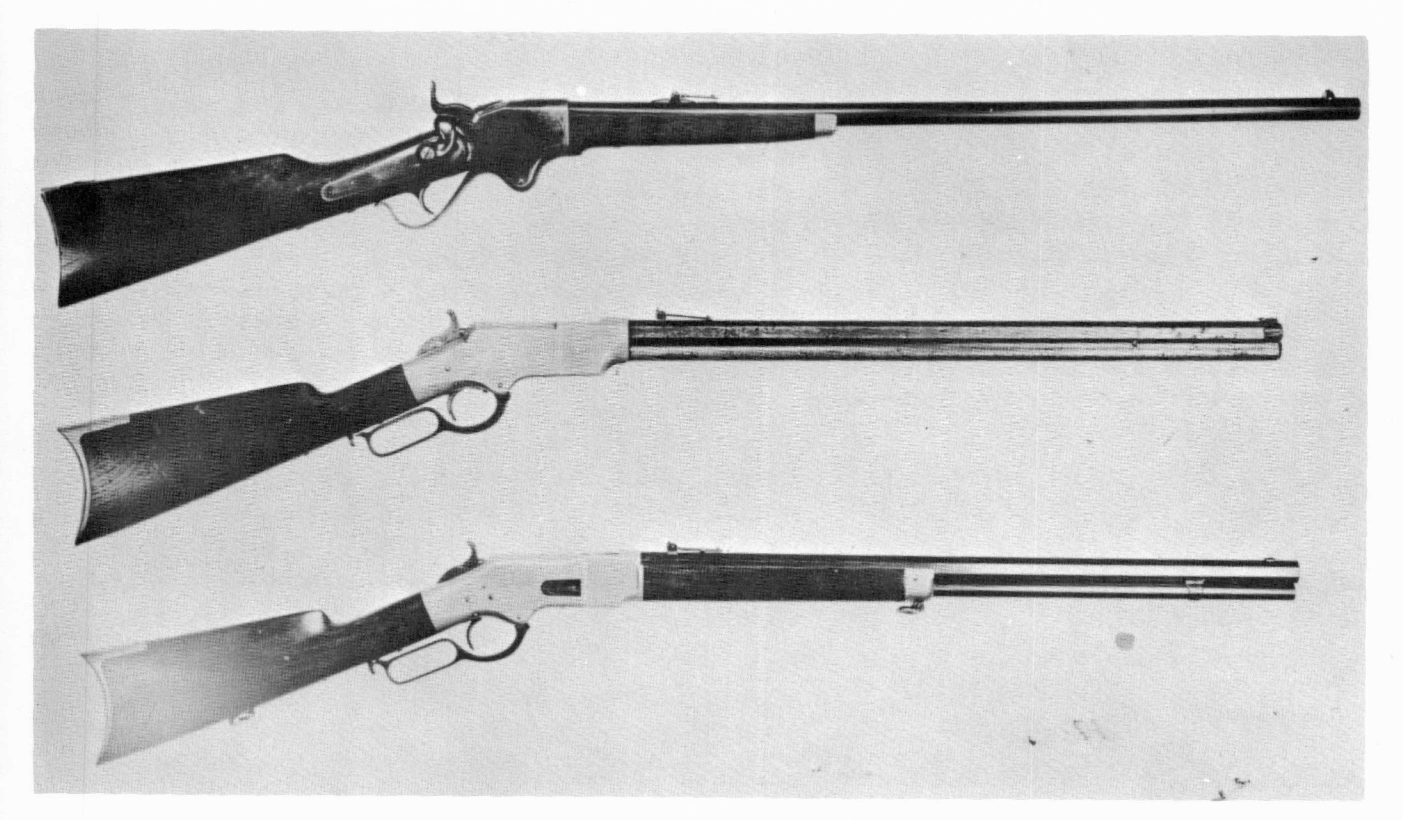

FIGURE 8-27 UPPER: Spencer Sporting Rifle; CENTER: Henry Model 1860 Rifle; LOWER: Winchester Model 1866 Rifle.

shown in the top illustration. Most of the surplus arms were carbines, which were very similar in appearance, but had a 20-inch barrel. The Model 1860 Henry is shown as the middle rifle in this illustration, and the Model 1866 Winchester in the lowest illustration. The close similarity between the Henry and the Model 1866 is readily apparent.

The most important single element in improving the model was a revised loading system invented by Nelson King and patented in 1866. While the Henry rifle had a long slotted magazine tube and a pivoting section at the front end of the barrel similar to that used on the Volcanic rifles, the Winchester Model 1866 had a spring loaded port on the right side of the receiver and a solid magazine tube which was closed at the front end. The cartridges were loaded one by one through the loading port against the magazine spring. This allowed a solid magazine tube to be fitted to the rifle and this tube in turn could be surrounded by a wooden forearm making the entire loading system much more rugged. Another advantage to the revised loading system was that the magazine tube could be reloaded with the action closed and a cartridge in the chamber. This meant that the hard pressed frontiersmen could slip a few extra cartridges in the magazine during a lull in the battle while still keeping the rifle at his shoulder and pointed at the enemy. The Model 1866 rifle shown in this illustration has been fitted with sling swivels. Receivers continued to be made of cast brass and the sighting systems remained very similar to the Henry with a fixed front sight and a rear sight which could be adjusted for considerable changes in elevation.

In the 1867 Winchester catalog, the following statement is made about the 1866 model:

> The Winchester Rifle remains in the mechanism for loading and firing precisely the same as the Henry, except the cartridge extractor. The latest improvements consist of an entire change in the magazine and the arrangements for filling it. By these changes, the gun is made stronger yet lighter; the magazine is closed and strongly protected; it is more simple in operation, requiring fewer motions in the one case and fewer pieces in the other. Not only can this gun be fired 20 times a minute continuously as a repeater, but it can be used as a single loader without any attachment to be changed for the purpose, retaining the magazine full of cartridges to be used in an emergency, when the whole 15 cartridges can be fired in 15 seconds, or at the rate of sixty shots a minute, or in double-quick time, in 7½ seconds, or at a rate of one hundred and twenty shots per minute, or two shots per second, loading from the magazine — an effectiveness far beyond that of any other arm.

Styles of Winchester Model 1866 Rifles

Model 1866 firearms are in Figure 8-28. Three basic models were offered, the sporting rifle, musket and carbine. The sporting rifle is shown at the bottom of Figure 8-27. The rifle had an octagonal 24-inch barrel and weighed 9½ pounds. The magazine capacity was 17 cartridges, which far exceeds the capacity of any modern rifle with the exception of a .22 rimfire rifle. One can well understand the willingness of a buyer to spend a large sum of money to secure a reliable .44 caliber rifle with this tremendous magazine capacity. The sporting rifle was offered in a round barrel version about 1871. The round barrel model cost less money, and weighed half a pound less but was otherwise very similar in specifications.

The very earliest Model 1866 rifles simply continued the serial numbers of the Henry rifles, and were referred to as "Improved Henrys." The transition in serial numbers was not abrupt, but occurred between 12,000 and 14,000. The first few thousand Model 1866 rifles were manufactured with flat sided receivers very similar to that on the Henry rifle in the middle illustration of Figure 8-27. These early rifles also had a flat plate covering the loading port. During 1867 or early 1868 the design was modified to provide a lip at the forward end of the receiver to extend over the wooden forearm. Careful

Model Name	Barrel Style	Barrel Length	Magazine Capacity	Weight of Rifle, Pounds
Sporting Rifle	Octagon	24	17	9½
Spotting Rifle	Round	24	17	9
Musket	Round	27	17	8¼
Carbine	Round	20	13	7¾

FIGURE 8-28 Styles of Winchester Model 1866 rifles.

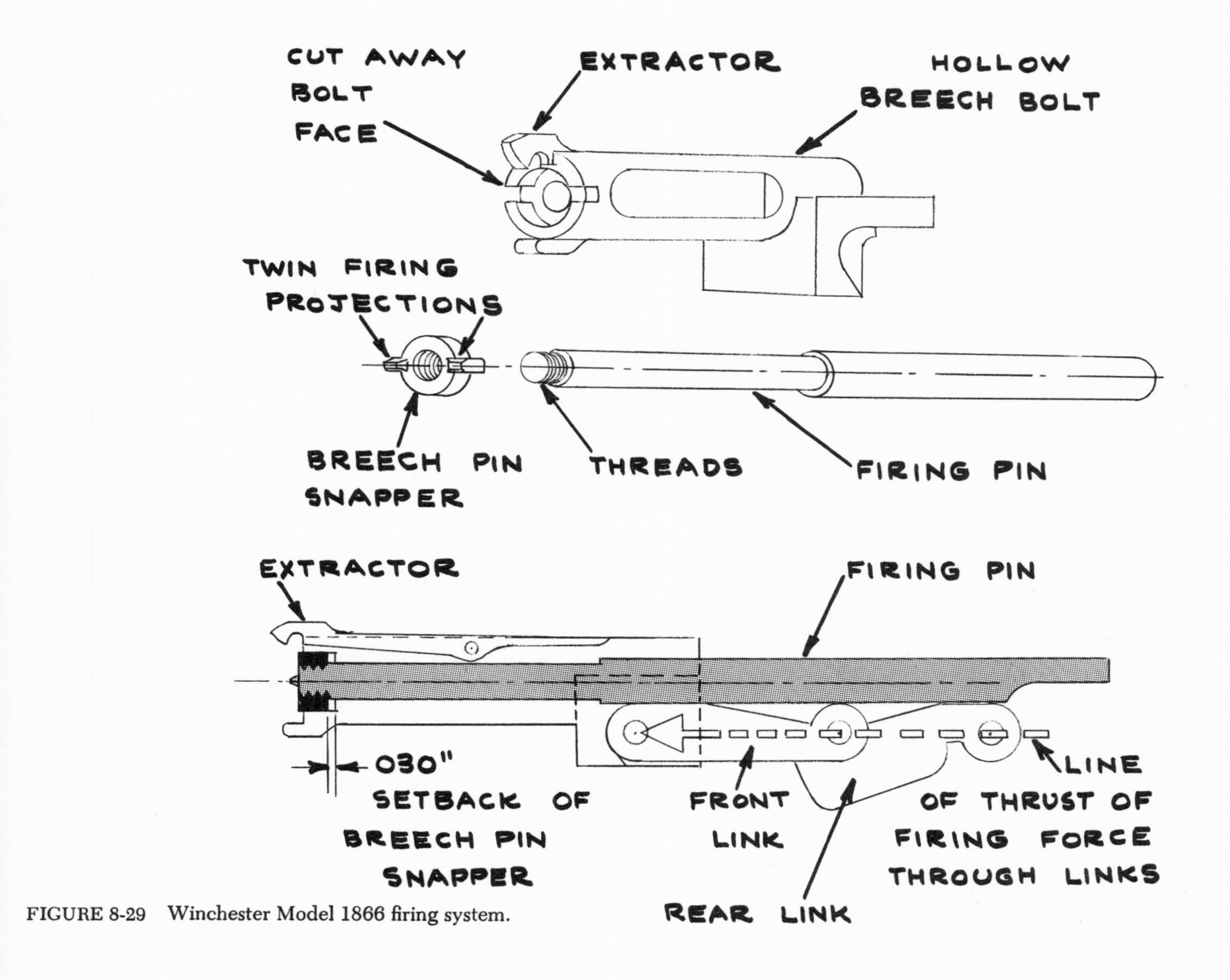

FIGURE 8-29 Winchester Model 1866 firing system.

examination of the Model 1866 in the figure will show this step in the receiver. This brass "rim" extends forward about 1/10 inch, and the brass is .040 of an inch thick. The wooden forearm is cut down to form a tenon to fit inside the rim. At this time, the loading port cover was modified to provide a concave surface to help guide the cartridge into the magazine. This final magazine design was so successful that it is still in use today on Winchester and competitive lever action rifles with tubular magazines.

The receivers and side plates for the Henry and Model 1866 rifles were cast of brass. A number of minor modifications were made in the receiver in both external and internal construction, evolving into a final shape shown in the bottom illustration of Figure 8-27. Note that the contours of the receiver in the hammer area have been softened, and there is a smooth blend of the top of the receiver just behind the carrier, compared with severe lines on the Henry receiver in both these places. There were a great many minor changes in internal configuration. For example, some brass side plates have cored out sections to reduce the weight and amount of machining. This was apparently too much trouble for by the early 1870's the side plates were plain brass ⅛-inch thick, machined all over.

The design of checkering on the hammer changed many times during the production life of the Model 1866, as did the design of the magazine tube. Early models had a threaded magazine end cap, while later models changed to a plug held with a cross screw. Some high serial number Model 1866 rifles have iron butt plates and forend caps, apparently taken directly from Model 1873 production lines.

The mechanical operation of the Model 1866 action

was similar to the Volcanic action, but the proportions of the parts were much larger and stronger. As an example, the pivot pins for the toggle links were .100 of an inch in diameter on the Volcanic rifles, compared with .155 of an inch on the Model 1866. The Model 1866 pins are two and a half times as strong as the pins in the Volcanic. Other components were similarly increased in size and strength. The bolt stroke was increased from .890 of an inch on the Volcanic to 1.370 inches on the Model 1866. The length of the carrier was increased to 1.370 inches to handle the .44 rimfire ammunition. The receiver, finger lever and links were all scaled up to larger dimensions.

The construction of the Model 1866 firing system is shown in Figure 8-29. The complex construction was necessary to provide a blow to the rim of the cartridge case with a firing pin in the center of the bolt. The way this problem was solved was to cut away most of the front of the bolt, and insert a "breech pin snapper" which was threaded onto the front of the firing pin. The breech pin snapper had two chisel-shaped firing pins which projected .025 of an inch beyond the face of the ring, and struck both sides of the cartridge case at the same time. In this way, the reliability of ignition was greatly increased. Unfortunately, this system had a real disadvantage. Only the outer rim of the case was supported on the solid breech bolt. The entire center of the case, was supported on the movable firing pin and breech pin snapper.

The rearward thrust on the Model 1866 firing pin assembly was rather high. The diameter of the breech pin snapper was .345 of an inch, and the .200-inch diameter threaded end of the firing pin was screwed in flush with the front of the snapper. Thus, the area for the cartridge to drive rearward was .099 of a square inch (including the two firing pin projections). With a probable maximum pressure in the cartridge of 15,000 pounds per square inch, the thrust on the firing pin assembly would be almost 1500 pounds. This force would be reduced by the work required to deform the copper cartridge case, but there is no doubt that the firing pin assembly moved smartly to the rear.

After the firing pin accelerated to a rearward velocity, it traveled only .030 of an inch before the breech pin snapper stopped on a shoulder in the bolt. This shoulder is shown in the lower illustrations in Figure 8-29. The heavy firing pin would continue to the rear, against the resistance of the hammer. This continued rearward motion put the threaded joint between the firing pin and breech pin snapper in shear. On old rifles which have seen much service the threads may be entirely worn out due to this battering.

The firing pin system was one of the critical areas of the design. Correspondence from Oliver Winchester to Civil War correspondents comments on breakage of the 1860 Henry firing pins. Management gave attention to securing better material and using great care in the manufacture of the Model 1866 firing pin assemblies, but the system did limit the maximum breech pressures of the .44 Henry ammunition to relatively low values.

Styles of Model 1866 Firearms

The Model 1866 was offered in three different styles in Figure 8-28. Originally only the octagonal barreled rifle model, and the round barreled carbine were manufactured. The first Model 1866 rifles had a receiver very similar to the Henry rifle. By late 1867, the Model 1866 had evolved into its own distinctive receiver, as

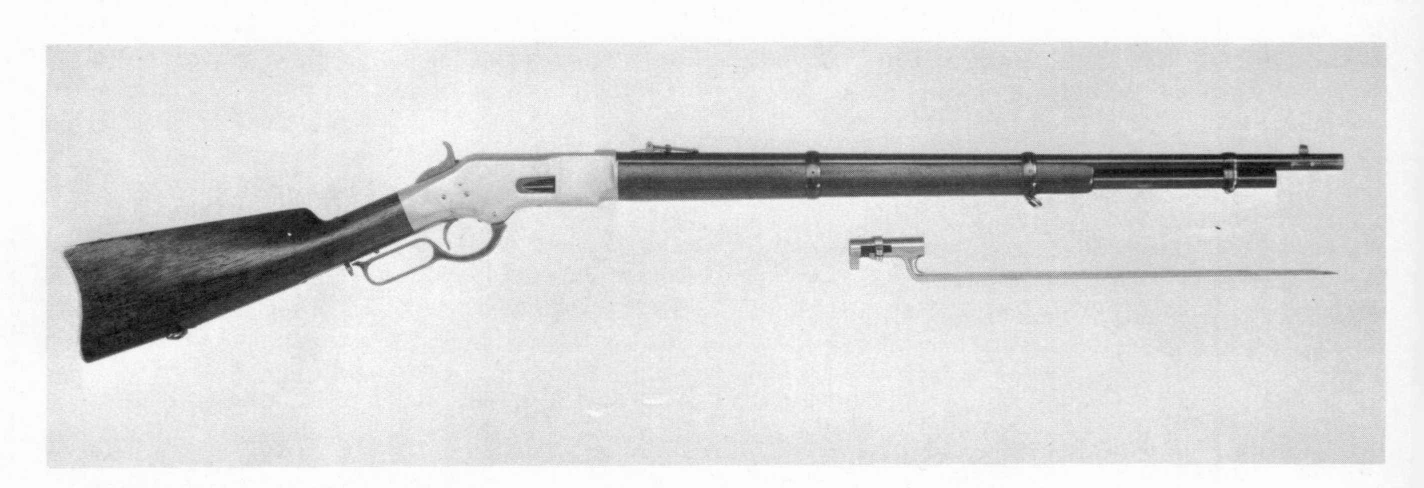

FIGURE 8-30 Winchester Model 1866 musket.

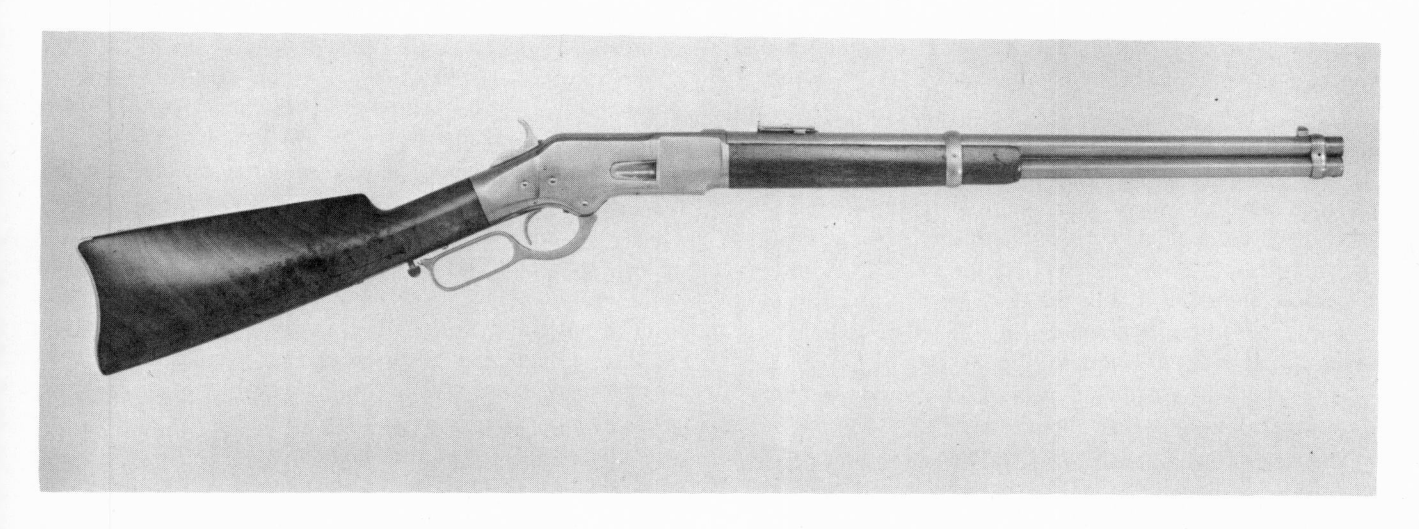

FIGURE 8-31 Winchester Model 1866 carbine.

shown in the bottom illustration of Figure 8-27. Further modifications were made over the years, but they were minor.

In 1869 a third model was added to the line. This was the Model 1866 musket shown in Figure 8-30. The musket was fitted with a 27-inch round barrel, and a long wooden forearm. They were offered with a triangular bayonet as shown in the illustration, or with the more modern saber bayonet at $2.00 additional. About 1871 the rifle model was offered with a round barrel at a lower price. This change reduced the weight of the rifle from 9½ pounds to an even 9 pounds.

The very compact Model 1866 carbine is shown in Figure 8-31. This model had a 20-inch round barrel and a magazine capacity of 13 rounds. These rifles were very light and handy for use on horseback and were an extremely popular model. The carbine is very similar in size, shape and balance to the current Model 94 carbines, which have proven to be outstanding rifles for use in brushy country and on horseback. Although the modern rifles have vastly improved ballistics and far stronger actions, the "human engineering" factors on this early model carbine were so well done that this type of design remains an excellent brush gun, or saddle carbine even today.

Manufacture of the Winchester Model 1866

During late 1866, the Winchester Company moved out of New Haven and into a building in Bridgeport which was part of the Wheeler and Wilson Sewing Machine Company. The move was apparently made because one of the directors of the corporation had surplus plant capacity in Bridgeport. This allowed the Winchester Company to expand the size of its operations from an average of slightly under 100 men to over 250 without making a heavy capital investment for new buildings. By 1870, the company had started to relocate to its permanent and present location in an area on the north side of New Haven, Connecticut.

A canal had been dug from New Haven Harbor all the way up into Massachusetts during the late 1820's and 1830's. During this period, New Haven was one of the leading ports on the New England coast and had a "long wharf" which extended out into the Harbor for over half a mile. Goods landed from the clipper ships were to be transhipped by the canal all through the lower New England area. In actual fact, the canal was only in profitable operation for ten years, but the charter had been cleverly written so that the canal company was permitted to construct a railroad along the towpath. By the time the Winchester Company moved back to New Haven in 1870, the railroad had taken over as the primary means of transportation. Multi-storied brick buildings were built parallel with the road named Canal Street. This was later renamed Winchester Avenue. One of these original buildings served the company from 1870 until 1965. It was originally three stories high. Later a fourth wooden story was added to provide additional space for the assembly of firearms. This building was a large U-shaped structure with an arched entrance way facing the road. The keystone with 1870 in large block letters was removed with an appropriate ceremony during demolition in 1965. The railroad line along the side of the Winchester plant is still in existence and portions of the old canal are still visible parallel to the railroad tracks a few miles north of the Winchester plant.

The Henry rifle was manufactured from 1862 to 1867. At that time, the production was shifted over to the "Improved Henry" which contained a wooden forearm and the improved loading system. In 1868, the "Improved Henry" became known as the Winchester Model 1866 rifle. When the new 1873 model was developed and finally placed into volume production in 1875, production of the old Model 1866 was dropped. It turned out that there was still a very significant sales demand for the 1866 model and production was resumed in October 1875.

Factory serial records start during 1875 at 125,000. Of this total about 13,000 were Henrys, leaving a probable total of 112,000 Model 1866 rifles manufactured between 1867 and near the end of 1875. The volumes start at modest figures and gradually build in the latter part of the 1860's reaching 22,600 in 1870 and 34,600 in 1871. The author doubts that all the orders were filled in either 1870 or 1871. Discussions of building the new plant in New Haven were carried out in the spring of 1870. By August of 1870 a decision had been reached to purchase a large tract of land from Oliver Winchester for $12,000 and construct the new manufacturing building adjacent to the railroad tracks.

During the Civil War, Oliver Winchester had commented that about 10,000 rifles had been manufactured while orders for at least 100,000 more had been received but could not be filled due to lack of production capacity. It is the author's opinion that the same situation occurred to a lesser extent in 1870 and 1871. With large foreign military contracts from France and Turkey, management no doubt secured maximum production from available equipment. At the same time, working capital was in very tight supply in the late 1860's. Even though the orders were coming in at a rapid rate, it appears very doubtful that management would invest large sums of money in doubling or tripling the production capacity in Bridgeport in order to manufacture a total of 34,000 rifles in 1871 when they were just finishing up and moving to the new manufacturing plant in New Haven. Another factor that makes it doubtful that large increases in production capacity would be installed for the 1866 model was that management was already hard at work on the extensive research and development required for the much more powerful 1873 Model rifle with its center-fire ammunition.

It is probable that the production capacity in the late 1860's and early 1870's allowed production of between 10,000 and 20,000 rifles per year. The average number of Model 1866 rifles produced between 1867 and 1875 amounts to 14,000 per year. Production must have really been strained in 1870, 1871 and 1872 to meet the commitments of the foreign orders.

The factory records of the serial numbers of rifles manufactured have been preserved after the year 1875. There appears to have been a gradually growing production capacity all through the late 1860's and 1870's. The Winchester model rifles required extensive machining of the internal components and fairly complex casting techniques to produce the brass receivers. It is undoubtedly true that some variations in production volumes could be secured by adding extra shifts, but the management was always careful to manufacture a high quality product and skilled workmen were required to maintain the tolerances, fits and clearances required. The production capacity was probably fully utilized until the slackening of orders following the business panic of 1873.

The Model 1866 Winchester came on the market immediately after the Civil War. It offered a drastically improved product at a crucial time in firearms history, and it rapidly achieved an excellent reputation for quality and reliability. These early model rifles actually had far greater impact on the settlement of the West than the later and more powerful 1886, 1894 and 1895 series of Winchester level action rifles which did not get out onto the frontier until after the Plains Wars and Indian skirmishes had drawn to a close. The 1866 model was timed perfectly for the westward expansion in the post-Civil War era and thousands of these "yellow boy" rifles with their distinct brass receivers were carried into the lonely corners of the unsettled country. Many examples remaining in private collections show the wide variety of uses on the frontier. Some rifles have been so extensively used on horseback that the forearm is almost worn through immediately forward of the receiver. Others that had fallen into Indian hands became decorated with rows of brass tacks up and down the buttstock and forearm. Some of these Indian rifles have been broken through the grip and repaired with rawhide. Many Model 1866 rifles have been used until they became unrepairable.

Ornately engraved Model 1866 rifles exist in many museums and some private collections. These rifles have carved a unique niche in American history, and this stature is reflected in the current values of an engraved Model 1866 rifle in excellent condition which are in the four-figure range, and increasing yearly. The production span of the Model 1866, from 1867 to 1898, saw the Winchester Company rise from a debt-ridden small venture into one of the largest and most prosperous businesses in New England.

Prices of the Winchester Model 1866

The 1869 Winchester catalog lists the Model 1866 with varnished stock and sling at $50. The musket with an angled bayonet and sling was listed at $47 and the carbine was the lowest priced model at $40. The copper rimfire cartridges were listed at $20 per thousand.

By 1874, the round barreled rifle model had been introduced at a price of $45. The price dropped to $28 in 1875 as the new Model 1873 center fire took over the premium priced position. This price held until 1878 when the price was cut again to $22. Although the retail price was increased to $24.00 in 1880, it had slumped to only $14.50 by 1884. The results of these price cuts were that modest sales volumes of the 1866 models were extended into the early 1890's. The volumes were never very great, but they were sufficient to keep the production line running and maintain the model in the line. The Model 1866 had a great deal to recommend it and it is little wonder that it maintained its popularity. For a mere $14.50 the purchaser received a well constructed, compact, lightweight rifle with a large magazine capacity. It fired medium powered ammunition which was moderate in cost. The mechanism had been developed to the point where it was extremely reliable and the whole package was an excellent tool for use on frontier situations, wherever moderate power was adequate.

AMMUNITION BUSINESS

The ammunition business closely paralleled firearms developments. Many different types of rimfire ammunition had been developed by the mid 1870's and Winchester vigorously pursued this business, manufacturing ammunition for a wide variety of competitive rifles as well as the Winchester Model 1866 and Henry rifles. The mechanical processes required in manufacturing ammunition were quite specialized and the development of satisfactory machinery was a long and very expensive process. Once the machines were developed, they could turn out vast quantities of high quality ammunition with a small number of workers. This contrasted sharply with the gunmaking business which generally utilized relatively simple machinery, such as drill presses, profilers, lathes and milling machines, but demanded high skill on the part of the workers, and a large number of workers to turn out the firearms. By 1874, Winchester manufactured a line of rimfire cartridges in .22, .25, .30, .32, .38, .41, .44, .46, .50, .52, and .56 caliber. These cartridges fitted a wide variety of single-shot breech- and repeating breech-loading rifles. By this period, Winchester could manufacture 250,000 cartridges per day. During the mid-1870's, the company was just starting the manufacture of paper and brass shotshells. Between 1874 and 1877, the company also received foreign orders for over 270 million loaded cartridges and components. The production capacity had risen to 2 million cartridges per day by 1879.

WINCHESTER MODEL 1873 RIFLE

The Model 1873 rifle was of great importance to the Winchester Repeating Arms Company. It was first manufactured only six years after incorporation of the company under the name Winchester and remained in the line until 1924 during which time a total of 720,610 rifles were manufactured. Over the 50-year span many variations were produced, as it was regular Winchester policy to improve the design and function of a model as experimental modifications were made and evaluated. There were further variations reflecting special requirements of the customer. Options offered included barrel lengths, barrels in octagonal, half octagonal, and round styles, full and half magazines, plain or set triggers, and special sighting equipment and stock shapes.

The Model 1873 Winchester rifle was an evolutionary design from the Model 1866, but the ammunition represented a radical change. The .44 Henry rimfire ammunition was loaded in a copper folded head cartridge case. The rim material had to be relatively thin so that the firing pin could deform it and cause ignition. The design of the Model 1866 allowed the center of the cartridge case head to move rearward with the firing pin approximately .030 of an inch, causing additional stress on the cartridge head material. These factors combined to limit the allowable pressure within the gun mechanism. Standard powder charges were 25 to 28 grains driving a 200- to 216-grain bullet.

The Model 1873 rifle was chambered for a .44/40 center-fire cartridge with a much heavier case made of brass. The stronger material and sturdier head structure could handle considerably higher pressure levels and the powder charge was increased to 40 grains. Manufacture of this new ammunition posed many difficult research and development problems. Oliver Winchester was sensitive to the complex problems involved and was painfully aware that much of his personal fortune had been required from 1857 to 1862 to keep the business alive while the .44 Henry rimfire cartridge and the Model 1860 Henry rifle were developed. A decade later this difficult and expensive process had

Model Name	Barrel Style	Barrel Length	Magazine Capacity	Weight of Gun, Pounds
Sporting Rifle	Octagon	24″	15	9
Sporting Rifle	Round	24″	15	8½
Carbine	Round	20″	12	7⅜
Musket	Round	30″	17	9½

FIGURE 8-32 Styles of Winchester Model 1873 firearms.

to be repeated to develop the more complex center-fire ammunition and a more powerful rifle to fire it.

Winchester management tried a new approach to product research and development. Thomas G. Bennett was hired after he graduated from Yale in the class of 1870. A project team was established which utilized the great reservoir of practical experiences of Winchester shop foreman and senior tool makers, and the more theoretical orientation of Mr. Bennett. This team worked for four years on the development of the Model 1873 rifle and its radically improved center-fire ammunition. The project team talked over new ideas and then the toolmakers and other machinists in the company fabricated new parts to test out the concepts. The guns and ammunition were assembled, tested and a continuous string of modifications and improvements incorporated into the designs. By 1873 the new rifle and ammunition were considered finalized and announced to the market. In fact, very serious manufacturing problems remained, particularly in the area of the new center-fire ammunition. These production problems were serious enough to delay introduction of the gun through most of 1873, and only 18 were shipped that year. By 1875 the new rifle was well launched and ammunition manufacturing capacity had been increased to handle both rimfire and centerfire designs.

Styles of Winchester 1873 Rifles

Model 1873 firearms had three models — sporting rifle, carbine, and musket. The specifications are shown in Figure 8-32. The sporting rifle was available with octagonal barrels, round barrels, or barrels that were octagon for the rear half and round for the front half. This last style was known as the "half octagon." Standard carbines had round 20-inch barrels, but some carbines are found with octagonal barrels, and barrels of odd lengths such as 14, 16 and 18 inches. The carbines were very light and compact with a 12-round magazine capacity and a gun weight of 7⅜ pounds.

Military versions of the Model 1873 Winchester were manufactured. These muskets were often fitted with 30-inch round barrels and weighed 9½ pounds. They were normally fitted with full length wooden forearms which protected the magazine tube.

Design Evolution of the Winchester Model 1873 Rifle

The design evolution of the 1873 can be divided into three periods. For the sake of clarity these will be defined as first, second and third styles. The first style rifles were produced from 1873 to 1879. The second style models were in production from 1879 to 1884, but there was some blending of features between these two styles. Most Model 1873 rifles were third style, produced from 1884 until 1924.

A very deluxe first style rifle is shown in Figure 8-33. This was a rare "one of one thousand" model assembled with all the refinements that manufacturing skill of the early 1870's could provide. The buttstock and forearm were made of finely figured walnut, which was checkered. A single set trigger mechanism has been fitted and a tang peep sight has been installed in addition to the regular rear sight. The features that identify this as a first style Model 1873 include the design of the finger lever, position of the trigger pivot pin, and the design of the dust cover on top of the receiver. The finger lever on the first style rifles is a thin band which only contacts the bottom of the stock at the extreme rear where a small lip is formed. Immediately to the rear of this lip is a small movable button which could be turned to lock the finger lever in an up position.

The receiver has been designed with higher sides in front than in the rear. Dovetail cuts were machined inside these high walls and a plate installed which slid over the top of the receiver to seal off the ejection port.

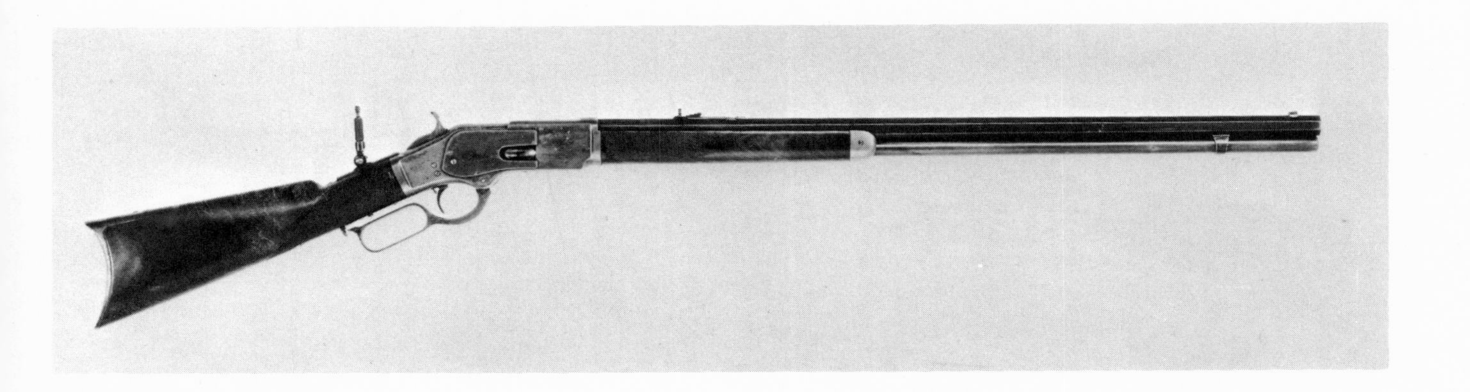

FIGURE 8-33 Winchester Model 1873 first style, "One of One Thousand" rifle.

As the rifleman operated the finger lever the dust cover was automatically drawn to the rear allowing ejection of the fired shell. When the rifle was merely being carried the dust cover tended to seal out dirt and keep the mechanism clean.

The rifle shown in Figure 8-33 has been fitted with a single set trigger mechanism which may be identified by a small slender adjusting screw located immediately behind the trigger.

A third style carbine is shown in Figure 8-34. The third style firearm utilized a dust cover running on a track which was machined into the top of the receiver. The most obvious change between the first, second and third styles is in the design of this upper track. In the second style the high receiver wall to the front was eliminated and a dovetail track was screwed onto the top of the rear of the receiver. The dust cover slid back and forth on this track. During 1882 a change was made to add more material to the top of the receiver at the back and to machine the dovetail track out of the receiver forging. All rifles made after 1882 may be considered third style rifles.

The Model 1873 carbine shown in Figure 8-34 is fairly similar to the design of lever action carbines of today. It has two barrel bands, one surrounding the forward section of the forearm and one encircling the barrel and magazine tube near the muzzle. The moderate weight of slightly under 7½ pounds, a short overall length and slim profile made the carbine an ideal arm for use in a saddle boot or for carrying in wooded country. The magazine capacity of 12 rounds gave ample firepower under emergency conditions.

The third type of Winchester Model 1873 was the military musket shown in Figure 8-35. Three barrel bands held a full length wooden forearm which provided protection to the magazine tube. A few muskets

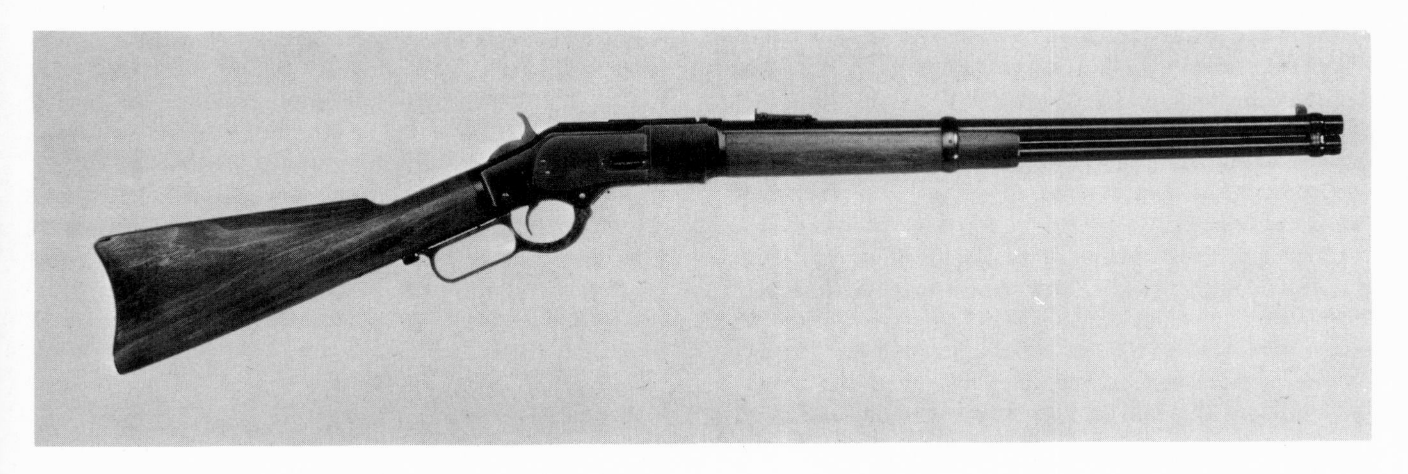

FIGURE 8-34 Winchester Model 1873 third style carbine.

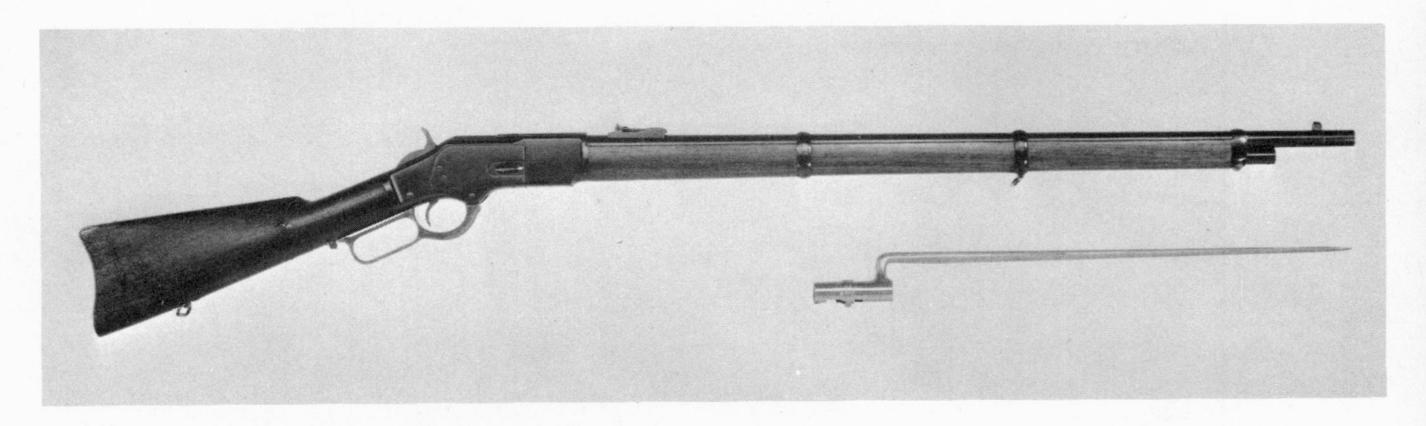

FIGURE 8-35 Winchester Model 1873 musket.

were made for the Spanish Government in 1879 with only one barrel band and a steel forearm cap to retain the front end of the forearm to the barrel. The musket shown in the figure is fitted with a triangular bayonet of typical Civil War design. It is fitted with a round 30-inch barrel and chambered for the .44/40 cartridge. The particular musket shown has all the features of the third style and represents fairly late manufacture.

Design Features of the Model 1873 Action

A cross-section drawing of a Model 1873 action is in Figure 8-36. A major improvement was the elimination of the complicated firing pin construction of the 1866 models. The Model 1873 was fitted with a rugged bolt which had a cylindrical hole in the center to take the firing pin. Early models had a bushing in the bolt face around the firing pin hole but second and third styles had solid bolt faces through which the firing pin protruded. This made a major improvement in strength since the breech face was locked solidly in place against the cartridge by the toggle linkage at the time of firing. Only the firing pin moved forward under the impact of the hammer blow and so the case head was thoroughly supported in all areas except the small firing pin hole in the center.

Cartridges were loaded into the tubular magazine through a loading port on the right side of the receiver. They were pushed rearward by the spring loaded magazine follower, into an opening in the brass carrier. As the finger lever was swung downward the toggle links holding the breech bolt forward were jackknifed downward causing the breech bolt to be drawn to the rear, cocking the hammer. The kinematics of these linkages can be seen by referring to the Henry patent, Figure 8-25. "Fig. 8" shows the links in a locked position and "Fig. 9" shows the links jackknifed. "Fig. 2" with the action fully open shows the links in a fully jackknifed position and the breech bolt all the way to the rear, cocking the hammer.

As the finger lever reached a nearly full open position, a diagonal surface on the finger lever (shown just below the pivot in Figure 8-36) struck the carrier lifter, raising the carrier assembly vertically. Springs were arranged so that the carrier was held in a fully up or fully down position. As the motion of the finger lever was reversed the breech bolt moved forward, pushing the fresh cartridge out of the brass carrier in a straight line into the chamber. When the finger lever reached a nearly closed position it struck another cam on the carrier lifter which snapped the carrier assembly downward.

A valuable safety feature known as the "trigger block" had been added to the design. The trigger mechanism was redesigned so that a small pivoted lever was fitted immediately behind the trigger. A trigger block pin projected through the hole in the bottom of the lower tang. The finger lever was redesigned with a solid boss immediately behind the trigger which contacted the lower tang. As the lever was drawn up into a fully upward position as shown in Figure 8-36 this boss on the finger lever lifted the trigger block and this in turn unlocked the trigger. Unless the lever was fully closed and the action locked the right angle bar at the end of the trigger block would drop down immediately behind the trigger and lock it in a forward position.

Since the Model 1873 rifle was locked by the toggle linkage mechanism it was very important that the two toggle links be exactly in line when the cartridge was

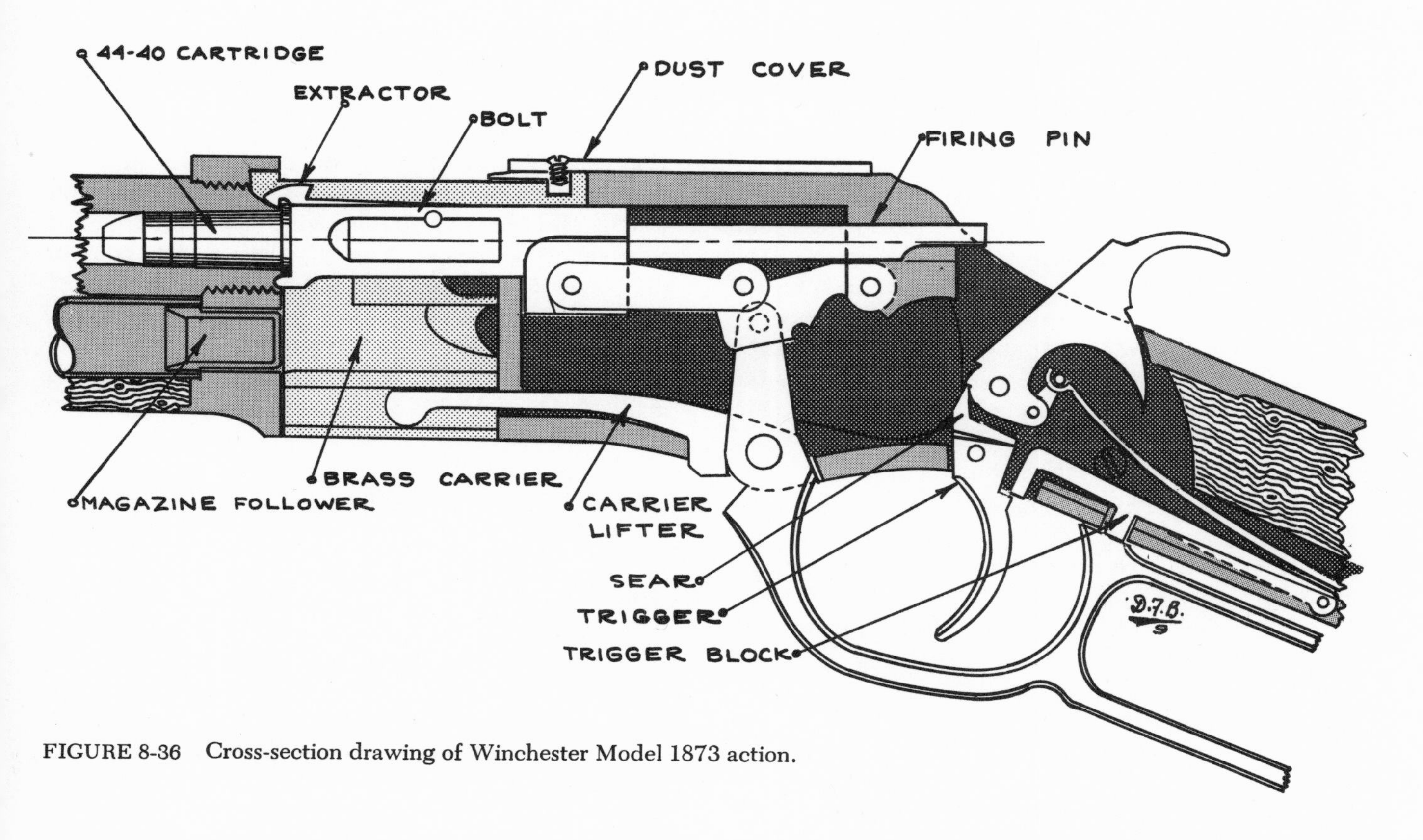

FIGURE 8-36 Cross-section drawing of Winchester Model 1873 action.

fired. The addition of the trigger block insured that the gun could not be discharged unless the lever was fully closed and the action locked tightly.

Ammunition for the Winchester Model 1873

The ammo for the Winchester Model 1873 rifles provided a significant increase in power level over the .44 Henry rimfire cartridge. The new center-fire ammunition had a further advantage of being easily reloaded, but manufacturing the new ammunition posed many technical problems for the Winchester management.

The complicated manufacturing processes required to produce rimfire ammunition had been successfully developed by 1860. The processes were tricky, for although copper is quite malleable in an annealed condition, it becomes harder and stronger, but more brittle as it is successively worked through cupping and drawing operations. At key points in the process the copper cups must be annealed. Ultimately techniques were developed so that the cartridge case had the right balance between increased hardness and tensile strength due to work hardening, and yet sufficient ductility so that the head did not split when struck by the firing pin, or as it moved rearward after firing against the firing pin assembly. Successful achievement of these difficult requirements opened the door to the production of many different calibers of rimfire ammunition. During the early 1860's Winchester added machinery and tooling to produce additional calibers so that by 1874 the plant had a capability of producing a diversified line of rimfire ammunition.

The difficult development of new machinery and processes had to be repeated for the .44/40 center-fire ammunition. A center-fire cartridge head is a much more complex design from a production standpoint with a swaged-in primer pocket and thick and thin sections. During the early 1870's production machinery and tooling was developed to produce this new more complex design, but start-up problems were severe so that adequate centerfire ammunition production was not achieved until 1874. The ballistic advantages of the new ammunition can be seen in the table below:

CARTRIDGE	BULLET WEIGHT (GRAINS)	MUZZLE VELOCITY (FPS)	MUZZLE ENERGY (FT-LBS)	EFFICIENCY (FT-LBS) (GRAIN)
.40 Volcanic	96	540	62	9.0
.44 Henry R.F.	200	1125	560	20.0
.44/40 C.F.	200	1300	752	18.8
.38/40 C.F.	180	1325	700	17.5
.32/20 C.F.	115	1234	388	19.4
.45/75 C.F.	350	1383	1485	20.0

All the Volcanic ammunition suffered from low velocity levels and poor exterior ballistics. The .40 caliber ammunition, for example, had a bullet weight of only 96 grains and a calculated muzzle velocity of approximately 540 feet per second. Such low velocity was due to severe gas leakage at the breech. The muzzle energy was only slightly over 60 foot-pounds and the efficiency was similar to that of a percussion revolver. The Henry rimfire ammunition of 1860 represented a tremendous improvement in performance. A 25- to 28-grain powder charge drove a 200-grain soft lead bullet at 1125 feet per second muzzle velocity for an energy level almost 10 times that of the Volcanic ammunition. Efficiency was excellent at 20 foot-pounds of muzzle energy per grain of propellant.

The .44/40 center-fire ammunition drove the same 200-grain soft lead bullet at 1300 feet per second muzzle velocity providing flatter trajectory, and an increase in muzzle energy to 750 foot-pounds. Efficiency remained high at 18.8 foot-pounds of muzzle energy per grain of propellant.

The drive for increased power in repeating firearms continued during the 1870's. The Spencer rifles of the Civil War had actually achieved muzzle energies of 900 foot-pounds with 450-grain lead bullets driven by 40 grains of black powder. The disadvantages to the Spencer ammunition lay in the heavy weight of the cartridges, and the low muzzle velocity of 930 feet per second in the carbines and 950 feet per second in the rifles which gave a very curved trajectory. What was wanted was a lightweight, reliable ammunition which would provide high power and extended range. The Army's decision to accept the 45/70 cartridge in 1873 put additional pressure on the development of powerful cartridges for repeating firearms. Winchester entered the Army trials with a powerful lever action rifle which contained many ideas introduced in the Model 1876 rifles. The Model 1876 was originally chambered for the .45/75 Winchester cartridge. A 74-grain black powder charge was used to drive a 350-grain soft lead bullet at 1383 feet per second muzzle velocity. This powerful cartridge provided 1485 foot-pounds of muzzle energy, almost double that of the .44/40 load and triple the energy level of the .44 Henry cartridge. Such powerful cartridges provided excellent long-range performance against heavy game. Theodore Roosevelt reported killing two elk with a single shot with the .45/75 cartridge at a range of 431 paces, or over 400 yards.

Ammunition for the Model 1873 Winchester is shown in Figure 8-37. The .44/40 was also known as the .44W.C.F. In 1878, Colt chambered their single action Army revolver for the .44/40 cartridge so the frontiersman could carry one ammunition for both rifle and revolver. This further boosted the popularity of the cartridge and it is estimated that the Model 1873 rifle in .44/40 caliber killed more game during the 19th century than any other single cartridge and rifle combination. The ammunition was compact, and lightweight and the 15-shot magazine capacity provided tremendous firepower. The rifle had a slim contour that easily fitted into a saddle boot or on the floor of a wagon. The mechanism had been developed to the point where it could endure rugged abuse and still give reliable service. The combination of features made the Model 1873 an extremely valuable weapon on the frontier where survival could easily depend on reliable firepower in an emergency.

The choice of .44 caliber for the first center-fire cartridge continued a Winchester tradition going back to 1860. The caliber provided good knock down power with the 200-grain soft lead bullet and the frontiersmen used it on everything from rabbits to buffalo. It is still an excellent short-range cartridge with good penetration at moderate ranges, and good brush-bucking ability with a modern jacketed .44/40 bullets. It is a chunky little cartridge with slight body taper. The taper of .471-inch diameter underneath the rim to .443-inch diameter at the mouth was just sufficient to provide easy extraction once a cartridge had been broken loose from the chamber. The dimensions shown in Figure 8-37 are from actual production drawings dated 1912 which were made available by Walter Bellemore. The length of all center-fire cartridges for the Model 1873 were controlled so that they would never exceed 1.6 inches. The dimensions shown on the drawing are maximum cartridge, and manufacturing tolerances were all in the direction of reducing dimensions. Thus the rim thickness on an actual cartridge might be as low as .058 of an inch but it should never exceed .065 of an inch.

In 1880 Winchester introduced the .38/40 center-fire cartridge for the Model 1873 rifle. This was a slightly bottlenecked cartridge offering a lighter bullet at a slightly higher velocity. The 40-grain black powder charge drove a 180-grain bullet at 1325 feet per second. Actual bullet diameter was .40 of an inch so the bullets were only .030 of an inch smaller in diameter than the .44/40.

The Model 1873 was also chambered for the .32/20 center-fire cartridge in 1882. Cases were of heavy construction and could be reloaded indefinitely. It was a very economical cartridge for the bullet weighed only 115 grains, and required only a 20-grain powder charge to achieve a muzzle velocity of 1234 feet per second.

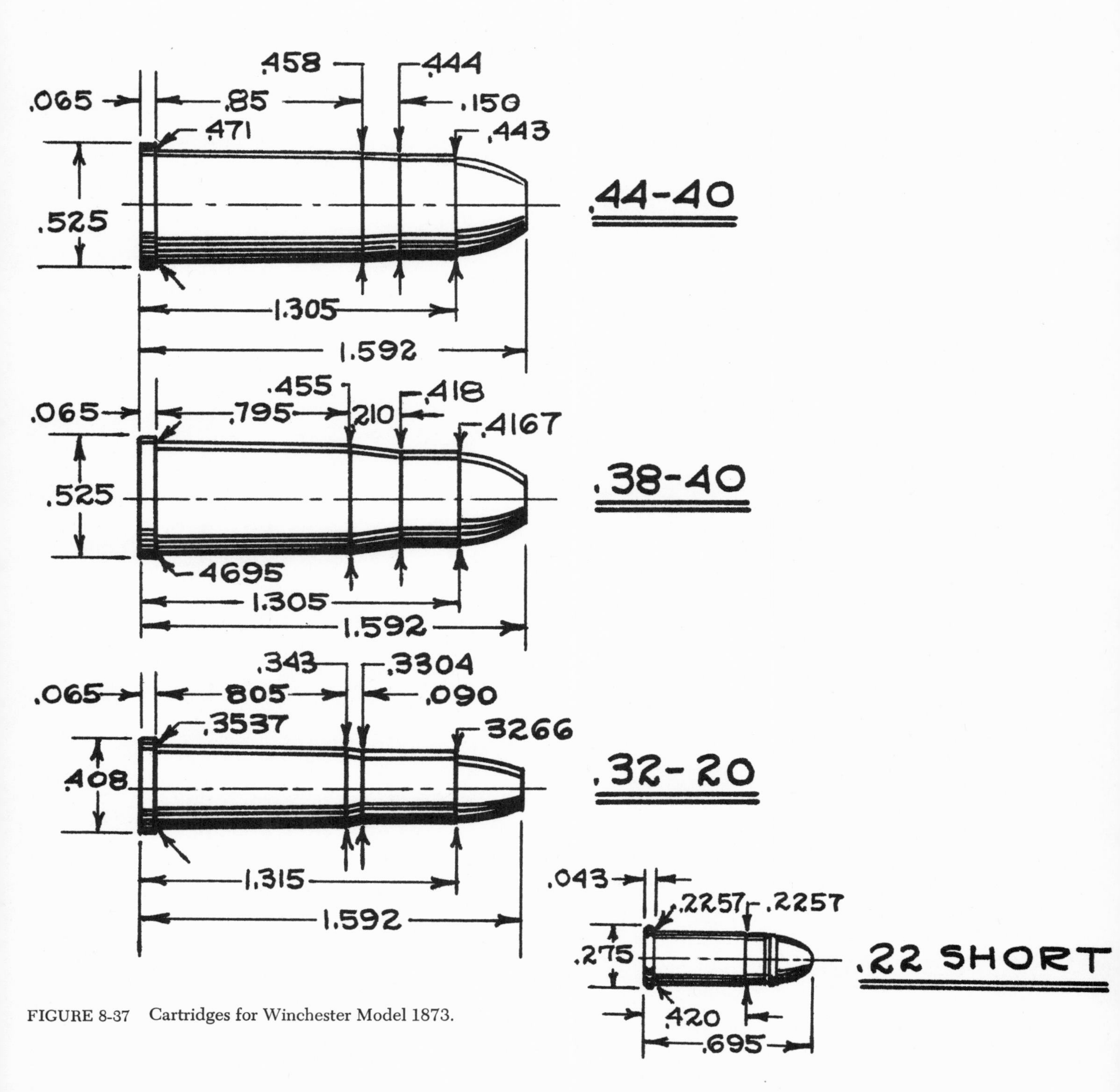

FIGURE 8-37 Cartridges for Winchester Model 1873.

The Model 1873 Winchester was also chambered for the .22 short and .22 long rimfire cartridges. These cartridges required extensive modifications to the design. The .22 short is the oldest American rimfire cartridge, dating back to Smith and Wesson's work in 1857. It was originally loaded with a charge of about 4 grains of black powder, providing a muzzle velocity of 977 feet per second at a range of 50 feet with a 30-grain bullet. The .22 long cartridge was originally loaded by Winchester in 1873 with a slightly higher powder charge which drove a 35-grain bullet at 1019 feet per second at 50 feet. The Model 1873 was much more popular in the center-fire calibers for they provided much greater power and the sturdy cartridge cases for this model could easily be reloaded at moderate cost.

Conclusions

American firearms underwent a revolutionary change in the century following the Declaration of Independence. At the beginning of the American Revolution the armies of the world were equipped with smoothbore flintlock muskets. A small percentage of each army was equipped with slower loading flintlock rifles, and officers were generally armed with swords and smoothbore flintlock pistols. Typical infantry manuals of the Revolutionary period define 20 or more specific steps to reload the musket in combat. The average soldier with his musket could not hit a man-sized target beyond 100 yards so that infantry battles in Europe were often fought at ranges as close as 30 yards with each side enveloped in a dense cloud of black powder smoke.

The early 19th century was a period of intense experimentation in all mechanical fields. Steam powered railroads became a reality and the steamship became a reliable method of ocean transportation. The development of water powered machinery made possible the production of more complex designs with more elaborate manufacturing processes. Inventors in Europe and the United States took advantage of the new techniques to overcome, step by step, the difficult problems of breech-loading firearms.

The American Civil War was a period of transition. Muzzle-loading rifles were standard in the armies of Europe and the United States in 1860. By 1865 American inventors had proven that repeating breech-loading firearms were not just a possibility but a practical reality.

The important international target matches of the 1870's pitted American skill with breech-loading firearms against the finest refinements of muzzle-loading techniques developed in Europe. American success with breech-loading rifles in the international matches of 1874 and 1877 proved that the extremely accurate muzzle-loading rifles of the Old World could be equaled or beaten in accuracy by the "newfangled" breech-loaders of the Americans. The development of powerful, accurate repeating rifles during the 1860's and 1870's meant that hardy young Americans in the post-Civil War era could penetrate the Far West and exist in the wilderness where their survival might depend on an ability to withstand heavy odds during an Indian attack. American firearms were exported around the world, and our leadership in this important area of technology rested upon the intense need for powerful, accurate firearms which could provide food and protection far from civilization.

COMPLETED